Systematic
POMOLOGY

Volume - 1

Dr. Om Prakash Pareek
Former Director
Central Institute for Arid Horticulture
(ICAR) Bikaner - 334 006 (Rajasthan)

Dr. Suneel Sharma
Prof. of Horticulture
Dept. of Horticulture,
CCS Haryana Agricultural University
Hisar (Haryana)

SCIENTIFIC
PUBLISHERS

Published by
SCIENTIFIC PUBLISHERS (INDIA)

Jodhpur –

5 A, New Pali Road
P.O. Box 91
Jodhpur - 342 001 INDIA

Delhi –

4806/24, Ansari Road
Daryaganj
New Delhi - 110 002 INDIA

Print 2026

ISBN: 978-93-6346-067-6 (SET) Vol 1-2

eISBN: 978-93-6346-068-3 (SET) Vol. 1-2

Visit the Scientific Publishers (India) website
at http://www.scientificpubonline.com

Printed in India

FOREWORD

Fruits have been an important source of human food ever since the dawn of civilization. Rich in nutrients such as vitamins, antioxidants, soluble fibre and minerals, fruits are considered to be the protective class of food. Globally, around 3000 species of different fruits exist, of which about 250 have considerable nutritional and commercial value and thus are being cultivated. Despite this, presently only around 30 species are commercially cultivated with a global production of 654.4 million tons.

The demand for fruits is likely to increase in view of increasing human population, rising income, overall social prosperity and appreciation for consuming healthy food for nutritional security. This obviously calls for widening of the global fruit basket as well as improving their production, productivity and quality.

In order to achieve this, a systematic documentation on description, identification, standard nomenclature and classification of available genetic diversity is a prerequisite.

In this context, the book 'Systematic Pomology' is indeed a welcome addition. Both Drs. O.P. Pareek and Suneel Sharma have provided a very useful account of nearly 375 fruit species belonging to 4 gymnosperm and 70 angiosperm families into a very systematic framework of phylogenetic system of nomenclature and classification developed in 2009 by the Angiosperm Phylogeny Group following the latest code of nomenclature. The general information on description of plant characters, identification, nomenclature and classification along with fairly exhaustive description of specific characteristics of different species are likely to be very helpful in identification of new genotypes/cultivars. Such a comprehensive account will certainly help in systematic introduction and selection of genetic materials in the fruit breeding programme considering their taxonomic proximities and specific characteristics related to fruit bearing, regularity, nutritive and edible quality including aroma and taste, and above all their resistance to biotic and abiotic stresses.

I am sure the information contained in this book will benefit especially the research workers in establishing/maintaining specific germplasm blocks, research orchards or even herbaria. The book is expected to serve as reference material for teachers, researchers, students and all those concerned with fruit flora, particularly those interested in their genetic resources, breeding and bioinformatics. Above all, this useful compilation would help the commercial fruit growers in selecting the most suitable fruit species/cultivars, locations for their planting and methods of orchard management for achieving higher productivity and profitability.

R. S. Paroda
Chairman, *TAAS*, Pusa Campus, New Delhi
Formerly, Secretary (DARE) and
Director General (ICAR)

PREFACE

Systematic Pomology is an integral part of the science of fruits. Its knowledge is a prerequisite for improvement as well as sustainable and profitable production of fruit crops. The nomenclature and classification of fruit plants had been traditionally done on the basis of the Bentham and Hooker's natural system of classification published in *Genera Plantarum* (1862-1883). Now after the development of the ordinal classification, using new systematic data especially on DNA sequences, for the families of flowering plants by the Angiosperm Phylogeny Group (APG), updated as APG III in 2009, adoption of the concept of phylogenetic nomenclature and classification in fruit species is more appropriate. Also, the latest Code of nomenclature for the cultivated plants should be adopted. Therefore the authors considered it necessary to put the fruit crops into the more systematic framework of the APG system of nomenclature and classification. This requirement has been felt ever since the authors taught the Systemaic Pomology course to postgraduate students. In fact, this interest has its roots when one of us (OPP) drew inspiration from the lectures of Prof. Ranjit Singh, an authority on citrus taxonomy, who taught the subject in the Horticulture Division of the Indian Agriculture Research Institute, New Delhi during 1962-63, and from the earlier publications from USA by Prof. F A Waugh (1916) and Prof. Q B Zeilinski (1955). The intention was also to consolidate and update the scattered information for those interested in the subject of fruit science.

With continued work on this task the present book has been brought out in two volumes. The subject matter of the book, having 40 chapters, has been presented in three parts. Part A, with 4 chapters, gives general information on methods for (i) description of plant characters, (ii) identification, (iii) nomenclature, and (iv) classification. In Part B and C, nearly 370 species belonging to 72 families have been grouped based on the Phylogenetic System of Classification of the APG. Part B has Gymnosperm fruits in 3 chapters and Part C has fruits of Angiosperms in 33 chapters. In each chapter, the fruits have been arranged giving their taxonomical status from family to the cultivar level with description of important pomological traits. Comparatively brief narrative is given on the characters at the levels of class, subclass, angiosperm clade, order and family. More emphasis has been laid on the description of characters at species level with considerably exhaustive description at the cultivar level. The book is richly illustrated with figures and photographs. Taxonomic keys have also been given for some species groups. This first volume contains 27 chapters; all the chapters of Part A and Part B and 20 chapters of Part C.

The remaining 13 chapters of Part C along with a references list, fairly exhaustive glossary and an index are continued in the second volume.

The book is intended to serve as a reference material for researchers, teachers, students, fruit growers and all concerned with fruit flora particularly those interested in their genetic resources, breeding and bioinformatics. The knowledge will be useful to a gene bank curator to enable him to systematically maintain fruit germ plasm *in-situ* or *ex-situ* and in herbaria including their proper documentation, to the taxonomists for use not only in preparation of keys and correct identification but also in classifying the fruit genotypes into categories and in removing confusion arising from synonimity in nomenclature. Correct knowledge of origin and evolution of the genotypes will be useful in their systematic use in scientific studies based on the information on their relationships and differences (taxonomic proximities) and also in selecting genetic material (considering specific characters) for use in improvement programmes. In addition, the information would be useful to the commercial fruit growers as a guide book for systematic planting and culture of fruits by selection of the right genotype/cultivar considering their suitability for use as rootstock and as scion material to obtain high productivity and quality of fruits in the given environment.

The authors have drawn information from number of published texts, monographs, books and periodicals for compilation of this work. The authors gratefully thank the organizations Biodiversity International, formaly IPGRI Regional Office for Asia, Rome, Italy, ProMUSA, TFNet, Selangor, Malaysia and IITA, Nigeria for using line diagrams/drawings of plant species from their published work. Our special thanks are also due to Dr S.N. Pandey, ex-ADG, ICAR, Dr. Sanjay Singh and Sh Sanjay Patil, CHES, Bikaner, Ms. Monica Lisa, CCS HAU, Hisar, Dr Sunil Pareek MPUAT, Udaipur, Dr. Murlidharan, Date Palm Research Station, Mundra, for providing photographs of cultivars of fruit species used in this publication. Thanks are also due to Dr R.A. Sharma and Dr S. Kathju, CAZRI, Jodhpur for valuable suggestions on portions of the text. Authors are grateful to the Vice Chancellor CCS Haryana Agricultural University, Hisar, and the Director CIAH, Bikaner for the kind encouragement to undertake this task. The task would not have been accomplished without the inspiration, encouragement and support provided by the family members especially Mrs. Kamla Pareek and Mrs. Deepali Sharma.

O.P. Pareek
Suneel Sharma

CONTENTS

INTRODUCTION

The word 'pomology', combination of the latin word *pomum* (fruits) and the Greek word *logy* or *logos* (discourse, treatise or science), literally means the science of fruits. It has two main components, 'systematic pomology' and the other is the 'practice of fruit growing'. Systematic pomology deals with our knowledge of the fruits themselves and the trees, bushes and vines on which they grow comprising three distinct subjects: i) descriptive pomology (examining distinguishing characters of fruits), ii) nomenclature (naming from the pictured description), and iii) classification (grouping based on similarities and differences in characters) of fruits (Waugh, 1912). According to Hedrick (1925) systematic pomology is the study of the kinds of fruits and their relationships involving accurate description of their form, features and structure and relative disposition of their organs following a set of special technical rules to put them into groups based on degree of resemblance. Bailey has defined systematic pomology as the study of differences and resemblances of horticultural plants, their classification according to natural relationship and their description. Thus it is a part of plant taxonomy in that it includes identification, nomenclature and classification, but is usually more restrictive being limited to only the tree fruit, small fruit and nut crops of commerce (Zielinski, 1955). Plant taxonomy deals with the system to identify, name and classify plants by their affinities and structural resemblances in a manner by which their phylogenetic relationship can be established and their line of evolution be traced. The system when applied to various kinds of fruits based on the descriptions of their characteristics, resemblances and differences with respect to morphological, genetical, physiological, biochemical, biotechnological and eco-attributes is called systematic pomology. Thus, systematic pomology is a broad field concerned with scientific studies of diversity of fruit plants and their identification, naming, classification, evolution and development. In other words it is the study of systematics (botanical and horticultural relationship) and taxonomy (scientific grouping) of different fruit plants.

The information generated from the studies related to systematic pomology helps :

i. in identifying the plants and in classifying them into categories,

ii. in evolving better keys based on their character descriptions,

iii. to provide a standard nomenclature and terminology for exchange of information and ideas related to these plants,

iv. in removing the confusion from synonymy created by indiscriminate naming, avoiding giving indiscriminate fancy names and promoting correct labeling,

v. to answer the general human concerns of how a plant type originated, evolved changing over to the present form to enable their correlation with the ancient species and in understanding their genetic relations,

vi. in establishing or maintaining a garden, a germplasm block, a research orchard or even herbaria wherein different plants are arranged in a systematic botanical order,

vii. in identification of new genotypes or cultivars for introduction to suit the given environmental conditions for planting in a region,

viii. in using the correct related cultivars kept in a genetic resources repository for genetic improvement considering the limits of hybridiz-ation and in selecting correct cultivars for studies such as stock-scion relations,

ix. in selecting genetic material (considering specific characters) for a breeding programme considering their taxonomical proximities, such as:

    a. improvement in fruit bearing and its regularity;

    b. marinating better fruit quality attributes like nutritive value (biochemical constituents), edible quality, appearance, etc.;

    c. resistance to certain biotic stresses from fungal, bacterial and viral pathogens, insect pests and nematodes;

    d. resistance to certain abiotic factors such as water stress, temperature extremes and salinity;

    e. modifying plant size (stature) and form; and

x. in deciding the locations of planting, methods of orchard management, utilization of plant produce, etc.

Although the component of horticultural nomenclature was kept during the International Horticultural Congress in 1910, the importance of description of cultivars of horticultural plants and their systematic classification was recognized only during the 9th Horticultural Congress in 1930 when the rules for formation of a Horticulture Nomenclature Committee were agreed and added as an appendix to the 1935 *Botanical Code*.

PART A

Chapter 1

DESCRIPTION OF PLANT CHARACTERS

Accurate and detailed description of characters of a fruit bearing tree, bush or vine and its parts including those related to growth habit, hardiness and productivity is the first step to confirm nomenclatural identity or to assign it to correct taxa if it happens to be a new genotype. The botanists take into account the wild plants and describe the plants on the basis of the study of herbarium sheets. Type specimen is a preserved herbarium specimen of a plant on the description of which a valid species is originally established. This approach is not considered practicable by the horticulturists as they are concerned with the cultivated plant material, that too in the living state, and have to consider their minute characters. This is necessary also because of the existence of allopolyploids as in European plums and interspecific as well as intergeneric hybrids as in citrus fruits. It is also not possible to separate fruit species on the basis of flower or fruit colour as is done in *Bauhinias.* The process of evaluation begins with adoption of descriptors or description blanks or forms that have been developed for making records of the descriptions. The descriptors may either be in the form of a field book or loose sheets to be kept in record files or cards to be stored in card cabinets/catalogues. *Bioversity International* has published descriptors on several fruit species. These can be obtained from the Bioversity Headquarters, Biodiversity International or bioversity@cgiar.org or can be downloaded or from website, http://www.bioversityinternational.org/e-library/publications/categories/descriptors. For identification, nomenclature and classification of fruit plants the characters included in the descriptors are, in general, related to the following areas:

1. Habitat: Aquatic, terrestrial; Tropical, temperate, arctic; Hydrophytes, mesophyte, xerophytes.

2. Morphological characters: These are physical characters related to the plant for botanical description. There are two kinds of characters: inherent characters due to genetic variation, and those that are due to ecological conditions and vary with environmental fluctuation. The differences caused by environmental fluctuation are not permanent and, therefore, are not considered, e.g. date of fruit ripening, size and shape of fruit, etc. The rootstock used also influences the size of tree and fruit and leaf characters. Usually, quantitative characters are not useful. A standard format should be used for recording plant characters. The format of descriptor varies depending upon plant type (fruit) and purpose. A descriptor may include characters from the following list. Additional characters may be added where required.

A. General growth characters

(a) Habit: Annual, ephemeral, biennial, perennial; Trees, vines, herbs, shrubs; Epiphyte, parasite.

i. Tree:

Type: Caudex, excurrent, deliquescent, culm.

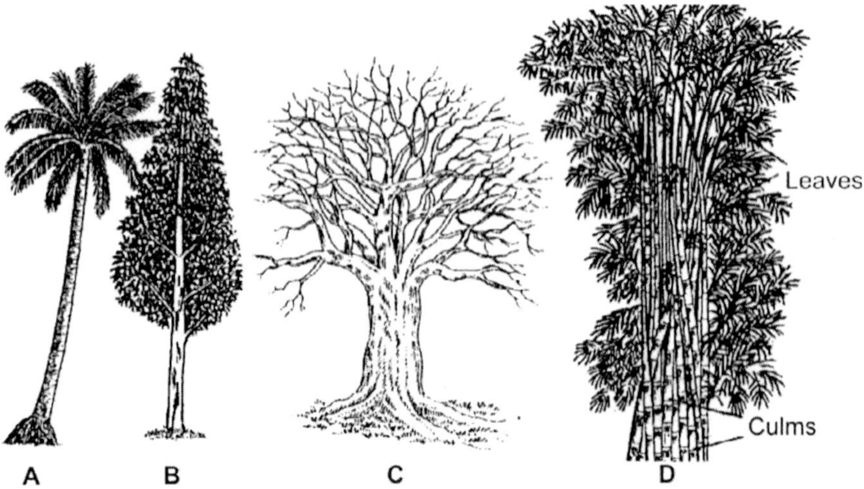

Fig. 1.1. Types of trees: A. caudex, B. excurrent, C. deliquescent and D. culm (Source: Pandey and Misra, 2008).

Stem axis: Acaulescent, arborescent, arboreous.

Crown shape: Upright, spreading, open, closed-headed, round-topped, irregular.

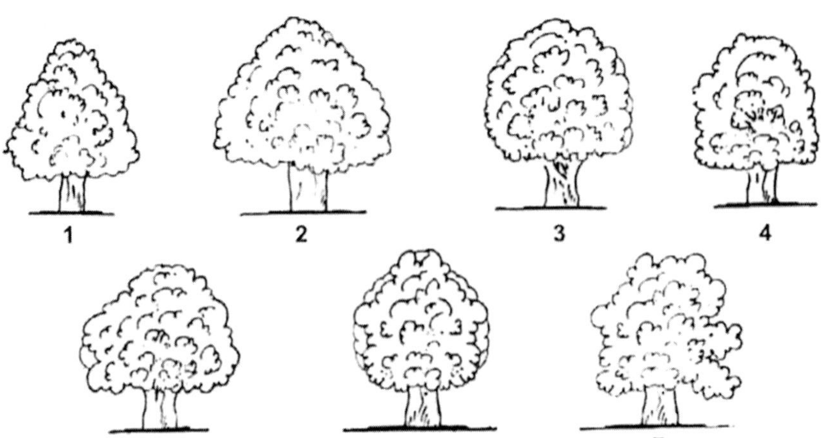

Fig. 1.2. Crown shape: 1. Pyramidal, 2. Broadly pyramidal, 3. Spherical, 4. Oblong, 5. Semi-circular, 6. Elliptical, 7. Irregular (Source: IPGRI, 2000).

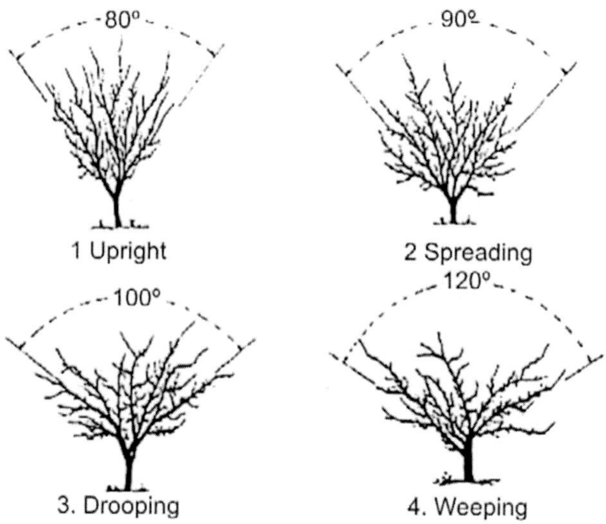

Fig. 1.3. Tree habit: 1. Upright, 2. Spreading, 3. Drooping, 4. Weeping (Source: Gülcan, 1985)

Branching: Racemose (monopodial), cymose (uniparous, biparous, multiparous).

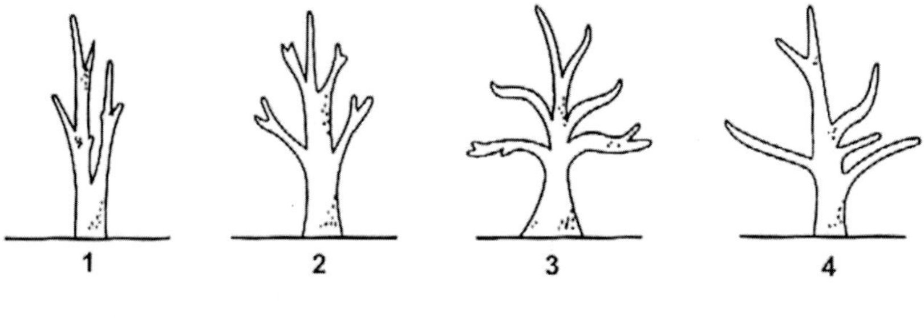

Fig. 1.4. Branching pattern: 1. Erect, 2. Opposite, 3. Verticillate, 4. Horizontal, 5. Irregular (Source: IPGRI, 2003).

Vigour: Vigorous, tall, semi-vigorous, dwarf.

Stature: Height; Spread.

ii. *Vine: Vigorous, semi-vigorous, dwarf, tall.*

iii. *Herb & shrub: Prostrate, erect, diffuse or weak-stemmed.*

b. Hardiness: Strong or weak; Hardy or susceptible to certain biotic and abiotic stress conditions.

c. Bark: Colour (dark brown, brown, grey, silvery); Patterns; Smooth, rough, streaked; Lenticels present, absent.

d. Foliage: Leaves abundant or sparse; Colour (dark green, light green).

B. Stem characters

a. Form: Creeper, trailer, climber (twiner, tendril climber, root climber, hook climber, adhesive climber, liana).

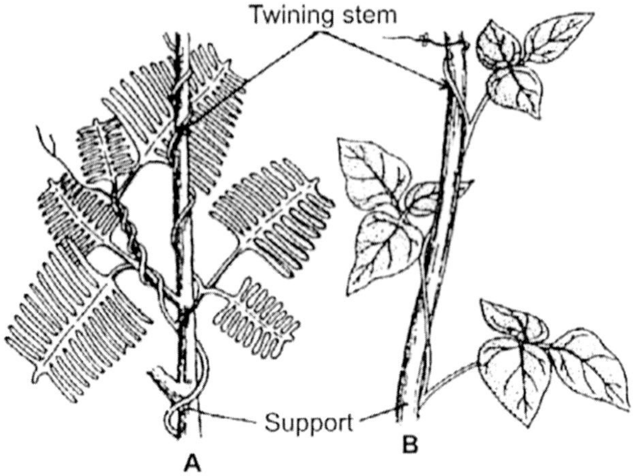

Fig. 1.5. Stem climber (Source: Pandey and Misra, 2008).

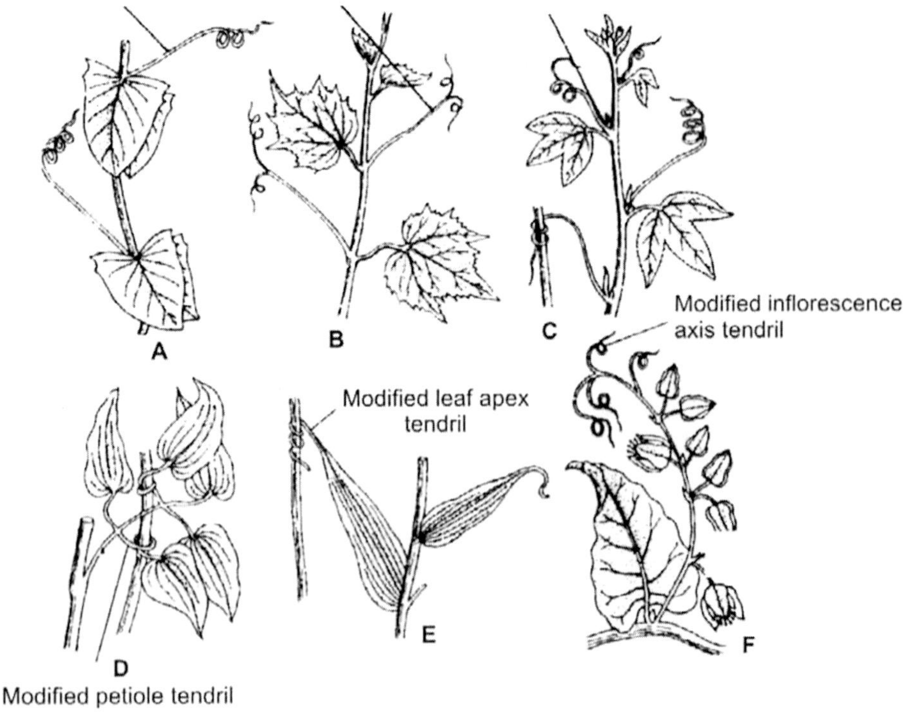

Fig. 1.6. Tendril climbers (Source: Pandey and Misra, 2008).

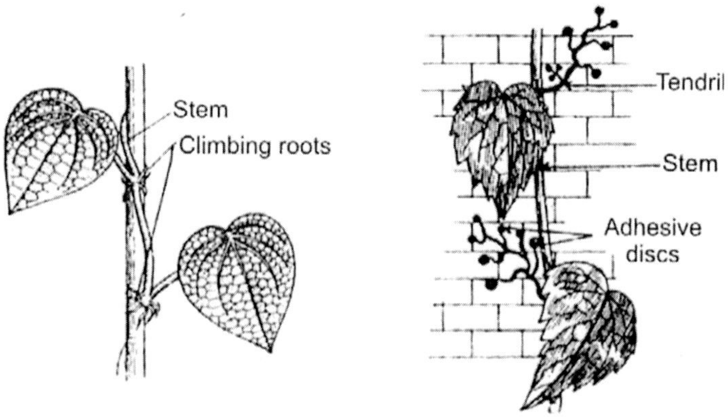

Fig. 1.7. Piper beetle and *Ampelopsis* (Source: Pandey and Misra, 2008).

Fig. 1.8. Hook climber (Source: Pandey and Misra, 2008).

b. Colour: Green, light green, grey, brown.

c. Twig/Shoot: Colour/pigmentation (purple, deep red, green, silvery); Hairiness; Presence and type of spines; Pith continuity, colour .

d. Modifications: Rhizome, tuber, bulb (truncated, imbricate), corm; Runner, stolon, sucker, offset; Phylloclade (cladophyll), cladode, thorn, stem tendril.

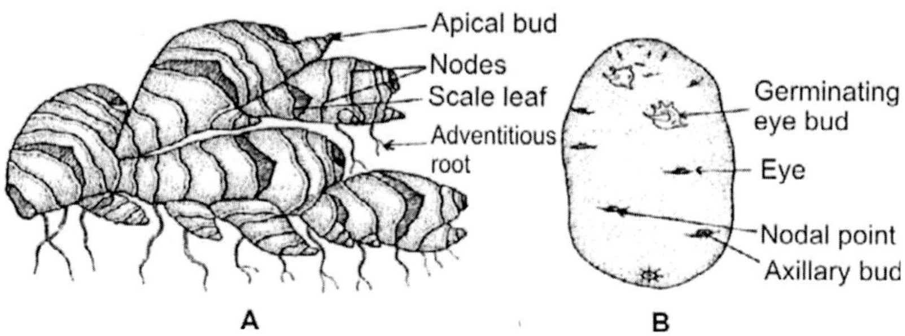

Fig. 1.9. A-rhizome and B-tuber (Source: Pandey and Misra, 2008)

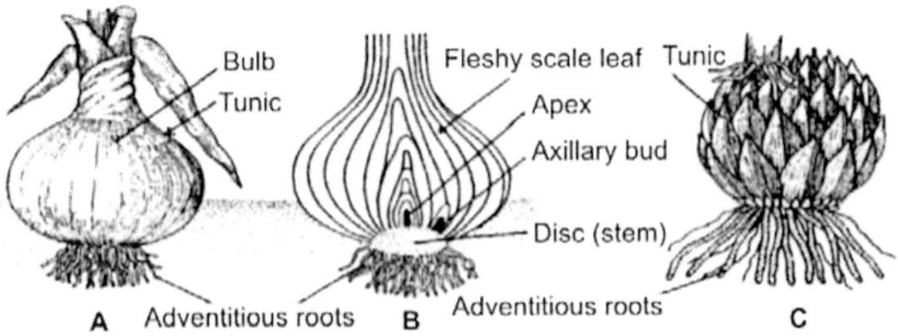

Fig. 1.10. A-tunicated bulb, B-L.S. of the bulb and C-scaly bulb (Source: Pandey and Misra, 2008).

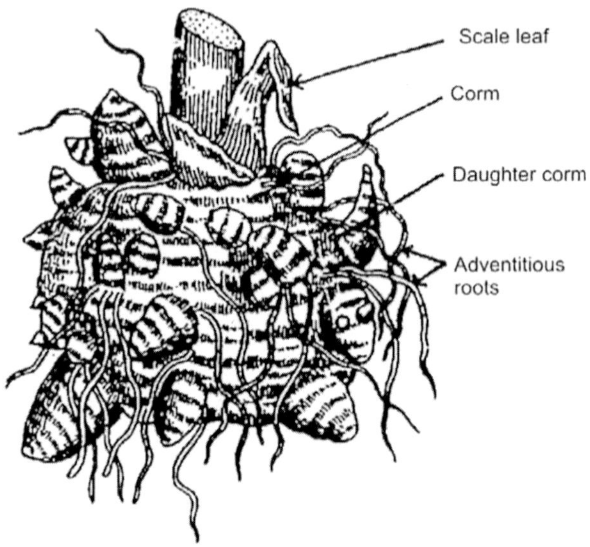

Fig. 1.11. Corm (Source: Pandey and Misra, 2008).

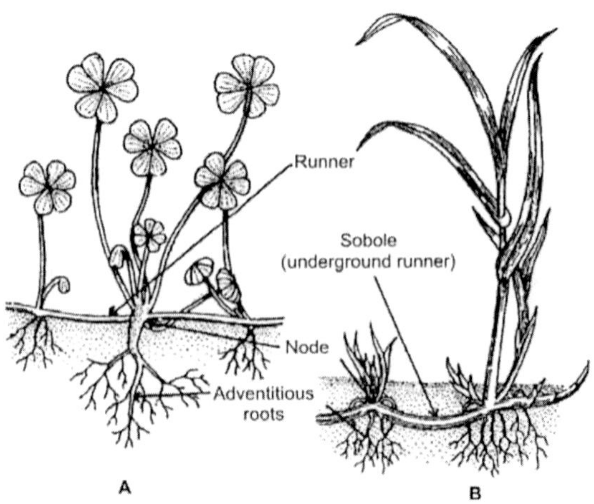

Fig. 1.12. A-runner and B-sobole (Source: Pandey and Misra, 2008).

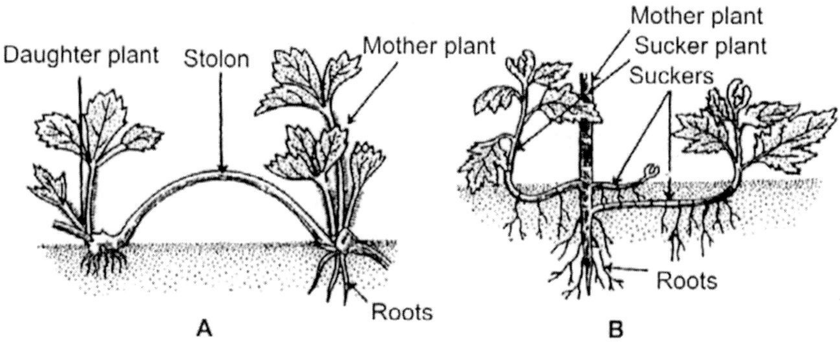

Fig. 1.13. A-stolon and B-sucker (Source: Pandey and Misra, 2008)

Fig. 1.14. Offset (Source: Pandey and Misra, 2008).

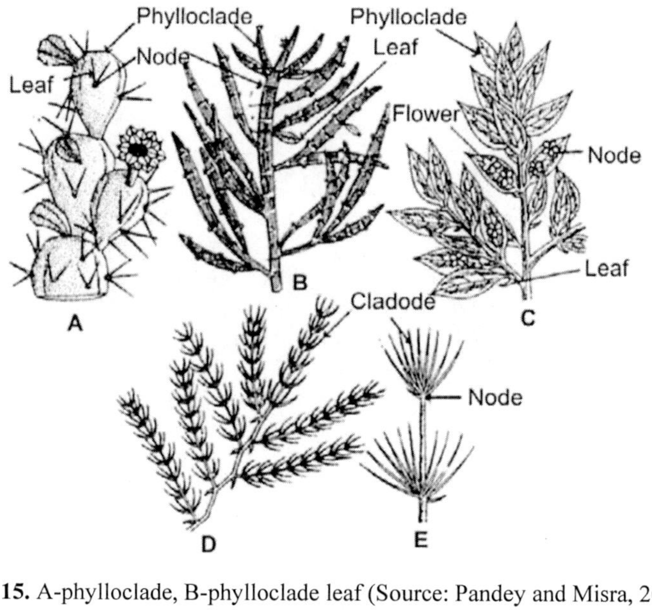

Fig. 1.15. A-phylloclade, B-phylloclade leaf (Source: Pandey and Misra, 2008).

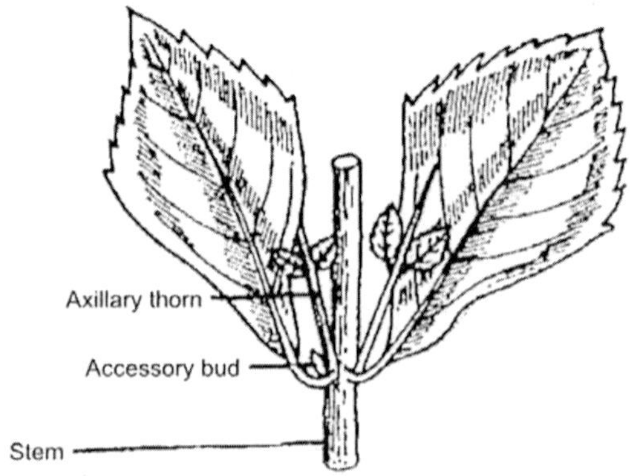

Fig. 1.16. Axillary branch modified into thorn (Source: Pandey and Misra, 2008).

C. Buds

a. Orientation: Apical, axillary (number per node); Sessile, stalked.

b. Shape.

c Size.

d. Surface: Smooth, pubescent, glandular.

e. Bud scales.

D. Root characters

a. Form: Tap, seminal, fibrous, normal, adventitious; Branched, unbranched.

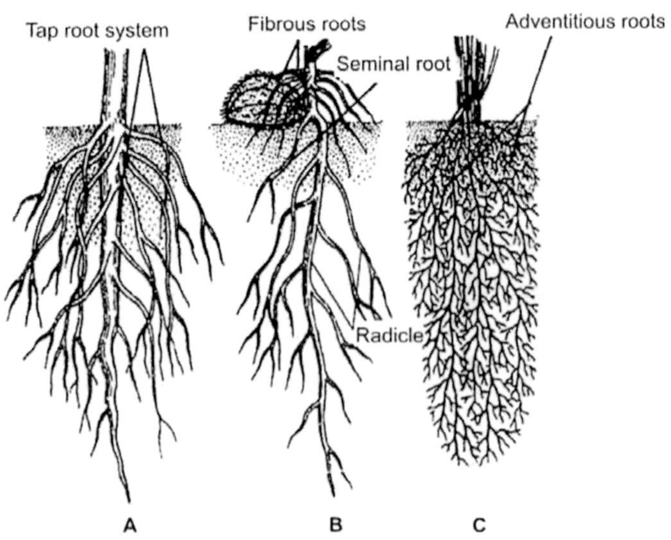

Fig. 1.17. A-tap root system, B-seminal roots in rice seedlings, and C-fibrous root system (Source: Pandey and Misra, 2008).

b. Modifications: Fusiform, conical, napiform; Tuberous, fasciculated, nodulose, moniliform, annulated; Epiphytic, parasitic; Assimilating, respiratory, reproductive, mycorrhizal; Prop, stilt, clinging, climbing, root buttresses, floating, contractile.

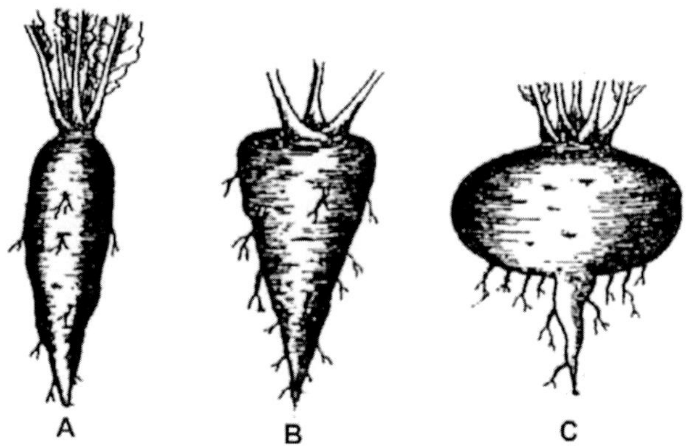

Fig. 1.18a. Modifications of root: A-fusiform, B-conical and C-napiform (Source: Pandey and Misra, 2008).

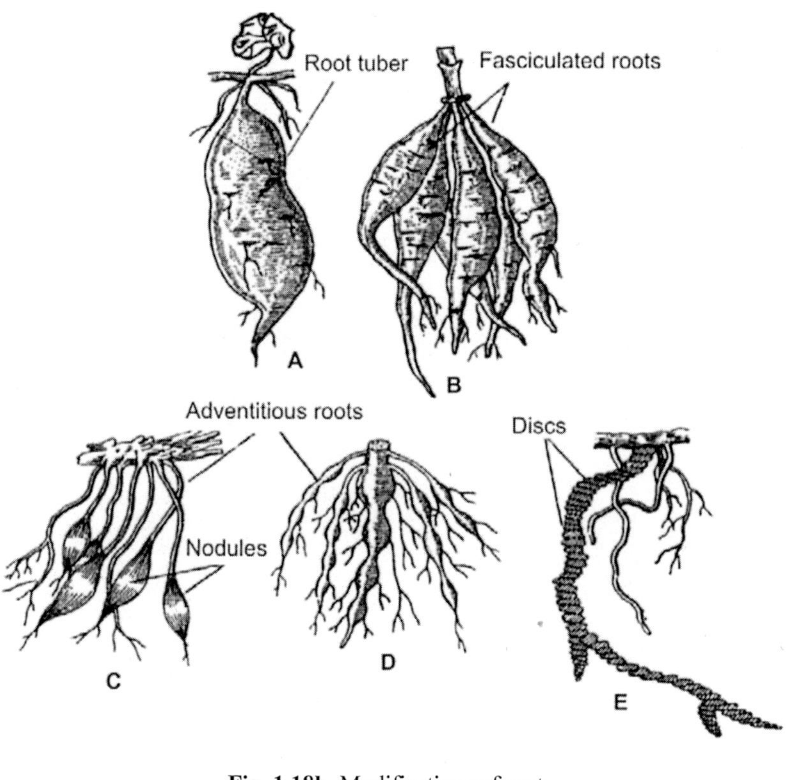

Fig. 1.18b. Modifications of root (Source: Pandey and Misra, 2008).

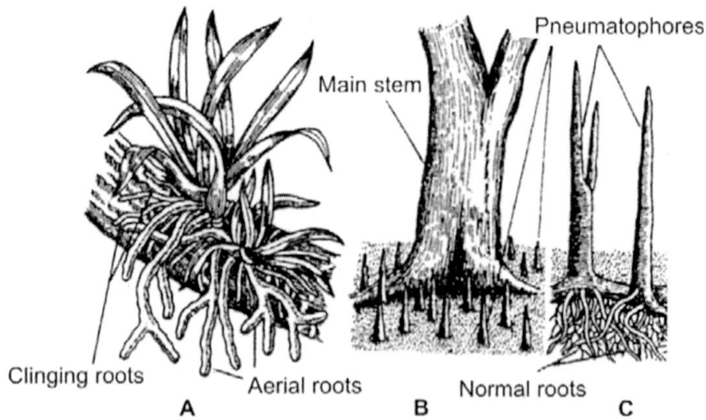

Fig. 1.18c. Modifications of root: A-aerial roots and B & C-respiratory roots (pneumatophores) (Source: Pandey and Misra, 2008).

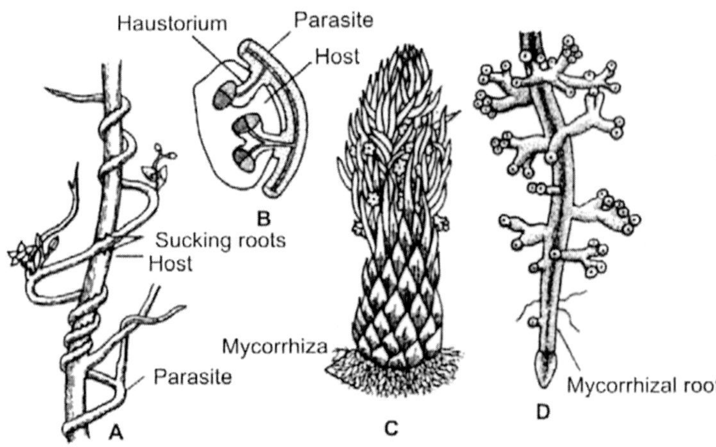

Fig. 1.18d. Modifications of root: A-haustorial roots, B-T.S. of host plant showing haustoria, C-mycorrhizal D-mycorrhizal root (Source: Pandey and Misra, 2008).

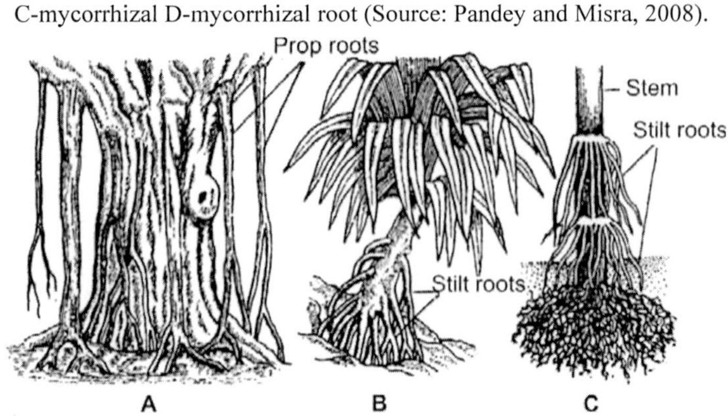

Fig. 1.18e. Modifications of root: A-prop roots, B-stilt roots and C-stilt roots (Source: Pandey and Misra, 2008).

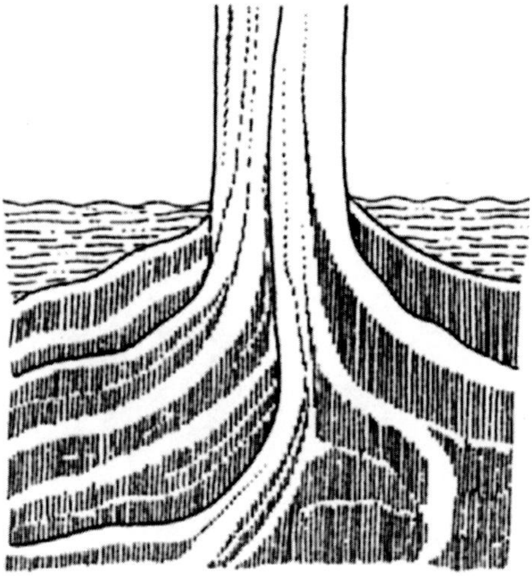

Fig. 1.18f. Modifications of root: Root buttresses (Source: Pandey and Misra, 2008).

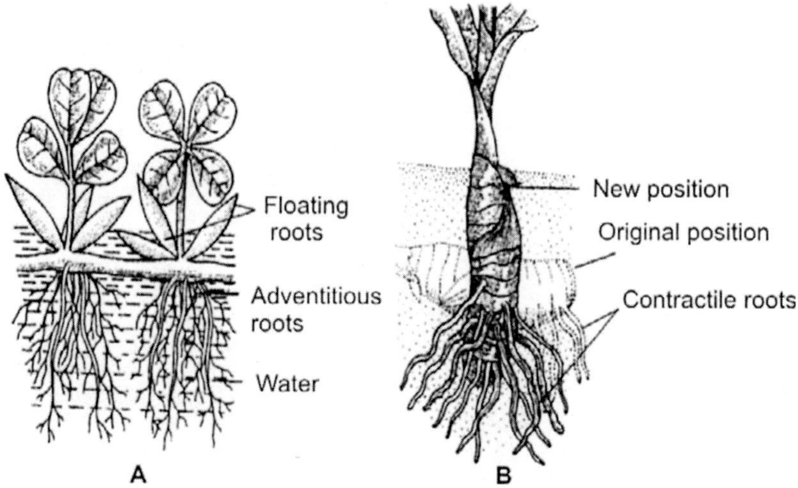

Fig. 1.18g. Modifications of root: A-floating roots and B-contractile roots (Source: Pandey and Misra, 2008).

E. Leaf characters

a. Kind: Cotyledonary, cataphylls or scale leaves, hypsophylls or bract leaves, prophylls, floral leaves or sporophylls, foliage leaves.

b. Duration: Caducous (fugacious), deciduous or annual, persistent.

c. Origin: Cauline, ramal, radical.

d. Phyllotaxy: Cauline, ramal, radical, spiral or alternate: orthostichous (distichous, tristichous, pentastichous, octastichous, etc.), parastichous; Cyclic; Opposite (opposite decussate, opposite superimposed); verticillate (whorled); Heterophylly, anisophylly.

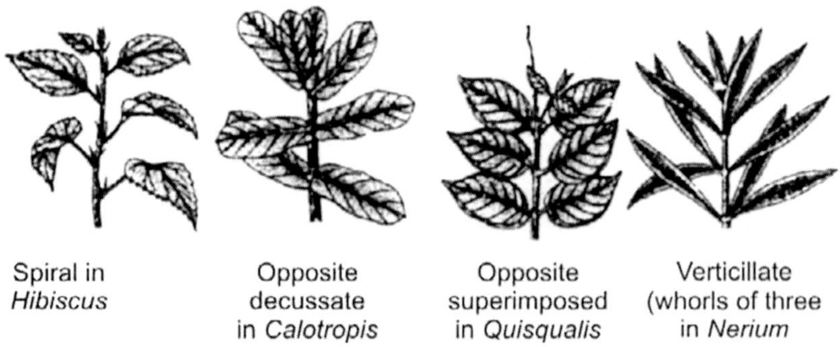

Fig. 1.19. Phyllotaxy: spiral, opposite decussate, opposite superimposed and verticillate (Source: Pandey and Misra, 2008)

e. Leaf parts

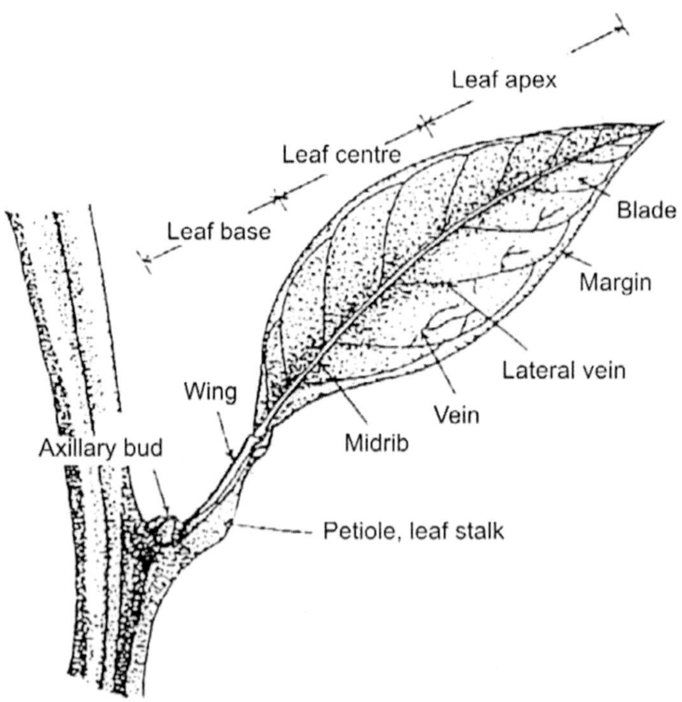

Fig. 1.20. Leaf parts

i. Hypopodium (Base): Pulvinus, sheathing, amplexicaul, decurrent.

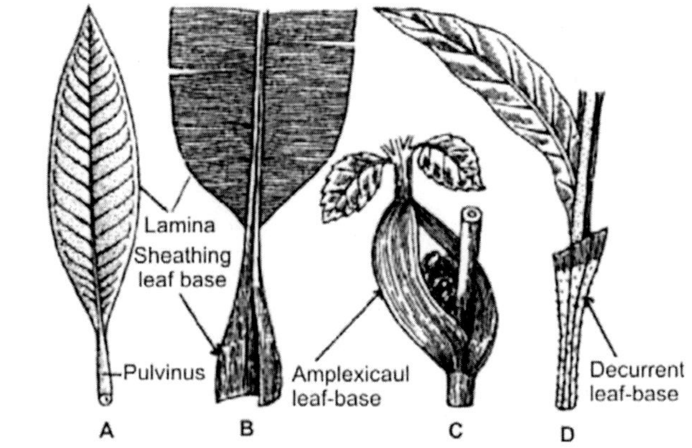

Fig. 1.21. Leaf base: A-pulvinus, B-sheathing leaf base, C-amplexicaul and D-decurrent (Source: Pandey and Misra, 2008)

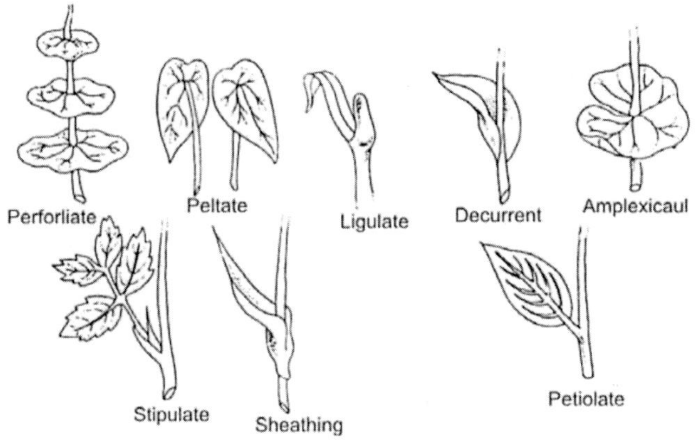

Fig. 1.22. Leaf attachment to stem

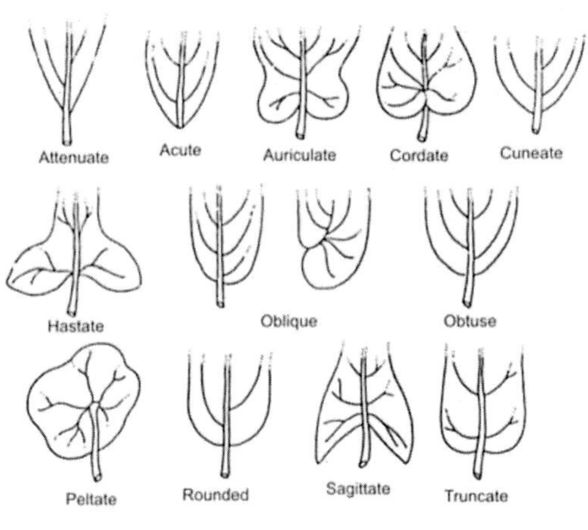

Fig. 1.23. Shape of leaf base

ii. Stipule: Ex-stipulate, stipulate; Adnate, free lateral, intrapetiolar, interpetiolar, ochreate; Tendriller, foliaceous, scaly, spinous, Caducous, deciduous; Stipels.

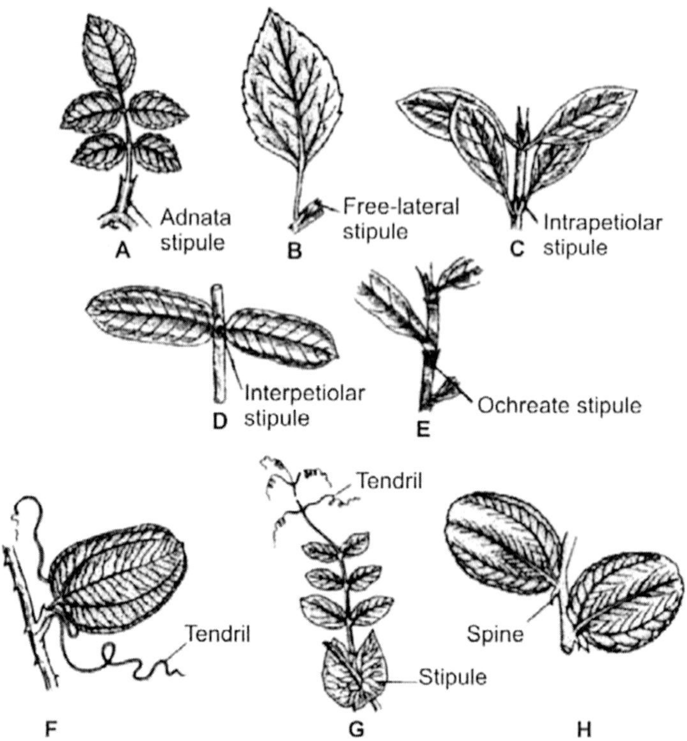

Fig. 1.24. Stipules: A-adnate, B-free lateral, C-intrapetiolar, D-interpetiolar, E-ochreate, F-tendrillar, G-foliaceous and H-spinous (Source: Pandey and Misra, 2008).

iii. Mesopodium (Petiole); Sessile, petiolate; Wing-like, winged, swollen (spongy), flattened, tendrillar, spinous; Presence of glands.

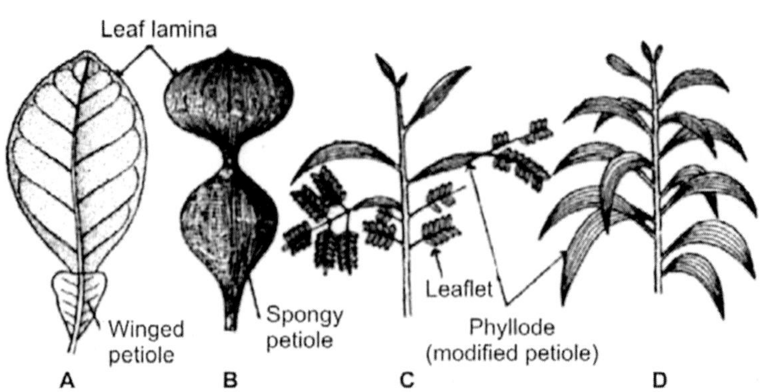

Fig. 1.25. Petiole: A-winged, B-spongy and C-phyllode. (C-young seedling part and D-mature leaf (phyllode) (Source: Pandey and Misra, 2008).

iv. Epipodium (Lamina): Dorsiventral, isobilateral, cylindrical.

1. Shape: Acicular, linear, lanceolate, oblong, ovate, cordate, sagittate, hastate, reniform, lunate, obovate, obcordate, spathulate, cuneate, elliptical, round.

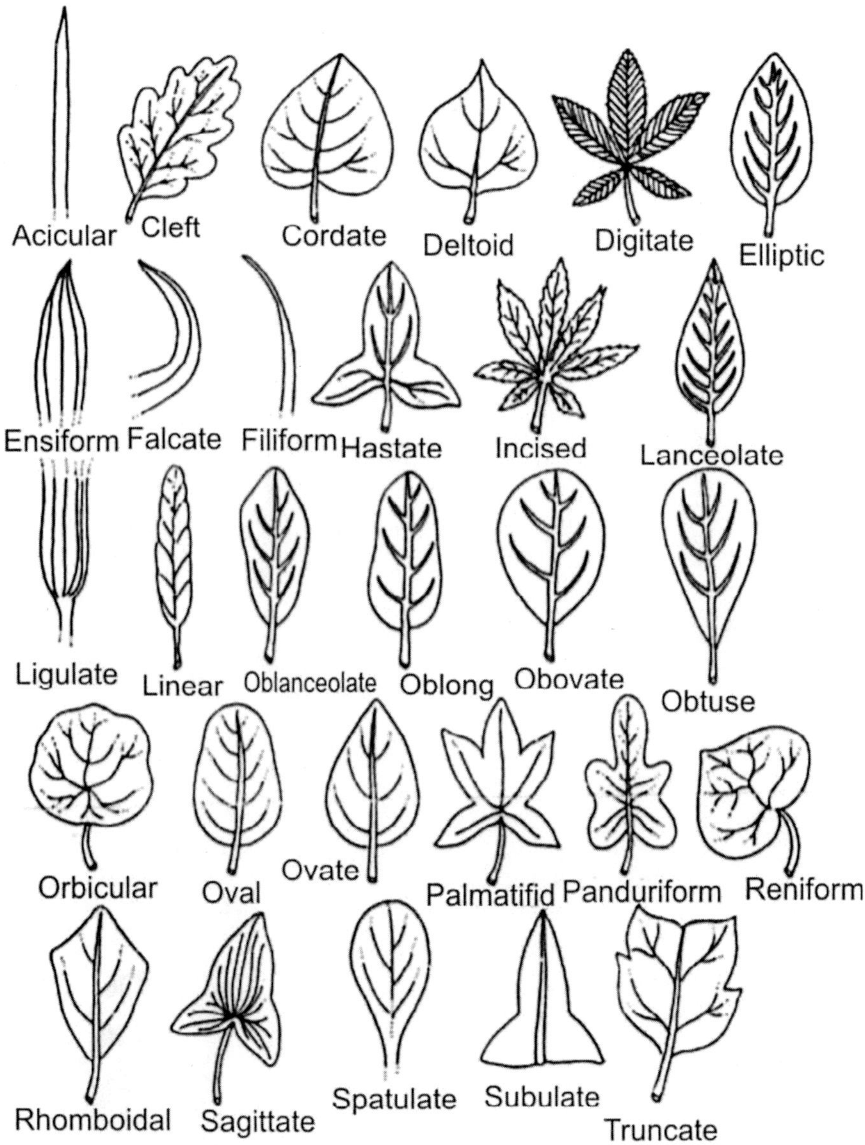

Fig. 1.26a. Shape of lamina.

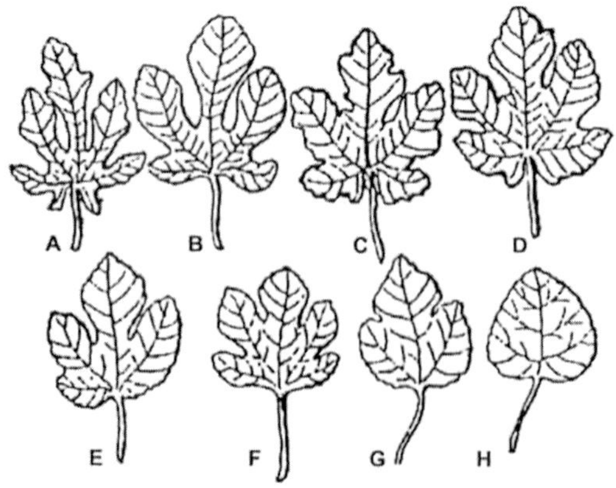

Fig. 1.26b. Shape of lamina (fig): A. Base calcarate, lobes linear, B. Base cordate, 5-lobed, lobes spathulate, C. Base calcarate, lobes lyrate, D. Base calcarate, lobes latate, E. Base cordate, 3-lobed, F. Base truncate, G. Base decurrent, H. Leaf not lobed (Source: IPGRI and CIHEAM, 2003).

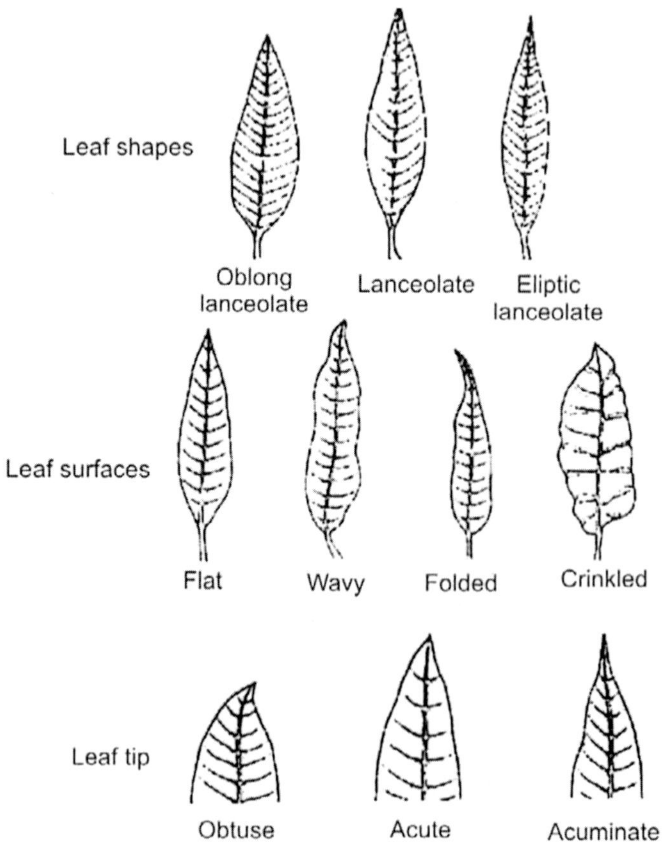

Fig. 1.26c. Shape of lamina (mango) (Source: IPGRI. 2006).

2. Size.

3. Margin: Entire, repand (wavy), serrate, biserrate, retroserrate, dentate, bidentate, crenate, bicrenate, spiny, lobed (incised).

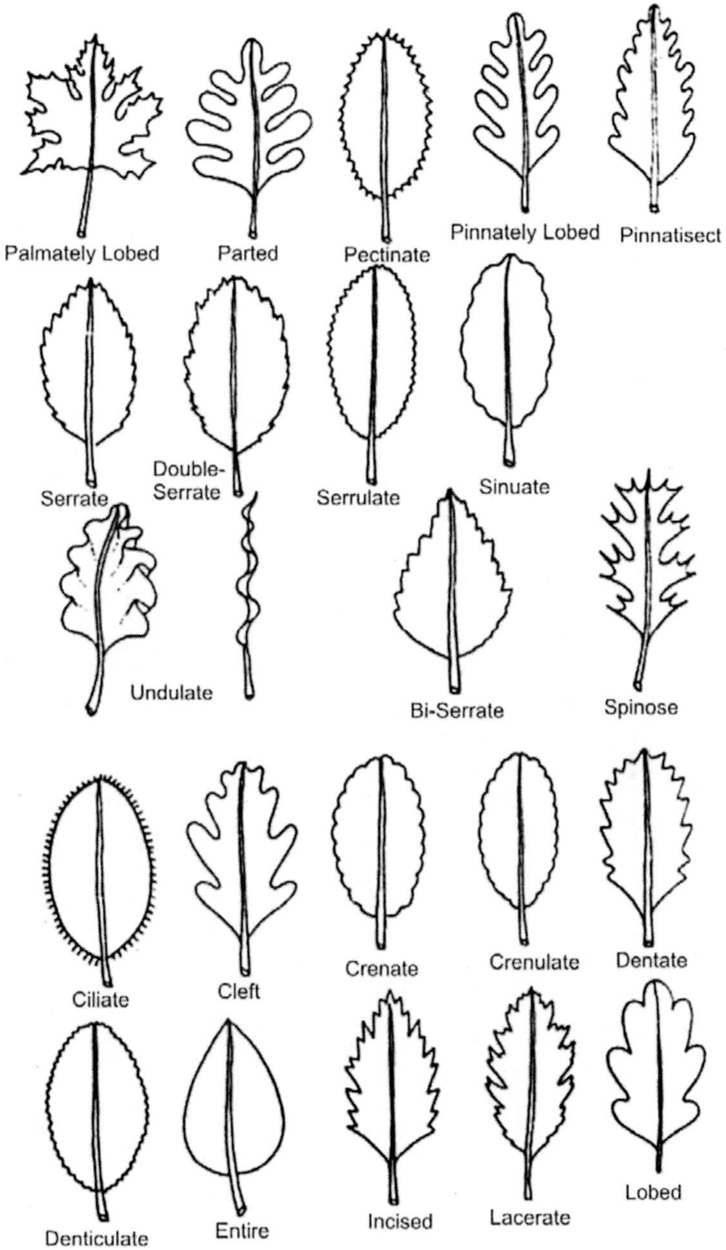

Fig. 1.27a. Leaf margin.

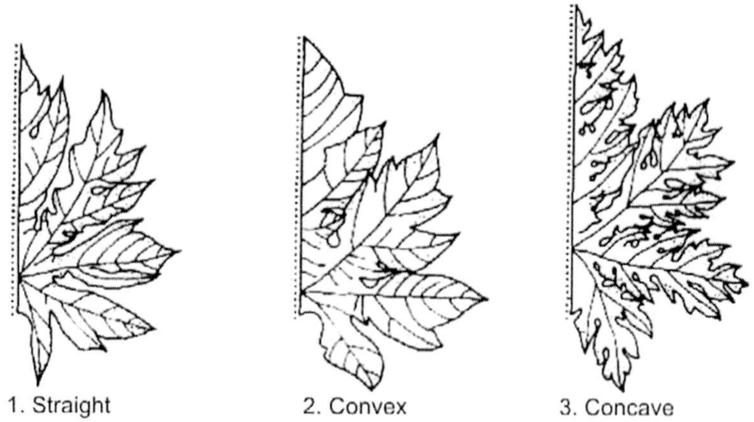

Fig. 1.27b. Leaf margin (papaya) (Source: IPGRI, 1988).

4. Incision: Simple, compound (pinnate, palmate).

Pinnate compound: Simple pinnate or unipinnate (paripinnate, imparipinnate), bipinnate, tripinnate, decompound.

Palmate compound: Unifoliate, bifoliate, trifoliate, quadrifoliate, multifoliate.

Fig. 1.28a. Leaf incision: A-simple, B-pinnate-paripinnate compound, C-pinnate-imparipinnate compound, D-bipinnate compound, E-tripinnate compound and F-decompound (Source: Pandey and Misra, 2008).

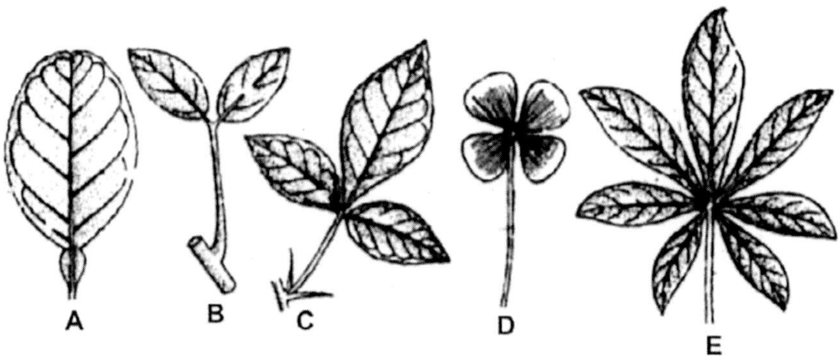

Fig. 1.28b. Leaf incision: Palmate compound leaves: A. unifoliate, B. bifoliate, C. trifoliate, D. quadrifoliate and E. multifoliate (Source: Pandey and Misra, 2008).

5. Apex: Acute, acuminate, obtuse, mucronate, cuspidate, tendrillar, cirrhose, truncate, retuse, emarginate.

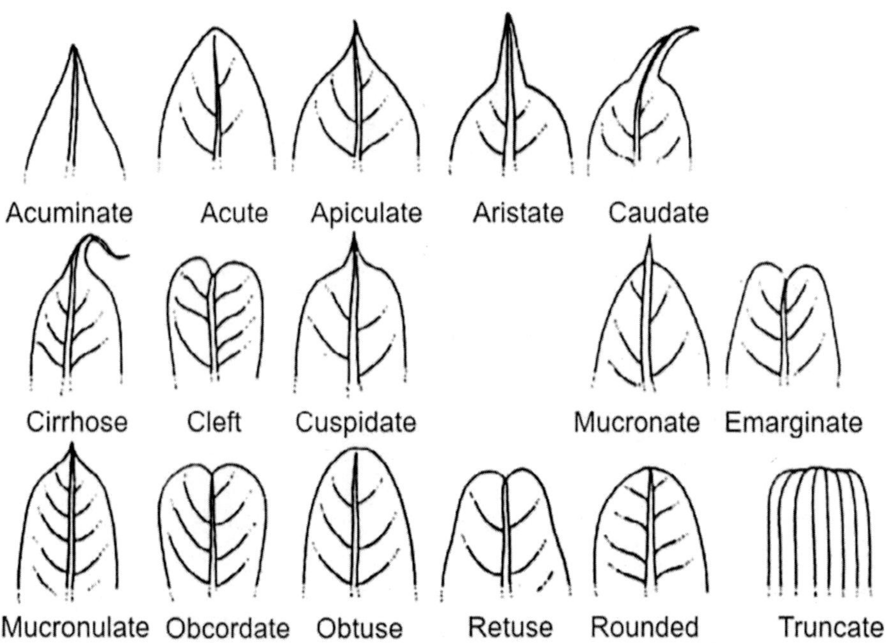

Fig. 1.29. Leaf apex (Source: Heywood *et al.,* 2007).

6. Surface: Glabrous, glaucus, scabrous viscose, rugose, gland dotted, spinose, hairy (pubescent, pilose, villose, tomentose, wooly, hirsute, hispid), spinose.

7. Venation: Reticulate (unicostate or pinnate, multicostate or palmate-convergent palmate, divergent palmate), parallel or striate (unicostate, multicostate-multicostate convergent, multicostate divergent).

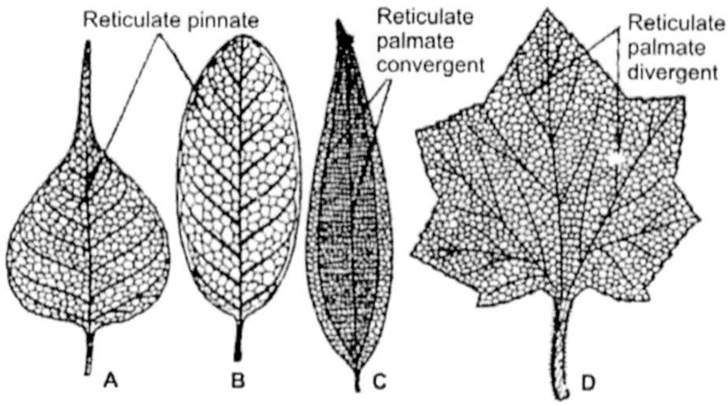

Fig. 1.30a. Leaf venation: Reticulate venation: A-unicostate, B-unicostate showing zuhmarginal veins, C-palmate convergent, D-palmate divergent (Source: Pandey and Misra, 2008).

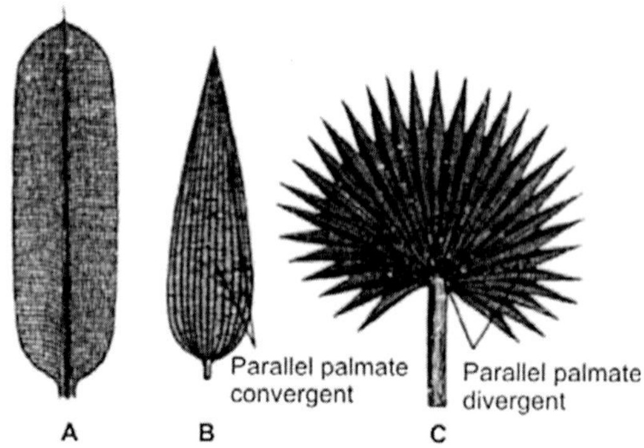

Fig. 1.30b. Leaf venation: Parallel venation: A-unicostate, B-palmate convergent and C-palmate divergent (Source: Pandey and Misra, 2008).

8. Modifications: Tendrillar, hooks, pitcher, bladder, fleshy, absorbing.

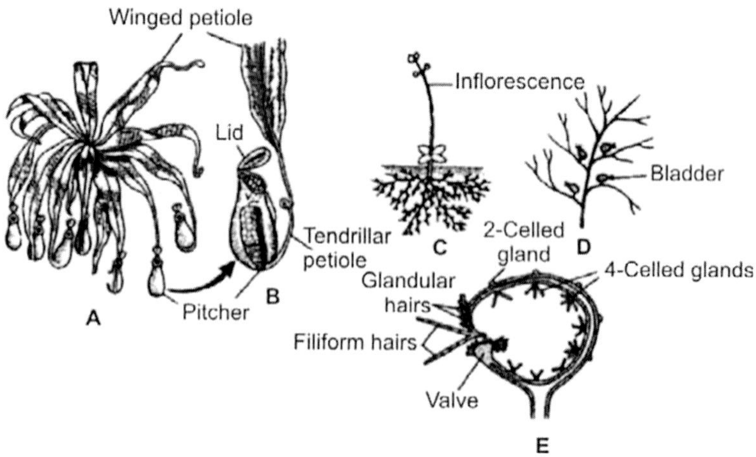

Fig. 1.31. Modifications of leaves in insectivorous plants: A-a plant of *Nepenthes*. B-a single leaf with pitcher, C-a plant of *Utricularia*. D-a part of leaf bearing bladders and E-C.S. of the bladder (Source: Pandey and Misra, 2008).

v. Bracts and bracteoles: Foliaceous or leafy, petalloid, spathy, involucral, scaly, cupule, epicalyx, glumes, flowering glume or lemma and bracteole palea.

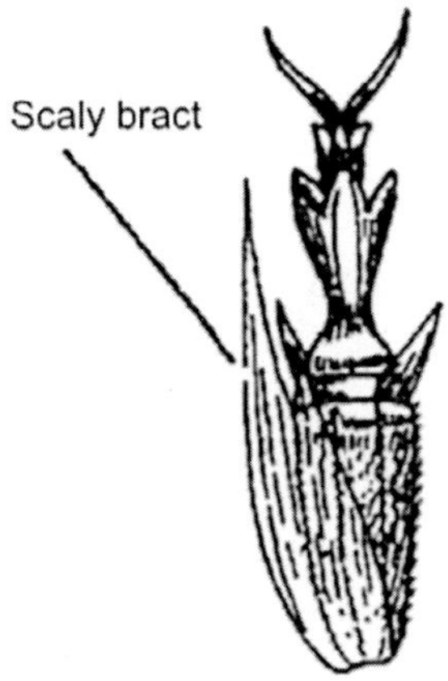

Fig. 1.32. Scaly bract of a floret (Source: Pandey and Misra, 2008).

F. Inflorescence: Simple (racemose or indefinite, cymose or definite).

a. Racemose: Raceme, spike, spikelet, catkin (ament), spadix, corymb, umbel, capitulum (head); (ray floret, disc floret).

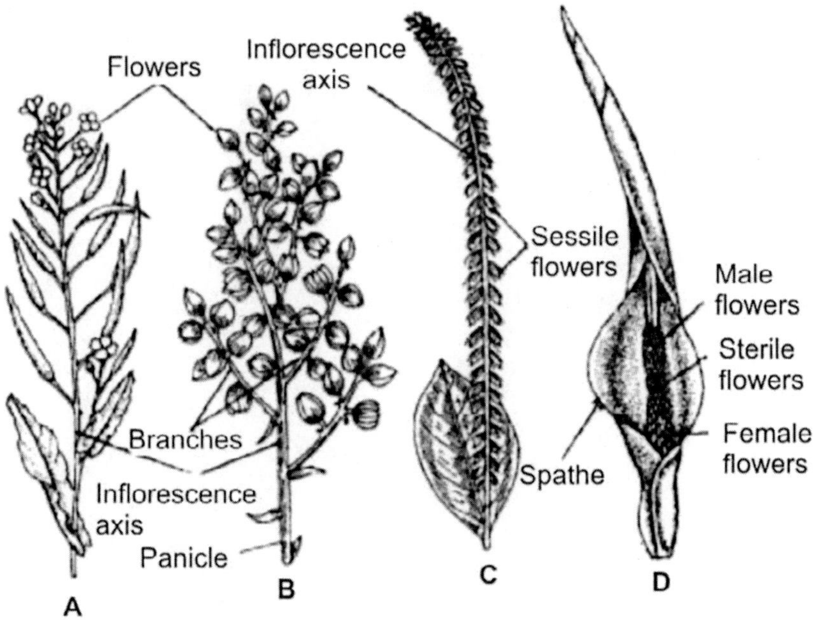

Fig. 1.33a. Inflorescence types: A-raceme, B-panicle, C-spike and D-spadix (Source: Pandey and Misra, 2008).

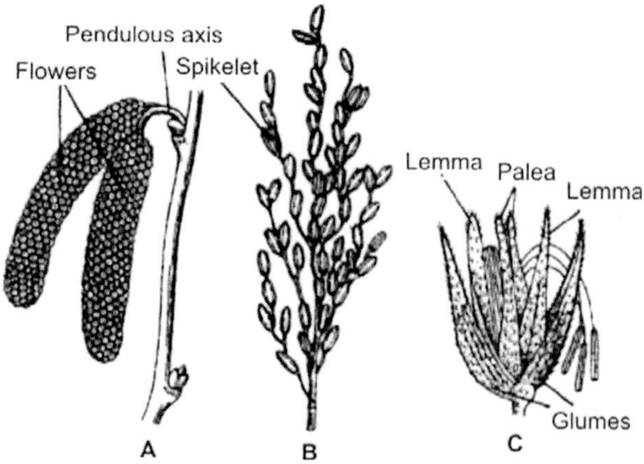

Fig. 1.33b. Inflorescence types: A-catkin, B-spikelet and C-spikelet with two florets (Source: Pandey and Misra, 2008).

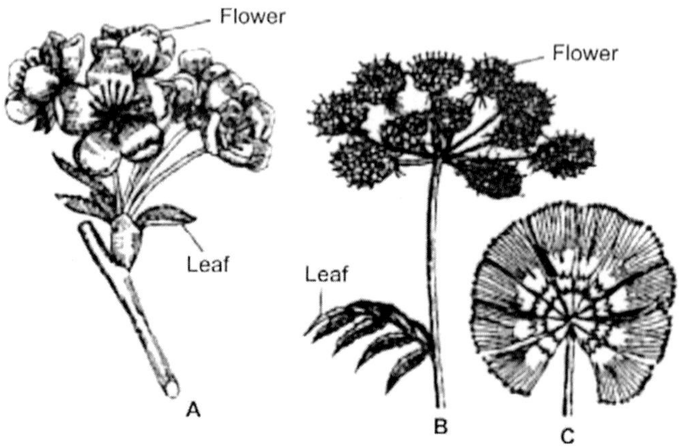

Fig. 1.33c. Inflorescence types: A-corymb, B-compound umbel, and C-a single umbel (enlarged) (Source: Pandey and Misra, 2008).

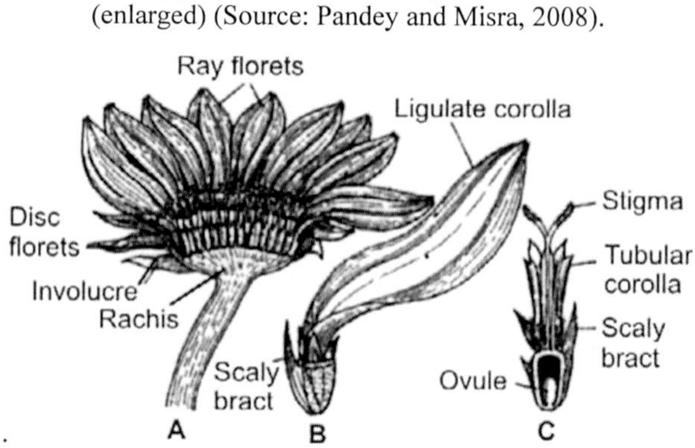

Fig. 1.33d. Inflorescence types: Capitulum inflorescence. A-L.S. of inflorescence, B-a ray floret and C-a disc floret (Source: Pandey and Misra, 2008).

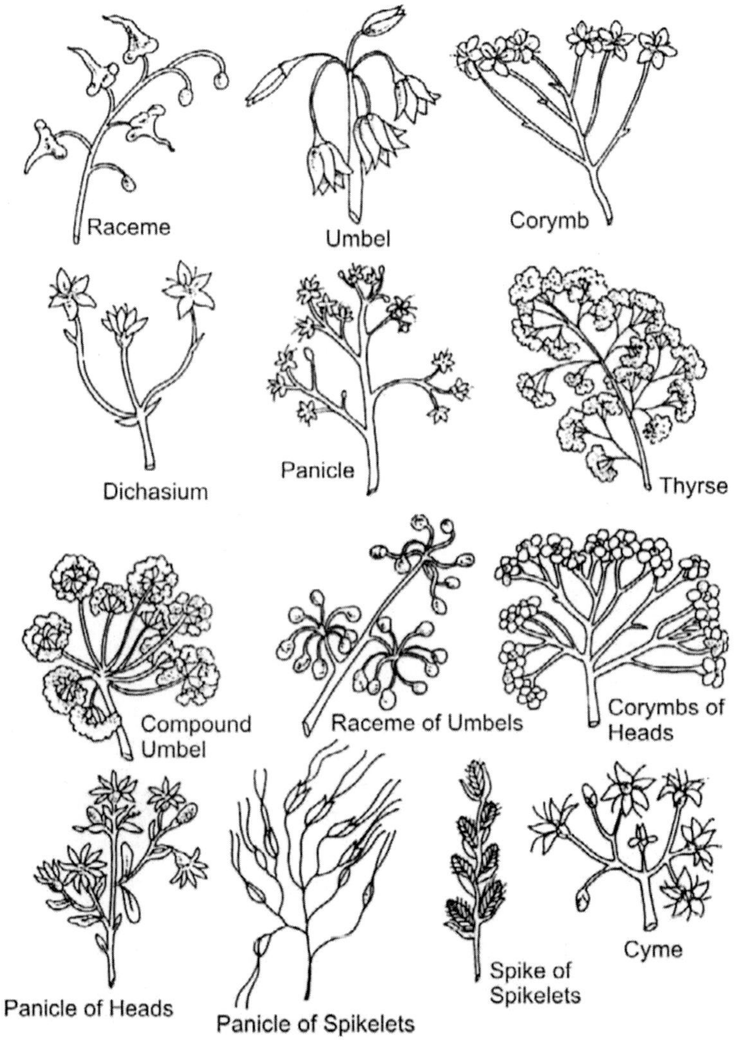

Fig. 1.33e. Inflorescence types.

b. Cymose: Monochasial or uniparous (helicoids or bostryx, scorpioid), dichasial or biparous, polychasial or multiparous.

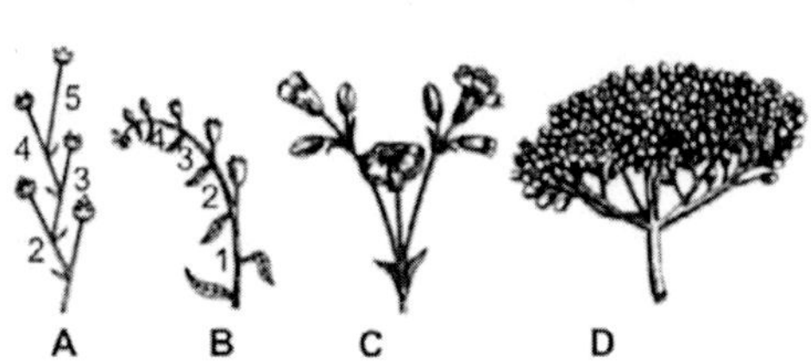

Fig. 1.33f. Inflorescence types: Monochasial (A-scorpoid cyme and B-helicoid cyme), C-dichasial cyme and D-polychasial cyme (Source: Pandey and Misra, 2008).

c. Compound: Raceme or panicle, spike of spikelets, corymb, umbel.

d. Special: Cyathium, verticillaster, hypanthodium.

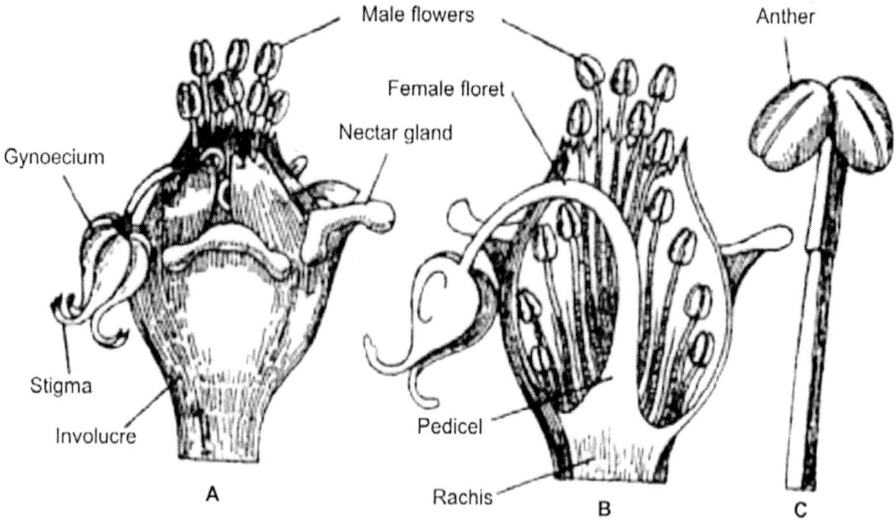

Fig. 1.34a. Inflorescence Special: Cyathium inflorescence. A-external view. B-L.S. of inflorescence and C-a male (staminate) flower (Source: Pandey and Misra, 2008).

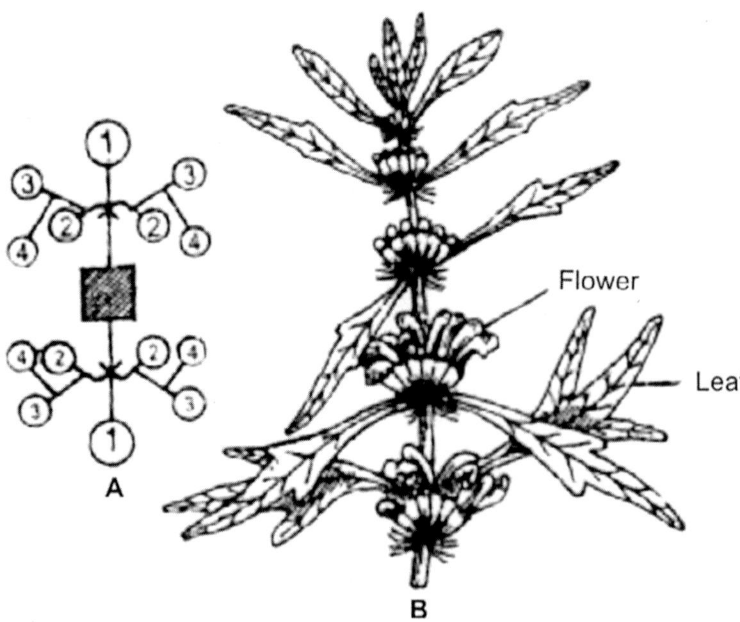

Fig. 1.34b. Inflorescence Special: Verticillaster inflorescence. A-flowering sequence and B-a twig with inflorescence (Source: Pandey and Misra, 2008).

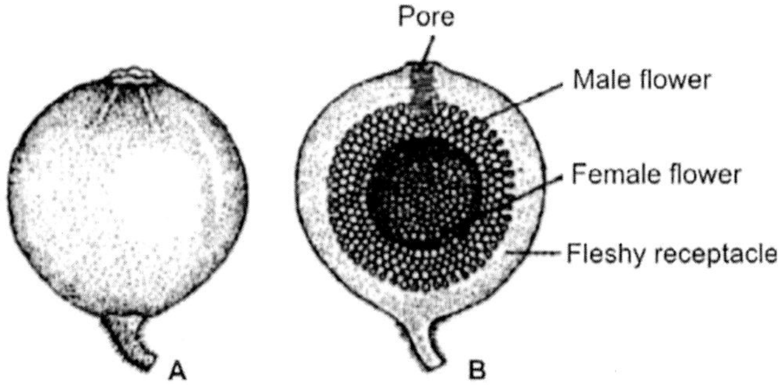

Fig.1.34c. Inflorescence Special: Hypanthodium inflorescence.
A-external view and B-L.S. of inflorescence (Source: Pandey and Misra, 2008).

e. Hairiness.

f. Special terms: Peduncle, scape, rachila, strobile, umbellule, cymule, cincinus (or cincinnus), drepanium, rhipidium, glomerule, tassel, thyrse (or thyrsus), secund.

G. Flower:

a. Flower parts: Calyx, corolla, androecium, gynoecium.

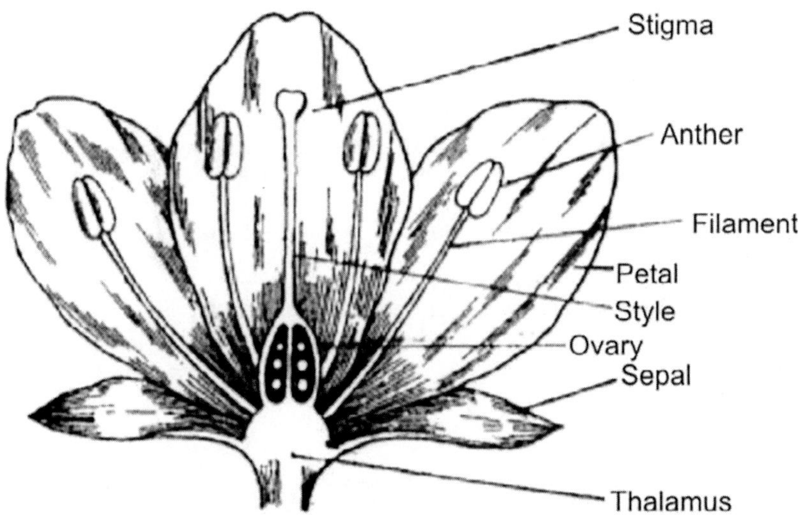

Fig. 1.35. L.S. of flower (Source: Pandey and Misra, 2008).

Dioecious, monoecious, polygamous; Complete, incomplete; Hermaphrodite, unisexual, staminate, pistillate, neuter; Actinomorphic, zygomorphic, asymmetric; Bracteate, ebracteate; Pedicellate, sessile; Hypogynous, perigynous, epigynous; Trimerous, tetramerous, pentamerous; Nectaries present or absent.

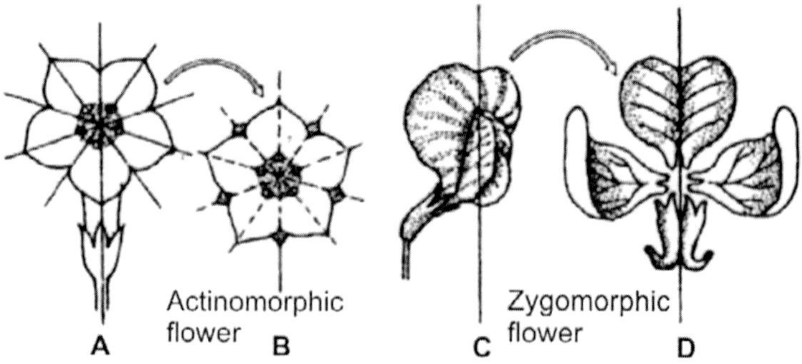

Fig. 1.36. Form of flower: A & B-actinomorphic (B-surface view) and C & D-zygomorphic (D-petals separated) (Source: Pandey and Misra, 2008).

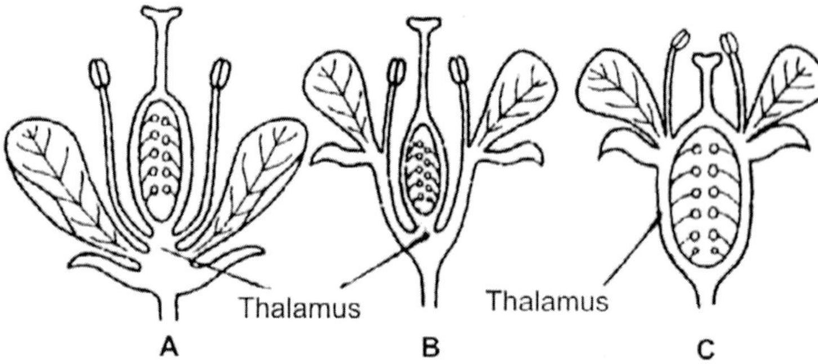

Fig. 1.37. Position of floral parts in relation to thalamus: A-hypogynous flower, B-perigynous flower and C-epigynous flower (Source: Chhabra, 2006).

b. Flower bud: Shape; Size; Colour; Presence of scales.

c. Rachis: Colour

d. Calyx: Number of sepals, polysepalous, gamosepalous, asepalous, petaloid; Caducous, persistent; tubular, cupulate, urceolate, campanulate, bilabiate, spurred, pappus, spinous, leaf-like, hooded; Aestivation: Valvate, twisted, imbricate, quincuncial, vexillary.

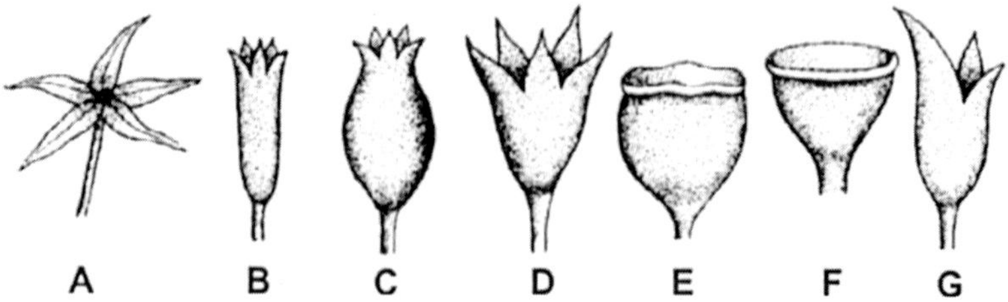

Fig. 1.38a. Forms of calyx: A-free; B-tubular, C-urceolate, D-campanulate, E-cupulate, F-infundibuliform and G-bilabiate (Source: Pandey and Misra, 2008).

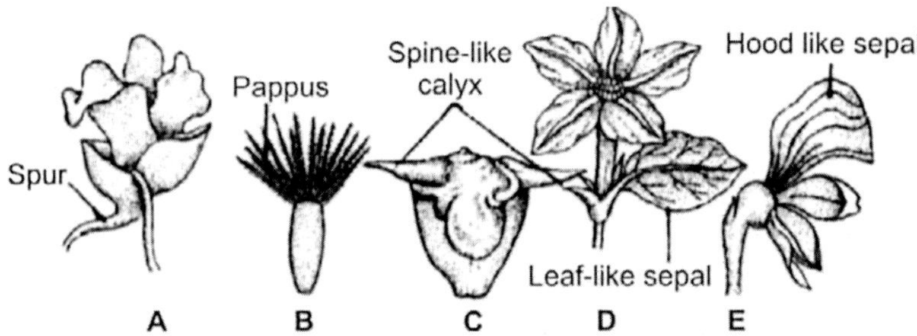

Fig. 1.38b. Forms of calyx: A-spurred. B-pappus, C-spinous, D-leaf-like and E-hooded (Source: Pandey and Misra, 2008).

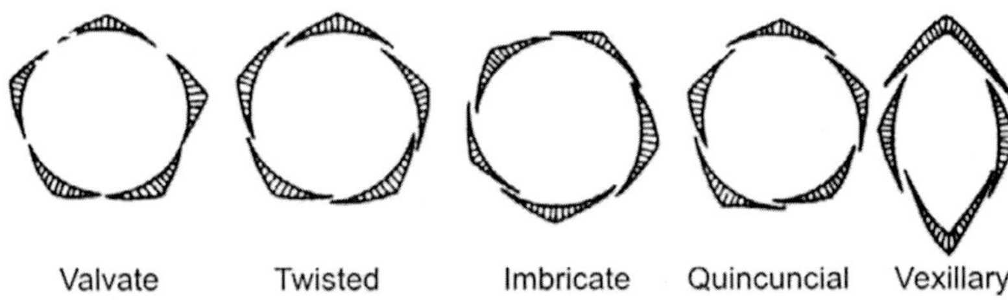

Fig. 1.39. Aestivation of the calyx (Source: Pandey and Misra, 2008).

e. Corolla: Number of petals, polypetalous, gamopetalous, apetalous, sepaloid; Caducous, persistent; cruciform, rosaceous, caryophyllaceous, papilionaceous, tubular, infundibuliform, campanulate, hypocrateriform, trumpet-shaped, urceolate, rotate, bilabiate ringent, bilabiate personate, ligulate; Aestivation: valvate, twisted, imbricate, quincuncial, vexillary.

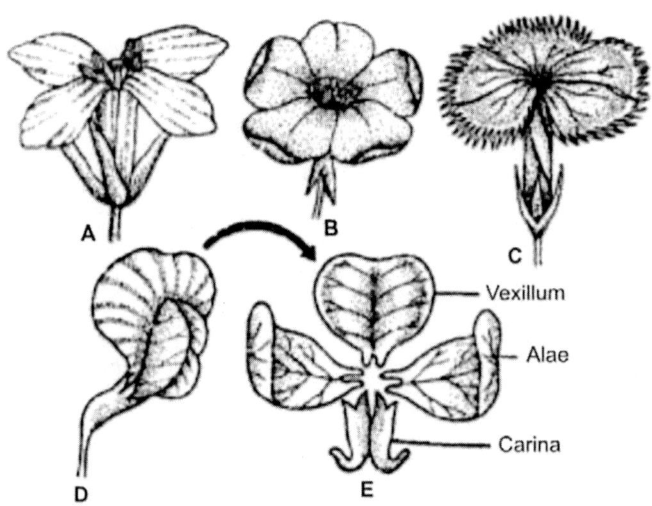

Fig. 1.40a. Forms of polypetalous corolla: A-cruciform, B-rosaceous, C-caryophyllaceous and D-papilionaceous (E-exposed petals of D) (Source: Pandey and Misra, 2008).

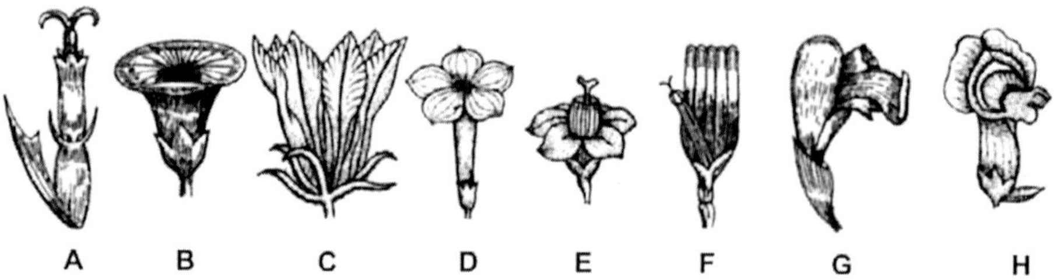

Fig. 1.40b. Forms of gamopetalous corolla: A-tubular, B-infundibuliform, C-campanulate, D-hypocrateriform, E-rotate, F-ligulate, G-bilabiate ringent and H-bilabiate personate (Source: Pandey and Misra, 2008).

f. Perianth: Gamopetalous, polypetalous, sepaloid, petaloid.

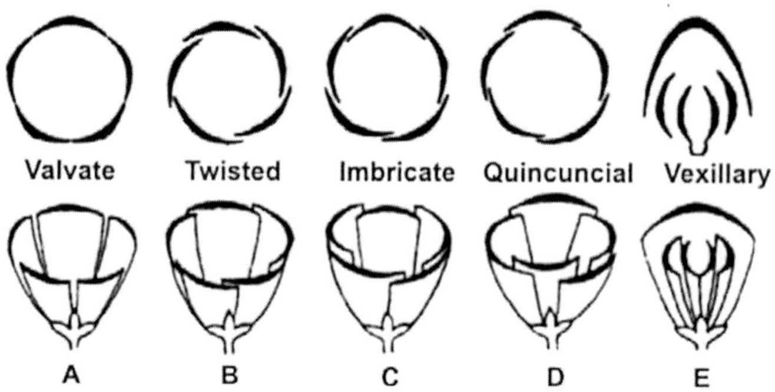

Fig. 1.41. Aestivation of corolla: A-valvate, B-twisted, C- imbricate, D-quincuncial and E-vexillary in two different views (Source: Pandey and Misra, 2008).

g. Androecium: Number of stamens (monandrous, diandrous, triandrous, tetrandrous, pentandrous, hexandrous, polyandrous).

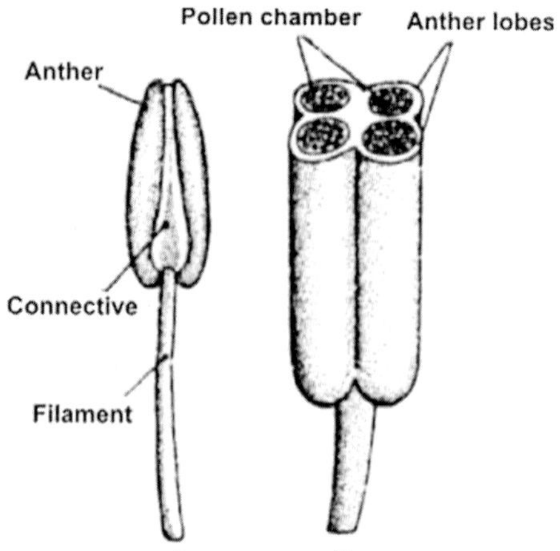

Fig. 1.42a. Parts of a stamen A and B-anther showing internal structure in T.S. (Source: Pandey and Misra, 2008).

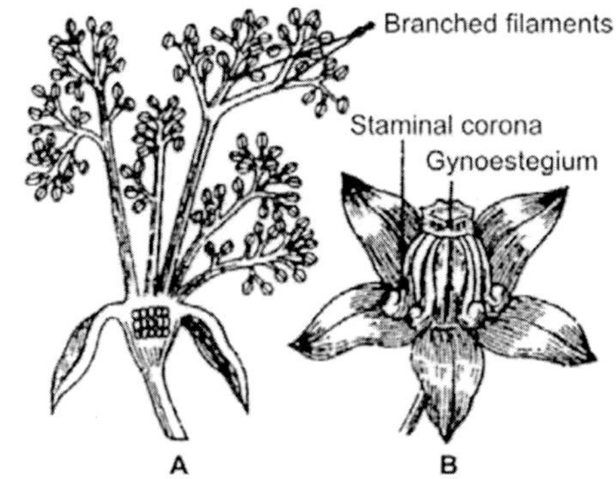

Fig. 1.42b. Parts of a stamen: A-branched stamens and B-gynostegium (Source: Pandey and Misra, 2008).

Cohesion of stamens: Monadelphous, diadelphous, polyadelphous, syngenesious, synandrous.

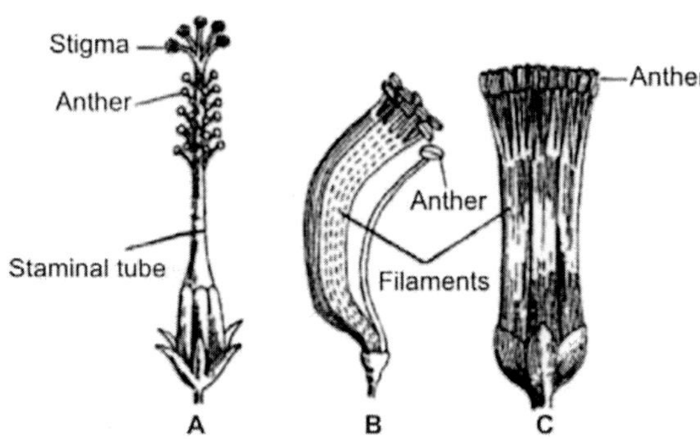

Fig. 1.43a. Cohesion of stamens:A-monadelphous, B and C-polyadelphous (Source: Pandey and Misra, 2008).

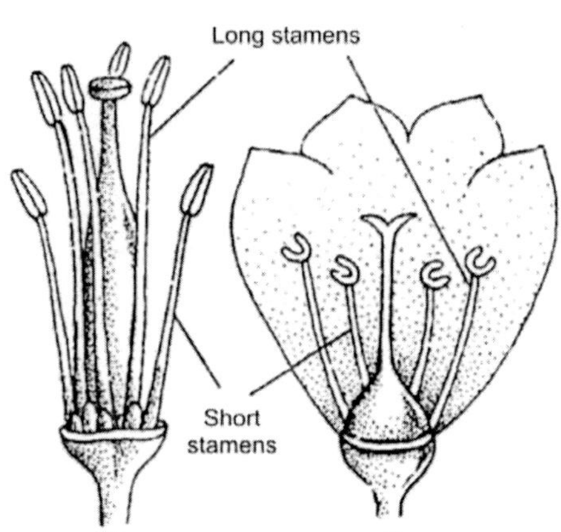

Fig. 1.43b. Cohesion of stamens: A-tetradynamous and B-didynamous (Source: Pandey and Misra, 2008).

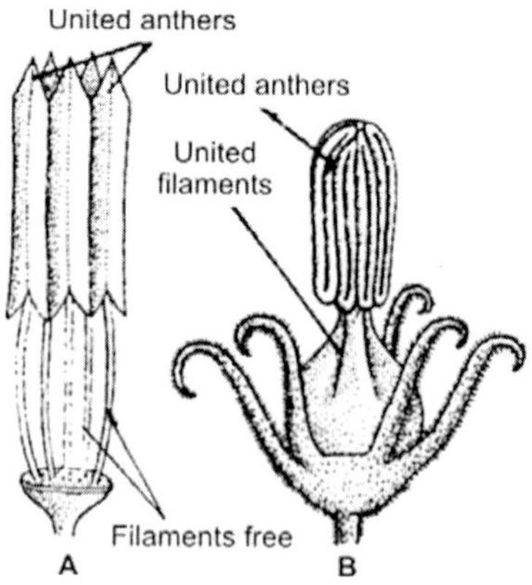

Fig.1.43c. Cohesion of stamens:A-syngenesious and B-synandrous (Source: Pandey and Misra, 2008).

Adhesion of stamens: epipetalous, epiphyllous, gynandrous.

Insertion of thalamus: Diplostemonous, obdiplostemonous.

Attachment of filament with anther lobe: Basifixed, dorsifixed, adnate, versatile.

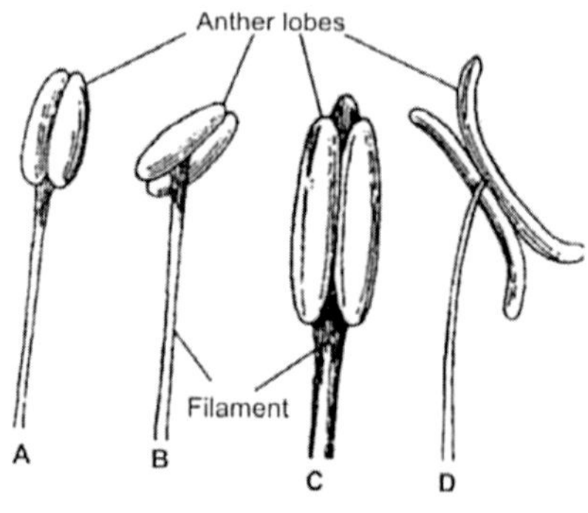

Fig. 1.44. Adhesion of stamens: A-basifixed, B-dorsifixed, C-adnate and D-versatile (Source: Pandey and Misra, 2008).

Dehiscence: extrose, introse, longitudinal, transeverse, porous or apical, valvular.

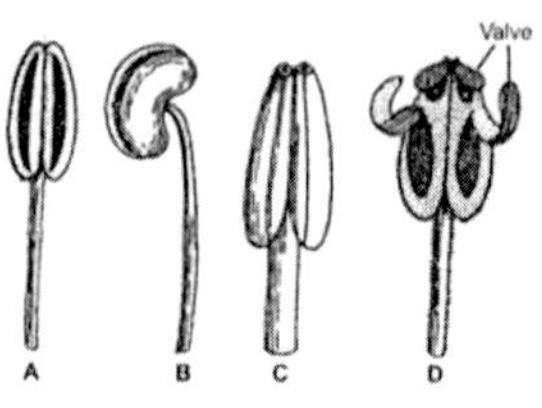

Fig. 1.45. Dehiscence of stamen: A-longitudinal, B-transverse, C-porous and D-valvular (Source: Pandey and Misra, 2008).

Filament: Long, short; Didynamous, tetradynamous; inserted, exserted, branched, gynostegium.

h. Gynoecium:

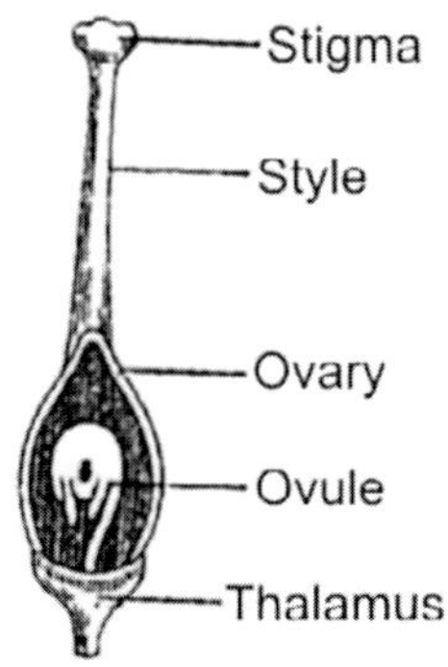

Fig. 1.46. A carpel showing different parts (Source: Pandey and Misra, 2008).

Number of carpels (monocarpellary, bicarpellary, tricarpellary, pentacarpellary, multicarpellary).

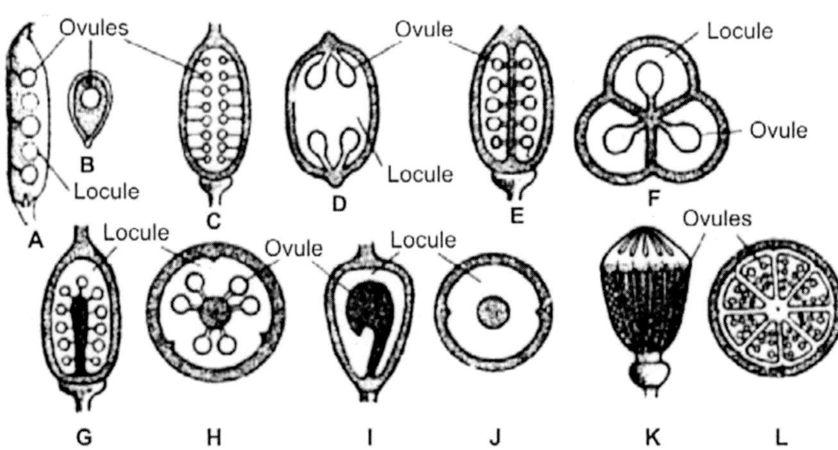

Fig. 1.47. Ovaries with placentation: A, B-monocarpellary with marginal placentation, C, D-bicarpellary with parietal placentation, E, F-tricarpellary with axile placentation, G, H-tricarpellary with free central placentation, I, J-bicarpellary with basal placentation and K, L-multicarpellary with superficial placentation (Source: Pandey and Misra, 2008).

Fusion of carpels: Apocarpous, syncarpous.

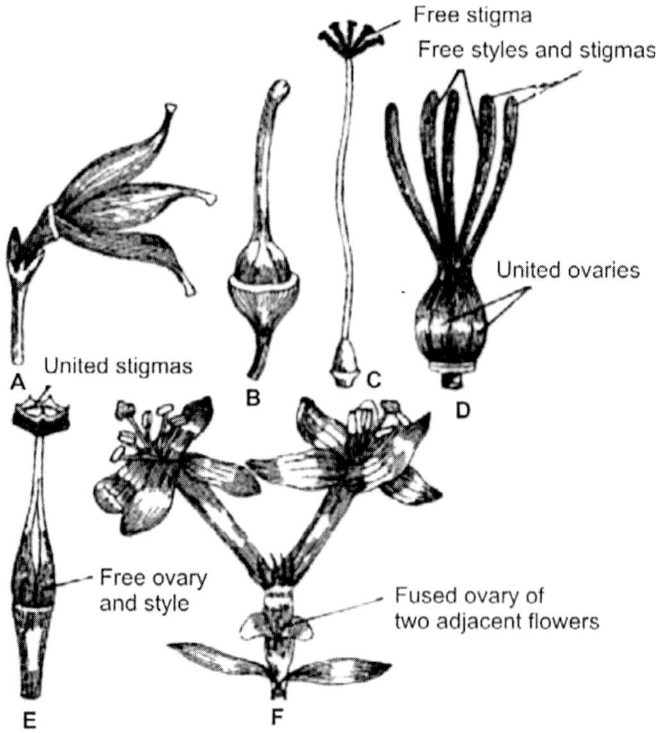

Fig. 1.48. Types of pistil: A-apocarpous, B-syncarpous, C-pistil with free stigmas, D-free style and stigma, E-ovary and style free and F-fused ovary of two adjacent flowers, i.e., syngynia (Source: Pandey and Misra, 2008).

Number of locules: unilocular, bilocular, trilocular, tetralocular, pentalocular, polylocular.

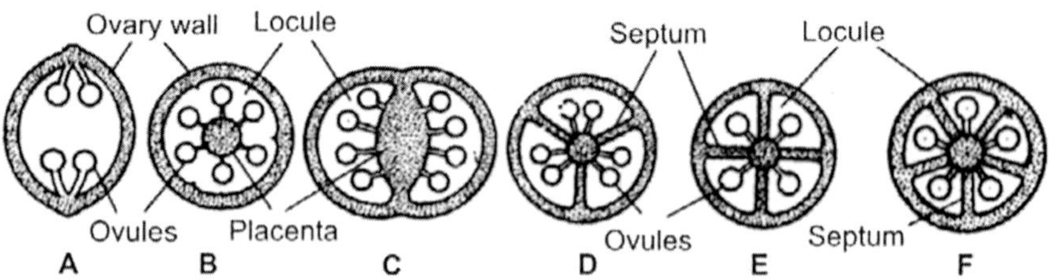

Fig. 1.49. Locules in ovary: A-B-unilocular, C-bilocular, D-trilocular, E-tetralocular and F-pentalocular (Source: Pandey and Misra, 2008).

Position of thalamus: superior, inferior, semi-inferior.

Placentation: Marginal, parietal, axile, free central, superficial, basal.

Style: Free, united, apical, lateral, gynobasic, branched.

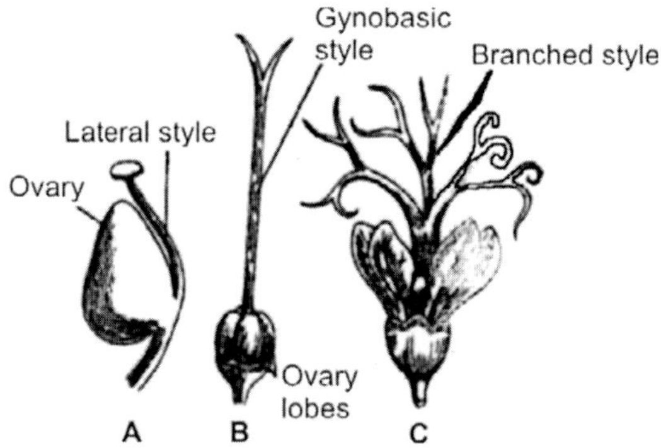

Fig. 1.50. Type of style: A-lateral, B-gynobasic and C-branched (Source: Pandey and Misra, 2008).

Stigma: Simple, capitates, discoid, lobed, bifid, bifid curved, bifid straight, sessile and straight, highly branched.

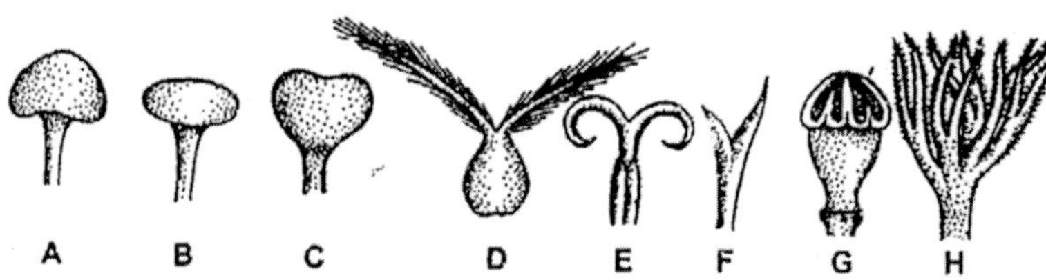

Fig. 1.51. Type of stigma: A-capitate, B-discoid, C-lobed, D-bifid. E-bifid curved, F-bifid straight, G-sessile and straight and H-highly branched (Source: Pandey and Misra, 2008).

Ovule: Orthostichous, anatropous, amphitropous, hemianatropous, campylotropous, circinotropous; Ategmic, unitegmic, bitegmic.

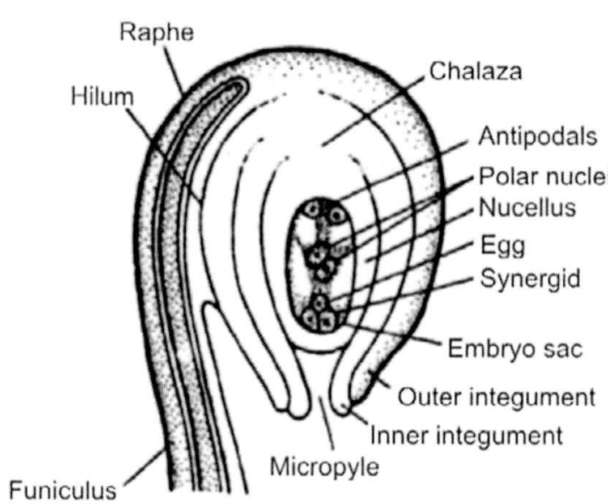

Fig. 1.52. L.S. of an ovule (Source: Pandey and Misra, 2008).

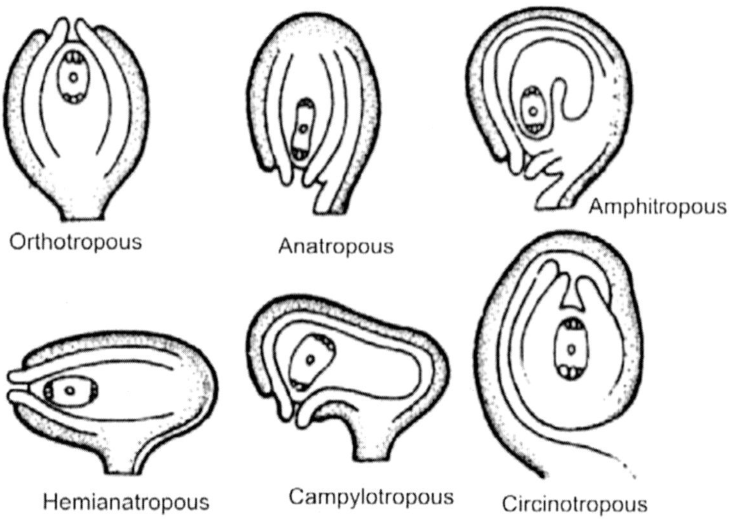

Fig. 1.53. Types of ovule (Source: Pandey and Misra, 2008).

i. Pollination: Autogamy, geitonogamy, homogamy, cleistogamy, allogamy, xenogamy, dicliny (unisexuality), dichogamy, protandrous, protogynous, heteromorphy, herkogamy; entomophily, ornithophily, cheiropterophily, malacophily, anemophily, hydrophily.

j. Floral formula (notations):

Br	Bracteate,	(C)	Corolla fused,	brl	Bracteolate,
P	Perianth,	⊕	Actinomorphic,	A	Stamens free,
%	Zygomorphic,	(A)	Stamens fused,	♂	Staminate,
G	Gynoecium free,	♀	Pistillate,	(G)	Gynoecium fused,
⚥	Bisexual or Hermaphrodite,	$\overline{G}$	Ovary inferior,	Ŏ	Neuter,
$\underline{G}$	Ovary superior,	Ep. K	Epicalyx,	∞	Indefinite,
K	Calyx free,	$\widetilde{CA}$	Epipetalous stamens,	(K)	Calyx fused,
$\widetilde{PA}$	epiphyllous stamens,	C	Corolla free		

For example, floral formula of *Hibiscus rosa-sinensis* is

⊕♂$Epi_{5-8}\ K_{(5)}\ C_5\ A_{(\square)}G_{(5)}$

ii. Method for sketching floral diagram

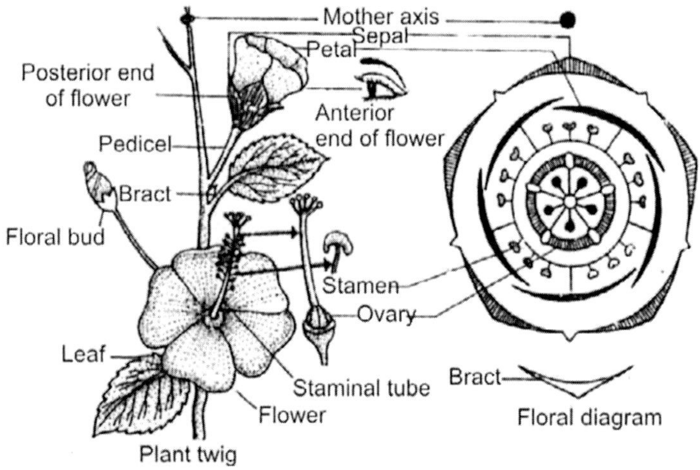

Fig. 1.54. Floral diagramme (Source: Pandey and Misra, 2008).

H. Fruit bunch/cluster: Round, elliptical, ovate, long, regular, irregular; compact, medium compact, loose; Length, breadth; Shoulder small, large, medium, double.

I. Fruit characters

a. Simple fruits

i. Dry fruits: Dehiscent or capsular (legume or pod, follicle, siliqua, silicula, capsule), indehiscent or achenial (achene, caryopsis, cypsela, samara, nut), and schizocarpic or splitting (lomentum, cremocarp, regma, carcerulus, double samara, samaroid).

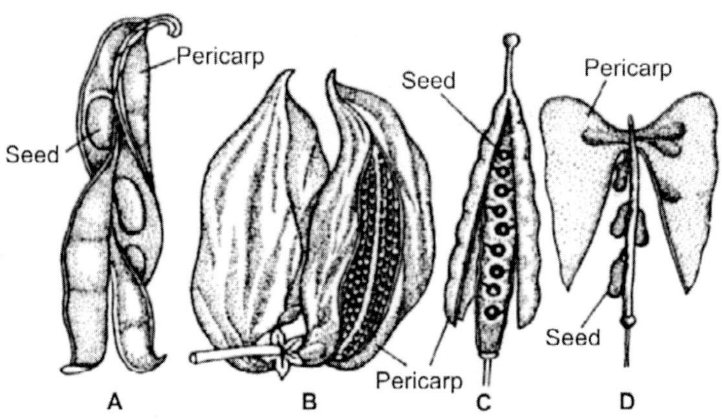

Fig. 1.55a. Type of dry fruits: A-legume, B-a pair of follicle, C-siliqua and D-silicula (Source: Pandey and Misra, 2008)

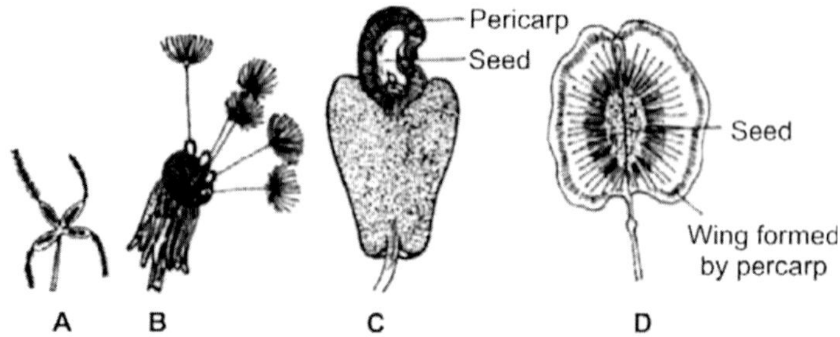

Fig. 1.55b. Type of dry fruits: A-achene, B-cypsela, C-nut, D-samara (Source: Pandey and Misra, 2008).

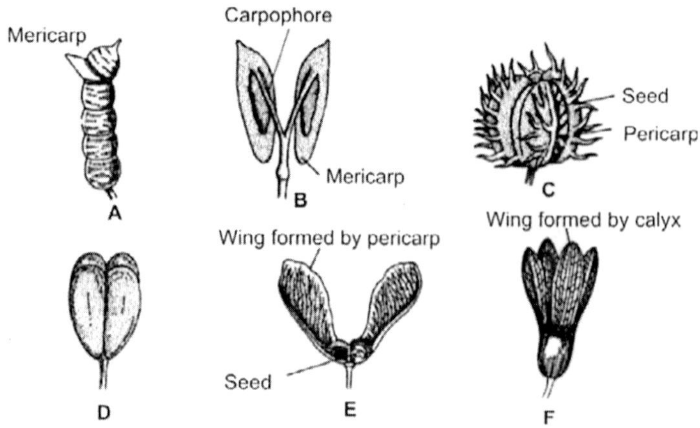

Fig. 1.55c. Type of dry fruits: A-lomentum, B-cremocarp, C-regma, D-carcerulus, E-double samara and F-samaroid (Source: Pandey and Misra, 2008).

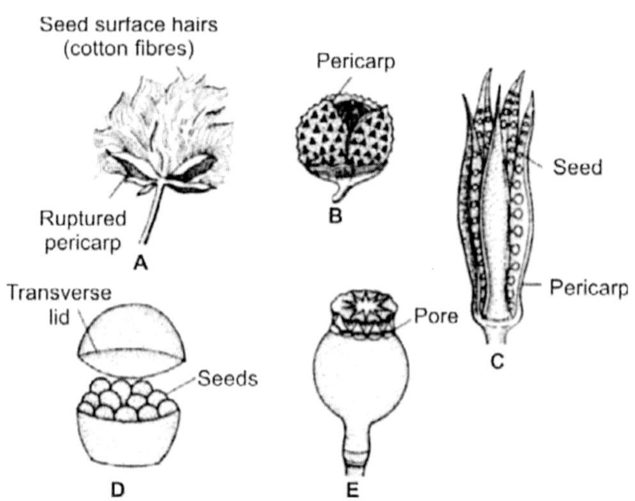

Fig. 1.56. Dehiscence in capsule fruits: A and C-loculicidal, B-septifragal, D-pyxidium and E-porous (Source: Pandey and Misra, 2008).

ii. Succulent fruits: drupe, berry, balausta, hesperidium, pome, pepo, amphisarca

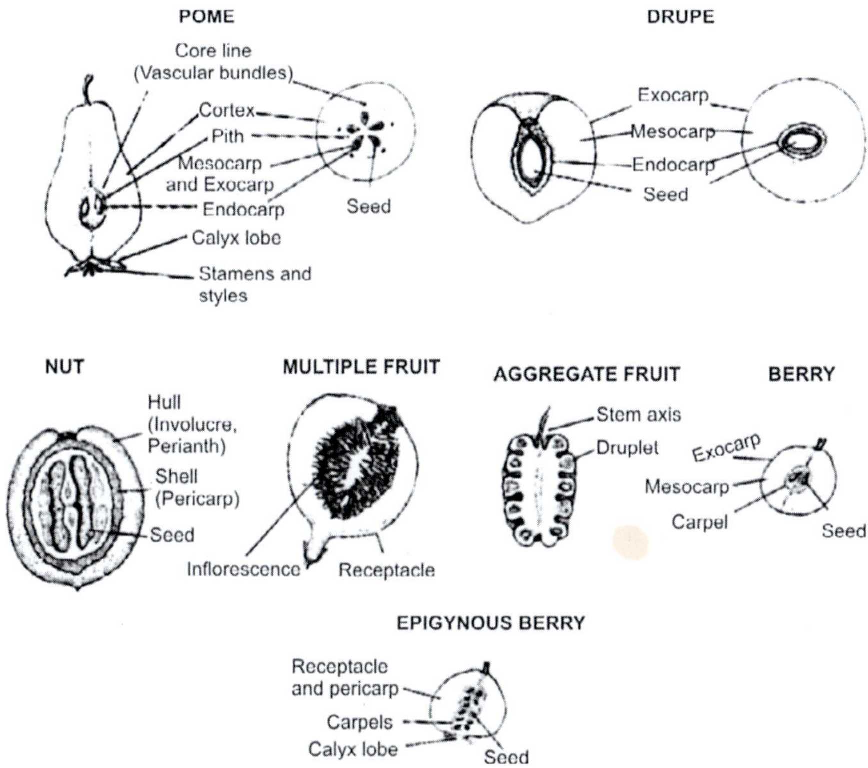

Fig. 1.57a. Type of succulent fruits (Source: Westwood, 1993).

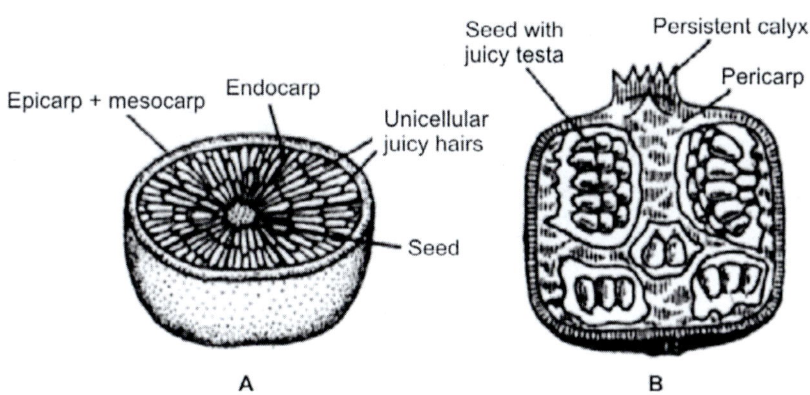

Fig. 1.57b. Type of succulent fruits: A-hesperidium (T.S.) and B-balausta (L.S.) (Source: Pandey and Misra, 2008).

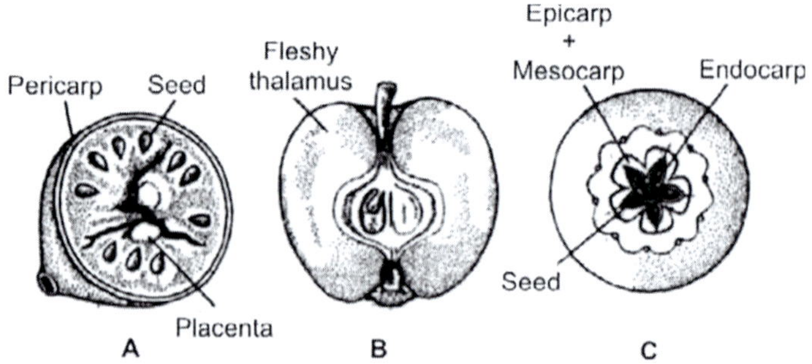

Fig. 1.57c. Type of succulent fruits: A-amphisarca (T.S.), B and C-pome (L.S. and T.S.) (Source: Pandey and Misra, 2008).

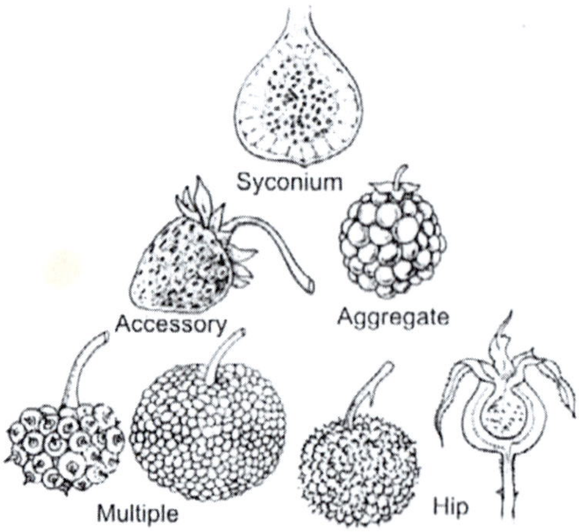

Fig. 1.57d. Type of succulent fruits.

b. Aggregate fruits: Etaerio of follicles, etaerio of achenes, etaerio of berries, etaerio of drupes.

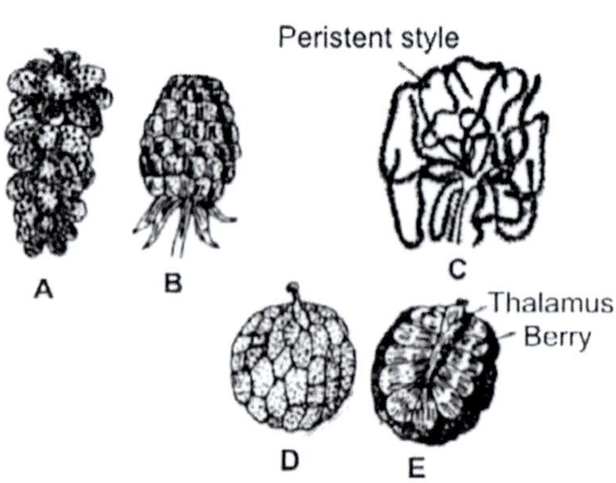

Fig. 1.58. Aggregate fruits: A-etaerio of follicles, B-etaerio of drupes, C-etaerio of achenes, D-etaerio of berries (E = L.S.) (Source: Pandey and Misra, 2008).

c. Compound (multiple) fruits: syconus, sorosis

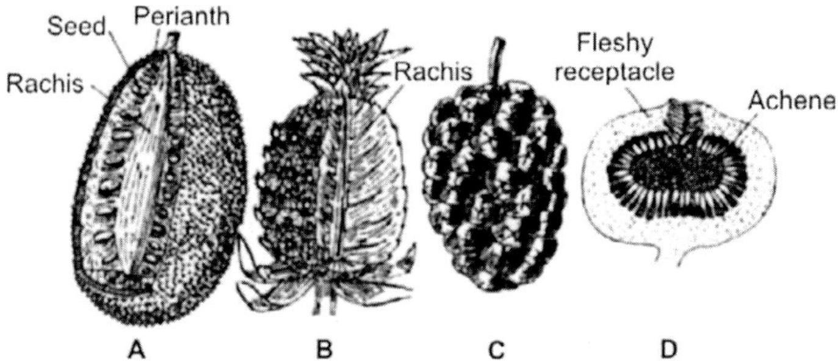

Fig. 1.59. Composite fruits: A-jackfruit (sorosis), B-pineapple (sorosis), C-mulberry (sorosis), and D-fig (syconus) (Source: Pandey and Misra, 2008).

d. Productivity: Prolific, light cropper, precocious, early bearing, late cropper, alternate bearing; early, medium, late.

e. Shape: Round, oblate, ovate, conic, oblong, truncate, obovate, turbinate, narrow-necked, acute, ribbed, cordate, lopsided, oblique, pyriform, regular, irregular, uniform, elliptical.

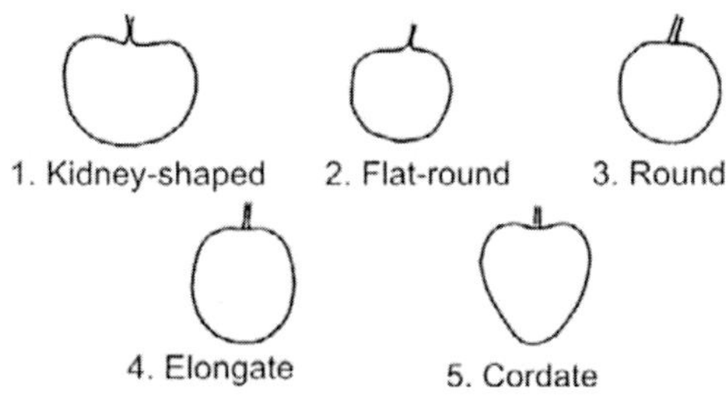

Fig. 1.60a. Shape of fruit (cherry): 1.kidney shaped, 2. Flat round, 3. Round, 4. Elongate, 5. Cordate (Source: Schmidt *et al.*, 1985).

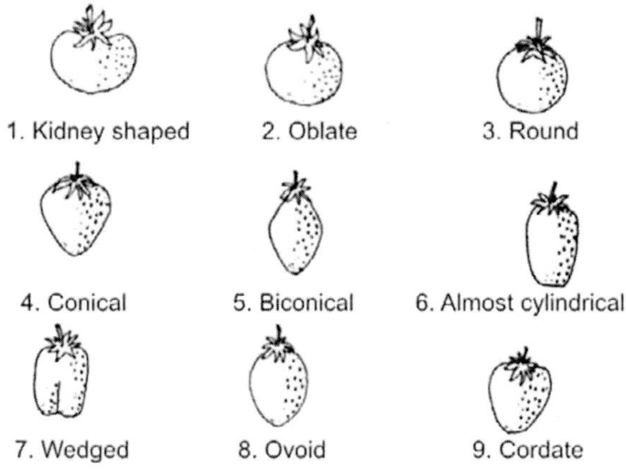

Fig. 1.60b. Shape of fruit (strawberry) (Source: Clamot *et al.*, 1986).

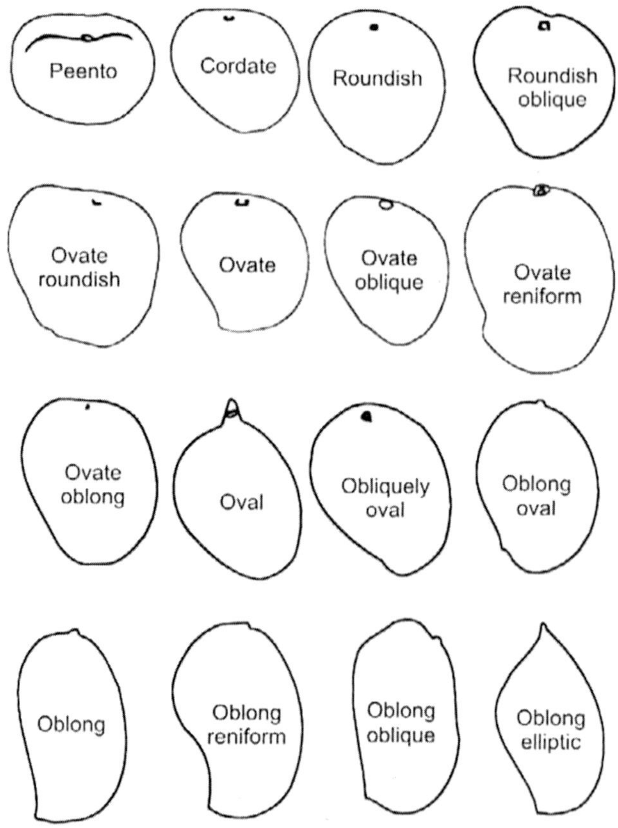

Fig. 1.60c. Shape of fruit (mango): peento, cordate, roundish, roundish oblique, ovate roundish, ovate, ovate oblique, ovate reniform, ovate oblong, oval, obliquely oval, oblong, oblong reniform, oblong oblique, oblong elliptic (Source: Sant Ram and Rajan, 2003).

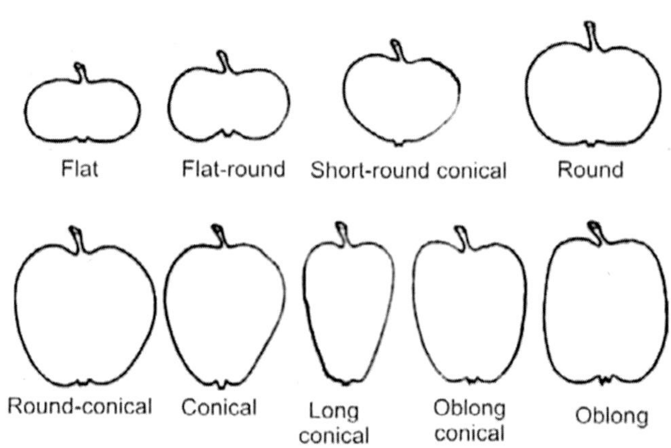

Fig. 1.60d. Shape of fruit (apple): flat, flat round, short round conical, round, round conical, conical, long conical, oblong conical, oblong (Source: Elzebroek and Wind, 2008).

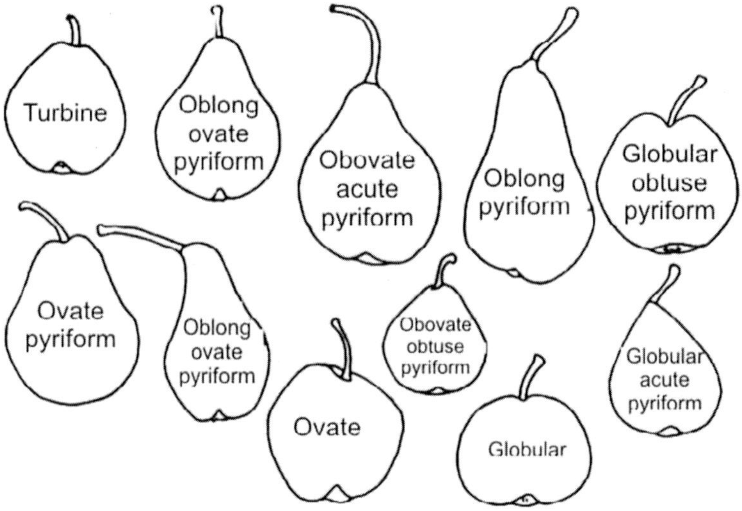

Fig. 1.60e. Shape of fruit (pear): turbinate, oblong ovate pyriform, obovate acute pyriform, oblong pyriform, globular obtuse pyriform, ovate pyriform, oblong ovate pyriform, ovate, obovate obtuse pyriform, globulate, globular acute pyriform (Source: Zielinski, 1955).

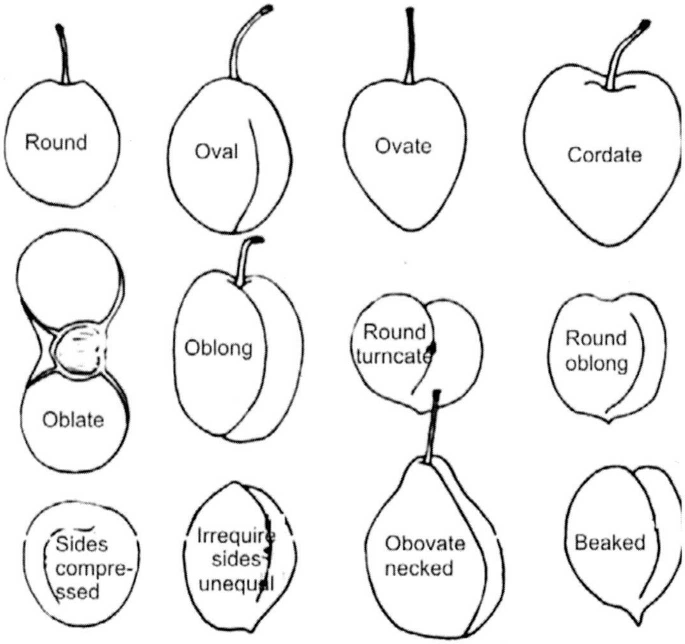

Fig. 1.60f. Shape of drupaceous fruit : round, oval, ovate, cordate, oblate, oblong, round truncate, round oblong, sides compressed, irregular sides unequal, obovate necked, beaked (Source: Zelinski, 1984).

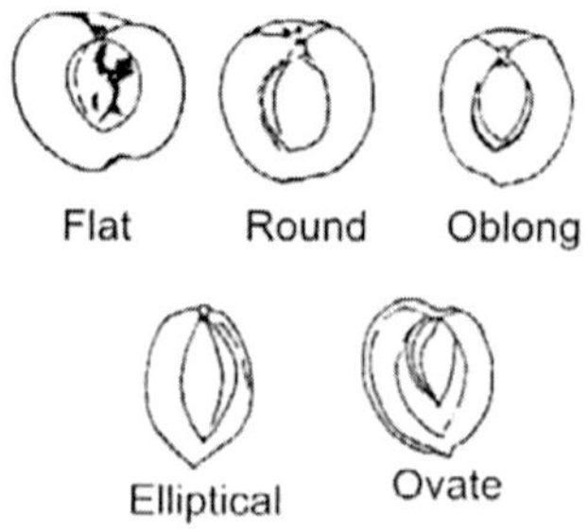

Fig. 1.60g. Shape of fruit (peach): flat, round, oblong, elliptical, ovate (Source: Bellini *et al*., 1984).

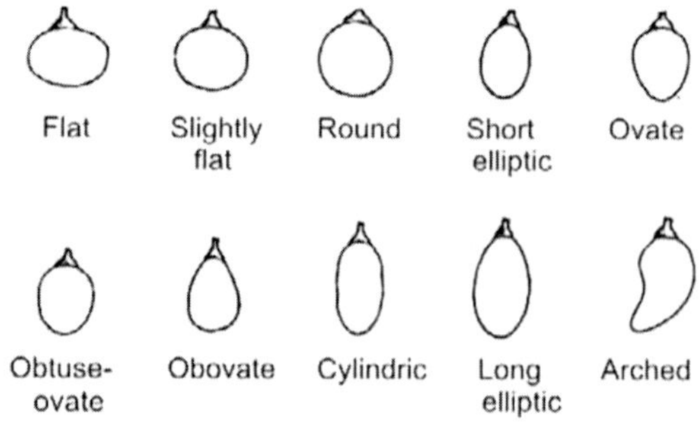

Fig. 1.60h. Shape of fruit (grape): flat, slightly flat, round, short elliptic, ovate, obtuse ovate, obovate, cylindric, long elliptic, arched (Source: IPGRI, UPOV, OIV. 1997).

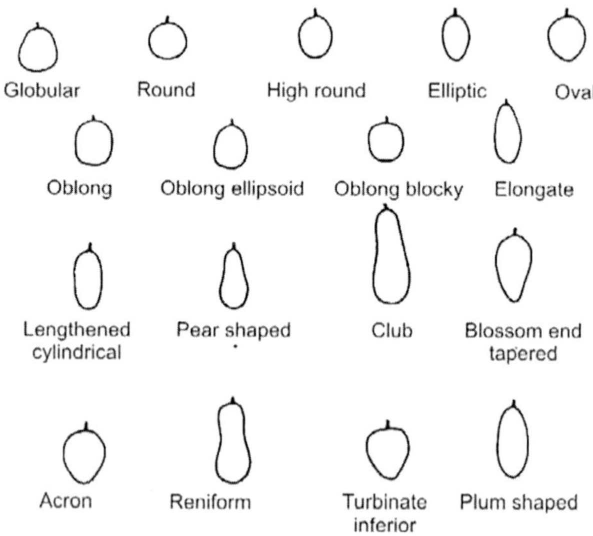

Fig. 1.60i. Shape of fruit (papaya): globular, round, high round, elliptic, oval, oblong, oblong ellipsoid, oblong blocky, elongate, lengthened cylindrical, pear shaped, club, blossom end tapered, acron, reniform, turbinate inferior, plum shaped (Source: IPGRI, 1988).

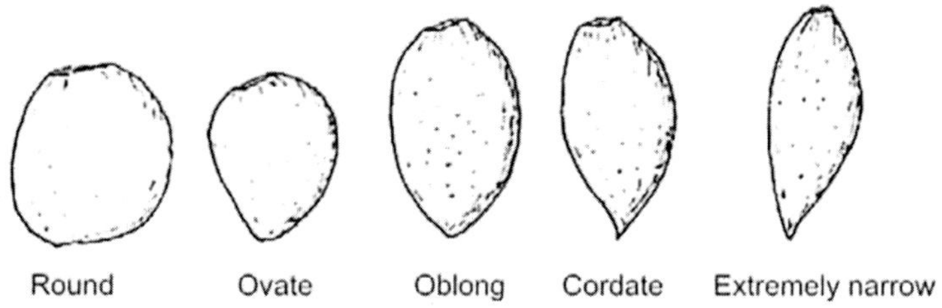

Fig. 1.60j. Shape of fruit (almond): 1. Round, 2. Ovate, 3. Oblong, 4. Cordate, 5. Extremely narrow (Source: IBPGR, 1988).

f. Apex: Pointed, rounded, depressed, tipped.

g. Stem end depression: Obtuse, acute, acuminate; Deep, medium, shallow; Wide, medium, narrow; Smooth, rough, russeted, pubescent, lipped.

h. Apical end depression: deep, medium, shallow; Broad, medium, narrow; Smooth, regular, irregular, wavy, crowned; Abrupt, rounded, sloping, flaring.

Fig. 1.61. Shape of stalk end of fruit (papaya): 1. Depressed, 2.flattened, 3. Inflated, 4. Pointed (Source: IPGRI, 1988).

i. Size.

j. Colour (under colour: or over colour): Striped,, streaked, marbled, blotched, mottled, blushed, washed.

k. Rind

i. Adherence with flesh: Tight, loose.

ii. Surface: Thick, medium thick, thin; Smooth, rough, wavy, wrinkled, ribbed, russeted, waxy, oily, dull, glossy, glabrous, glandular, rugose, hairy, scabious; Tough, brittle, medium tender, tender.

iii. Calyx: Persistent, deciduous; Open, closed, partly closed; United at base, separate at base; Convergent, erect, recurved.

iv. Calyx tube (depression just below the calyx lobes): Conical or cone shaped, funnel-shaped, urn-shaped.

v. Remnants of stamens: Basal, medium, marginal.

vi. Suture: Continuous, broken; broad, medium, narrow; Deep, medium, shallow.

vii. Dots: Rough, depressed, sub-depressed; Round, stellate, star-shaped, oblong, elliptical; Small (inconspicuous), large (conspicuous): Numerous, few, scattered.

viii. Bloom: waxy, whitish substance; Heavy, moderate, scant.

ix. Oil glands: Large, small, medium; Deeply imbedded, lightly imbedded; Few, numerous.

l. Pedicel: Long, medium, short; Thick, medium thick, slender, clubbed.

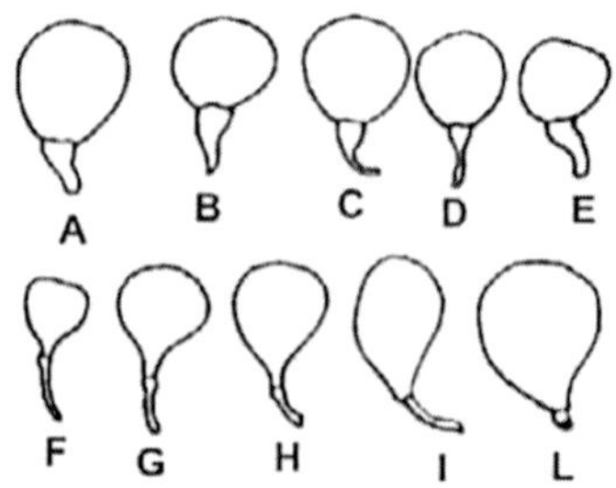

Fig. 1.62. Type of fruit pedicel (fig): 1. Variously enlarged (A-E), 2. Long and slender (F-I), 3. Short and thick (L) (Source: IPGRI and CIHEAM, 2003).

m. Pulp/Flesh: Fine, melting, soft, juicy, buttery, pulpy, mealy, meaty, coarse-grained, medium coarse-grained, gritty, granular, crisp, breaking, firm, tough, dry.

i. Quality: Rating (from Best to Poor).

ii. Use; Culinary, cooking, dessert.

iii. Flavour: Sweet, sugary, vinous, subacid, mild subacid, acid or sour, bitter, astringent, neutral, insipid or flat, aromatic, sprightly, nutty, tart, musky, mild, strong, delicate, rancid, pungent, bland, acrid, warm, burning, cooling, nauseous, pricking saline.

iv. Juice: Quantity, colour, quality.

v. Segments: Number; Regularity.

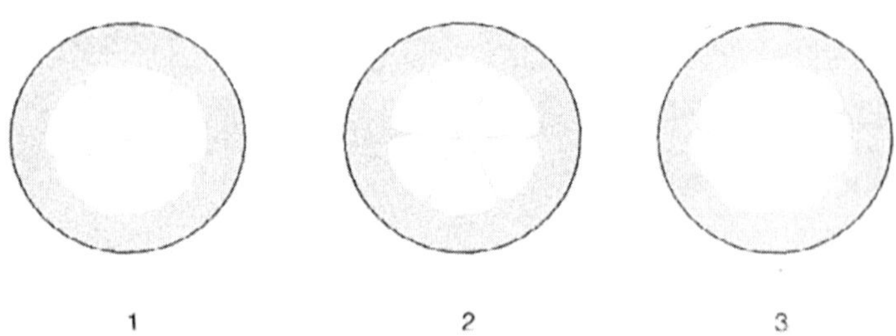

Fig. 1.63. Number of arils per fruit (mangosteen) (Source: IPGRI, 2003).

vi. Juice sacs: Size, shape, orientation.

vii. Septa: Tough, tender, medium tender; Thick, medium thick, thin.

viii. Core: Solid, loose, sessile or basal, medium, distant; Closed, open; Large, medium, small.

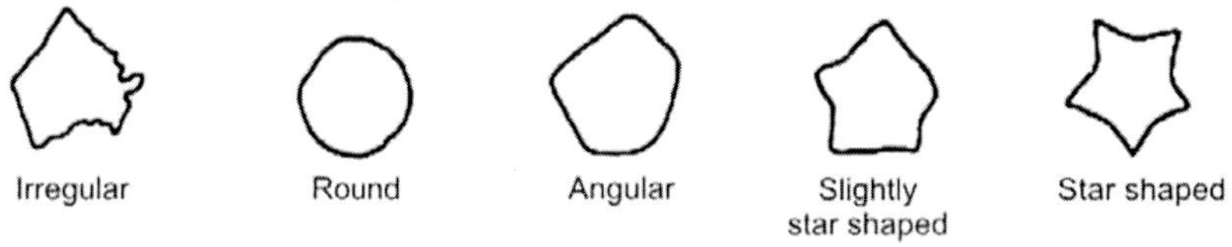

Fig. 1.64. Shape of central cavity of fruit (papaya): 1. Irregular, 2. Round, 3. Angular, 4. Slightly star shaped, 5.Star shaped (Source: IPGRI, 1988).

ix. Core lines: Clasping, meeting.

x. Carpels (parchment-like walls of seed): Roundish, cordate, obcordate, elongated, oblong, ovate, obovate; Open, closed; Axile, abaxile; Smooth, tufted.

xi. Stone: smooth, rough, pitted, ridged, furrowed, grooved, winged, uneven; Free, half free, cling.

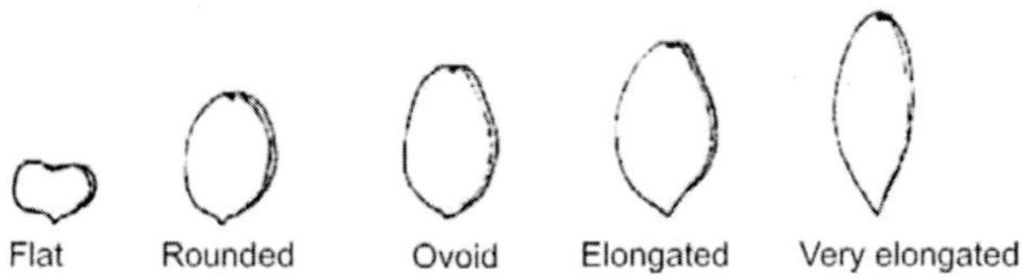

Fig. 1.65. Shape of stone (peach): 1. Flat, 2. Rounded, 3. Ovoid, 4. Elongated, 5. Very elongated (Source: Bellini *et al.,* 1984).

J. Seed characters

a. Number.

b. Shape:

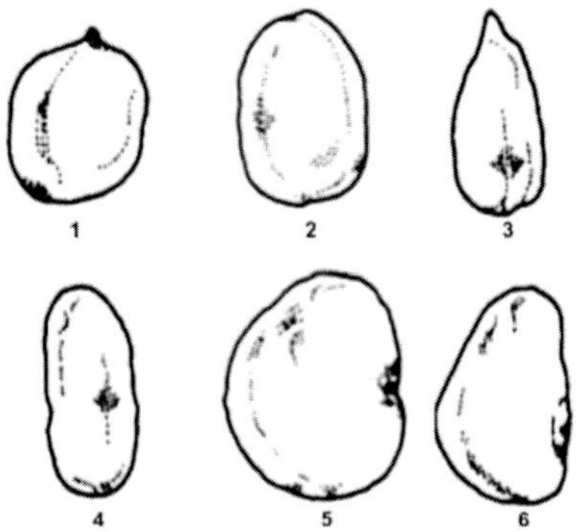

Fig. 1. 66. Shape of seed (jackfruit): 1.Spheroid, 2. Ellipsoid, 3. Elongate, 4. Oblong, 5. Reniform, 6. Irregular, 7. Other (Source: IPGRI, 2000).

c. Size.

d. Colour.

e. Surface: Smooth, rough, markings/venation.

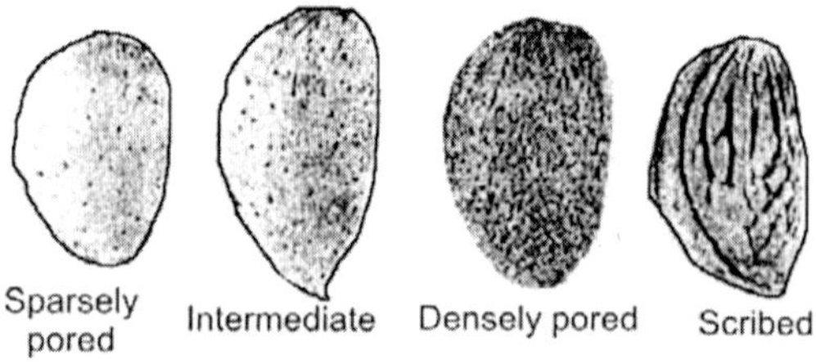

Fig. 1.67a. Markings on the stone (almond) (Source: Gülcan, 1985).

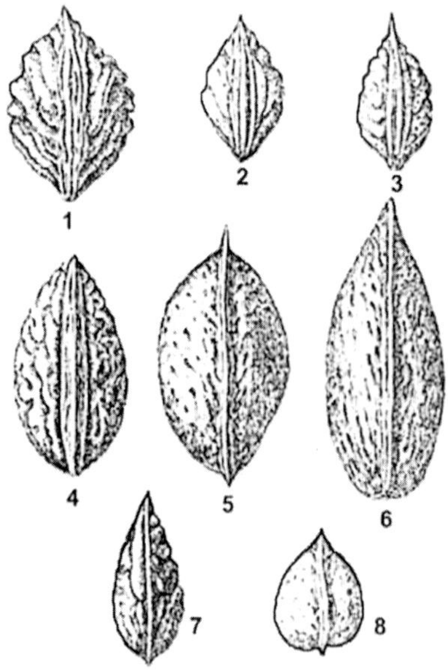

Fig. 1.67b. Markings on the stone fruits (almond, peach) (viewed sideways): 1. Common English peach, 2. Double, Crimson flowered Chinese peach, 3. Chinese Honey peach, 4. English almond, 5. Barcelona almond, 6. Malaga almond, 7. Soft shelled French almond, 8. Smyrna (Source: Darwin, 1868)

f. Endosperm: Endospermic, non-endospermic; Number of cotyledons.

g. Chalaza: Near centre, above centre, at top.

h. Raphe: Large, small

These attributes are helpful to identify the plants and to put them in correct groups. Besides the descriptions of microstructural features of seed surface its inner cells also have taxonomical use. The descriptions can be made either by growing the plant material at one location, preferably on one type of rootstock or by visiting their original places of growing. While making description at their original place there can be duplication of the same plant as the differences may be because of environmental conditions. When the former method is used, the environmental conditions of the location may not be suitable for expression of the true characters of the collected plant material. Besides, collection, planting and growing of plant material at one location is not only troublesome but also time consuming.

3. The physiological reactions of different cultivars can be used to establish relationships. Some such tests are :

i. Taking the serum from the blood of the rabbit which was injected with protein extract of one plant and mixing it with the protein extract of the other plant. Appearance of precipitate shows close relation between the two plants.

ii. Relationships are established in citrus on the basis of colour reaction of plant extract which is due to the presence of certain glucosides.

iii. Different cultivars of sour orange show different reactions to the virus.

iv. Rate of respiration, transpiration, etc.

v. Differences in certain biochemical constituents in cytoplasm may be the basis to classify plants.

4. Characters of pollen grains such as their structure, size and shape which are known to differ from species to species.

5. Genetic characters related to hybridization somaclonal variation, cibridization, etc. as these affect species delimitation, e.g. the plants within a species normally hybridize freely and those in different species do not. The way different genes in different plant groups express themselves and the changes in characters of a particular species through cibridization, somatic mutations and gene transfers should also be kept in view.

6. Characters of cytoplasm, number of nuclei, particularly orgenelles in the nucleus (the number of chromosomes, their morphology and any irregularity during their pairing at the time of meiosis, etc.) are used to establish relationships. In addition to chromosome number, DNA content in nucleus of a species, distribution and amount of constitutive heterochromation, cytochemical distinction between different heterochromation types, location of transcriptionally active nuclear organizers, and genomic DNA component and its relation to heterochromation bands are important criteria to establish relationships.

7. Anatomical characters such as size and number of stomata, cell size, number of vascular bundles (as used for classification in sweet orange). Embryological characters such as size, shape and other features of embryos at a particular stage of maturity can determine whether the plants are closely related. Electron-microscopic and microscopic studies of leaves and their surfaces are also important in taxonomical classification of different species and cultivars.

8. Ecological conditions bring about changes in the expression of the characters. For example, plants growing in desert environment develop different characters when shifted from irrigated areas; red pigment in Blood Red Malta, the pale yellow pigment in Mosambi and green colour in mandarins may not be present in all ecological situations. The green colour in the mandarin when transported from southern India to the northern State of Uttar Pradesh (Lucknow) vanished even within the transit period.

⑧ ⑧ ⑧

Chapter 2

PLANT IDENTIFICATION

Identification is the process of determining whether the unknown plant is identical with or similar to the already known plant (named specimen). In practice one commonly identifies a plant by direct comparison or use of keys and arrives at a name. The process can utilize virtually all of our sense organs. It can be done by vision, smell, feel (touch) and occasionally by taste. The object is viewed as a whole and its identity recognized by a holistic mental process. Alternatively, the identity is decided by analytic approach that entails using specialized descriptive terminology of morphological characters of its parts such as stem, bud, leaf, flower, placentation, ovule, fruit, etc. The diagnostic characterization involves listing or assessment of the features of a taxon that distinguish it from all other taxa. It may involve studying a live plant, a plant specimen, or a plant image in making a decision. Comparison with the available written descriptions in plant manuals or with preserved herbarium specimen, photographs or illustrations can be done to determine the family, genus and species to which the plant belongs. The latest floras and checklists of the region and monographs can also be seen; which usually contain exhaustive information including keys about the taxon. The keys used in the floras are usually diagnostic stating only the conspicuous features. Cultivated plants are particularly difficult to identify because they include a large number of cultivars and hybrids and their number constantly grows. Several identification methods and tools are used by taxonomists for identification.

A. Expert identification

Expert identification is perhaps the best way to identify a specimen as the expert will usually know the taxa of that group over a wide geographical range. He may use prepared monographs and synopses of the group in question along with the latest revisions. This method, however, may be time consuming as it requires valuable time of expert and presents problems creating delays in his visits or in sending the specimen. Expert determination is often essential for certain groups where species or iftraspecific identification is very difficult.

B. Comparison

This is an excellent method of identification as it is done by comparison of the unknown plant with named specimen, photographs, illustrations or descriptions. Its reliability is dependent on the accuracy and authenticity of the specimen, photographs, illustrations or descriptions used in the comparison. Lack of availability of suitable materials makes the method time consuming and virtually impossible.

i. **Specimen comparison:** Comparing with a live or preserved plant collection, usually an identified herbarium specimen, is the best as many feature of plant (e.g. colouration and surface features) are often not adequately visible from photographs or illustrations or denoted in written descriptions.

ii. **Image comparison:** An unknown plant is identified by visually comparing it with photographs or illustration of the known taxa. It requires great caution as two or more taxa may look very similar to one another since the morphological features are not easily visible in photographs or illustrations.

iii. **Comparing written description:** Various features of the unknown plant are compared with the written descriptions of possible known taxa. Comparison with the written descriptions available in plant manuals can be done to determine the family, genus and species to which the plant belongs.

C. Identification keys

The most widely followed method is use of keys or similar devices (synopses, outlines, etc.). It does not require the time, materials or experience for comparison and recognition. Keys are a type of taxonomic literature and are most useful devices for identification. Taxonomic key consists of a series of contrasting or contradictory statements or propositions requiring the identifier to make comparisons and decisions based on statements in the key as related to the material to be identified. The series of choices leads the user to the correct name of the unknown item by sequentially choosing between two (or more) statements based on the characters of the plant until the possibilities are narrowed down to one. Each time a choice is made; one or more taxa are eliminated. Thus correct identity of a specimen is determined by a process of elimination. Keys are, therefore, constructed using contrasting characteristics to divide the possible names in the key into smaller and smaller groups. The choices may be herbaceous verses woody, zygomorphic verses actinomorphic flower, etc. The identity is confirmed in steps; first step determines the family, then the genus and then species. Most keys are artificial or practical and do not necessarily reflect their phylogeny. Rarely, a key may be natural or phylogenetic in which diagnostic (or even apomorphic) features are used to delimit "natural' groups which are usually formal taxa. Thus, it may or may not split a larger group into smaller, natural (monophyletic) subgroups.

The most common key is a dichotomous key. "Dichotomous" means "divided into two parts". Thus, dichotomous keys always give two choices in each step. Two contrasting choices (statements or leads) are presented at each step. The pair of choices (leads) is called a *couplet.* The key presents a series of couplets each presenting choice between two mutually exclusive and parallel statements. The lead of a couplet may be indented and/or numbered. Identification proceeds by selecting the lead of a couplet that best fits the organism. The first contrasting characters in each couplet are referred to as the *leads or primary character.* Being conspicuous and clear cut, these are usually the best contrasting diagnostic characters, sometimes referred to as key characters. Following the lead are *secondary key characters.* The key always has a flowchart structure. Modern dichotomous keys are conventionally published either in indented or bracketed style. Although various other styles have been proposed, these traditional formats serve the purpose well.

Indented key: The *indented* or *yoked* key is the most widely used in manuals for the identification of vascular plants. The key is arranged in such a way that each subsequent subordinate couplet after the first couplet is indented one step further to the right. An example of the indented key is shown below:

1. Fruit more than twice as long as broad, with a skin in three or more distinct segments .... Banana

1. Fruit less than twice as long as broad, with a skin not in segments

2. Fruit with thick aromatic skin

3. Skin yellow; fruit with a marked protuberance at one end .... Lemon

3. Skin orange; fruit rounded at both ends .... Orange

2. Fruit with a thin, non-aromatic skin

4. Fruit with a single 'stone' in the centre .... Plum

4. Fruit with several separate seeds in the centre

5. Fruit greenish-yellow, hairy .... Gooseberry

5. Fruit blackish-purple, glabrous .... Black currant

Bracketed key: The *bracketed* or parallel key always puts two couplets next to each other in consecutive lines on the page. At the end of each line there is either a name or a number referring to a couplet later in the key as shown below:

1.	Fruit more than twice as long as broad, with a skin in three or more distinct segments .... Banana
	Fruit less than twice as long as broad, with a skin not in segments 2
2	Fruit with thick aromatic skin 3
	Fruit with a thin, non-aromatic skin 4
3.	Skin yellow; fruit with a marked protuberance at one end .... Lemon
	Skin orange; fruit rounded at both ends ....Orange
4.	Fruit with a single 'stone' in the centre .... Plum
	Fruit with several separate seeds in the centre 5
5.	Fruit greenish-yellow, hairy .... Gooseberry
	Fruit blackish-purple, glabrous .... Black currant

The indented key makes visual identification easier as it groups together elements having similar morphology. For example, while *Centunculus* and *Samolus* are grouped under 'leaves alternate', *Lysimachia* and *Anagallis* are grouped under 'leaves opposite'. But it may prove uneconomical because additional pages are required owing to the indented lines for each couplet. Also, the second part of the couplet occurs much later than its first part on a page which may cause confusion. In contrast, the bracketed key makes good use of the page space and both the parts of couplet are adjacent but the grouping is not immediately apparent.

A large amount of knowledge about reliable and efficient identification procedures may be incorporated in good single-access keys. Characteristics that are reliable and convenient to observe most of the time and for most species (or taxa), and which further provide a well-balanced key (the leads splitting number of species evenly) will be preferred at the start of the key. However, in practice it is difficult to achieve this goal for all taxa in all conditions. If the information for a given identification step is not available, several potential leads must be followed and identification becomes increasingly difficult. Although software exists that helps in skipping questions in a single-access key, the more general solution to this problem is the construction and use of multi-access keys, allowing a free choice of identification steps and are easily adaptable to different taxa (e.g., very small or very large) as well as different circumstances of identification (e.g., in the field or laboratory).

Polyclave: The multi-access or multi-entry key containing data necessary to construct many different dichotomous keys is called polyclave. Polyclaves of various kinds allow one to select the characteristics for use in identifying each specimen, taking his choices from some character set and repeating an elimination process until a tentative identification is made. A printed data table, chart or matrix giving the status of various taxa for useful characteristics is used as a polyclave by listing the possible taxa on scratch paper and crossing out those which do not agree with the specimen's characters. It consists of a list of numerous character states whereby a user selects all the states that match the specimen. It permits the use of a limited subset of information to narrow down the possibilities. This uses one punched card per taxon having characters represented by holes around the margin of the card. Sometimes each card may represent a single character. If a taxon possesses a particular character, the hole for that character is notched. The taxon cards are sorted by running a large needle through the hole for the character into the stacked cards. The operation follows step by step elimination process. The usefulness of a dichotomous key, listing only floral characters, gets limited if the plant specimen lacks flowers. But a polyclave key has listing of not only floral characters but also the features of roots, stems, leaves, fruits and seeds. Polyclaves are readily mechanized, as shown by the familiar edge-punched cards and the less familiar window keys, as well as various mechanical devices. All polyclaves are now implemented by a computer algorithm. Although well intended, character-set algorithms seem to offer no advantages over polyclaves. However, pattern recognition methods, using no formal characters, might be employed effectively for identification in some cases. Such techniques linked with optical scanners, spectroscopy or chromatography could offer fully automated identification.

Guidelines for preparing a key: Most keys whether dichotomous or polyclave rely on written statements used to make choice and narrow down to identify the specimen. Although the keys are the most practical and common methods for identification, they cannot be foolproof and should, therefore, be regarded only as guides. Visual images in the form of photographs or drawing can be used to clarify the meaning of contrasting characters or character states.

Keys have been constructed for identification of varieties/cultivars of cultivated plants by using characters conspicuous for the given category. For example, in case of raspberries, presence or absence of glands on the petiole, peduncle, pedicel and calyx, and whether these glands are stalked or sessile, the form of the leaflets on young canes, the character and abundance of bristles on the young cane, and character of the fruit; and in case of peach, leaf and flower characters (e.g. size and showy petal). Hedrick has published keys to several temperate fruits using characters such as sweetness in cherries, season of ripening in pears, sweetness and colour in apple, colour of fruit in plums and flesh characteristics in peach and apricot. These major characters in turn are followed by the couplets with more minor characters such as suture, stone, shape of fruit, length of stem, etc. The major considerations in key construction should be ease, quickness and accuracy. Some of the guidelines are as follows:-

1. Identify all groups to be included in a key.
2. Prepare a description of each taxon.
3. Select "key characters" states. The two parts of the couplet should be made up of contrasting statements so that one part will apply and the other will not. Use acroscopic, morphological characters and constant character states when possible. Avoid characteristics that can only be seen in the field or on specially prepared specimens. Use features that are readily observable and available throughout the growing season. Avoid using geographical location as a sole separating character.
4. Prepare a Comparison Chart.
5. The major couplet should as far as possible divide the entire set of taxa in more or less two groups. Use at least two characters per lead when possible.
6. The couplets should start with a noun followed by adjectives. The first word of each lead of the couplet should be identical. For example, if the first lead of a couplet begins with the word *stamens,* the second lead of the same couplet must begin with the word *stamens.* The leads of consecutive couplets should not begin with the same word, since this may cause confusion when one looks away to observe the plant specimen. The successive leads start with different words.
7. Use parallel construction and comparative terminology in each lead of a couplet.
8. Mention the name of the plant part before descriptive phrases, e.g., leaves or flowers blue not blue flowers, leaves alternate not alternate leaves.
9. Use characters that are precisely defined using measurements, with ranges that do not overlap avoiding those based on vague generalities like 4-8 versus 6-10 mm long, large versus small and southern versus northern.
10. The couplets should have positive statements avoiding unqualified negative statements. For example, use “leaf apex acute” versus “leaf apex acuminate” and not “leaf apex not acute”.
11. Construct strictly dichotomous keys.

12. Follow key format (indented or bracketed).
13. It may be necessary to provide two sets of keys in some groups; flowering versus fruiting material, vegetative versus flowering, or staminate versus pistillate in dioecious plants.
14. Construct separate keys for dioecious plants, for flowering or fruiting materials and for vegetative materials when pertinent.
15. Couplets of a key may be numbered or lettered, or may use some combination of lettering and numbering, or may be left blank in the case of indented keys.
16. Place those groups with numerous variable character states in a key several times when necessary.

While using the keys, following guidelines are to be considered

1. Obtain as much information as possible about the characters of the unknown plant before starting to use the key.
2. Select keys appropriate for the plant material to be identified from the flora, manual, monograph or revision, relating to the geographic area if the locality from where the plant was obtained is known.
3. Read the introductory comments on format details, abbreviations, etc. before using the key.
4. Read both the leads (choices) of the couplet carefully before making a choice. Even though the first lead may seem to describe the unknown plant, the second lead may be more appropriate.
5. Be sure you understand all the terms in each choice. Use a glossary to understand the meaning of the terms.
6. Measure several similar structures when measurements are used in the key. Do not base your decisions on a single observation. It is often desirable to examine several specimens, e.g. measure several leaves and not a single leaf. Attempts to use the key are likely to fail if specimen consists of a single leaf or just a flower.
7. Try both choices when dichotomies are not clear or when information is insufficient, and make a decision as to which of the two answers best fits the descriptions.
8. If both choices seem possible, try going both ways.
9. Confirm your choices by reading both ways.
10. Verify your results by comparing the specimen with an illustration or with an authentically named herbarium specimen.
11. If the specimen doesn't seem to fit the key and all choices are unlikely, retrace your steps to correct a probable mistake.

⑧ ⑧ ⑧

Chapter 3

NOMENCLATURE

Nomenclature involves assigning correct name to a properly identified plant to know exactly to what it pertains, to avoid confusions arising from situations when more than one name is available for a plant or the same name is used for more than one plant and also to ensure that the name reflects plant relationships. Providing single "correct" name for every plant helps in biodiversity conservation, communication, information retrieval and for maintaining a useful reference system and continuity in literature.

Initially the system of naming began by giving brief descriptions. This gave rise to polynomial system of nomenclature but that proved too cumbersome as the number of plants increased. Then a trinomial system of nomenclature was followed. Rivinus discovered a binomial system in 1750. This was popularized by Carl Linnaeus after laying down some rules. His publications, *Critica Botanica* in 1737, *Philosophia Botanica* in 1751 and the most comprehensive *Species Plantarum* in 1753, formalized the name of a genus with a single epithet to form the name of a species. Thus the binomial system of plant nomenclature was established. Most wild plants fit neatly into the nested hierarchy of ranks, species into genera, genera into families, etc., used in Linnaean classification which aligns with Darwinian descent with modification. Linnaeus used a third name as a variety within a species, including both wild and horticultural variants. From about 1400 CE, Latin was adopted as the language for biological nomenclature and has continued to be used for preciseness, conciseness and stability in plant nomenclature. The horticultural varieties were written in Latin and some have persisted to this day.

The first comprehensive effort to lay out rules to bring an agreement between the botanists in assigning precise and understandable names that do not change quite often was made when Alphonse Louise de Candolle drew up the following four simple '*lois*', or laws, in a conference attended by about 150 persons at Paris in 1867:

1. One plant species shall have no more than one name.
2. No two plant species shall share the same name.
3. If a plant has two names, the name which is valid shall be that which was the earliest one to be published after 1753.
4. The author's name shall be cited, after the name of the plant, in order to establish the sense in which the name is used and its priority over other names.

The Paris Code of Nomenclature, however, did not prove practical owing to its violation by some people. The Americans formed the Rochester Code in 1892. First International Botanical Congress was held in 1900. During the second Congress at Vienna in 1905, efforts were made to bring the Paris Code and the Rochester Code together. As a result, the first set of international rules governing the naming of plants were adopted and published as the *International rules of Botanical Nomenclature*. These are referred to as the *Vienna Rules* (not *Vienna Code*). After World War II the responsibility for the *Botanical Code* was taken up by the International Association for Plant Taxonomy. Subsequently, revised versions of these *Rules* were produced in the meetings of the International Botanical Congress held at six-yearly interval. Some of the important versions are *Cambridge Rules* (1935), *Stockholm Code* (1952), *Seattle Code* (1969), *Leningrad Code* (1975), *Sydney Code* (1981), *Berlin Code* (1987) and *Tokyo Code* (1993).

The International Code of Botanical Nomenclature (ICBN)

At the 17th International Botanical Congress held at Vienna in July 2005, the edition of *International rules of Botanical Nomenclature* revised as *Tokyo Code* was formulated as "Vienna Code" to be called the *International Code of Botanical Nomenclature* (ICBN). The formation and use of botanical names of plants in Latin form are governed by the ICBN or Botanical Code (McNeill, 2004; McNeill *et al.*, 2006). The ICBN (first published as such in 1952) was formulated at the Stockholm Congress of 1950.

Taxonomic groups (taxa): The *Code* deals with the naming of taxonomic groups (taxa) and these are arranged in a hierarchical order in consecutively subordinate ranks, the higher rank being inclusive of all lower ranks. The principal ranks of taxa in descending sequence are kingdom (regnum), division (or phylum), class, order, family, genus, and species. Only the final three ranks are in general use for the nomenclature of cultivated plants and the species is usually considered the basic rank. However, the APG classification recognizes only Tricolpates (Eudicots), Asterids, Rosids, Euasterids, Eurosids above the order level as monophyletic clades for which no formal taxonomic names are used. Each scientific name of a particular rank ends in a certain suffix according to the rules and recommendations of the ICBN. For example, Asteridae is a taxon at the rank of subclass, Asterales is at the rank of order, and Asteraceae is at the rank of family, etc. The names of families are plural adjectives used as nouns and are formed by adding the suffix *–aceae* to the stem, which is the name of an included genus. However, nine traditional family names with the suffix -ae, *viz.* Compositae (=Asteraceae), Cruciferae (=Brassic-aceae), Gramineae (=Poaceae), Guttiferae (=Clusiaceae), Labiatae (=Lamiaceae), Leguminosae or Papilionaceae (=Fabaceae), Palmae (=Arecaceae), and Umbelliferae (=Apiaceae) are also accepted as an exception. The name of subfamily ends with the suffix *-oideae*. However, within the Fabaceae (=Leguminosae), the subfamily name Papilionoideae is an acceptable alternative to the Faboideae. The name of a genus is a noun, or word treated as such, and begins with a capital letter. It is singular, may be taken from any source whatever, and may even be composed in an arbitrary manner. The etymology of a generic name is not always complete. They lack meaning. The name of a subdivision of a genus, such as subgenus, section, or series, is a combination of a generic name and subdivisional epithet connected by a term denoting its rank. The epithet is written with a capital initial letter and, when written in connection with a specific epithet, is placed in parentheses.

The name of a species is a binary combination (binomen) in Latin form of generic name followed by a single species epithet written in italics followed by the name of the author which is not written in italics. The taxa above the rank of genus are not underlined or italicized. If the epithet is of two words they must be joined by a hyphen or united into one word. The epithet can be taken from any source whatever and may be constructed in an arbitrary manner. Specific epithets which are nouns are grammatically independent of the generic name. Specific epithets, when adjectival in form, agree in gender with the name of their genus. They are written with a lower-case initial letter.

Authorship: Scientific names are associated with one or more authors, the person(s) who validly published the name. For example, the family Rosaceae can be cited as 'Rosaceous Jessieu' because de Jessieu validly published the family name, the name of the tribe Conostylideae with authorship is 'Conostylideae Lindley', the genus *Mohavea* is '*Mohavea* A. Gray', the species *Mohavea confertiflora* is '*Mohavea confertiflora* (Bentham) Heller', and the subspecies *Monardella linoides* subsp. *viminea* is '*Monardella linoides* A. Gray subsp. *Viminea* (Greene) Abrams.' Author names are often abbreviated such as Haemodoraceae R. Br. (for Robert Brown) or *Liquidambar styraciflua* L. (L. being standardized abbreviated for Linnaeus). The author name is important, especially when two people have used the same name in describing two different plants. If the name was revised or changed, the previous author is in parenthesis.

Infraspecific names: Populations may acquire slightly different characters in different geographical areas, especially if isolated, e.g. more robust habit, darker veins, unique flower and fruit characters. These may be distinguished as subspecies within one species. Distinct populations and individuals occurring sporadically within the geographical range of a species or subspecies may be recognized as varieties (*varietas*) and forms (*forma*). A botanical variety is found in the wild and described as such and that found in cultivation is a cultivated variety or cultivar (cv.). However, the rank of botanical variety and cultivar can be similar. For example, a white flowered selection of a blue flowered plant if first found in the wild would be var. *alba* and if first found in cultivation is cv. Alba. The rules by which botanical infraspecific taxa are named specify that the name shall consist of the name of the parent species followed by a term which denotes the rank of the subdivision, and an epithet which is formed in the same ways as specific epithets, including grammatical agreement when adjectival. The name of a subdivision of a species, such as *subspecies* (subsp. or ssp.), *varietas* (var.), *subvarietas* (subvariety or subvar.), and *forma* (f.), is a combination of a species name and a subspecific epithet connected by a term denoting its rank. Technically, the rank of subspecies is above that of variety. However, in practice, subspecies and variety are used interchangeably. These form a hierarchy, and further subdivisions are permitted, but the Code does not define the characteristics of any rank within the hierarchy. Consequently, infraspecific classification is subjective.

Hybrid names: Spontaneous interbreeds or deliberate crosses between species in the same genus (or between subspecies or varieties within the same species) are given hybrid names with multiplication sign and treated like species names. Graft hybrids (graft-chimaeras) are indicated by a plus sign. For the name of a hybrid between parents from two different genera, a name can be constructed from the two generic names, in part or in entirety (but not both in their entirety) as a condensed formula and are indicated by the multiplication sign x, or by the addition of the prefix northo to the term denoting the rank of the taxon; intergeneric hybrids (between two different genera) have the x before the name (e.g. x *Mahoberberis* for hybrids between the genera *Mahonia* and *Berberis* and x *Fatshedera* for hybrids between the genera *Fatsia* and *Hedera*. Interspecific hybrids (between two or more species) have the 'x' before the epithet of species name (e.g. *Mentha* x *piperita*). The 'x' is not underlined or italicized like the Latin names.

Valid names: All valid names must be accompanied by valid description in scientific publications and in well recognized languages, e.g. English, Russian, German, French and Spanish. Names of persons should be avoided in the nomenclature, e.g. *P. simonii*. When two names are given simultaneously to one plant, the one published earlier gets priority, e.g. *C. limon* and *C. limonia*, the former got preference. Since a plant can have only one correct name, which is determined by priority, its other validly published names are synonyms. The names may be revised if (a) the previous workers have overlooked the characters in classifying plants, (b) on the basis of differences found out later, e.g. *Pyrus malus, Malus malus, Malus domestica* and *Malus sylvestris* (separate name should be there for genus and species). *Malus pumila* has been put separate than *Malus sylvestris* as the latter has much more pubescence. *Fortunella japonica* was previously named as *Citrus japonica* and (c) when one name is given to two plants. If the name becomes well established, it is not changed. If there is any doubt as to whether a name is correct or not, the nomenclatural type is consulted. A nomenclatural type is almost always a single specimen, e.g., a standard herbarium "sheet" for vascular plants, but it may also be an illustration. The type serves the purpose of acting as a reference for the name. The different types that are designated by ICBN are as follows:-

1. Holotype – It is a specimen used by the author in the original publication as the nomenclatural type.
2. Isotype – It is a duplicate specimen of the holotype, i.e., from the same collection with the same locality, date and number as the holotype.
3. Lectotype – It is specimen selected from the original material, when no holotype was designated at the same time of publication or as long as it is missing or destroyed.
4. Neotype – It is a specimen selected to serve as a substitute of holotype when all the material on which the name of taxon was based is missing.
5. Cotypes – A cotype is a second specimen from the same plant from where the holotype was collected. It is occasionally mentioned in the literature.
6. Syntype – It is one of the two or more specimens cited by an author of a species when no holotype was designated; or a syntype is any one of the two or more specimen originally designated as types. In most cases, where no holotype was designated, there will also be no 'paratypes', since all the cited specimen will be syntypes.

7. Topotype – It is a specimen collected from the same locality from where the holotype was collected.

International Code of Nomenclature for algae, fungi, and plants: The name International Code of Botanical Nomenclature was changed to International Code of Nomenclature for algae, fungi, and plants (ICN) in July 2011 during the International Botanical Congress at Melbourne. This Melbourne Code replaced the Vienna Code of 2005 as the set of rules and recommendations dealing with the formal botanical names that are given to plants, fungi and a few other groups of organisms, all those "traditionally treated as plants". The name of the Code is partly capitalized and partly not. The lower-case for "algae, fungi, and plants" indicates that these terms are not formal names of clades, but indicate groups of organisms that were historically known by these names and traditionally studied by botanists, mycologists, and phycologists. This includes blue-green algae (Cyanobacteria); fungi, including chytrids, oomycetes and slime moulds; photosynthetic protists and taxonomically related non-photosynthetic groups. There are special provisions in the ICN for some of these groups, as there are for fossils. Botanical Code is vested in the International Union of Biological Sciences (IUBS), though this is delegated to the International Commission for Botanical Nomenclature, which meets every six years during International Botanical Congresses. At these meetings, proposals to amend the Code are considered and voted on, the result being a new edition, usually published in the year following the Congress. The ICN is based on the following principles, which have evolved from the de Candollean Lois, and are the philosophical basis of the code and provide guidelines for the taxonomists who propose amendments or deliberate on the suggestions for modification of the Code:

- Botanical nomenclature is independent of zoological, bacteriological, and viral nomenclature.
- A botanical name is fixed to a taxon by a type. This is almost invariably dried plant material and is usually deposited and preserved in a herbarium, although it may also be an image or a preserved culture. Some type collections can be viewed online at the websites of the herbaria in question.
- A guiding principle in botanical nomenclature is priority, the first publication of a name for a taxon, but the formal starting date for purposes of priority is 1 May 1753, the publication of *Species Plantarum* by Linnaeus. However, to avoid undesirable (destabilizing) effects of strict enforcement of priority, conservation of family, genus, and species names is possible.
- The intent of the Code is that each taxonomic group ("taxon", plural "taxa") of plants has only one correct name that is accepted worldwide, provided that it has the same circumscription, position and rank. The value of a scientific name is that it is an identifier; it is not necessarily of descriptive value.
- Names of taxa are treated as Latin.
- The rules of nomenclature are retroactive unless there is an explicit statement that this does not apply.

The ICN can only be changed by an *International Botanical Congress* (IBC), with the International Association for Plant Taxonomy providing the supporting infrastructure. Each new edition supersedes the earlier editions and is retroactive back to 1753, except where different starting dates are specified. The Nomenclature Section held just before the 18th International Botanical Congress in Melbourne, Australia in July 2011 made following changes in the way to name new plants, algae, and fungi.

- The *Code* will permit electronic-only publication of names of new taxa; no longer will it be required to deposit some paper copies in libraries.
- The requirement for a Latin validating diagnosis or description was changed to allow either English or Latin for these essential components of the publication of a new name.
- "One fungus, one name" and "one fossil, one name" are important changes for fungi and for fossils; the concepts of *anamorph* and *teleomorph* (for fungi), and *morphotaxa* (for fossils) have been eliminated.
- As an experiment with "registration of names", new fungal descriptions will require the use of an identifier from "a recognized repository"; the only repository so far recognized is MycoBank.
- The title of the *Code* was broadened to make explicit that it applies not only to plants, but also to algae and fungi.

Cultivated plant names

Early listing and documentation of plants made little distinction between those that were anthropogenic and those that were natural wild kinds. The first record of a named cultigen occurs in *De Agri Cultura*, written about 160 BCE by Cato the Elder (234–149 BCE) in a list that includes 120 kinds (cultivars) of fig, grape, apple and olive. The cultivar names were mostly of one word and denoted its provenance (the geographical origin of the place where the plant selections were made). The record made in 827 CE show that herbs such as sage, rue, fennel, opium poppy, mint, radish, gallica rose, bottle gourd and melon were grown by the Romans in monastery gardens. Similar lists of plants occur in records of plants grown in Villa gardens in 742–814 CE.

From about 1500 CE, the publication of herbals were the formal documentation of plants. By the late 16th century the number of different plant kinds described in Europe had risen to about 4,000. In 1623 Gaspard Bauhin published his *Pinax theatre botanici* compiling a list of about 6000 kinds of plants. The combined works of Valerius Cordus (1515–1544 CE) published in 1562 included many named cultivars including 30 apples and 49 pears, presumably local German selections. John Parkinson's *Paradisi in Sole* (1629) lists 57 apples, 62 pears, 61 plum, and 35 cherry and 22 peach cultivars.

The influx of new plants into Western Europe largely to the botanic gardens of Amsterdam, Leiden, Chelsea and Paris necessitated their recording. The tradition of documenting garden plants was established by Philip Miller (1691–1771) in Chelsea Physic Garden, London. In 1724 Miller produced a two-volume compendium of garden plants called *The Gardeners and Florists Dictionary*. Linnaean binomials were adopted in its revised and enlarged 8th edition in 1768.

Plant explorations in the early 18th century created need for description of thousands of new organisms. This brought out difficulties in communication about plants. Carl Linnaeus attempted to name all the known organisms of his time. Friedrich Alefeld (1820–1872) distinguished three infraspecific taxonomic categories: *Uterart* (subspecies), *Varietaten Gruppe* and *Kultur-Varietat*, all with Latin names. This appears to have laid the ground for the later establishment of the cultigen classification categories, cultivar and Group. German botanist Karl Koch (1865) expressed resentment at the continued use of Latin for cultigen names. In 1867 during the fourth Horticultural and Botanical Congress, Alphonse de Candolle stated that "*Seedlings, half-breeds (métis) of unknown origin or sports should receive from horticulturist's fancy names in common language, as distinct as possible from the Latin names of species or varieties*." Cultivated plant taxonomists then faced the challenges such as the use of large plant name databases, ways of dealing with the use of non-scientific names in commerce (known as trade designations), especially for plant labels in nurseries, intellectual property and plants, adapting to modern technology, in particular molecular techniques, to the creation and identification of cultivars, maintaining germplasm collections of cultivars, including herbaria, and recording and registration of cultivars. Horticulturists were also confronted with problems relating to names of various lengths, written and published in many languages with much duplication.

Botanical and horticultural exploration rapidly increased in the 19th century. New plants including valuable economic plants from the tropics enriched the existing collections. This provided the common global heritage of economic and ornamental cultigens that formed the stock for modern plant selection, breeding and genetic engineering. As the community of people dealing with the cultigens of commerce grew, the divergence re-emerged between taxonomy serving scientific purposes and utilitarian taxonomy meeting human needs. The *Botanical Code* focuses on the needs of plant taxonomists to maintain order and stability for the scientific names of all plants and is thus plant-centred. It was not until the mid-19th century that the nomenclatural path for cultigens began to diverge from mainstream plant taxonomy. The nomenclatural path for plants used in the commercial world of agriculture, forestry and horticulture was required to cater to the needs of people and is thus human-centred.

International Code of Nomenclature for Cultivated Plants

The International Horticultural Congress at Brussels in 1910 added a horticultural nomenclature component in conjunction with International Botanical Congress. The *Règles de Nomenclature Horticole* was established on submission by the Royal Horticultural Society. The use of simple descriptive Latin names (e.g. *compactus*, *nanus*, *prostratus*) for horticultural variants was accepted. Also names in local language were accepted; which were not to be translated and should consist of a maximum of three words, preferably one word. This first *Horticultural Code* consisted of 16 Articles. It was not until the *9th Horticultural Congress* in London in

1930 that the rules of a Horticulture Nomenclature Committee were agreed and added as an appendix to the 1935 *Botanical Code.*

The ICBN requires that the units of taxonomy, the taxa being named, are in some way nested in a hierarchy of ranks. Variation at and below the species level, whether in wild or cultivated plants, is not readily accommodated in a hierarchical structure. As a result of discussions at the 1950 International Botanical Congress in Stockholm and the 18th International Horticultural Congress in London in 1952, the first *International Code of Nomenclature for Cultivated Plants* (ICNCP) was published in 1953. The ICNCP, also called *Cultivated Plant Code*, do not require an extensive and obligatory hierarchy of entities and provides the rules by which to communicate and hence name the enormous diversity of cultivated plants at and below the species level. It thus supplements the *ICN* and gives rules and recommendations for naming of cultivated plants. William Thomas Stearn (1911–2001) first wrote this *Cultivated Plant Code* (Wageningen). Subsequently this *Code* was followed by editions – in 1958 (Utrecht), 1961 (update of 1958), 1969 (Edinburgh), 1980 (Seattle), 1995 (Edinburgh), 2004 (Toronto) and 2009 (Wageningen). The *Code* specifies in its title that it is dealing with *cultivated plants* (not wild). It defines the scope of the *Code* for plants that have evolved under natural selection with human assistance. It requires the use of special classification categories, the cultivar, Group and grex, that do not conform with the hierarchy of ranks implicit in the *Botanical Code* as its Preamble states that "*The purpose of giving a name to a taxon is not to indicate its characters or history, but to supply a means of referring to it and to indicate to which category it is assigned.*

A *Horticultural Taxonomy Group* (*Hortax*), a small committee of plant taxonomists and horticulturists with a professional interest in the classification and nomenclature of cultivated plants, was formed in the UK in 1988. The committee meets to discuss topics of relevance to the ICNCP. Meanwhile a parallel organization, the *Nomenclature and Registration Working Group* of the *Vaste Keurings Commissie* was formed in the Netherlands. The newsletter *Hortax News* was superseded in February 2006 by the first issue of *Hanburyana*, a journal produced by the Royal Horticultural Society in London and dedicated to horticultural taxonomy. This filled a gap left when the American journal *Baileya* ceased publication in the early 1990s. International Association for Cultivated Plant Taxonomy was launched at the Sixth Symposium on the Taxonomy of Cultivated Plants at Wageningen in 2007. The *Cultivated Plant Code* is the responsibility of the *International Commission for the Nomenclature of Cultivated Plants.* International Society for Horticultural Science (ISHS) published the *Cultivated Plant Code* following the structure of the *Botanical Code.* Amendments to the *Cultivated Plant Code* are prompted by international symposia for cultivated plant taxonomy which allow for rulings made by ICNCP. While the Botanical Code governs the names of plants in the wild, its rules also apply to cultivated plants where ranks such as family, genus, species and subspecies are concerned. The *Cultivated Plant Code* is to provide two extra categories, Group and Cultivar, with which to classify plants that are brought into or selected in cultivation. Trade designations, are not governed by either Code, although the *Cultivated Plant Code* makes recommendations to avoid confusion between commercial names and those governed by the Codes.

The word "cultivar" coined by L.H. Bailey came into general circulation with this Code. It was defined in 1980 in *Cultivated Plant Code* as, "The term *cultivar* denotes an assemblage of cultivated plants which is clearly distinguished by any characters (morphological, physiological, cytological, chemical, or others), and which, when reproduced (sexually or asexually), retains its distinguishing characters". Brickell (1995) redefined cultivar as, "A cultivar is a taxon that has been selected for a particular attribute or combination of attributes, and that is clearly distinct, uniform, and stable in its characteristics and that, when propagated by appropriate means, retains those characteristics" in the ICNCP. The words "variety" and "form" (or their equivalent in other languages) or "strain" must not be used as synonyms for the word cultivar.

Cultivars arise from various breeding processes, selection from wild or cultivation sources or by spontaneous or induced mutation. The clones [asexually propagated from any part of a plant or derived from aberrant (abnormal) growth], graft-chimaeras (composed of tissues from two different plants and originated by grafting, e.g. Syringa `Correlata', which combines tissues from *Syringa* x *chinensis* and *Syringa vulgaris* may be given cultivar names. F_1 hybrids (the result of a repeatable single cross between two pure-bred lines), cultivar groups [e.g. Tulipa Darwin Group; *Solanum tuberosum* 'Desiree' (Red-skinned Group)], and a number of other categories are specifically listed as items that can be given cultivar names. The term Grex is used for a hybrid group of known parentage.

The cultivar epithet, when attached to the binomial or genus name, forms the full cultivar name. To distinguish cultivar epithets from the scientific part of a name, they are enclosed in single quotation marks or apostrophes and should never be written in italics, e.g. *Mangifera indica* 'Langra' or underlined. Cultivar names can be more than one word. They should not be preceded by the abbreviations cv., var. or f. In genera where there are many cultivars or where a well-known cultivar has given rise to many others through plant breeding, collective name is used (Group epithet) to encompass cultivars which share certain defined characters. A Group, however, does not have to contain, or be solely composed of, cultivars. Group names always include the word "Group" and, when used with a cultivar name, are put in parentheses (curved brackets), never in single quotation marks. For example, *Solanum tuberosum* (Maincrop Group) 'Desirée' is a cultivar within a Group of potatoes called Maincrop. Where complex groups of hybrids may result from repeats of a particular cross, each Group is given a grex name (=flock in Latin) which covers all offspring resulting from crossing those particular parents. In contrast to Group, parentheses are not used with grex names, and grex is abbreviated to gx. For example, *Pleione* Shantung gx 'Muriel Harberd' is a cultivar within *Pleione* Shantung grex. Trade designations that sometimes resemble cultivar epithets should not be enclosed in single quotation marks and whenever possible should be printed in a typeface which contrasts with the cultivar epithet, usually small capitals. They should always be cited together with the true cultivar name.

The relevant extracts, relating to Principles and Rules & Recommendations subdivided into Articles, from the *Cultivated Plant Code* (Brickell *et al.*, 2009) published by ISHS are presented below:

The Principles

Principle 1: ICNCP, also known as the *Cultivated Plant Code*, is to promote uniformity, accuracy, and stability in the naming.

Principle 2: With the exception of any Latin component within their names, the form of which is governed by the International Code of Botanical Nomenclature (ICBN or Botanical Code), the nomenclature of names in the categories of cultivar, Group, and grex (taxa of plants whose origin or selection is primarily due to intentional human activity), is governed by this Code.

Principle 3: The naming of taxa governed by this Code is based upon priority of publication.

Principle 4: Names of plants governed by this Code must be universally and freely available for use by any person to denote a taxon.

Principle 5: This Code regulates the terminology to be used for categories of taxa governed by this Code and the names to be applied to those individual taxa. The Code recognizes that the names established for taxa of plants using terminology peculiar to some national and international legislation, take precedence over names formed under the provisions of this Code.

Principle 6: The practice of applying trade designations as marketing devices in addition to properly established names of taxa of plants are not to be recognized as being names regulated under this Code.

Principle 7: The formation and use of common names of plants are not regulated by this Code.

Principle 8: International registration of cultivar, group, and grex names and the publication and promotion of lists of such names are of the greatest importance for promoting uniformity, accuracy, and stability in the naming of cultivated plants.

Principle 9: The selection, preservation, and publication of designations of nomenclatural standards are strongly encouraged in stabilizing the application of cultivar and group names and to avoid duplication of such names.

Principle 10: The Rules and Recommendations of this Code should be endorsed and applied by all those responsible for the promotion and use of names for cultivated plants.

Principle 11: The provisions of this Code are retroactive unless stated otherwise.

Rules and Recommendations

Article 1. Relationship with ICBN: Plants in cultivation may be named in accordance with the ICBN at least to the level of genus, or to the level of species or below. Plants recognized as cultivars, Groups, or grexes may be given epithets. Hybrids between taxa may receive names or in addition, may be named as cultivars, Groups, or grexes.

Article 2. The Cultivar: A cultivar is an assemblage of plants that (a) has been selected for a particular character or combination of characters, and (b) is distinct, uniform, and stable in these characters, and (c) when propagated by appropriate means, retains those characters. The botanical categories *varietas* (var.) and *forma* (f.) are not equivalent to cultivar.

Cultivars differ in their mode of origin or reproduction. These may be plants of the same clone (asexually propagated from any part of the plant), derived from topophysic or cyclophysic clone, aberrant growth of a cultivar, presence of intracellular organism, same chimaera, graft-chimaera, seed derived from uncontrolled pollination, line or multiline, F1 hybrid, changed ploidy level, genetically modified plants, etc.

Article 3. The Group: The Group is formal category which may comprise cultivars, individual plants or combination thereof on the basis of defined character-based similarity. Criteria for forming and maintaining a Group may vary according to required purposes of particular users.

Article 4. The Grex: The grex is formal category for assembling plants based solely on specified parentage. The parents of a grex are restricted to the rank of species or another grex.

Article 5. The Graft-Chimaera: A graft-chimaera is a plant that results from grafting the vegetative tissues of two or more plants belonging to different taxa, and is thus not a sexual hybrid. Graft-chimaeras below the rank of genus may be recognized as cultivars.

Article 6. The Denomination Class: A denomination class is the unit within which the use of a cultivar, Group, or grex epithet may not be duplicated except when reuse of an epithet is permitted. It is a single genus or hybrid genus unless a special denomination class has been determined by the ISHS Commission for Nomenclature and Cultivar Registration.

Article 7. Publication: Publication is affected in accordance with Art. 25.

Article 8. Names and Epithets: The name of a cultivar or Group consists of a combination of the name of the genus or lower taxon to which it is assigned with a cultivar or Group epithet. The name of a grex consists of the name of the genus to which it is assigned together with a grex epithet.

Article 9. Date of a Name: The date of the name of a cultivar, Group, grex, or the generic name of an intergeneric graft-chimaera is that of its establishment.

Article 10. Established Names: An established name is one that is in accordance with Art. 27. It might not be in conformity with the requirements of local legislation.

Article 11. Accepted Names: The accepted name is the earliest established one that must be adopted for a cultivar, Group, grex, or generic name of an intergeneric graft-chimaera. But a Group may have more than one accepted name and if appropriate International Cultivar Registration Authority publishes its decision to designate a more widely used name or anyone else may publish a proposal.

Article 12. Conserved Names: A conserved name is one that, although otherwise contrary to the rules of the Code, must be adopted for a cultivar, Group, or grex by a ruling of IUBS International Commission for Nomenclature of Cultivated Plants.

Article 13. Trade Designations: A trade designation is not a name regulated under this Code but is a device that has been used for marketing a cultivar, Group, or grex in place of its accepted name. A trade designation is not to be confused with a synonym. A synonym is an established name that is not accepted name.

Article 14. Cultivar Status: Cultivar status is indicated by enclosing the cultivar epithet within single quotation marks, e.g. *Pinus sylvatica* 'Repens'. Double quotation marks and the abbreviations cv. and var. are not to be used within a name to distinguish cultivar epithets.

Article 15. Group Status: Formal Group status is indicated by use of the word Group as the first or final word in the Group epithet, e.g. *Begonia* Elatior Group. When the word Group has to be abbreviated, the concentration 'Gp' is to be employed.

Article 16. Grex Status: Grex status is indicated by the use of the word "grex", or by the standard concentration "gx", e.g. *Cymbidium* Alexanderi gx 'Westonbirt'.

Article 17. Trade Designation Status: Trade designation must always be distinguished typographically from cultivar, Group, and grex epithets, e.g. *Choisya ternata* 'Limo' as *Choisya ternata* GOLDFINGERS.

Article 18. Starting Point in Nomenclature: Establishment of cultivar, Group, and grex names in any denomination class is treated as starting with a list or publication designated for that denomination class by the ISHS Commission for Nomenclature and Cultivar Registration.

Article 19. Conservation of Names: If a name, contrary to the Rules of this Code, has been (a) designated as accepted by an International Registration Authority, or (b) proposed to be accepted by anyone else, or (c) the designation or proposed acceptance is in dispute, the name can be conserved as accepted name on publication of ruling to this effect by the IUBS International Commission for the Nomenclature of Cultivated Plants.

Article 20. Names of Wild Plants brought into Cultivation: Plants brought from the wild into cultivation and which are not subsequently classified as cultivars or Groups retain the names that are applied to the same plants growing in nature.

Article 21. Names of Cultivars:

i. The name of a cultivar is a combination of the correct name of the genus or lower taxon to which it is assigned under the ICBN, or its unambiguous common name, with a cultivar epithet.

ii. The minimum requirement is for a cultivar epithet to accompany the name of the genus in Latin form or a common name equivalent. When a cultivar can be assigned to a taxon at species rank or below, the name of that taxon (or its common name equivalent) may accompany the cultivar epithet.

iii. Each word of a cultivar epithet must start with an initial capital letter, e.g. *Malus domestica* 'Beauty of Bath'.

iv. A cultivar epithet remains unaltered when the name of the taxon to which it is assigned is changed.

v. The final epithet in Latin form of the correct name under ICBN of a taxon at the rank of species or below is to be retained as cultivar epithet if the taxon is subsequently reclassified as a cultivar, e.g. *Mahonia japonica* and *Primula denticulata* var. *cachmeriana* are to be written as *Mahonia* 'Japonica' and *Primula denticulata* 'Cachmeriana'.

vi. The epithet of any name in Latin form even if not published prior to January 1, 1959 under the ICBN and meet the requirement for a cultivar may be adopted as cultivar epithet, if the plants to which it is applied are now considered to represent a cultivar.

vii. If a cultivar epithet in Latin form established before January 1, 1959 has been repeated within a denomination class but within different taxa, the cultivar epithet must be linked to the name of the taxon to which it applies, e.g. as *Juniperus chinensis* 'Variegata' and not *Juniperus* 'Variegata'.

viii. If a cultivar epithet is an adjective derived in Latin form, it must agree in gender with that of the name of the genus to which it is assigned.

ix. If a cultivar epithet is an adjective derived from an epithet in Latin form transferred to a genus with another gender, the gender of the epithet is changed to agree with that of the new genus.

x. If a noun is used as part of a cultivar epithet and is qualified with an adjective, the latter agrees with the gender of the noun, not the gender of the generic name concerned.

xi. For a cultivar name to be established on or after January 1, 1959, its epithet is to comprise a word or words in any language but may not be entirely in Latin except under (v) and (vi) above; if they are current in a language other than Latin as terms, common phrases (as Habeas Corpus), personal names (as Caesar) and place names (as Nova Scotia); as a novel invention (e.g. 'NuMex Crimson' onion); Japanese vernacular name transcribed into a Roman script (e.g. *Nelumbo* 'Oga'); and in the form of a code of up to 10 characters (e.g. 'M9').

xii. For a cultivar to be established on or after January 1, 1996, its epithet must consist of no more than 30 characters (Roman letters, numbers, and permitted punctuation marks or symbols) overall excluding spaces and the demarcating marks.

A cultivar epithet should be as short as practical and should not consist of nor contain excessively long words that may be difficult to write or pronounce.

A cultivar name whose epithet is or contains the name of a living person should not be published unless that person has given permission for their name to be used.

xiii. A cultivar name may not be established if on or after January 1, 2004 its epithet consists solely of a single letter of Arabic or Roman numerals or a single letter or numerals in combination with a punctuation mark.

xiv. A name is not established if on or after January 1, 1959 the cultivar epithet a) contains the words "form" or "variety" or their abbreviations or equivalents in other languages; b) it is the name of a genus or the common name of a species or other denomination class if use of such epithet might lead to confusion; and c) if it might exaggerate the merits of the cultivar and which might become confusing through the later introduction of new cultivars having comparable characters.

xv. A name is not established if on or after January 1, 1996 its cultivar epithet a) contains the words "cultivar", "grex", "group", "hybrid", "maintenance", "mixture", "selection", "series", "sport", "strain", their equivalents in any language or their plural forms or the words "improved" and "transformed" or their equivalents in any language; b) when written in Roman script containing punctuation marks except the apostrophe ('), comma (,), up to two non-adjacent exclamation marks (!), the period or full-stop (.), or the hyphen (-), the forward slash (/) or backward slash (\) symbols; c) contains the Latin or common name(s) of the genus to which it is assigned; and d) if it is so similar to an existing epithet in denomination class to which the cultivar is assigned that the name might cause confusion.

xvi. A name is not established if its cultivar epithet contains fractions or symbols except as specified under (xv) above.

xvii. A cultivar name should not be published if -

a. its epithet might cause confusion by consisting of terms that are likely to be encountered in the market place.

b. its epithet consists solely of a word or that may be descriptive (adjectival) and that could refer to some character or characters common or with the potential to become common in cultivation of the denomination class concerned.

c. it may give the impression that the cultivar has one or more characters that it does not possess.

d. its epithet may give the impression that the cultivar is derived from or related to another when this is not the case.

e. its epithet may give false impression concerning the identity of its raiser, breeder, introducer or origins.

f. its epithet might cause offence.

Article 22. Names of Group: The name of a Group is the combination of the correct name of the genus under the ICBN, or its unambiguous common name, or lower taxon to which it is assigned, with a Group epithet.

A Group epithet must be either one word or several words with which the word "Group", or its equivalent in other modern languages, is associated.

Each word of a Group epithet must start with an initial capital letter. The word "Group" or its equivalent in other languages is always to be written with a capital initial letter when rendered in a Roman script.

In forming the part of a Group epithet associated with word "Group", reading "Group" for "cultivar" should be followed throughout (e.g. *Beta* Spinach Beet Group).

The word "Group", or its equivalent in any language, is considered part of the Group epithet. It can only occur once in a Group epithet.

If a Group epithet is formed from a grex epithet established prior to January 1, 2004, the former grex epithet is used with the word "Group" replacing the word "grex" to form the Group epithet.

The name of a Group should not be published if its epithet is the same as, or is confusingly similar to an epithet of a cultivar name that has been previously established in the denomination class concerned unless it is thought that the category of Group is more appropriate than the category of cultivar.

Article 23. Names of Grexes: The name of a grex is a combination of the correct name of the genus under the ICBN, or its unambiguous common name, with a grex epithet. Each word of a grex epithet must start with an initial capital letter.

In forming the part of a grex epithet associated with word grex, reading "grex" for "cultivar" should be followed throughout.

As from January 1, 2010, a "grex" epithet may not be established if it is identical to that of a nothospecific epithet with the same parentage.

Article 24. Names of Graft-Chimaeras: Graft-Chimaeras are designated either by a formula or, when they are a union between two genera, by a generic name in Latin form. The formula for a graft-chimaera is the accepted names of the component taxa arranged in alphabetical order linked by the addition sign "+". A space must be left on each side of the addition sign in such formulae.

When a component taxa of a graft-chimaera belongs to different genera a unique name in Latin form may be formed by combining part of the genus of one of the compound genera connected by a vowel to the full name of the other component genus, prefixing the addition sign "+". A space is left between the addition sign and the generic name. The generic name thus formed must not be the same as that of another genus or hybrid genus validly published under the provisions of the ICBN.

Article 25. Conditions of Publication: Publication is effected under this Code only by printed or similarly duplicated material, including indelible autograph to the general public or at least to botanical, agricultural, forestry, or horticultural institutions with accessible libraries. The issue of microform and unpublished theses is not regarded as a means of effective publication.

Generic names of intergeneric graft-chimaeras are not published if, on or after January 1, 1953, they appear either in works of indelible autograph or in trade catalogues or non-scientific newspapers nor are they published if they appear in seed-exchange lists on or after January 1, 1973.

Copies of publications, especially trade catalogues, containing new cultivar or Group names should be sent to appropriate International Cultivar Registration Authorities and, if possible, to libraries that maintain collections of such publications.

Article 26. Date of Publication; On or after January 1, 1959 publication is deemed to be effected only if the publication containing the name of the cultivar, Group, grex, or the genetic name of the intergeneric graft-chimaera is clearly dated at least to the year.

The date of publication is the date on which publication took place.

Article 27. Conditions of Establishment: In order to be established names governed by this Code must (a) be published on or after the starting-point date for the relevant denomination class, (b) appear in dated publication, (c) have a form that complies with the provisions for a cultivar or for a Group, or for a grex or for a generic name of an intergeneric graft-chimaera, and (d) for a cultivar or Group published after January 1, 1959, be accompanied by a description or by reference to a previously published description.

A description is a word or words that (a) indicate one or more recognizable characters of a cultivar or Group, or (b) distinguishes the new cultivar or Group from one whose name has been previously or simultaneously being established.

The names of grexes and the generic names of intergeneric graft-chimaeras are established if the accepted names of both parents of the grex or graft-chimaera concerned are stated at the time of publication.

The name of a cultivar is established if it is accepted under an equivalent term in a register maintained by a statutory plant registration authority.

A name that has not been accepted by the author or one that has been provisionally listed is not regarded as being established.

Names are not established if, at the time of publication, no plants existed for which the name is proposed.

When two or more cultivar, Group, or grex names are simultaneously published in the same work for what the author considers to be the same cultivar, Group, or grex, only one may be established.

The description of any new cultivar or Group should be sufficiently full to make clear how the cultivar or Group differs from similar cultivars or Groups.

Reference to a previously published description should include (a) the author's name, (b) the full title of the publication, (c) the page number on which the description appears, and (d) the year of publication.

A coloured illustration, or a reference to a previously published illustration, should be provided to accompany the description of a new cultivar or Group.

When publishing a new cultivar, Group, or grex names, the parentage and history, the derivation or meaning of the epithets, and the names of the raiser or breeder, nominant, and introducer should be stated when known.

A specimen of a new cultivar or Group, either living or dried, should be sent to the appropriate International Cultivar Registration Authority along with any coloured photographic, illustrative, or other relevant material.

Article 28. Citation of Authors' Name: It is not necessary to cite the name of the author.

Article 29. Choice of Names: When two or more cultivar, group or grex names have been established, the name with the epithet based on the earliest validly published Latin epithet is to be accepted regardless of original rank.

When there are two or more names in use for the same cultivar, grex, or within the same language for a Group, the name that best preserves existing usage is to be chosen without regard to any rank or to the principle of priority.

If a hitherto recognized species or infraspecific taxon is no longer thought to represent a distinct taxon, the name of which is provided for under the ICBN, and if this would otherwise enforce an undesirable change of epithet for a cultivar or Group, the epithet of the name of the former taxon (a) may be incorporated into an existing cultivar epithet provided that the latter is also in Latin form, or (b) may form the epithet of a cultivar.

Article 30. Re-use of Epithets: The epithet of a cultivar, Group, or grex must not be re-used within the same denomination class for any other cultivar, Group, or grex unless re-use of the cultivar, Group, or grex epithet is accepted by an appropriate International Cultivar Registration Authority.

An International Cultivar Registration Authority may only accept re-use of a cultivar, group or grex epithet if that authority is satisfied that the original cultivar, Group, or grex (a) is no longer in cultivation, and (b) has ceased to exist as breeding material, and (c) may not be found in a gene or seed bank, and (d) is not a known component in the pedigree of other cultivars, Groups, or grexes, and (e) the name has rarely been used in publication, and (f) re-use is likely to cause confusion.

An epithet whose re-use has been accepted by an International Cultivar Registration Authority may never be re-used subsequently in that denomination class.

Article 31. Rejection of Names: Names are to be rejected and are not to be used if they are contrary to the Rules of the Code.

The name of a cultivar accepted and published by a statutory plant registration authority, even if using alternative terms, must not be rejected.

If an established name is subsequently successfully challenged as being in conflict with prior right such as use of a trademark or the known name or abbreviation of an intergovernmental or international organization that it is excluded from trademark protection by international convention, the established name is to be rejected and a replacement name provided.

A cultivar, group, or grex name is to be rejected if its publication is against the expressed wish of its raiser or breeder.

Where, a name has been rejected earlier and a replacement name has been provided, the rejected name may not now be accepted.

A cultivar name whose epithet is in a language other than Latin and that exactly duplicates another in the denomination class to which it is assigned is to be rejected.

A replacement name that is superfluous on its establishment is to be rejected.

If it is thought that a cultivar, group, or grex epithet might cause undue offence, the decision of the IUBS International Commission for the Nomenclature of

Cultivated Plants, on application, shall be published; rejection becomes effective from the date of publication of the ruling.

Article 32. Translation of Epithets: When a cultivar or grex name appears in a publication using a different language from that of original publication, the epithet may not be translated but may be transliterated or transcribed.

Article 33. Transliteration of Epithets: if a cultivar, Group, or grex epithet in one alphabetic script needs to be rendered in another alphabetic script, it may be transliterated character by character.

Article 34. Transcription of Epithets: If a cultivar, Group, or grex epithet in a non-alphabetic script needs to be rendered in an alphabetic script it may be transcribed.

Article 35. Spelling of Epithets: The correct spelling of epithets in Latin form that were originally published under the provisions of the ICBN but that are subsequently used as cultivar, Group or grex epithets is to be determined in accordance with the provisions of ICBN.

The correct spelling (orthography) of an epithet in a language other than Latin is that as provided on its establishment. The original scripts are the basis for correcting any spelling mistakes or any orthographical irregularities in transliterations, transcriptions or translations. An unintentional mistake in the original spelling is, however, to be corrected.

Accents and other diacritical marks are to be retained in cultivar, Group, and grex epithets.

The ligatures "æ" and "œ" indicating that the letters be pronounced together are to be transcribed as the separate letters "ae" and "oe" respectively.

The German letter "β" in an epithet may be transcribed as "ss"; the ampersand "&" to be transcribed as "and"; the symbol "#" meaning "number" as the contraction "No".

Cultivar, Group, and grex epithets or parts of such epithets must not be abbreviated. But a cultivar, Group, or grex epithet originally established using the initials of personal names must not have those initials spelled out in full.

The second and subsequent elements of a hyphenated word are to start with a lower case letter.

When a cultivar, Group, or grex epithet contains a possessive noun in singular, the apostrophe together with the letter "s" is to be written after the noun. When plural, the apostrophe is to be written after the plural noun.

Names of Hybrid Genera

1. The formation of names for hybrids between plants of different genera is governed by the provisions of the ICBN.
2. Hybridity is indicated by use of the multiplication sign "x", either between the names of the taxa involved (a "hybrid formula") or by assigning a name prefixed by the multiplication sign (for hybrid genera, a "condensed formula") or by use of prefix "northo" with the indication of rank. Names

given to hybrids between species or between infraspecific taxa are not condensed formulae but must conform to all the provisions of the ICBN for names of the equivalent rank.

3. In case of a condensed formula, the multiplication sign ("x", not italicized) should be placed so as to indicate that it belongs to the name or epithet but is not actually part of it.
4. The name for a hybrid genus arising from a cross between members of two genera is a condensed formula in which the names adopted for the parental genera are combined into a single word, using the first part or the whole of one, the last part or the whole of the other (but not the whole of both) and, optionally, a connecting vowel.
5. The name for a hybrid genus derived from four or more genera is formed from the name of a person to which is added the termination *–ara.* No such name may exceed eight syllables. Such a name is regarded as a condensed formula.
6. The name for a hybrid genus derived from three genera is either (a) a condensed formula in which the three names adopted for the parental genera are combined into a single word not exceeding eight syllables, using the whole or first part of one, followed by the whole or any part of another, followed by the whole or last part of the third (but not the whole of all three) and, optionally, one or two connecting vowels, or (b) a name formed from the name of a person to which is added the termination *–ara* provided that the resulting name does not exceed eight syllables.
7. When a hybrid generic name is formed from the name of a person by adding the termination *–ara,* that person should preferably be a collector, grower or student of the group.
8. When a condensed formula is derived from names of genera, the parental names used in its formation must be those that are accepted by the author of the condensed formula as correct for the parental taxa.
9. Name of hybrid genera ending in *–ara*, which are equivalent to condensed formulae, are applicable only to plants which are accepted taxonomically as being derived from the parents named.
10. In order to be validly published (established) the name of a hybrid genus must be effectively published with a statement of the names of the parent genera, but no description or diagnosis is necessary, whether in Latin or in any other language.
11. Since the names of hybrid genera are condensed formulae or are treated as such, they do not have nomenclatural types and their application is determined entirely on stated parentage.
12. For purposes of priority, names of hybrid genera are subject to the same Rules as are those of non-hybrid genera.
13. Names of hybrid genera that appear on or after January 1, 1953 in trade catalogues or non-scientific newspapers and on or after January 1, 1973 in

seed-exchange lists are not validly published (established) in those publications.

14. Names published merely in anticipation of the existence of a hybrid genus are not validly published (established).

Registration of Names

1. Registration is the acceptance of a cultivar, Group, or grex name by an authority responsible for registering such names.
2. An International Cultivar Registration Authority (ICRA) is an organization appointed by the ISHS Commission for Nomenclature and Cultivar Registration to be charged with the registration of cultivar, Group, or grex names. The act of registration is completed by publication of such names which also ensures their establishment.
3. A statutory plant registration authority is an organization established by national legal enactment or by international treaty, which, as part of its remit, establishes variety denominations or other names for pants.
4. An International Cultivar Registration Authority is not obliged to register a name accepted by a statutory registration authority.
5. Acceptance of a cultivar or Group name by an International Cultivar Registration Authority does not imply judgment on the distinctness of that particular cultivar or Group, nor on its agricultural, horticultural or silvicultural merit.
6. An International Cultivar Registration Authority may also record trademarks if they have been used as marketing devices for cultivars, Groups, or grexes. Such marks if recorded must never be given nomenclatural status and must not appear in a publication by an International Cultivar Registration Authority.

The ICRA maintains a register of the names within the group of interest and this is published and placed in the public domain. One major aim is to prevent the duplication of cultivar and Group epithets within a genus, as well as ensuring that names are in accord with the latest edition of the *Cultivated Plant Code*. New names and other relevant data are collected by and ICRA and each new epithet, submitted to it is checked to ensure that it has not been used before and that it conforms with the *Cultivated Plant Code*. The details about the plant such as parentage, the names of those concerned with its development and introduction, and basic description highlighting its distinctive characters are recorded.

Nomenclatural Standards

1. A nomenclatural standard is preferably a herbarium specimen to which the name of a cultivar or Group is permanently attached.
2. A nomenclatural standard may have been originally nominated as a voucher specimen or as the type specimen under the provisions of the ICBN.

3. An image, other than one maintained digitally, may be designated as a nomenclatural standard when a specimen is not made available or when essential characteristics are recognized from a suitable illustration.
4. If a nomenclatural type cannot be interpreted unambiguously, a nomenclatural standard may be designated in support of that type provided that designation of the nomenclatural type will always take precedence over the nomenclatural standard.
5. The nomenclatural standard for a clonal cultivar whose name is established under the provisions of a statutory plant registration authority after January 1, 2004 must be prepared from the same stock as that used to support recognition of that cultivar by the statutory plant registration authority.
6. The nomenclatural standard for a seed-raised cultivar whose epithet is established under the provisions of a statutory plant registration authority after January 1, 2004 must be prepared from plants grown from seed deposited in and maintained by seed laboratories nominated for maintaining such germplasm under prevailing statutory provisions.
7. Designation of a nomenclatural standard and the citation of the institution holding such a standard are effected by publication.
8. In the event that more than one nomenclatural standard has been designated for the same cultivar or Group, the earliest designation takes precedence.
9. A nomenclatural standard that is a dried specimen should be recognized by keeping it in a specially marked folder.
10. Where practical, nomenclatural standards should be maintained as part of a portfolio into which any specimens, illustrations, colour chart references (with specified edition), and other information such as a copy of the original publication of a name may be assembled for reference purposes. Where appropriate, the standard portfolio should also include details of parentage and the origins of the cultivar or Group and should cite the date and place of establishment of the same.
11. Duplicates of nomenclatural standards should be circulated to other institutions with collections of such standards, especially those in other countries.
12. The exact citation of any living material from which a nomenclatural standard was prepared, and the date of its collection, should be noted with such a standard.
13. If the breeder or raiser of the cultivar or Group, nominant, introducer, or author of its name is no longer available or willing to examine material for preparation of a nomenclatural standard, the advice of other experts should be sought in verifying material for such a standard.
14. Herbarium specimens require expert preparation and raiser of new cultivars or Groups are strongly advised to donate plant material to a recognized herbarium willing to accept such material so that suitable nomenclatural standards may be prepared.

Modification of the Code

The Code may be modified only by action of the International Union of Biological Sciences (IUBS).

Cultigen names

The Greek philosopher Hippo (5th century BC) expressed the opinion that cultigens were produced from wild plants as a result of the human care bestowed on them. Theophrastus (370–285 BCE), the "Father of Botany" and a pupil of both Plato and Aristotle, accepted the view that human action produced cultigens from wild plants. Liberty Hyde Bailey (1858-1954) an American horticulturist, botanist and cofounder of the American Society for Horticultural Science felt the need for special categories for those cultivated plants that had arisen by intentional human activity and which would not fit neatly into the Linnaean hierarchical classification of ranks used by the *Cultivated Plant Code*. For such plants he coined the word cultigen (the word derived from the conflation of the Latin "*cultus*" meaning cultivated and "*gens*" meaning kind). He noted two *gentes* or kinds (singular, *gens*) of plants; those of known origin or nativity, of known habitat, "*that are discovered in the wild*", were referred to as indigens and the other kind of domesticated group of unknown or indefinite origin (that "*arise in some way under the hand of man*") having such characters as to separate it from the indigens as cultigens or "... *a species, or its equivalent, that has appeared under domestication*..." This definition restricts the idea of the cultigen to plants at the rank of species. Thus, in the Glossary of his *Manual of Cultivated Plants* published in 1924 L.H. Bailey designated the plants in cultivation originating under domestication from the native plants as cultigens and the other as indigens (indigenous or native to the region). At the same time he proposed the term cultivar to distinguish varieties originating in cultivation from botanical varieties known first in the wild. This definition of the cultigen permits the recognition of cultivars. In his *Hortus Second* in 1941 and *Hortus Third* in 1976 *Bailey* returned to the idea of the cultigen having the rank of species indicating that the terms cultigen and cultivar are not synonymous and that cultigens exist at the rank of species only. According to him "*A cultigen is a plant or group of apparent specific rank, known only in cultivation, with no determined nativity, presumably having originated, in the form in which we know it, under domestication.*

Cultigen is a general purpose term for plants whose origin or selection is primarily due to intentional human activity. Thus, the cultigens are anthropogenic or "man made" plants deliberately altered or selected by humans. These arise as a result of simple selections of variants from the wild or cultivation including intentional or accidental hybrids and vegetative sports (aberrant growth that can be reproduced reliably in cultivation); ancient selections of crops; selections from the existing cultivated stocks or from variants within wild populations that are maintained as recognizable entities solely by continued propagation; plants that are the result of plant breeding and selection programmes; the results of deliberate repeatable single crosses between two pure lines to produce desirable plants of a particular general appearance (but not genetically identical); genetically modified plants (plants modified by deliberate implantation of genetic material); clonal material reproduced by cuttings, grafting, budding, layering, etc.; graft-chimaeras (plants grafted to produce mixed tissue, the graft material possibly from wild plants, special selections, or hybrids); and any plants that have been altered by humans but which have not been given formal names. The term cultigen is occasionally applied in a very general sense to any organisms that do not have a wild or uncultivated counterpart, but is domesticated or raised in captivity. However, the domesticated plants are simply wild plants or plants introduced directly from the wild, rather than being specially selected for particular desirable characteristics, but may have genetically "changed" in some way from its wild counterparts, either by conscious or unconscious selection. Because cultigens are defined by their mode of origin and not by where they are growing, plants meeting this definition remain cultigens whether they are naturalized in the wild, deliberately planted in the wild, or growing in cultivation. These plants are usually the plants of commerce that are used in horticulture, agriculture and forestry.

The definition and use of the term cultigen in horticulture has varied but generally, unlike usage in botany, it encompasses cultivars. Botanical Glossary of *The New Royal Horticultural Society Dictionary of Gardening* defines cultigen as, "*a plant found only in cultivation or in the wild having escaped from cultivation; included here are many hybrids and cultivars*", being essentially the same as the definition of the cultigen published by Bailey in 1924. Recent usage in horticulture has, however, maintained a distinction between cultigen and cultivar, nevertheless *allowing the inclusion of cultivars* within the definition. Thus cultigen and cultivar may be confused with one another. The term cultigen encompasses not only plants with cultivar names but others as well, while cultivar is a formal classification category in the ICNCP. Since many domesticated plants were more like botanical varieties than species, Bailey (1923) established a new classification category "the cultivar" for these. The more appropriate etymology of the word cultivar has been suggested to be a contraction of the words "cultigen" and "variety". He defined cultivar as "*... a race subordinate to species, that has originated and persisted under cultivation; it is not necessarily, however, referable to a recognized botanical species. It is essentially the equivalent of the botanical variety except in respect to its origin*". In the *Cultivated Plant Code* (1953) Bailey's term cultivar was introduced. In *Baileya* published in 1954, distinction between the term *cultivar* and the *variety* has been made. Choosing classification categories for cultigens is not clear cut. The replacement of the expression "cultivated plant" with the word "cultigen" is not universally accepted.

The term *taxon* was introduced by German biologist Meyer in the 1920s. The term *culton* (pl. *culta*) has been suggested to replace the word taxon when speaking about cultigens. Cultigens may be named by the traditional method of scientific naming under the *International Code of Botanical Nomenclature*. Many of the most important cultigens, like maize (*Zea mays*) and banana (*Musa acuminata*), are so named. Now it is more common for cultigens to be given names in accordance with the principles, rules and recommendations laid down in the *Cultivated Plant Code* which provides for the names of cultigens in three classification categories, the cultivar, the Group (formerly Cultivar-group), and the grex. The *Cultivated Plant Code* does not recognize the use of trade designations and other marketing devices as scientifically acceptable names. Not all cultigens have been given names according to the *Cultivated Plant Code*. Apart from ancient cultigens, there may be occasional anthropogenic plants such as those that are the result of breeding, selection and tissue grafting that have not been given names according to the *Cultivated Plant Code* because of lack of commercial value.

In botanical literature the word cultigen is generally used to denote a plant which, like the wheat (*Triticum aestivum*) is of unknown origin, but presumed to be an ancient human selection. Plants like these have been given binomials according to the *Botanical Code* and therefore have names that have the same form as those of plants that occur naturally in the wild. As the cultigens are the result of deliberate human selection there is no difference, in principle, between them and modern plants with additional names under the *Cultivated Plant Code*. The use of binomials for cultigens occurs for the most part because they were following the accepted nomenclatural conventions that predated the *Cultivated Plant Code*. In theory cultigens can be named under either Code or both, although in practice almost all have cultivar names governed by the *Cultivated Plant Code*.

Wider use of the term cultigen has been proposed for the following reasons:

- supports current usage in horticulture
- assists clarity in non-technical discussions about "wild" and "cultivated" plants (for example, cultivated plants as commonly understood (plants in cultivation) are not the same as the "cultivated plants" of the *Cultivated Plant Code*, and the distinction between "wild" and "cultivated" habitats is becoming progressively blurred)
- has the potential to simplify the language and definitions used in the Articles and Recommendations of the *Cultivated Plant Code*
- gives greater precision and clarity to the definition of the respective scope, terminology and concepts of the *Botanical Code* and the *Cultivated Plant Code*
- avoids the potential for confusion within the *Cultivated Plant Code* over its scope, that is, whether it is concerned with:
    - where plants are growing (in the wild or in cultivation)
    - how they originated (whether they are the result of intentional human activity or not)
    - whether it simply provides a mechanism for regulating the names of those cultigens requiring special classification categories that are not part of the Linnaean hierarchy of the *Botanical Code* i.e. cultivar and Group names

Trade designations and marketing names

Plant labels in retail outlets with appealing marketing names that are easy to use, pronounce and remember with an intention to maximize market share are referred as "trade designations". These are outside the scope of the *Cultivated Plant Code*.

Plants protected by Plant breeders' rights (PBR) may have a "true" cultivar name – the recognized scientific name in the public domain, and a "commercial synonym" an additional marketing name that is legally protected; e.g. *Rosa* Fascination = 'Poulmax', the ‘Poulmax’ being the true scientific name. Quoting the original code name allows correct identification of cultivars around the world. The peak body coordinating Plant breeders’ rights is the Union for the Protection of New Varieties of Plants (*Union internationale pour la protection des obtentions végétales*, UPOV) and this organization maintains a database of new cultivars protected by PBR in all countries.

⑧ ⑧ ⑧

Chapter 4

CLASSIFICATION

Classification of plants is an arrangement of organisms into groups on the basis of similarities. The groups are, in turn, assembled into more inclusive groups, until all the organisms have been assembled into a single most inclusive group. In the sequence of increasing inclusiveness, the groups are assigned to a fixed hierarchy of categories such as species, genus, family, order, class and division, the final arrangement constituting a system of classification. Once established, a classification provides an important mechanism of information storage, retrieval and usage. It facilitates the identification of plants and enables tracing their relationship with each other.

In the prehistoric days, primitive tribes identified and classified plants on the basis of their usefulness for edible or medicinal purpose. The folk taxonomy was based either on their gross similarities like trees, shrubs, herbs, etc. or on their economic value such as forest plants, cultivated plants, cereals, etc. Early civilizations in China, India, Egypt and Babylonia had flourishing culture of utilization of plants for various purposes in their lives. Written records in Sanskrit show that crops such as wheat, barley, melons and cotton were grown in India during Vedic Period (2000 to 800 BC). Medicinal uses of several plants are mentioned in the *Atharva Veda* written around 2000 BC. Parasara (250 to 120 BC) compiled *Vriksh Ayurved* dealing with descriptions of morphology including details of internal structure of plants along with their physiology and byproducts. Plants were classified into *ganas* (families) such as *Samiganyan* (legume) and *Savastikaganyan* (crucifer). Charak (1st century AD) recognized flowering trees and herbs of different growth patterns in his *Charak Samhita* and provided description of their uses in Indian medicine.

In devising ways of classifying organisms the philosopher Aristotle (384–322 BC) established the idea of a *fundamentum divisionis* — the principle that groups can be progressively subdivided. This is congruent with the relatively recent idea of evolution as descent with modification. Biological classification follows this principle of groups within groups, known as a nested hierarchy, but this form of classification does not necessarily presuppose evolution. The pioneering work with scientific approach to plant classification was started by the Greek philosopher and Aristotle's student Theophrastus (372-287 BC). The attempts were continued by several workers. In his *Enquiry into Plants* (1916) and *The causes of plants* (1927), Theophrastus described 500 kinds of plant, dividing them into groups: trees, shrubs, under-shrubs and herbs with further subdivision into wild and cultivated, flowering and non-flowering, deciduous or evergreen.

Pliny the Elder (29–79 AD), author of *Naturalis historiae*, following utilitarian approach, classified plants according to their medicinal properties and listed "cultivars" named after people, places or special plant characteristics. Dioscorides (1st Century AD), a Greek doctor, produced *Materia Medica* of the herbals giving an account of nearly 600 medicinal plants which led to the modern pharmacopoeia. After addition of illustrations, the manuscript became known as *Codex Juliana*. During the period of Muslim Empire (610-1100 AD), concentration was more on preparing lists of plants useful in agriculture and medicine, e.g. *Canon of medicine* authored by Ibn-Sina (Avicenna) and another list of nearly 600 plants by Ibu-ul-Awwan.

During the Middle Ages, Albertus Magnus (1193-1280 AD) recognized monocots and dicots based on the structure of stem and separated vascular from non-vascular plants. The botanical-medical books were produced by herbalists from Germany (e.g. *Herbarium vivae eicones* during 1530-1536 by Otto Brunfels with illustrations prepared from living plants; *New kreuterbuch* in 1539 by Jerome Bock giving descriptions of 567 species classified as herbs, shrubs and trees; *Historia plantarum* in 1561 by Valerius Cordus, Italy; *Commentartii in sex libros Pedacii Dioscorides* in 1544 by Pierandrea Mathiola and *Herball* during 1551-1568 by William Turner, England. There was a widespread realization of the value of plants in human life. Consequently extensive explorations in Europe, Asia and Africa and in the New World resulted in enormous increase in the list of plant names and necessitated a true botanical classification to take into account the whole plant kingdom as it exists in nature.

The Italian botanist, Andrea Cesalpino made a beginning of plant taxonomy. He prepared a herbarium of 768 plants in 1563 and preserved it in the Museum of Natural History at Florence. His *De Plantis libri* contained descriptions of 1520 species of plants grouped into herbs and trees. His German contemporary Joachin Jung (1587-1657) defined several terms to describe different components of plant. The Swiss botanist, Gaspard Bauhin (1560-1624), also formed a herbarium of 4000 specimens and published *Pinax theatri botanici* in 1623 that contained a list of 6000 species of plants along with synonyms and introduced binomial nomenclature keeping several species under one generic name. John Ray, in the revised edition of his *Methodus plantarum nova* (1703), included 18000 species dividing the plant kingdom into herbac (herbs) and arboreous (trees) and subdividing them as monocots and dicots. His attempt was perhaps the first to group plants based on whether they resembled or differed. Between about 1470 and 1670, 600 to 1000 different kinds of plants were listed including the cultigens Gallica, Centifolia, the rose of uncertain origin. Up to about 1650 plants had been grouped either alphabetically or according to utilitarian folk taxonomy (medicinal uses or whether they were trees, shrubs or herbs). Between 1650 and 1700 there was a move from the utilitarian back to a scientific natural classification based on the characters of the plants themselves.

J. P. de Tournefort (1656-1708), French botanist, was the first to clearly establish genera in his system of classification published in 1694 in *Elements de botanique* that contained 698 genera and 10,146 species. Although still using the broad groupings of "trees" and "herbs", he began to use flower characteristics as distinguishing features and provided a clear definition of the genus as a basic unit of classification. This became a precursor of scientific classification organizing plant variation into equivalent groups or ranks. Many of his genera were later adopted by Carl Linnaeus.

Rapid advances were made since 1600 AD mainly during the period of Carolus Linnaeus (1707-1778). The Linnaean system or the ranked system of classification includes assigning appropriate position and rank to a new taxon (a taxonomic group assigned to any rank; pl. taxa), dividing a taxon into smaller units, uniting two or more taxa into one, transferring its position from one group to another and altering its rank. Later Lamarck (1778), de Jussieu (1774), de Candolle (1806-1893), Bentham and Hooker (1862-1883), Eichler (1875), Engler (1892), von Wettstein (1907), Bessey (1915), Rendle (1925), MEZ-ZIEGENSPECK (1926), Tippo (1942) and Hutchinson (1948) proposed their systems of classification. The systems of classification so far proposed fall into one of the three types, artificial, natural and phylogenetic wherein the taxonomic entities are classified in different fashions.

A. Artificial system: Camerarius in 1694 pointed out that stamens were male sex organs and style and ovary form female sex organs of a flower and that pollen was necessary for seed set. The Swedish scientist Linnaeus published a paper on the sexuality of plants in 1729. Linnaeus utilized the number of stamens for primary classification of the flowering plants. The system is usually based on few characters or even on a single character, e.g. number of stamens, cohesion of stamens, hairiness of plants, etc., to classify organisms for convenience, primarily as an aid to identification. The system of Linnaeus was thus very simple in application. This is based on arbitrary, easily observable characters such as habit, colour, number, form or similar features taking only the floral parts of the plants, more particularly the number, size and cohesion of stamens, into consideration and divided the plants into 24 classes. These classes were further subdivided into orders such as monogyna, digyna, etc. on the basis of carpel characters. His classification is called the "sexual system of classification". This was very largely supported by the followers of the dogma of "Species Creation" and the theory of "Constancy of Species". The system thus fits into this greatest and the last approach towards Artificial System of classification. Taking over the collections made by Linnaeus, the English botanist J. E. Smith, founded the Linnaean Society of London in 1788 and handed over the herbarium to this Society. He, however, ignored the natural or phyletic relations that have much practical importance. Although Linnaeus provided a cataloguing scheme for a large number of plants and a system to bring unrelated plants together there was still need for a more objective classification.

B. Natural system: Natural classification uses overall similarity in grouping taxa, a concept initiated by the French botanist M. Adanson (1727-1806) and culminated in the extensively used classification of Bentham and Hooker. Adanson (1763) recognized 58 natural orders in his *Familles des plantes*. *Flore Francaise* by another French botanist J. B. P. Lamarck contained principles of natural grouping of species, orders and families along with a key to identification of plants. This system, apart from indexing and cataloguing, arranges the plants in order of their relationship with each other as is found in nature utilizing all the available information on several characters. Bernard Jussieu (1699-1776), a contemporary of Linnaeus evolved the first natural system of classifying plants. Antoine Laurent de Jussieu (1748-1836) published this classification along with his own additions in *Genera plantarum* in 1789. He gave 15 orders and 100 families, most of which are recognized even today. Following him Augustine De Candolle (1778-1841) introduced the term 'taxonomy', derived from the term 'taxon' meaning any group of plants, in *Theorie elementaire de la botanique* published in 1813. His son, Alphonse De Candolle revised it in 1844 using anatomy for the purpose of classification, particularly presence or absence of vascular structures, recognizing 213 different natural orders. Thus, Monocots having scattered vascular bundles were separated from the Dicots wherein the vascular bundles form a ring.

Working at Kew Gardens, two English botanists, George Bentham (1800-1884) and J. D. Hooker (1817-1911) published *Genera plantarum* in 1862-63, a classification of seed plants recognizing dicotyledons, gymnosperms and monocotyledons as distinct groups and 192 Cohors or families (Table 4.1). This was the last work based on the concept that the species is a constant entity, although now it is well known that species also undergoes changes. Hooker later wrote a book, *Index Kewensis*.

Table 4.1. Summary of Bentham and Hooker's system of classification (*Genera Plantarum*).

Dicotyledonum (Leaves with reticulate venation, pentamerous flowers and seeds with 2 cotyledons, exogenous growth, tap root system)

Polypetalarum (Corolla consisting of separate petals)

Series i. Thalamifloræ (Sepals distinct, stamens many, petals and stamens attached to the receptacle, hypogynous, disc absent)

Cohors i. Ranales (Floral parts arranged in spiral, cyclic or spiroocyclic manner, carpels free, gynoecium apocarpous)

1. Ranunculaceæ, 2. Dilleniaceæ, 3. Calycanthaceæ, 4. Magnoliaceæ, 5. Annonaceæ, 6. Menispermaceæ, 7. Berberideæ and 8. Nymphæaceæ.

Cohors ii. Parietales (Carpels united to form unilocular ovary, placentation parietal)

9. Sarraceniaceæ, 10. Papaveraceæ, 11. Cruciferæ, 12. Capparideæ, 13. Resedaceæ, 14. Cistineæ, 15. Violarieæ, 16. Canellaceæ and 17. Bixineæ.

Cohors iii. Polygalinæ (Syncarpous,ovary 2-3 septate)

18. Pittosporeæ, 19. Tremandreæ, 20. Polygalæ and 21. Vochysiaceæ.

Cohors iv. Caryophyllinæ (Placentation axile)

22. Frankeniaceæ, 23. Caryophylleæ, 24. Portulaceæ and 25. Tamariscineæ.

Cohors v. Guttiferales (Stamens numerous, calyx imbricate, ovary with 3-8 carpels, axile placentation)

26. Elatineæ, 27. Hypericineæ, 28. Guttiferæ, 29. Ternstroemiaceæ, 30. Dipterocarpeæ and 31. Chlenaceæ.

Cohors vi. Malvales (Stamens numerous, calyx valvate)

32. Malvaceæ, 33. Sterculiaceæ and 34. Tiliaceæ

Series ii. Disciflorǣ (Calyx consisting of united or distinct sepals which may be free or adnate to ovary, disc present, ovary superior and immersed in disk of flower, stamens usually definite in number, hypogynous)

Cohors vii. Geraniales (Pentamerous flowers, disc annular or broken into glands, androecium obdiplostemonous, multicarpellary ovary, syncarpous, axile placentation, ovule pendulous, raphe usually ventral)

35. Lineæ, 36. Humiriaceæ, 37. Malpighiaceæ, 38. Zygophylleæ, 39. Geraniaceæ, 40. Rutaceæ, 41. Simarubeæ, 42. Ochnaceæ, 43. Burseraceæ, 44. Meliaceæ and 45. Chailletiaceæ

Cohors viii. Olacales (Androecium diplostemonous, ovule pendulous and raphe usually dorsal)

46. Olacineæ, 47. Ilicineæ and 48. Cyrillaceae.

Cohors ix. Celastrales (Androecium haplostemonous, ovule erect, raphe ventral)

49. Celastrineæ, 50. Stackhousieae 51. Rhamneae 52. Ampelideae

Cohors x. Sapindales (Androecium diplostemonous, ovules ascending, often 1-2 in each locule, raphe ventral or inverted, usually compound leaves, exstipulate, flowers usually in panicles).

53. Sapindaceae 54. Sabiaceae 55. Anacardiaceae 56. Coriarieae 57. Moringaceae

Series iii. Calyciflorae (sepals united, rarely free, petals in one or two series, perigynous or epigynous, ovary generally inferior)

Cohors xi. Rosales (indefinite stamens, often twice or more the number of petals, styles distinct)

58. Connaraceae, 59. Leguminosæ, 60. Rosaceæ, 61. Saxifragaceæ, 62. Crassulaceæ, 63. Droseraceæ, 64. Hamamelideæ, 65. Bruniaceæ and 66. Halorageæ.

Cohors xii. Myrtales (usually definite stamens, perigynous or epigynous, axile placentation, ovary syncarpous, divided into locules)

67. Rhizophoraceæ, 68. Combretaceæ, 69. Myrtaceæ, 70. Melastomaceæ, 71. Lythraceæ and 72. Onagraceæ.

Cohors xiii. Passiflorales (leaves usually much lobed or divided, tendril climbers, stamens 5, ovary syncarpous, placentation parietal)

73. Samydaceæ, 74. Loasaceæ, 75. Turneraceæ, 76. Passifloraceæ 77. Cucurbitaceæ, 78. Begoniaceæ and 79. Datisceæ

Cohors xiv. Ficoidales (Perianth undifferentiated, ovary syncarpous, ovules in basal or axile placentation)

80. Cactaceæ and 81. Ficoideæ,

Cohors xv. Umbellales (Umbel inflorescence, ovary syncarpous having 1 ovule per locule)

82. Umbelliferæ, 83. Araliaceæ and 84. Cornaceæ

- **Dicotyledones**

Gamopetalæ (Corolla partially or completely fused, perianth dichlamydeous, heterochlamydeous)

Series i. Inferæ (Ovary inferior, stamens as many as the petals alternating with them)

Cohors i. Rubiales (Stamens epipetalous, distinct anthers, ovary with 2-many locules each with 1-many ovules)

85. Caprifoliaceæ and 86. Rubiaceæ.

Cohors ii. Asterales (Stamens are epipetalous, distinct anthers or united, ovary with 1 locule and 1 ovule)

87. Valerianeæ, 88. Dipsaceæ, 89. Calcereæ, 90. Compositæ,

Cohors iii. Campanales (Stamens free, not adnate to corolla, ovary with 2-6 locules each with many ovules),

91. Stylidaceæ, 92. Goodenovieæ and 93. Campanulaceæ.

Series ii. Heteromereæ (Ovary superior; stamens in two or more series epipetalous or free from corolla opposite the petals or are double the number of petals, carpels more than 2)

Cohors iv. Ericales (Stamens double the number of petals or isomerous and alternating with them, ovary has 2-many locules)

94. Vacciniaceæ, 95. Ericaceæ, 96. Monotropeæ, 97. Epacrideæ, 98. Diapensiaceæ, 99. Lennoaceæ.

Cohors v. Primulales (Stamens as many as corolla lobes and opposite the petals, ovary with 1 locule and placentation axile)

100. Plumbagineæ, 101. Primulaceæ and 102. Myrsineæ.

Cohors vi. Ebenales (Stamens as many as corolla lobes or many and opposite them, ovary with many locules, few large seeds)

103. Sapotaceæ, 104. Ebenaceæ and 105. Styraceæ.

Series iii. Bicapellatæ (Stamens as many as corolla lobes and alternating with them or fewer, ovary superior with 2 carpels)

Cohors vii. Gentianales (Corolla actinomorphic, leaves opposite)

106. Oleaceæ, 107. Salvadoraceæ, 108. Apocynaceæ, 109. Asclepiadaceæ, 110. Loganiaceæ and 111. Gentianaceæ.

Cohors viii. Polemoniales (Corolla actinomorphic, leaves alternate)

112. Polemoniaceæ, 113. Hydrophyllaceæ, 114. Boragineæ, 115. Convolvulaceæ and 116. Solanaceæ.

Cohors ix. Personales (Corolla zygomorphic, posterior stamen often reduced, ovules usually more than 4)

117. Scrophulariaceæ, 118. Orobanchaceæ, 119. Lentibulariaceæ, 120. Columelliaceæ, 121. Gesneriaceæ, 122. Bignoniaceæ, 123. Pedaliaceæ, 124. Acanthaceæ,

Cohors x. Lamiales (Corolla zygomorphic to oblique and, posterior stamen reduced, ovules 4),

125. Myoporineæ, 126. Selagineæ, 127. Verbenaceæ, 128. Labiatæ Incertae Sedis, and 129. Plantagineæ.

- **Dicotyledones**

Monochlamideæ or Incompletae (Presence of one or incomplete whorl of perianth or perianth altogether absent, sepaloid perianth, petals absent) Vol III. It has no division into cohors.

Series i. Curvembryeæ (Ovule generally one, embryo coiled, seeds mostly with mealy endosperm)

130. Nyctaginaceæ, 131. Illecebraceæ, 132. Amaranthaceæ, 133. Chenopodiaceæ, 134. Phytolaccaceæ, 135. Batideæ and 136. Polygonaceæ.

Series ii. Multiovulatæ Aquaticæ (ovary syncarpous, ovules many, plants aquatic)

135. Podostemonaceæ

Series iii. Multiovulatæ Terrestres (ovary syncarpous, ovules many, plants terrestrial)

138. Nepenthaceæ, 139. Cytinaceæ and 140. Aristolochiaceæ

Series iv. Microembryeæ (Embryo very minute, ovary apocarpous or syncarpous with single ovule)

141. Piperaceæ, 142. Chloranthaceæ, 143. Myristicaceæ and 144. Monimiaceæ

Series v. Daphnales (Woody or herbaceous plants, sepaloid perianth, stamens perigynous, ovary with one carpel and 2-4 ovules)

145. Laurineæ, 146. Proteaceæ, 147. Thymelæaceæ, 148. Penæaceæ and 149. Elæagnaceæ

Series vi. Achlamydosporeæ (Usually inferior ovary, one locule, with 1-3 ovules, seeds endospermic, without testa)

150. Loranthaceæ, 151. Santalaceæ and 152. Balanophoraceæ

Series vii. Unisexuales (Flowers unisexual, perianth usually absent)

153. Euphorbiaceæ, 154. Balanopseæ, 155. Urticaceæ, 156. Platanaceæ, 157. Leitneriaceæ, 158. Juglandaceæ, 159. Myricaceæ, 160. Casuarinaceæ and 159. Cupuliferæ

Series viii. Ordines Anomali (Families of uncertain relationship)

161. Salicineæ, 163. Lacistemaceæ, 164. Empetraceæ and 165. Ceratophyllaceæ

- **Gymnospermeæ** Vol III (1) (Naked seeded plants)

166. Gnetaceæ, 167. Coniferæ and 168. Cycadaceæ

- **Monocotyledones** (Leaves with parallel venation, trimerous flowers, seeds with one cotyledon) (Vol III (2))

Series i. Microspermæ (inner perianth lobes petaloid, inferior ovary, microscopic seeds, many, exalbuminous)

169. Hydrocharitaceæ, 170. Burmanniaceæ and 171. Orchidaceæ

Series ii Epigynæ (Perianth biseriate, inner petaloid, inferior ovary, seeds large, few to many)

172. Scitamineæ, 173. Bromeliaceæ, 174. Haemodoraceæ, 175. Iirideæ, 176. Amaryllideæ, 177. Taccaceæ and 178. Dioscoreaceæ

Series iii Coronarieæ (Perianth biseriate, inner whorl petaloid, corolla-like flowers, superior ovary, seeds albuminous)

179. Roxburghiaceæ, 180. Liliaceæ 181. Pontederiaceæ, 182. Philydraceæ 183. Xyridaceæ, 184. Mayaceæ, 185. Commelinaceæ and 186. Rapataceæ

Series iv Calycineæ (Perianth biseriate, sepaloid, calyx-like flowers, superior ovary, seeds albuminous)

187. Flagellarieæ, 188. Juncaceæ and 189. Palmæ

Series v. Nudifloreæ (Perianth usually absent or reduced, superior ovary, seeds albuminous)

190. Pandaneæ, 191. Cyclanthaceæ, 192 Typhaceæ, 193. Aroideæ and 194. Lemnaceæ

Series vi. Apocarpæ (Perianth in 1-2 series or absent, superior ovary, carpels free, one or more, apocarpous, seeds exalbuminous)

195. Triurideæ, 196. Alismataceæ and 197. Naiadaceæ

Series vii. Glumaceæ (Minute flowers, perianth reduced, bracts large, scaly, ovary or locules with one ovule)

198. Eriocaulaceæ, 199. Centrolepidaceæ 200. Restiaceæ, 201. Cyperaceæ and 202. Gramineæ

Publication of *The Origin of species* by Charles Darwin in 1859 changed the outlook on classification of plants considering that the organisms undergo a continuous and gradual change under the influence of environmental conditions and that there exists some relationship in the sense of common descent between different species. On acknowledging the existence of evolutionary process, the natural system of classification became inadequate. In 1883, A.W. Eichler (1875) gave a unified system dividing the entire plant kingdom into two subgroups, Cryptogamae and Phanerogamae, the latter into two classes, Angiospermae and Gymnospermae, and Angiospermae into Monocotyledons and Dicotyledons. Based on this, Adolf Engler and Karl Prantl developed a system of classification which differed from the Eichler's only in some details. But there was a confusion as to which was the most primitive family. One large and artificial group of plants having only one perianth (monochlamydeous flowers) was considered the most primitive. But now monocots are considered advanced and not primitive in comparison to dicots. Although the systems of Bentham and Hooker and of Engler and Prantl are now obsolete, but owing to their strength of thorough treatment, are still being followed in the floras around the world.

Natural system of the eighteenth and nineteenth centuries that used morphology in delimiting the overall similarity has undergone considerable refinement in recent years. As against the sole morphological features as indicators of similarity in natural systems, overall similarity is now judged on the basis of features derived from all the available fields of taxonomic information (phonetic relationship) based on data from sources such as morphology, anatomy, embryology, phytochemistry, ultra structure and in fact, all other fields of study. Phonetic classifications were strongly advocated by Sneath and Sokal (1973) but did not find much favour with major systems of classification. It has, however, been very prominently used in modern phylogenetic systems to decide the realignments within the system of classification.

C. Phylogenetic system: Phylogenetic system of classification is the grouping of the plants in relation to their genetic relationship with each other reflecting the course of evolution. It thus connects the system with the descent of plants and enables one to determine at a glance the ancestors or derivatives of the individual. The evolutionary descent or relationship of a group of organisms is depicted either through a phylogram, phylogenetic tree or a cladogram. The classification is constructed with the premise that all the descendants of a common ancestor should be placed in the same group (i.e., group should be monophyletic). If some descendants have been left out, rendering the group paraphyletic, these are brought back into the group to make it monophyletic (merger of Asclepiadaceae with Apocynaceae and of Capparaceae with Brassicaceae in recent classifications). Similarly, if the group is polyphyletic (with members from more than one phyletic lines), it is split to create monophyletic taxa (e.g. genus *Arenaria* split into *Arenaria* and *Minuartia*). This approach is known as cladistics.

Evolutionary taxonomic classification differs from a phylogenetic classification in that the gaps in the variation pattern of phylogenetically adjacent groups are regarded as more important in recognizing groups. It accepts leaving out certain descendants of a common ancestor (i.e., recognizing paraphyletic groups) if they are not significant, thus failing to provide a true picture of the genealogical history. The characters considered to be of significance in the evolution (and the classification based on these) are dependent on expertise, authority and intuition of systematists.

This system is close to the Natural system as the plants showing gross similarities are usually related. But it is not possible to classify plants by strictly following this system as the species are undergoing changes and the existing knowledge pertaining to origin and relationships of all taxa is incomplete. Consequently, the system that is now being followed is a mix up based on the combination of partly natural and phylogenetic systems.

American botanist, C. A. Bessey (1845-1915) laid the foundation of the modern phylogenetic classification based on that of Bentham and Hooker and published in 1915. This is outlined below:

Class 1. Alternifoliae (Monocotyledoneae)

Subclass 1. Strobiloideae (5 orders)

Subclass 2. Cotyloideae (3 orders)

Class 2. Oppositifoliae (Dicotyledoneae)

Subclass 1. Strobiloideae

Superorder 1. Apopetalae-polycarpellatae (7 orders)

Superorder 2. Sympetalae- polycarpellatae (3 orders)

Superorder 3. Sympetalae- dicarpellatae (4 orders)

Subclass 2. Cotyloideae

Superorder 1. Apopetalae (7 orders)

Superorder 2. Sympetalae (3 orders)

Bessey considered angiosperms to have evolved monophyletically from Cycadophyta. He believed in the strobiloid theory of the origin of the flower, the latter having originated from a vegetative shoot with spiral phyllomes, of which some modified to form sterile perianth, fertile stamens and carpels. He represented evolutionary relationships through an evolutionary tree known as *Besseyan cactus*. Classification resembling Bessey's was developed by the German Hans Hallier (1808-1932) and that resembling Engler's was published by the Austrian systematist Westtstein (1862-1931) and also by English botanist Alfred Rendle (1865-1938). The British botanist John Hutchinson (1884-1972) associated with the Royal Botanic Gardens at Kew published a system of classification based on 24 principles in 1973 in *The Families of Flowering Plants*. He recognized 411 families but placed several closely related families in distant groups. Deriving from the classifications of Bentham and Hooker and Engler and Prantl, Lyman Benson (1979) published a classification in his book *Plant Classification* in 1957, dividing monocotyledons directly into 13 orders.

A number of contemporary workers improved the system of classification as and when new information and data from paleobotany, phytochemistry and ultrastructure became available. It was largely accepted that Angiosperms are a monophyletic group (consisting of the descendants of a common ancestor) and that dicots were more primitive than the monocots. The Russian botanist Armen Takhtajan (1997) as well as Arthur Cronquist (1988) of New York Botanical Garden placed angiosperms in division Magnoliophyta divided into two classes, Magnolipsida (dicots) and Liliopsida (monocots). Takhtajan recognized 11 subclasses, 55 superorders, 175 orders and 458 families in dicots and 6 subclasses, 16 superorders, 57 orders and 131 families in monocots. Whereas Takhtajan attached more importance to cladistics, Cronquist gave more weightage to the phenetic relationship in the placement of groups. Similar classification was proposed by the Hungarian C. R. de Soo in 1975. The American taxonomist Robert Thorne (2003) also proposed a similar classification but ranked angiosperms as a class and not division. He divided the class Angiospermae (Magnoliopsida) into 10 subclasses, placing monocot taxa between primitive dicots and the more advanced Eudicots and recognized 33 superorders, 90 orders and 489 families. Thorne's phylogenetic shrub showing relationship between different groups is left empty in the centre of the diagram to indicate early extinct angiosperms, those nearer the centre being the primitive groups and those nearer the periphery the advanced ones. The classification proposed by Rolf Dahlgren (1932-87) is closely similar to the earlier versions of Thorne's. Some more proposals such as Sporne (1976), Stebbins (1974), Doweld (2001) and Wu *et al.* (2002) on the Takhtajan-Cronquist pattern have also been published.

Angiosperm Phylogeny Group (APG)

Until detailed genetic evidence became available, the classification of flowering plants (also known as angiosperms, Angiospermae, Anthophyta or Magnoliophyta) was based on their morphology (particularly that of the flower) and their biochemistry (kinds of chemical compounds they contained or produced). Classification systems were typically produced by an individual botanist or by a small group. The result was a large number of such systems and their updates that tended to be favoured in different countries; e.g. the Engler system in continental Europe; the Bentham & Hooker system in Britain (particularly used by Kew); the Takhtajan system in the former Soviet Union and countries within its sphere of influence; and the Cronquist system in the USA. The classifications were not phylogenetic as these were not based on strictly monophyletic groups.

The use of cladistic methodology and the incorporation of morphological, anatomical, embryological, palynological, karyological, chemical and molecular data and particularly the multiple gene sequence data have been useful in assessing higher level angiosperm relationships. The genetic evidence that became available, analyzed by phylogenetic methods, confirmed or clarified some relationships in existing systems of classification, but radically changed others. Many changes were proposed. Bremer and Wanntorp (1981) suggested that Angiosperms should not be divided into Monocotyledons and Dicotyledons but instead directly into the monophyletic groups. A global consortium of botanists from major institutions worldwide came together under the title of the 'Angiosperm Phylogeny Group' or APG and provided a widely accepted system for angiosperm classification based largely on genetic (DNA) information. The first attempt was made in 1998 (APG I) with the following principles for classification that remained unchanged in subsequent revisions:

- The Linnean system of orders and families should be retained. "The family is central in flowering plant systematics". An ordinal classification of families is proposed as a "reference tool of broad utility". Orders are considered to be of particular value in teaching and in studying family relationships.

- Groups should be monopyletic (i.e. consist of *all* descendants of a common ancestor). The main reason why existing systems are rejected is because they do not have this property, they are not phylogenetic.
- A broad approach is taken to defining the limits of groups. Thus of orders, it is said that a limited number of larger orders will be more useful. Families containing only a single genus and orders containing only a single family are avoided where this is possible without violating the over-riding requirement for monophyly. Although orders and families are used, above this level, named clades are freely employed in addition.

The APG I grouped 462 families into 40 putative monophyletic orders and a small number of informal monophyletic higher groups such as monocots, commelinoids, eudicots, core eudicots, rosids, eurosids I, eurosids II, asteroids, euasterids I and euasterids II. Under these informal groups, were also listed a number of families without assignment to order, and a number of families were listed both at the beginning and at the end of the classification. This was an ordinal classification of flowering plant families primarily on the basis of genetic characteristics as a "reference tool of broad utility". The broad approach adopted was to define the limits of orders that resulted in the recognition of 40 orders, compared to 232 in Takhtajan's classification. Other features of the proposed classification include:

- Formal, scientific names are not used above the level of order, named clades being used instead. Thus eudicots and monocots are not given a formal rank on the grounds that "it is not yet clear at which level they should be recognized". A substantial number of taxa whose classification had traditionally been uncertain are given places, although there still remain 25 families of "uncertain position".
- Alternative classifications are provided for some groups, in which a number of families can either be regarded as separate or can be merged into a single larger family. For example, the Fumariaceae can either be treated as a separate family or as part of Papaveraceae.

Cladistic information brought out that a simplistic division of angiosperms into monocots and dicots does not reflect phylogenetic history. Thus a major outcome of the classification was the disappearance of the traditional division of the flowering plants into monocots and dicots. The monocots were recognized as a clade, but not the dicots. A number of former dicots were placed in separate groups basal to both monocots and the remaining dicots (eudicots or 'true dicots'). Judd *et al.* (1999) made some modifications by shifting some of the families from informal groups where these were assigned in 1998 and recognized 51 orders. Another revision was done in 2003 (APG II) to update APG I (Table 4.2). Broad circumscriptions of taxa by placing small families containing only one genus in a larger group resulted in considerable refinement with more families and some orders coming out of the unplaced taxa.

Table 4.2. Angiosperm classification based on APWEB, 2003

- Anita Grade
  - Order Nymphaeales
    - Family Nymphaeaceae
- Magnoliid Complex
- Magnoliids
  - Order Magnoliales
    - Family Annonaceae
  - Order Laurales
    - Family Lauraceae
- Two clades of uncertain position
- Monocots
  - Order Alistmatales
- Family Araceae
  - Order Pandanales
    - Family Pandanaceae
- Commelinoid Clade
  - Order Arecales
    - Family Arecaceae (Palmae)
  - Order Zingiberales
    - Family Musaceae
  - Order Poales
    - Family Bromeliaceae
- Eudicots (Tricolpates)
  - Order Ranunculales
    - Family Berberidaceae
  - Order Proteales
    - Family Proteaceae
    - Family Nelumbonaceae
- Core Eudicots (Core Tricolpates)
  - Order Caryophyllales
    - Family Cactaceae
    - Family Polygonaceae
  - Order Santalales
    - Family Lauraceae
- Two clades of uncertain position
- Monocots
  - Order Alistmatales
    - Family Vitaceae
  - Order Myrtales
    - Family Myrtaceae
    - Family Combretaceae
    - Family Lythraceae
    - Family Trapaceae

Eurosids I
- Order Zygophyllales
  - Family Zygophyllaceae
- Order Celastrales
- Order Cucurbitales
  - Fabids (Euosids II)
- Order Oxalidales
  - Family Oxalidaceae
- Order Malpighiales
  - Family Malpighiaceae
  - Family Euphorbiaceae
  - Family Clusiaceae (Guttiferae)
  - Family Passifloraceae
  - Family Chrysobalanaceae
  - Family Phyllanthaceae
- Order Fabales
  - Family Fabaceae (Leguminosae)
- Order Rosales
  - Family Elaeagnaceae
  - Family Rosaceae
  - Family Moraceae
  - Family Rhamnaceae
  - Family Ulmaceae
  - Family Urticaceae
- Order Fagales
  - Family Betulaceae
  - Family Myricaceae
  - Family Jaglandaceae
  - Family Fagaceae

Malvids (Eurosids II)
- Order Huerteales
- Order Brassicales
  - Family Capparaceae
  - Family Caricaceae
  - Family Moringaceae
- Order Malvales
  - Family Tiliaceae
  - Family Sterculiaceae
  - Family Bombacaceae
- Order Sapindales
  - Family Meliaceae
  - Family Burseraceae
  - Family Anacardiaceae
  - Family Rutaceae

Family Sapindaceae

Asterids Clade (= Sympetalae)

Order Cornales

Family Cornaceae

Order Ericales

Family Sapotaceae

Family Ebenaceae

Family Ericaceae

Family Lecythidaceae

Family Actinidaceae

Lamiids (Euasterids I)

Family Boraginaceae

Order Garryales

Order Solanales

Family Solanaceae

Gentianales

Family Rubiaceae

Family Apocynaceae

Family Loganiaceae

Order Lamiales

Family Oleaceae

Family Verbenaceae

Campanulids (Euasterids II)

Order Apiales

Order Aquifoliales

Order Asterales

Order Dipsacales

Family Caprifoliaceae

Family Adoxoaceae

Non-Angiosperm Taxa

Ginkgos (Ginkgoales)

Ginkgoaceae

Conifers (Coniferales)

Araucariaceae

Cuppressaceae

Pinaceae

Gnetophytes

Gnetaceae

Some of the main changes made in APG II are:

- Many of the previously unplaced families are now located within the system.
- Several major families are restructured.

The APG II recognized 457 families and 45 orders and changing the name Commelinoids to Commelinids. The angiosperms are no longer to be divided into traditional dicots and monocots. Commelinids are distinct from other monocots, and these two, forming the traditional monocots are better placed between primitive angiosperms and the Eudicots. In 2007, a linear ordering of the families in APG II was proposed for herbarium specimens.

Subsequent revision was done in 2009 (APG III) to update APG II retaining the broad outline of the system but reducing the number of previously unplaced families and genera. Consequently, the number of orders increased from 45 to 59; only 10 families were not placed in an order and only two of these (Apondanthaceae and Cynomoriaceae) were left entirely outside the classification. The use of 'bracketed' families was discontinued in favour of larger, more inclusive families. As a result, the APG III system contains only 415 families. For example, Agavaceae and Hyacinthaceae are no longer regarded as distinct from the broader Asparagaceae. There were only five taxa (two small families of parasitic plants and three genera) that remained unplaced in the angiosperm tree. Now in almost all cases APG III uses the broader concept instead of two alternate versions permitted in APG II, wider (one larger family) and narrower (2-10 more narrowly defined families), which makes the classification simpler. Some unusual relationships have unravelled, e.g. Rafflesia (the "corpse flower") found in the Indonesian rainforest, noted for producing the largest individual flower in plants, is actually related to the poinsettia (Euphorbia pulcherrima), one of the world's smallest flowers.

Some modifications suggested to improve the system are linear ordering of the families (Haston *et al.,* 2009) and use of formal taxonomic ranks in place of the informal clade names, above the ordinal level (Chase and Reveal, 2009). Chase and Reveal (2009) have reduced the flowering plants to a single subclass composed of the formally recognized 16 superorders and the group as a whole is recognized as the subclass Magnoliidae. The system is now being followed by major herbaria, including Kew, World Checklist of Selected Plant Families and the floras. A web site for the APG system, APweb, hosted by the Missouri Botanical Garden, is maintained which is regularly updated incorporating views published on areas of angiosperm taxonomy.

Levels of Classification

All living things are classified into Kingdoms, *Animalia* (animals), *Mycetae* (fungi), *Bacteria*, *Monera* (blue-green algae), *Protista* (other algae including diatoms) and *Plantae* (green plants). Cryptogams and Phanerogams are two main divisions of the plant kingdom (Plantae). Cryptogams include Thallophytes (algae, fungi, bacteria and viruses), Bryophytes (moss, liverworts) and Pteridophytes (ferns). They do not produce flowers or seeds and their mode of reproduction is not easily discernible. They have naked embryos called spores, i.e. they have reproductive organs that are inconspicuous and are thus called Cryptogamae or those with hidden reproductive organs. The Phanerogams produce flowers and are called the flowering plants. The flowering plants have distinct male and female organs which respectively contain male and female gametes or sexual cells that fuse during sexual reproduction and form seed embryo sporophyte. Thus this division is also called Spermatophyta, meaning seed bearing plants containing ovules. The Spermatophytes or Magnoliophytes are originally woody plants producing secondary xylem through activity of secondary meristem (cambium) and show heterospory with two kinds of spores (microspores and megapores), which produce two kinds of gametophytes (male or microgametophytes and female or megagametophytes). Thus the characteristic features of the Divison Magnoliophyta are: (1) presence of enclosed seed; ovules are enclosed in a more or less completely closed cavity formed by one or several separate or united sporophylls or carpels; very often surrounded by distinct floral envelopes i.e. perianth; (2) process of pollination; transfer of pollen grain from the male organ that are deposited not directly on the micropyle of the ovule but on the receptive female organ called stigma where they germinate and send a pollen tube through the style to complete the process of double fertilization inside the ovule; (3) extremely simplified and specialized male and female gametophytes devoid of gametangia (antheridia and archegonia); and (4) triple fusion; one of the two male gametes fusing with the egg cell (syngamy), and the other with two free or already fused polar nuclei of the central cell of the female gametohyte resulting in a diploid zygote and a triploid primary nucleus of the endosperm (although in the Podostemaceae and Orchidaceae the endosperm fails to develop or degenerates early in ontogeny) and sieve tube elements in the phloem tissue accompanied by one or more companion cells that are derived from the same mother cell. After the pollination and fertilization, the ovary develops into the fruit and the ovules into the seeds.

The flowering plants fall into two classes, Gymnosperms and Angiosperms (Magnoliopsida or Angiospermopsida). Gymnosperms are tall trees or bushes. They produce cones instead of flowers. Cones are woody reproductive structures that produce exposed ovules or naked seeds, i.e. seeds not enclosed in fruits and with only an integument as covering. They have primitive and very simple unisexual flowers and a simple process of fertilization to which endosperm formation precedes. The reproductive process is slow; up to a year may pass between pollination and fertilization and seed maturation may require 3 years. Polyploids are rare; they have not undergone extensive allopolyploid speciation. All are woody plants; trees, shrubs, lianas and few epiphytes and no true aquatics. They have well developed roots, and long pointed leaves. Pollination is by wind, no animal pollination and no double fertilization. The class Gymnospermae contains four major lineages: Cycadaceae (cycads), Ginkgoaceae (ginkgos), Pinaceae (conifers) and gnetophytes. They remain green throughout the year and are called evergreen plants.

The Angiosperms have embryo usually with two cotyledons, sometimes one, rarely with three or four. Cotyledons are commonly with three vascular bundles. Leaves are mostly petioled. Venation is typically reticulate, either pinnate or palmate and mostly not closed (with free vein endings). Leaf traces are 1-3, seldom more. Prophylls and bracteoles are usually paired. Plumule is terminal. Vascular bundles are usually arranged in a ring, seldom in two or more rings or scattered. Mostly a tap root system is present from which side branches arise. The root cap and epidermis are mostly of a common ontogenetical origin. Plants are woody or herbaceous, frequently secondarily arborescent. Epicuticular wax ultrastructure is mostly of *Aristolochia*-type, but in Winteraceae and Canellaceae they are of *Berberis*-type. Plastids are of the sieve elements of S-type or less often of P-type. Flowers are mostly 5- or (less frequently 4-merous and only in some mainly archaic groups 3-

merous). Floral nectaries are of various types but never septal or nectaries are absent. Pollen grains are typically triaperturate or of triaperturate derived type, except in some archaic families, where they are distally uniaperturate or rarely biaperturate.

The subclass Magnoliidae includes woody or herbaceous plants. Secretory cells with oily contents are ordinarily present in the parenchymatous tissues. Vessels are with sclariformis simple perforations or the vessels are absent. Sieve-element plastids usually contain protein crystalloid (Pc-type) or filaments (Pf-type), often also starch, in some families only starch (S-type). Stomata are commonly paracytic. Flowers are bisexual or less often unisexual, frequently spiral or spirocyclic, actinomorphic. Stamens are mostly numerous. Tapetum is usually secretory. Microsporogenesis is successive or simultaneous. Pollen grains are 2-celled or less often 3-celled, 1-colpate, 2-colpate, 3-6-colpate, rugate, porate or often inaperturate. Gynoecium is mostly apocarpous. Ovules are bitegmic or much less often unitegmic, usually crassinucellate. Endosperm is cellular or nuclear. Seeds are mostly with small or minute embryo and copious endosperm, sometimes accompanied or largely replaced by perisperm. Cotyledons are typically 2, but occasionally 3 or 4 (Degeneriaceae, Idiospermaceae). The plants commonly produce neolignans and/or benzyl isoquinoline alkaloids, but without ellagic acid and iridoid compounds.

The subclass includes a number of relatively very archaic orders and families of flowering plants most probably evolved from a common ancestral stock with the superorder Nymphaeanae as basal group. These have a very disharmonious combination of both primitive and derived characters. It constitutes 10 phyletic groups (Core Angiosperms or Mesangiosperms, Monocots, Commelinids, Eudicots, Core Eudicots, Rosids, Fabids:eurosid I, Malvids:eurosid II, Asterids, Lamiids:euasterid I, and Campanulids:euasterid II) that represent distinctly related 'orders'. An 'order' comprises one or more 'families'. A large family may be divided into phyletic units such as 'subfamilies' and a subfamily into 'tribes' and 'subtribes'.

A family or a subfamily may comprise of one or more 'genera' and a genus may have one or more 'species'. The species is the basic unit in the taxonomy of plants. The species constitutes a group of plants having similar, not identical, characters. It is defined as a collection of individuals which are very much alike and assumed to be more closely related or more recently descended from the same ancestor. The 'genus' is sometimes subdivided into subgenera, sections, subsections and series.

A species may sometimes be divided into subspecies, varieties, forms, races, strains, clones, and others, depending on such minor characters as the yield and quality of the produce, resistance to diseases, plant vigour, flower characters, etc. which may not justify for the status of a separate species. Botanical variety is a group of plants under a species, e.g. *Prunus persica* var. *nucipersica.* Horticultural variety is a group of plants formed with an economic point of view. The ones propagated vegetatively are called 'cultivars' and those propagated asexually are called 'clones'. 'Biotype' is species in a narrow sense. It is a group of genetically identical plants which may not necessarily be homozygous. Ecotype is separated from a species by geographical barriers and has adapted itself for survival in the given conditions. Strain is a division of a cultivar showing a difference in the characters of economic importance such as yield, colour, etc. However, strain is not recognized and all the strains are now separate cultivars. The recognized taxonomic ranks are given in Table 4.3.

Table 4.3. Recognized taxonomic ranks*

Main	Secondary	Further	Termination	Name of taxa
Domain				Eukarya
Kingdom (Regnum)			-bionta	Plantae
Division (Phylum)			-phyta	Magnoliophyta
		Subdivision (Subphylum)	-phytina	Magnoliophytina
Class			-opsida	Magnoliopsida (Angiosperms)
		Subclass	-idae	Magnoliidae
		Superorder	-anae	
Order			-ales	
		Suborder	-ineae	
		Infraorder	-aria	
		Superfamily	-acea, -ariae	
Family			-aceae	
		Subfamily	-oideae	
	Tribe		-eae	
		Subtribe	-inae	
Genus				
	Section			
	Series			
Species				
		Subspecies		
	Variety			
	Form			

*APG classification recognizes only Tricolpates (Eudicots), Asterids, Rosids, Euasterids, Eurosids above the order level as monophyletic clades for which no formal taxonomic names are used.

The ICBN recognizes five infraspecific ranks: subspecies, variety, subvariety, form and subform, although only subspecies (for geographical races), variety (for local populations which are morphologically and possibly ecologically distinct) and form (for atypical individuals within a population) are mostly used for cultivated plants as well as wild plants. For cultivated plants, three hierarchical categories between species and cultivar have been suggested: convarietas, group, subgroup (if necessary) and cultivar or race.

Taxonomic position (up to species level) of the fruit crops that occur in different agro-climatic areas spread over the diversity regions of the world and have significant role in human food and nutrition has been outlined in Table 4.4 (the taxonomic ranks as per updated classification by APG III, 2009 and the synonymy of Magnoliidae presented by Reveal and Chase, 2011).

Table 4.4. Taxonomic position of fruit crops.

Kingdom: PLANTAE		
Division: MAGNOLIOPHYTA (SPERMATOPHYTA; SPERMATOPHYTES)		
Class: Gymnospermae (Gymnosperms)		
Ginkgopsida	**Pinopsida**	**Gnetopsida**
Subclass **Ginkgoidae**	Subclass **Pinidae**	Subclass **Gnetidae**
Order **GINKGOALES**	Order **PINALES**	Order **GNETALES**
Ginkgoaceae	**Pinaceae**	**Gnetaceae**
Maidenhair tree (***Ginkgo biloba*** L.)	**Chilgoza pine (*Pinus gerardiana* Wall. ex D. Don.)** **Stonepine (*Pinus pinea* L.)**	**Spanish joint fir** (***Gnetum gnemon*** **L.)**
Class: Magnoliopsida (Angiospermopsida) [Angiosperms] Subclass **Magnoliidae**		
Super Order/Order	**Family**	**Genus/Species**
NYMPHAEANAE **NYMPHAEALES** *EURYALALES*	**Nymphaeaceae** Waterlily family *(=Euryalaceae)*	**Gorgan nut or Fox nut** *(Euryale ferox* **Salisb.)**
[CORE ANGIOSPERMS – MESANGIOSPERMS]		
MAGNOLIANAE **MAGNOLIALES** *ANNONALES*	**Annonaceae** Annona family	**Cherimoya (*Annona cherimola* Mill.)** **Sweet sop (*Annona squamosa* L.)** **Atemoya or Hanuman phal *(Annona atemoya* Hort. ex Wester)** **Bullock's Heart (*Annona reticulata* L.)** **Soncoya (*Annona purpurea* Moc. and Sesse ex Dunal)** **Ilama (*Annona diversifolia* Safford)** **Wild custard apple (*Annona senegalensis* Auct. non Pers.)** **Pond apple (*Annona glabra* L.)** ***Annona cutemoya*** **Biriba (*Rollinia mucosa* (Jacq.) Baill.)** **Burahol (*Stelechocarpus burahol* (Blume) Hook.f.)** **Pawpaw (*Asimina triloba* (L.) Dunal)**
MAGNOLIANAE **LAURALES**	**Lauraceae** Laurel family	**Avocado (*Persea americana* Mill.)**

LILIOPSIDA (MONOCOTS, MONOCOTYLEDONS, MONOCOTYLEDONAE)

LILIANAE **ALISMATALES** *=ARALES*	**Araceae** Arum family *=Philodendraceae, Pothaceae*	**Ceriman (*Monstera deliciosa* Liebm.)**
LILIANAE **PANDANALES**	**Pandanaceae** Screwpine family	**Karuka *(Pandanus brosimus* Merr. & L.M.Perry*)***

	[COMMELINIDS]	
LILIANAE **ARECALES** *(=COCOSALES)*	Arecaceae Palm family *(=Borassaceae, Cocosaceae, Palmae, Phoenicacea)*	**Palmyra palm (*Borassus flabellifer* L.)** **African fan palm (*Borassus aethiopum* C. Mart.)** **Coconut *(Cocos nucifera* L.)** **Date palm (*Phoenix dactylifera* L.)** **Date sugar palm (*Phoenix sylvestris* Roxb.)** **Acai palm (*Euterpe oleracea* C. Mart.)** **Babassu *(Attalea speciosa* C. Mart. ex. Spreng.)** **Buriti palm (*Mauritia flexuosa* L.f.)** **Pataua *(Jessenia bataua* (Mart.) Burret.)** **Pejibaye *(Bactris gasipaes* Kunth)** **Rakum palm (*Salacca wallichiana* Mart.)** **Salak palm (*Salacca zalacca* (Gaertner) Voss)** **Sugar palm (*Arenga pinnata* (Wurmb.) Merr.)** **Tucuma (*Astrocaryum aculeatum* G.F.W. Meyer** **Doum palm (*Hyphaene thebaica* (L.) Mart.)**
LILIANAE **ZINGIBERALES** *(=MUSALES, CANNALES)*	**Musaceae** Banana family	***Musa acuminata* Colla.** ***M. balbisiana* Colla.** **Cultivated banana (AA diploid, AAA triploid, AAB triploid, AB diploid, ABB triploid, ABBB tetraploid)** **African banana or Ensete (*Ensete ventricosum* (Welw.) Cheesman), Wild plantain or Indian bread (*Ensete superbum* (Roxb.) Cheesman syn. *Musa superbum* Roxb.)**
LILIANAE **POALES** (=*BROMELIALE)*	**Bromeliaceae** Bromeliad family	**Pineapple (*Ananas comosus* (L.) Merril)**
	[EUDICOTS]	
RANUNCULANAE *=(BERBERIDANAE)*	**Berberidaceae** Barberry family	**European barberry or Barberry *(Berberis vulgaris* L.)**
RANUNCULALES = (*BERBERIDALES)*	Lardizabalaceae	**Akebia or Chocolate vine or Five-leaf akebia (*Akebia quinata* (Houtt. Decne)**
PROTEANAE **PROTEALES** *= (NELUMBONALES)*	**Nelumbonaceae** **Water lotus family**	**Lotus (*Nelumbo nucifera* Gaertn.)** **American lotus (*Nelumbo lutea* Willd.)**
	Proteaceae Protea family	**Macadamia nut (*Macadamia integrifolia* Maiden et Betche)**
	[CORE EUDICOTS]	
DILLENIANAE **DILLENIALES**	**Dilleniaceae**	**Elephant apple (*Dillenia indica* L.)**
SAXIFRAGANAE **SAXIFRAGALES**	**Grossulariaceae** *= (Ribesiaceae)*	**European gooseberry (*Ribes grossularia* L.)** **Wedge leaf gooseberry (*Ribes hirtellum* Michx.)**

		American black currant (*Ribes americana* Mill.) **Black currant (*Ribes nigrum* L.)**
	ROSIDS	
ROSANAE (=*VITANAE)* **VITALES** *(=LEEALES)*	**Vitaceae** Grape family *(=Ampelopsidaceae)*	**European or Old World grape (*Vitis vinifera* L.),** **Fox grape or concord grape (*Vitis labrusca* L.)** **Muscadine grape (*Vitis rotundifolia* Michx.)** **Wild grape *(Ampelocissus latifolia* (Roxb.) Planch.)** **Summer grape (*Vitis aestivalis* Michx.)**
	[FABIDS: EUROSID I]	
ZYGOPHYLLALES *(=BALANITALES)*	**Zygophyllaceae** (=*Balanitaceae)*	**Desert date (*Balanites aegyptiaca* (L.) Delile)**
FABALES *(=CAESALPINIALES, MIMOSALES)*	**Fabaceae** Legume family (=*Caesalpiniaceae, Lathyraceae, Leguminosae, Mimosaceae, Papilionaceae, Tamarindaceae*)	**Subfamily Caesalpinioideae** **Tamarind (*Tamarindus indica* L.)** **Carob (*Ceratonia siliqua* L.)** **Yeheb nut (*Cordeauxia edulis* Hemsl.)** **West Indian locust (*Hymenaea courbaril* L.)** **Subfamily Mimosoideae** **Khejri (*Prosopis cineraria* (L.) Druce)** **Tree bean (*Parkia roxburghii* G. Don.)** **African locust bean (*Parkia biglobosa*) (Jacq.) Benth.)** **Manila tamarind (*Pithecellobium dulce* (Roxb.) Benth)** **Subfamily Faboideae (syn. Papilionoidae)** **Tahiti chestnut (*Inocarpus edulis* Forst.)** **Tonka bean (*Dipteryx odorata* (Aubl.) Willd.)**
ROSALES (=*AMYGDALALES, ARTOCARPALES, FICALES, MORALES, RHAMNALES,)*	**Rosaceae** *(=Amygdalaceae, Malaceae, Mespilaceae, Potentillaceae, Prunaceae, Pyraceae, Sorbaceae, Cydoniaceae, Fragariaceae)*	**Subfamily Rosoideae** **Strawberry (*Fragaria* x *ananassa* Duch.)** **White rose (*Rosa alba* L.)** **European blackberry (*Rubus fruticosus* auct. Aggr.)** **Subfamily Maloideae** **Quince (*Cydonia oblonga* Mill.)** **Asian flowering quinces or Japanese quince (*Chaenomeles speciosa* (Sweet) Nak.)** **Medlar (*Mespilus germanica* L.)** **American mountain ash (*Sorbus americana* Marshall)** **Loquat (*Eriobotrya japonica* (Thunb.) Lindl.)** **European pear (*Pyrus communis* L.)** **Nashi (*Pyrus pyrifolia* (N.L.Burman) Nakai)**

	Kainth (*Pyrus pashia* D. Don.)
	Ussurian pear (*Pyrus ussuriensis* Maxim.)
	Snow pear (*Pyrus nivalis* Jacq.)
	Apple (*Malus × domestica* Borkh.) syn. *M. pumila* Mill.)
	Service berry (*Amelanchier spp.*)
	Saskatoon berry (*Amelanchier alnifolia* Nutt.)
	Black chokeberry (*Aronia melanocarpa* (Michx.)Ell.)
	English hawthorn (*Crataegus monogyna* Jacq.) Common hawthorn (*Crataegus monogyna* Jacq.)
	Crabapple (*Malus baccata* (L.) Borkh.)
	Subfamily Amygdaloideae
	Almond (*Prunus dulcis (*Mill.) D.A.Webber syn. *P. amygdalis* Batsch; *P. communis* (L.) Archang.)
	Peach (*Prunus persica* (L.) Batsch.)
	Nectarine (*Prunus persica* var. *nucipersica* (Suckow) C.K. Schneid syn. *Prunus persica* var. *laevis* Gray
	Chinese peach (*Prunus davidiana* (Carr.) Franch.)
	Apricot (*Prunus armeniaca* L.)
	Russian apricot *(Prunus armeniaca* var. *ansu* Maxim.)
	Siberian apricot (*Prunus sibirica* L.)
	Japanese apricot (*Prunus mume* Sieb. et Zucc.)
	Old world plums or Japanese plum (*Prunus salicina* Lindl.)
	European plum (*Prunus domestica* L.)
	Myrobalan or cherry plum (*Prunus cerasifera* Ehrh.)
	Apricot plum (*Prunus simonii* Carr.)
	American red plums (*Prunus americana* S.Wats.)
	Sweet cherry (*Prunus avium* L.)
	Tart or sour cherry (*Prunus cerasus* L.)
	Mahaleb cherry (*Prunus mahaleb* L.)
	Himalayan cherry or Paja (*Prunus cerasoides* D.Don.) syn. *P. puddum* Franch.
	Black cherry (*Prunus serotina* Ehrh.)
Elaeagnaceae	**Seabuckthorn (*Hippophae rhamnoides* L.)**
	Oleaster (*Elaeagnus angustifolia* L.)
Rhamnaceae	**Chinese jujube (*Ziziphus jujuba* Mill. non Lam.)**
Buckthorn family *(=Ziziphaceae)*	**Sour jujube (*Ziziphus acidojujuba* C. Y. Cheng et M. J. Liu)**
	Ber (*Ziziphus mauritiana* Lamk.)
	Jharber *(Ziziphus nummularia* (Burm.f.) Wight & Arn.)

		Japanese raisin tree (*Hovenia dulcis* Thunb.)
	Moraceae	**Subfamily Moroideae**
	Mulberry family	**White mulberry (*Morus alba* L.)**
	(=Artocarpaceae, Ficacea)	**Black mulberry (*Morus nigra* L.)**
		Red mulberry (*Morus rubra* L.)
		Subfamily Aurtocarpoideae
		Fig (*Ficus carica* L.)
		Jackfruit (*Artocarpus heterophyllus* Lamk.)
		Breadfruit (*Artocarpus altilis* (Parkinson Fosberg; syn. *Artocarpus communis* J.R.Forst. & G.Forst.)
		Monkey jack (*Artocarpus lakoocha* Roxb.)
		Chempedak (*Artocarpus integer* (Thunb.) Merr.)
		Marang (*Artocarpus odoratissimus* Blanco)
		African breadfruit (*Treculia africana* Decne.)
		Che (*Cudrania tricuspidata* Bur. ex Lavallee)
	Urticaceae Nettle family	**Trumpet tree and snakewood (*Cercropia peltata* Linnaeus)**
		Amazon grape (*Pourouma ceropiaefolia* Mart.)
FAGALES	**Fagaceae**	**Spanish chestnut (*Castanea sativa* Mill.)**
(=BETULALES, QUERCALES, JUGLANDALES, MYRICALES)	Beech family *(Castaneaceae, Quercaceae)*	**American sweet chestnut (*Castanea dentata* (Marshall) Borkh.)**
		American beechnut (*Fagus grandifolia* Ehrh.)
	Myricaceae Bayberry family	***Kafal* (*Myrica esculenta* Buch.-Ham.)**
	Juglandaceae Walnut family	**Hickory and pecan (*Carya* spp.)**
		Shagbark hickory nut (*Carya ovata* (Mill.) K. Koch)
		Pecan (*Carya illinoinensis* (Wangenh) K. Koch)
		Persian or English walnut (*Juglans regia* L.)
		Butternut (*Juglans cinerea* L.)
		Japanese or siebold walnut (*Juglans ailantifolia* Carr.)
		Manchurian walnut (*Juglans mandshurica* Maxim.)
		Chinese walnut (*Juglans cathayensis* Dode)
		Eastern black walnut (*Juglans nigra* L.)
		North Californian black walnut (*Juglans hindsii* (Jeps.) Rehder)
	Betulaceae syn. Corylaceae	**Filbert and hazelnut (*Corylus* spp.)**
		European hazelnut (*Corylus avellana* L.)
	Birch family	**American hazlenut (*Corylus americana* L.)**
	(=Corylaceae)	**Turkish cobnut (*Corylus colurna* L.)**
CUCURBITALES	**Cucurbitaceae** Gourd family	**Oyster nut (*Telfairia pedata* (Sm. ex Sims) Hook.)**
		Telfairia nut (*Telfairia occidentalis* Hook. f.)
		Cassabanana (*Sicania odorifera* (Vell.) Naudin)
OXALIDALES	**Oxalidaceae**	**Carambola (*Averrhoa carambola* L.)**

(=ELAEOCARPALES)	Oxalis family *(=Averrhoaceae)*	**Bilimbi (*Averrhoa bilimbi* L.)**
	Cunoniaceae	**Davidson's plum (*Davidsonia pruriens* F. Muell)**
	Elaeocarpaceae	**Indian olive (*Elaeocarpus floribundus* Blume)**
		Ceylon olive (*Elaeocarpus serratus* L.)
MALPIGHIALES *(=PHYLLAN-THALES, SALICALES, CHRYSOBALANALES, EUPHORBIALES, FLACOURTIALES, GARCINIALES, IRVINGIALES, PANDALES, PASSIFLORALES)*	**Euphorbiaceae** Spurge family	**Mogongo nut (*Schinziophyton rautanenii* (Schinz.) Radcl-Sm.)**
		Orinoco nut (*Caryodendron orinocense* Karst.)
		African walnut (*Plukenetia conophora* Müll. Arg.)
	Phyllanthaceae	**Aonla (*Phyllanthus emblica* L.)**
		Otaheite gooseberry (*Phyllanthus acidus* (L.) Skeels)
		***Baccaurea* species**
		Bignay (*Antidesma bunius* (L.) Spreng.)
		Masuku (*Uapaca kirkiana* Müll. Arg.)
	Malpighiaceae	**Barbados cherry (*Malpighia glabra* L.**
	Malpighia family	**Nance (*Byrsonima crassifolia* (L.) Kunth.**
	Chrysobalan-aceae	**Cocoplum (*Chrysobalanus icaco* L.)**
	(=Licaniaceae)	**Sansapote (*Licania platypus* (Hemsl.) Fritsch)**
		Hissing tree (*Parinari curatellifolia* Planch. ex Benth.)
		Couepia (*Couepia longipendula* Pilg.)
	Passifloraceae	**Passionfruit (*Passiflora edulis* Sims.)**
	Passionflower family	**Purple passionfruit (*Passiflora edulis* forma *edulis*)**
		Yellow passionfruit (*Passiflora edulis* f. *flavicarpa* Deg.)
		Giant granadilla (*Passiflora quadrangularis* L.)
		Sweet calabash (*Passiflora maliformis* L.)
		Banana passionfruit (*Passiflora mollissima* [Kunth] Bailey)
		Maypop (*Passiflora incarnata* L.)
		Water lemon (*Passiflora laurifolia* L.)
		Sweet granadilla (*Passiflora ligularis* Juss.)
	Salicaceae	**African dove plum (*Dovyalis abyssinica* (A. Rich.) Warb.)**
	Willow family *(=Flacourtiaceae)*	**Kei apple (*Dovyalis caffra* (Hook.f. et Harv.) Warb.)**
		Kitembilla (*Dovyalis hebecarpa* (Gardner) Warb.)
		Governor's plum (*Flacourtia indica* Merr.)
		Lovi-lovi (*Flacourtia inermis* Roxb.)
		Paniala (*Flacourtia jangomas* Raeusch.)
		Rukam (*Flacourtia rukam* Zoll. & Moritzi)
	Caryocaraceae	**Pequi (*Caryocar brasiliense* Cam.)**

	Irvingiaceae	**Bush mango (*Irvingia gabonensis* Baill.),**
	Calophyllaceae	**Mammee apple (*Mammea americana* L.)**
	Clusiaceae	**Mangosteen (*Garcinia mangostana* L.)**
	(=Cambogiaceae,	**Mundu (*Garcinia dulcis* Kurz)**
	Garciniaceae,	**Gamboge (*Garcinia tinctoria* W.F. Wight)**
	Guttiferae)	**Som-Khack (*Garcinia atrovirdis* Griff. ex T. Anderson)**
		Cerapu (*Garcinia prainiana* King)
		Gorakha (*Garcinia cambogia* Desrouss)
		Imbe (*Garcinia livingstonei* T. Anders.)
		Kokam (*Garcinia indica* Choisy)
		Cowphal (*Garcinia cowa* Roxb.)
		Bakuri (*Platonia insignis* Mart.)
		Madrono (*Rheedia madruno* Planch. and Triana)

[MALVIDS: EUROSID II]

Super Order/Order	**Families**	**Genera/Species**
MYRTALES	**Combretaceae**	**Indian almond (*Terminalia catappa* L)**
(=TRAPALES,	Combretum family	**Baheda (*Terminalia bellirica* (Gaertn.) Roxb.)**
COMBRETALES,		**Chebulic myrobalan (*Terminalia chebula* Retz.)**
LYTHRALES)		**Okari nut (*Terminalia okari* C.T. White)**
	Lythraceae	**Pomegranate (*Punica granatum* L)**
	Loosestrife family *(=Punicaceae, Trapaceae)*	**Water chestnut (*Trapa natans* L. var. *bispinosa* (Roxb.) Makino syn. *T. bicornis* Osbeck)**
	Myrtaceae	**Guava (*Psidium guajava* L.)**
	Myrtle family	**Costa Rican guava (*Psidium friedrichsthalianum* (Berg) Niedenza)**
	(=Eugeniaceae)	**Cattley guava (*Psidium cattleianum* Sabine**
		Yellow strawberry guava (*P. cattleianum* var. *lucidum*)
		Feijoa (*Feijoa sellowiana* O. Berg
		Water apple (*Syzygium aqueum* Burm. f. (Alston)
		Java rose apple (*Syzygium samarangense* (Blume) Merr. and Perry)
		Rose apple (*Syzygium jambos* (L.) Alston.)
		Malay rose apple *Eugenia malaccensis* L.
		Pitomba (*Eugenia luschnathiana* Klotzsch ex Berg)
		Araca-boi (*Eugenia stipitata* McVaugh)
		Grumichama (*Eugenia dombeyi* (Sprengel) Skeels)
		Surinam cherry (*Eugenia uniflora* L.)
		Camu-camu (*Myrciaria dubia* McVaugh)
		Jaboticaba (*Myrciaria cauliflora* (DC) Berg)
		Rumberry (*Myrciaria floribunda* Berg)
		Downy myrtle (*Rhodomyrtus tomentosa* Wight.)
		Chilean cranberry (*Ugni molinae* Turcz.)

		Allspice (*Pimenta dioica* (L.) Merrill.) syn. *P. officinalis* L.)
SAPINDALES	**Burseraceae**	**Java almond (*Canarium indicum* L.)**
(*=BURSERALES,*	Torchwood family	**Pili nut (*Canarium ovatum* Engler)**
CITRALES,	*Balsameaceae*	**African pear (*Dacryodes edulis* (G.Don) H.J. Lam.)**
HIPPOCASTANALES,		
RUTALES,	**Anacardiaceae**	**Mango (*Mangifera indica* L.)**
SIMAROUBALES,	Cashew family	**Binjai (*Mangifera caesia* Jack. ex Wall.)**
SPONDIADALES)	*(=Spondiadaceae,*	**Horse mango (*Mangifera foetida* Lour.)**
	Pistaciaceae)	**Kuwini (*Mangifera odorata* Griffith)**
		Bambangan (*Mangifera pajang* Kostermans)
		Gandaria (*Bouea gandaria* Blume)
		Cashew (*Anacardium occidentale* L.)
		Pistachio (*Pistacia vera* L.)
		***Pistacia chinensis* Bunge**
		Ambarella (*Spondias dulcis* Soland ex Parkinson)
		Yellow mombin (*Spondias mombin* L.)
		Amra (*Spondias pinnata* (Linn. f.) Kurz)
		Purple mombin (*Spondias purpurea* L.)
		Marula nut (*Sclerocarya birrea* (A. Rich.) Hochst.)
		Chironji (*Buchanania lanzan* Spreng.)
	Sapindaceae	**Litchi (*Litchi chinensis* Sonn.)**
	Soapberry family	**Longan (*Dimocarpus longan* Lour.)**
	(=Hippocastanaceae)	**Rambutan (*Nephelium lappaceum* L.)**
		Pulasan (*Nephelium ramboutan-ake* (Labill.) Leenh.)
		Akee (*Blighia sapida* Koenig)
		Mamoncillo (*Melicoccus bijugatus* Jacq.)
		Fijian longan (*Pometia pinnata* J.R. and G. Forst)
		Pitombeira (*Talisia esculenta* (St. Hil.) Radlk.)
		Yellow genip (*Talisia oliviformis* (Kunth) Radlk.)
		Guarana (*Paullinia cupana* Kunth.)
	Rutaceae	**Wampee (*Clausena lansium* (Lour.) Skeels.)**
	Rue family	**Box orange (*Severinia buxifolia* (Poir.) Tenore)**
	(=Aurantiaceae,	**Kumquats (*Fortunella* Swingle)**
	Citraceae)	**Large round kumquat (*Fortunella crassifolia* (Poir.) Tenore)**
		Oval kumquat (*Fortunella margarita* (Lour.) Swingle)
		Malayan kumquat (*Fortunella polyandra* (Ridl.) Tan.)
		Hong Kong wild kumquat (*Fortunella hindsii* (Champ.) Swing.)

		Trifoliate orange (*Poncirus trifoliata* (L.) Raf.)
		Australian finger lime or Mexican orange (*Microcitrus australasica* Swingle)
		Citron (*Citrus medica* L.)
		Fingered citron (*Citrus medica* var. *sarcoclactylis*)
		Grapefruit (*Citrus paradisi* Macf.)
		Lemon (*Citrus limon* (L.) Burm. f.)
		Sour lime (*Citrus aurantifolia* (Christm.) Swingle)
		Tahiti or Persian lime (*Citrus latifolia* Tanaka)
		Sweet lime (*Citrus limettioides* Tanaka)
		Mandarin (*Citrus reticulata* Blanco)
		Satsuma mandarin (*C. unshiu* Marcovitch)
		King mandarin (*C. nobilis* Loureiro)
		Mediterranean mandarin (*Citrus deliciosa* Tenore)
		Calamondin (x *Citrofortunella mitis* (Bunge) Wijnands syn. *C. madurensis* Loureiro.)
		Rangpur or Canton lemon (*Citrus limonia* Osbeck)
		Ugli (*Citrus reticulata* Blanco x *C. paradisi* Macf)
		Pummelo (*Citrus grandis* (L.) Osbeck)
		Sweet orange (*Citrus sinensis (L.)* Osbeck)
		Sour orange (*Citrus aurantium* L.)
		Rough lemon or Jambhri (*Citrus jambhiri* Lush.)
		Karna khatta (*Citrus karna* Raf.)
		Bael (*Aegle marmelos* (L.) Corr.)
		Wood apple (*Feronia limonia* (L.) Swingle)
		White sapote (*Casimiroa edulis* Llave and Lex.)
		Intergeneric hybrids (Citranges, Citrangequats, Citrangedins, Citrangors, Cicitranges, Citrumellos, Citremons, Citrandarins, Citrumquats, Procimequat, Limequats, Orangequats, Eremolemons, Eremoranges, Eremoradias, Citrangermors, Lemonage, Lemonimes, Lemandarins, Tangors, Tangelos, Clement, Minneola, Orlando, Seminole)
	Meliaceae	**Langsat (*Lansium domesticum* Correa)**
	Mahogany family	**Santol (*Sandoricum koetjape* (Burm.f.) Merr. syn. *S. indicum* Cav.)**
MALVALES	**Muntingiaceae**	**Jamaica cherry (*Muntingia calabura* L.).**
(=*BOMBACALES,*	**Malvaceae**	**Subfamily Grewioideae**
BIXALES,	Mallow family	**Phalsa *(Grewia asiatica* L. syn. *Grewia subinaequalis* DC)**
STERCULIALES,	*(=Bombacaceae,*	
STERCULIALES,	*Durionaceae,*	***Grewia asiatica vestita* (Wall. ex Brandis) Mast.)**
TILIALES,	*Grewiaceae,*	

CISTALES)	*Philippodendraceae,* *Sterculiaceae,* *Tiliaceae)*	**Subfamily Helicteroideae** **Durian (*Durio zibethinus* Murr.)** **Subfamily Malvoideae** **Kola nut (*Cola acuminata* Schott and Endl.)** **Cocoa (*Theobroma cacao* L.)** **Cupuassu (*Theobroma grandiflorum* (Willd. ex Spreng.) K.Schum.)** **Subfamily Bombacoideae** **Baobab (*Adansonia digitata* L.)** **Malabar chestnut (*Pachira aquatica* Aubl.)** **Matisia (*Quararibea cordata* Vischer syn. *Matisia cordata* Humb. & Bonpl)**
BRASSICALES *(=SALVADORALES,* *CAPPARALES,* *CARICALES,* *MORINGALES)*	**Moringaceae**	**Drumstick tree (*Moringa oleifera* Lam.*)***
	Caricaceae Papaya family	**Papaya (*Carica papaya* L.)** **Mountain papaya (*Vasconcellea pubescens* A.DC. syn. *Carica candamarcensis* Hook.)** **Babaco (*Vasconcellea x heilbornii* V. M. Badillo syn. *Carica heilbornii* V. M. Badillo)** **Toronche, chamburo (*Vasconcellea monoica* (Desf.) A.DC. syn. *Carica monoica* Desf.)** ***Vasconcellea quercifolia* A. St.-Hil. syn. *Carica quercifolia* (A. St.-Hil.) Hieron.** ***Vasconcellea cauliflora* (Jacq.) A.DC. syn. *Carica cauliflora* Jacq.**
	Salvadoraceae	**Indian mustard tree (*Salvadora oleoides* Decne)**
	Capparaceae Caper family	***Ker* (*Capparis decidua* (Forsk.) Edgew.)**
SANTALANAE **SANTALALES** *(=OLACALES)*	**Olacaceae**	**Galo nut (*Anacolosa frutescens* Blume)** **African walnut (*Coula edulis* Baill.)** **Tallow wood plum (*Ximenia americana* L.)**
	Santalaceae	**Quandong (*Santalum acuminatum* (R.Br.) A.DC.)**
CARYOPHYL-LANAE *(=POLYGONANAE)*	**Polygonaceae** Buckwheat family	**Seagrape (*Coccoloba uvifera* L.)**
CARYOPHYL-LALES *(=OPUNTIALES,* *SIMMONDSIALES,* *CACTALES)*	**Cactaceae** Cactus family *(=Opuntiaceae,* *Cereaceae,* *Nopaleaceae)*	**Prickly pear (*Opuntia ficus-indica* Mill.)** **Barbados gooseberry (*Pereskia aculeata* Plum. ex Mill.)** **Strawberry pear (*Hylocereus undatus* Britt. and Rose)**
	ASTERIDS	
ASTERANAE *(=CORNANAE)* **CORNALES**	**Cornaceae** Dogwood family	**Cornelian cherry (*Cornus mas* L.)**
ASTERANAE **ERICALES** *(=ACTINIDIALES,* *LECYTHIDALES,* *SAPOTALES,*	**Lecythidaceae**	**Brazil nut (*Bertholletia excelsa* Humb. et Bonpl.)** **Monkey pot or sapucaia nut or paradise nut (*Lecythis elliptica* H.B.K., *L. pisonis* Cambess., *L. zabucajo* Aubl.)**

VACCINIALES, DIOSPYRALES)	**Sapotaceae** Sapodilla family *(=Achradaceae)*	**Sapodilla (*Achras zapota* (L.) van Royen)** **Khirni *(Manilkara hexandra* (Roxb.) Dubard)** **Miracle berry (*Synsepalum dulcificum* (Schumach. & Thonn.) Daniell.)** **Argan tree (*Argania spinosa* (L.) Skeels)** **Shea butter tree (*Vitellaria paradoxa* Gaertn. f.)** **Mamey sapote (*Calocarpum sapota* (Jacq.) Merr.)** **Star apple (*Chrysophyllum cainito* L.)** **Canistel (*Pouteria campechiana* (Kunth.) Baehni)** **Abiu (*Pouteria caimito* (Ruiz & Pav.) Radlk.)** **Mahua (*Madhuca longifolia* Macbr.)** **Indian butter tree (*Madhuca butyracea* (Roxb.) Pierre ex Dubard)**
	Ebenaceae Ebony family *(=Diospyraceae)*	**Japanese persimmon (*Diospyros kaki* L.f.)** **American persimmon (*Diospyros virginiana* L.)** **West African ebony (*Diospyros mespiliformis* Hochst. ex A. DC *)*** **Velvet apple (*Diospyros blancoi* A.DC)** **Black sapote (*Diospyros digyna* Jacq.)** **Date plum (*Diospyros lotus* L.)** **Nepal Ebony persimmon *(Diospyros tomentosa* Roxb.)** **Mabola persimmon (*Diospyros discolor* Willd.)**
	Actinidiaceae Actinidia family	**Kiwifruit (*Actinidia deliciosa* A.Chev.) C.F.Liang et A.R.Ferguson *)*** **Hardy kiwi (*Actinidia arguta* (Siebold and Zucc.) Planch. ex Miq.)**
	Ericaceae Heath family *(=Vacciniaceae)*	**Subfamily Vacciniaceae** **Lowbush blueberry (*Vaccinium angustifolium* Aiton.)** **Highbush blueberry (*Vaccinium corymbosum* L.)** **Cranberry (*Vaccinium macrocarpon* Ait.)** **Lingon berry (*Vaccinium vitis-idaea* L.)**

[lamiids: euasterid I]

GENTIANALES *(=APOCYNALES, LOGANIALES, RUBIALES, STRYCHNALES)*	**Rubiaceae** Madder family	**Spanish tamarind (*Vangueria madagascariensis* J.F.Gmel.)** **Borojoa *(Borojoa patinoi* Cuatr.)** **Genipap (*Genipa americana* L.)**
	Loganiaceae Logania family *(=Strychnaceae)*	**Kaffir orange (*Strychnos spinosa* Lam.)**
	Apocynaceae Dogbane family *(=Carissaceae)*	**Karonda (*Carissa carandas* L.)** **Natal plum (*Carissa grandiflora* A.DC.)** **(*Carissa bispinosa* (L.) Desf.)**

		Bush plum (*Carissa spinarum* L.) **Cow tree (*Couma utilis* (Mart.) Müell. Arg.)**
BORAGINALES *(=CORDIALES)*	**Boraginaceae** Borage family *(=Cordiaceae)*	**Gonda (*Cordia myxa* L.)** ***Gondi* (*Cordia gharaf* Forsk.)**
SOLANALES	**Solanaceae** Nightshade family	**Tree tomato (*Solanum betaceum* Cav. syn. *Cyphomandra betacea* Sendt.)** **Cape gooseberry (*Physalis peruviana* L.)** **Orinoco apple (*Solanum topiro* Humb. et Bonpl.)** **Naranjilla (*Solanum quitoense* Lam.)**
	Caprifoliaceae	**Blue honey suckle or honey berry (*Lonicera caerulea* L.)** **Goji berry or wolf berry (*Lycium barbarum* L.)**
LAMIALES	**Oleaceae** Olive family	**Olive (*Olea europaea* L.)**
	Lamiaceae Mint family	**Black plum (*Vitex doniana* Sweet)**
	Verbenaceae Verbena family	
	[campanulids: euasterid II]	
DIPSACALES *(=ADOXALES, SAMBUCALES)*	**Adoxaceae** *(=Viburnaceae, Sambucaceae)*	**Elderberry (*Sambucus canadensis* L.)** **Highbush cranberry (*Viburnum trilobum* Marsh.)**

⑧ ⑧ ⑧

Part B
GYMNOSPERMAE (GYMNOSPERMS)

The gymnosperms are the group of seed producing plants including conifers, cycads, ginkgo and gnetophytes. The plants are woody having pycnoxylic or manoxylic wood, the latter made up of tracheids, rarely of vessels. The venation of leaves is dichotomous or derived there from. Megasporangia are surrounded by an integument to form ovules, additionally protected by inclusion in cones or cone-like structures, rarely fully exposed, such as in ginkgo and cycas. Functional reproductive units are mostly unisexual. Gametophytes are more strongly reproduced than the pteridophytes, the female ones mostly with reduced archegonia and the male ones 4 to more-celled. Pollen are mostly unisulcate. Exine is alveolar or granular. Fertilization takes place with a pollen tube and the male gametes are rarely motile. Seeds are provided with a primary endosperm.

Chapter 5

GINKGOALES

Ginkgoales contains only one extant species, *Ginkgo biloba*, the ginkgo tree. It is monotypic within the monotypic class Ginkgopsida of the division Ginkgophyta. The order includes five families of which only Ginkgoaceae remains extant.

Family Ginkgoaceae

The trees are deciduous with long and short shoots having resinous and slightly mucilaginous wood, spreading and petiolate leaves having flattened blades, dichotomously flabelliform in living species (but more linear in some fossil members), bilobed or entire, without midribs, but with numerous fine, occasionally dichotomous radiating veins; spirally arranged, distant on long shoots, more crowded and clustered on short lateral spur shoots, associated with scale leaves, with some short shoots eventually reverting to a long shoot growth form. The shoots are glabrous, of annually periodic growth with small, pointed and slightly scaly resting buds. Male and female cones arise always on separate trees. Male cones are catkin-like, in small groups of about 4-8 each in the axils of leaves or scale leaves at the ends of the short spur shoots, amongst and emerging with or before the foliage leaves that are quickly deciduous. Pollen is wind-borne, without air bladders. Subsequent fertilization is by motile spermatozoids. Female (ovuliferous) organs are drupe-like, in the axils of leaves or scale leaves in sparse groups at the apices of short shoots amongst the leaves, each long-stalked with two distal terminal ovules of which usually only one develops. The ovules swell to become ellipsoid globose, fleshy orange-yellow, slightly glaucous at maturity, the outer layer pulpy and odoriferous, surrounding an inner stony layer (Kramer and Green, 1990). It is a monotypic family.

Genus *Ginkgo* L.

It is a genus of highly unusual non-flowering plants.

Maidenhair tree
(*Ginkgo biloba* L.; yinguo (silver fruit), bái guŏ (white fruit), icho, eunhaeng)

It is indigenous to eastern China. The ginkgo was widespread during the Jurassic and Cretaceous periods but by the end of Pliocene it disappeared from the fossil record except from a small area of central China. The fossils related to the modern ginkgo date back 270 million years making it a "living fossil". The tree has been cultivated in China since ancient times. The trees planted in the temples are believed to be 1500 years old. Because of its status in Buddhism and Confucianism, it is widely planted in Japan and Korea where it has naturalized, spreading into natural forests. Trees are exceptionally hardy and withstand air pollution, high salinity, high winds and frost remarkably well.

The tree is deep rooted, deciduous and very large reaching a height of 20-35 m. Old trees produce aerial roots (known as chichi or zhongru). The crown is angular having long and somewhat erratic branches growing shoots with regularly spaced leaves. Spur shoots or short shoots develop from the axils of these leaves on second year growth. These shoots have very short internodes and their leaves are usually unlobed which appear clustered at the tip. After a number of years, the short shoot may change into a long shoot or *vice versa*. On the long shoots, the distinctive leaves are fan-shaped, bilobed and have more than four parallel veins per segment. The leaves are usually 5-10 cm long. Two veins radiate out into the leaf blade at the base and fork dichotomously.

The tree is dioecious. The reproductive structures are formed only on the spur shoots. The male flowers are yellowish catkins in long clusters at the end of the side boughs. The female flowers are bare, grouped in pairs, lengthily pedunculate and equipped with two free ovules. Male plants produce small pollen cones with sporophylls each bearing two microsporangia spirally arranged around a central axis. Female plants do not produce cones. The fertilization of ginkgo seeds occurs via motile sperm as in ferns. The sperm is large, about 250-300 micrometres, having a complex multi-layered structure, which is continuous belt of basal bodies forming the base of several thousand flagella that actually have a cilia-like motion. The flagella/ cilia apparatus pulls the body of the sperm forwards. Two sperms are produced, one of which successfully fertilizes the ovule. Large ovules have stuffed substances of reserve that ginkgo drops on the ground rather tardily in season. The higher pole of the ovule is constituted of a mini cavity filled with liquid, the pollinic room. This room presents a tiny opening, the micropyle, which produces a viscous droplet to trap a grain of pollen if it is presented and the micropyle is then closed. Finally the pollen germinates and produces true spermatozoids, which swim towards the female cell and penetrate to amalgamate with it. It is widely held that fertilization of ginkgo seeds occurs just before or after they fall in early autumn. Embryo ordinarily occurs in seeds just before and after they drop from the tree. Two ovules are formed at the end of a stalk, and after pollination, one or both develop into apricot-like structures, technically not fruits, but the seeds. The seed is 1.5-2.0 cm long. Its soft and fleshy outer layer (sarcotesta) is light yellow-brown, soft, and fruit-like. It is attractive in appearance, but contains butanic acid and gives off an unpleasant odour like rancid butter when fallen. Beneath the sarcotesta is the hard sclerotesta (the shell) and a papery endotesta surrounding the female gametophyte at the centre. This egg-shaped seed is edible and much sought after. These are known as ginkgo nuts or white nuts or *li zi* in Chinese. The nut-like gametophytes inside the seeds are a traditional Chinese food. The seeds (nuts) are nutritious and contain 13% protein and 3% fats comprising linoleic, oleic, palmitic and linolenic acids. Consuming over 5 seeds a day may cause poisoning to children owing to the presence of 4-methoxypyridoxine (MPN). Contact with the fleshy sarcotesta covering the seeds may cause skin ailments in some people.

Some male cultivars have been recognized in the USA. The popular cultivar 'Autumn Gold' is a clone of a male genotype.

Chapter 6

PINALES

The order comprises all the extant conifers such as cedar, celery-pine, cypress, fir, juniper, larch, pine, redwood, spruce and yew. The tree is branched, tracheid side wall pits are with torus and phloem is with scattered fibres and resin ducts/cells. Plants are monoecious, microsporangiophore/filament is simple with terminal microsporangia. The reproductive structure known as a cone is produced. Ovuliferous scales are flattened, ±united with bract scales. Ovules lack pollen chamber. Pollen tube is unbranched, growing towards the ovule. Gametes are non-motile, siphonogamy. Seed coat is dry, not vascularized. The families included are Araucariceae, Cephalotaxaceae, Cupressaceae, Pinaceae, Podocarpaceae, Sciadopityaceae and Taxaceae.

Family Pinaceae

The plants are highly resinous shrubs or trees, deciduous or evergreen. The leaves are usually with resin canals, acicular, linear or oblong, solitary and spirally arranged in all shoots, or in some genera only on new growth, and later densely grouped on short, lateral shoots; soft, stiff, flexible, rigid or asperous in texture. Shoots are glabrous, pubescent or hairy, usually with distinctive rhythmic annual growth increments. Male and female cones are usually on the same tree, female cones often appearing later in the life of the tree and borne mostly on higher branches. Male cones are catkin-like, solitary or grouped and axillary with numerous spirally arranged microsporophylls with two pollen sacs. Female (ovuliferous) cones are solitary, in irregular groups or whorled, erect, suberect or pendant, sessile or shortly-stalked, rounded or elongate, each with numerous spirally arranged scales and more or less conspicuous bracts, the former each with ovules on their upper surface, leathery or becoming stiff, woody, flexible, papery leathery with age, and sometimes highly resinous, in 1-3 seasons and eventually dismembering the tree or the scales opening on the tree to release seed. Seed is winged or unwinged, two in each scale, cotyledons in variable number, sometimes numerous (Kramer and Green, 1990).

Genus *Pinus* L.

The shrubs and trees are tall, monoecious and evergreen. Leaves vary from small and scale-like to long and linear lanceolate to very long and narrowly linear that are variously distributed. The leaves are solitary and spirally arranged, or (mostly) in fascicles of 1-5 with persistent or deciduous scarious basal sheaths. Male cones arising in the axil of a scale leaf are numerous and closely clustered around the bases of young shoots, with numerous scales. Pollen is with two air bladders. Female cones are terminal or subterminal, elongate to ovate, symmetric or oblique and mostly woody. At least 80 species are widely distributed in the northern hemisphere, South to Central America, North Africa, and the Philippines and Sumatra (Kramer and Green, 1990).

Chilgoza
(*Pinus gerardiana* Wall. ex D. Don.; noosa pine, neoza)

The pine tree is evergreen, small to medium, occasionally attaining a height of 24 m and diameter of 3.6 m having thin, glabrous, silver gray and mottled bark. Branches are short and horizontal forming a compact architecture. Young shoots are olive green and ridged. The needle-like leaves are in clusters of three, 5-10 cm long, stiff, dark green and partly persisting for 3-4 years. The pine is monoecious. Male cones are 7.5-13 mm long borne on lower branches and the oblong ovoid female cones are 15-23 x 10-13 cm in size borne on top branches. The reflexed scales are thick, woody and are of about 3.8 x 2.5 cm size. The seed is cylindrical, pointed at the tip, 2-2.5 cm long, dark brown with inconspicuous and caducous wing and oily endosperm (Sehgal and Chauhan, 1991; Pandey and Misra, 1992).

Stonepine
(*Pinus pinea* L.; Italian stonepine or parasol, pignolia or umbrella pine)

It is native of northern Mediterranean region. The tree is evergreen, needle-leaved growing up to 30 m in height with an umbrella-shaped crown. Leaves are 10-20 cm long and are borne in pairs. Male and female reproductive structures (strobili or cones) are borne separately on the same tree. Seeds are borne in cones of 8-14 x 10 cm size. The cones require 3 years to develop and produce seeds. Seeds are 15-20 x 7-11 mm in size having caducous wings of less than 1 mm.

No standard cultivar is known. However, lot of variability is observed in nature with respect to kernel size from which selections can be made. A thin-shelled form is found in Italy in which it is possible to break the shell even by fingers (Menninger, 1977; Rosengarten, 1984).

⑧ ⑧ ⑧

Chapter 7

GNETALES

An order of chiefly tropical or xerophytic woody gymnospermous plants, mostly vines, but a few trees having vessels in the wood, large flat opposite leaves that have reticulate venation and compound male and female strobili. The seeds have two cotyledons and may be brightly coloured. It consists of a single family Gnetaceae, 1 genus *Gnetum* and about 30 species. These are practically unknown as fossils but are sometimes considered on structural grounds to be near or on the ancestral line of the angiosperms.

Family Gnetaceae

The plants are mostly dioecious trees, shrubs or vines for the greater part. The branches are nodose. Leaves are decussate, simple, entire, pinnately nerved and exstipulate. Spikes are ramified or simple, axillary or cauline, each with two opposite basal scales and several collars containing moniliform hairs and sessile flowers, either numerous spirally arranged male flowers below a ring of some sterile female ones or a ring of few fertile female flowers. The female flower has an ovule enclosed in a fleshy outer envelope (perianth) and two thinner inner envelopes (integuments), the innermost with a tubillus. The sterile female flowers are without the middle envelope. Male flower has a claw-shaped, transversely splitting perianth and a central stamen with two (in *G. gnemoides*) apical and yellow microsporangia, which open by an apical median split. Seed at maturity remains enclosed in the fleshy outer envelope which turns red, pink or yellow, the middle envelope forms a hard and ribbed testa with the thin inner envelope and the small embryo embedded in copious endosperm. The only genus *Gnetum* has about 30 species of which 7 are in tropical America, 2 in western Africa and the remainder in tropical Asia from Bombay to Fiji.

Genus *Gnetum* L.

It is a genus of gymnosperms, the sole genus in the order and family with 30 or more species of tropical evergreen trees, shrubs and lianas.

Spanish joint fir

(***Gnetum gnemon* L.**; melinjo; melindjo; mennjau)

It is native of Malaysia. It occurs in a wild state in rain forests at elevations up to 1200 m and is common on river banks in New Guinea. It is distributed from

Assam to Caroline Islands and Fiji. Some related species having edible fruits are *G. costatum* K. Schumann (found growing in Papua New Guinea), *G. latifolium* Blume (found growing in Malaysia to Philippines) and *G. tenuifolium* Ridley (found growing in Malaysia).

The tree is dioecious, slender, evergreen, 5-10 m tall having a straight trunk and simple, elliptical and opposite leaves of 7.5-20 x 2.5-10 cm size. The inflorescence is solitary and axillary, 3-6 cm long, pale yellow, emerging also from older wood and bearing flowers in whorls at the nodes. Female flowers are globose and tipped, 5-8 at each inflorescence node. Fruit is nut-like, ellipsoid, 1-3.5 cm long, shortly apiculate, velvety and is yellow turning red to purple on ripening with one large horny seed. The seed is covered with a tough husk (seed coat) and a thin edible rind.

Of the 6 botanical varieties, only *G. gnemon* var. *gnemon* has tree form and bears large fruits and is cultivated in the Philippines, Sulawesi, Sumba, New Guinea and Fiji. The others are shrubs and bear very small fruits. *G. gnemon* var. *tenerum* is a 3 m tall shrub with oblong beaked flower and the much smaller fruit has acute apex.

⑧ ⑧ ⑧

PART C

MAGNOLIOPSIDA (ANGIOSPERMOPSIDA) [ANGIOSPERMS]

Chapter 8

NYMPHAEALES

The plants are herbaceous without cambium and aquatic with generally submerged or floating leaves, 4-celled uniseriate secretory trichomes with a large terminal cell. The tissues are parenchymatous without ethereal oil cells and with conspicuous air passages and laticifers. Vascular bundles are closed, scattered, or less commonly in one or more rings. Vessels are absent. Sieve element plastids are of S-type. Leaves are spiral, involute, peltate (divided), simple with entire toothed margin, stipulate (the stipules median axillary), or exstipulate. Stomata are anomocytic. Flowers are solitary, often large, bisexual, actinomorphic, mostly spirocyclic. Perianth is basically 3-merous. Stamens are usually numerous, extrorse or latrorse with free filaments, tetrasporangiate anthers opening longitudinally. Tapetum is secretory. Microsporogenesis is mostly simultaneous. Pollen grains are 3-celled (*Cabomba*) or 2-celled and 1-colpate, zonocolpate or inaperturate, mostly in monads. Gynoecium is apocarpous or syncarpous. Carpels are 1-50, large to very large. Ovules are 3-400, usually anatropous with cup-shaped outer integument, bitegmic, crassinucellate. Endosperm is usually cellular. Female gametophyte is of *Polygonum*-type or rarely also both *Polygonum* and *Oenothera*-type (Orban and Bouharmont, 1998). Fruits are of various types. Seeds are operculate with palisade exotesta, mostly with small embryo, 4 nucleate embryo sac, scanty endosperm, with or without perisperm and arillus. Benzyl isoquinoline alkaloids are absent, but contain pseudoalkaloids based on sesquiterpenes and ellagitannins (no benzylisoquinolins) (Takhtajan, 2009). The order consists of three families.

Family Nymphaeaceae (water lilies)

It is a cosmopolitan family of large flowered water plants, the water lilies. It contains about 6 genera and 55-60 species (Heywood *et al.*, 2007). It occurs in fresh water habitats (lakes and ponds, rivers and streams, springs, marshes, ditches, canals and tidal waters), in both temperate and tropical regions.

The fresh water aquatic herbs are normally perennial having long horizontal rhizomes that are sometimes tuberous, or short and erect. The leaves are submerged, floating or emergent, simple, peltate, cordate or sagittate, with or without stipules; the lamina is ovate to orbicular, entire or dentate. In *Victoria amazonica*, the leaves may attain 2 m diameter, with spines on the surface and petioles and upturned rims. They are able to support weight of 40-75 kg due to the network of tubular veins on their undersides. The flowers are often large and showy, actinomorphic, hermaphrodite and solitary, borne above the water surface on stout peduncles. The sepals are 4-9, green or coloured, and petaloid (*Nuphar*). The petals are 3 to many (absent in *Ondinea*), white, yellow, pink, red, blue or purplish in colour. Stamens are 3 to numerous. The ovary is inferior or semi-inferior (*Barclaya, Euryale, Nymphaea*) or superior (*Nuphar, Ondinea*). The carpels are 3-40, united or partly free. The fruit is a spongy berry-like capsule, dehiscing by the swelling of mucilage within or indehiscent. The seeds often have aril (*Nymphaea*, *Ondinea*). The flowers are pollinated by insects, especially beetles.

Genus *Euryale* Salisbury

The plants are herbaceous, annual or perennial, short and upright caudex. Leaves are floating, prickly, peltate, and long-petioled with orbicular blade of 30-200 cm having actinodromous venation with prominent parenchymatous ribs. The flowers are epigynous having four persistent prickly sepals, 20-35 purple-violet petals, 78-92 stamens, gradating from flattened to conventional filaments, introrse dehiscence, 8-16 syncarpous carpels, cup-shaped stigma, prickly and irregularly dehiscent fruit and large arillate seeds. It contains one species, *E. ferox* Salisb. occurring from northern India eastward into Japan (Takhtajan, 2009).

Gorgan nut

(Euryale ferox Salisb.; *makhana;* fox nut; prickly water lily)

The plant is prickly aquatic herb having circular, purple and spiny leaves that are 30-40 cm in diameter, ribbed beneath and dark green and uneven above. The leaves have prominent veins on the purple undersides, densely pitted with spines. These are attractive because of the colouration and puckering. The flowers are bluish mauve, about 5 cm broad, prickly outside and open during the day. Flowers are short lived and are barely held above the water level. The calyx is reddish inside and 20-30 petals are violet blue or purple and are shorter than the calyx lobes. Stamens are numerous. The fruit is a small, oval, spongy, and prickly, many seeded (8-20) and black globular berry bearing the remains of the calyx on its top and remains submerged in water. The seeds are black and roundish, 4-15 mm in diameter having a thick and hard outer wall and are eaten raw or after roasting.

⑧ ⑧ ⑧

[CORE ANGIOSPERMS – MESANGIOSPERMS]

Chapter 9

MAGNOLIALES

The plants are woody trees or shrubs with multilacunar nodes. Vessels are scalariform or less frequently with simple perforations, scalariform lateral pitting, opposite (*Magnolia fraseri* and *Liriodendron*). Fibres are with bordered pits. Rays are heterogeneous or rarely homogeneous (in some temperate species of *Magnolia*). Axial parenchyma is apotracheal. Sieve element plastids are of S- and Psc-types.

Leaves are alternate, simple, entire or seldom 2-10-lobed, pinnately veined with stipules or exstipulate. Stomata are paracytic or rarely anomocytic. Flowers are usually solitary, terminal or axillary, bisexual or very rarely unisexual (*Kmeria*). Perianth is well developed with free and imbricate segments, variously spiral to cyclic in three or more series, more or less similar and are petaloid or less often clearly differentiated into sepals and petals arranged in whorls of three. Stamens are numerous, free, spirally arranged, originating centripetally, more or less ribbon-shaped (laminar), mostly three-veined and typically not clearly differentiated into filament and anther. The anthers are tetrasporangiate, the microsporangia are paired and tapetum is secretory. Microsporogenesis is simultaneous. Pollen grains are 2-celled, boat-shaped, psilate or more or less rugulose, sulcate and aperturate. Gynoecium is sessile or stipitate, apocarpous or less frequently more or less syncarpous. Carpels are solitary (in *Degeneria* and sometimes in *Michelia montana*) or more frequently several to numerous and spirally arranged (except in *Pachylarnax*), conduplicate, semi-sealed (*Manglletia* and *Elmerillia*) or more commonly fully sealed. Ovules are two to numerous, large to very large, anatropous, bitegmic, crassinucellate with massive parietal tissue. Female gametophyte is of *Polygonum*-type. Ovaries are superior. Endosperm is cellular. Fruit carpels are indehiscent. Seeds are large, frequently fleshy or arillate with sarcotesta having small to minute embryo, copious and oily endosperm, sometimes ruminate. Sesquiterpene lactones are present (Takhtajan, 2009). It contains six families.

Family Annonaceae

It has 2 subfamilies (Annonoidae with free spirally arranged carpels and Monodoroideae with united cyclically arranged carpels), 135 genera and 2500 species, nearly all tropical and native to the Old and New World (Heywood *et al.*, 2007). Some are subtropical and a few are native to temperate region of North East America. Commercially, the most significant genera are *Annona* and *Rollinia* (Sanewski, 1991). The important edible fruits are cherimoya, sugar apple or sugar sop, sour sop and the ilama. The North American pawpaw is ornamental but also provides edible fruits. The other members of the family yield useful products such as drugs, dye, perfumes and wood.

The trees and shrubs are usually evergreen and aromatic with resin canals and septate pith in the stems. The leaves are entire, alternate, simple, glaucous, typically distichous and without stipules. The flowers are fragrant, frequently open before all floral parts are fully developed. These are often odd (ugly) in appearance, solitary, hypogynous, regular and trimerous. Sepals are usually 3. The petals are usually 6, in two series and mostly valvate (not overlapping). Stamens are numerous, arranged spirally. Protogyny is widespread. Filaments are thick and short. The anthers are 4-celled at anthesis. The carpels are usually many and separate, resulting in the fruit being an aggregate of berries (apocarp). In *Annona* species, the berries coalesce with a receptacle to form an aggregate (syncarp). In the cherimoya, the carpels are closely crowded or fused together with the stalk of the receptacle to form a syncarpium. The fruits in other genera are dry or capsular. The seeds have ruminate endosperm and are of complicated construction.

Genus *Annona* L. (2n = 14, 28, 42)

The genus contains about 110 species found in tropical America, 4 in tropical Africa and a few are cultivated for fruit throughout the tropics (Kubitzki *et al.*, 1993). The genus exhibits a large genetic diversity, reflecting the different centres of origin of the species. Most of them are believed to have originated in the hot humid lowlands of Central America and northern South America. The cherimoya (*A. cherimola*) originated in the subtropical Andean highlands (Popenoe, 1970). The chromosome number for most *Annona* species is 2n = 2x = 14 or 16, with the exception of *A. glabra* which is tetraploid (Kessler, 1993). Many of the species are apparently sexually compatible, e.g. the atemoya is a natural hybrid between *A. cherimola* and *A. squamosa* (Jordán and Botti, 1992).

The plants are small (7 m), evergreen trees and shrubs or almost woody herbs with simple or stellate hairs. The leaves are entire, alternate and exstipulate. The flowers are perfect, are yellowish with 3 to 6 tepals and numerous stamens and pistils. These are solitary or in small clusters, terminal leaf-opposed, supra-axillary or cauliflorous. Sepals are 3, valvate. Petals are 6, valvate or imbricate, in 2 whorls, subequal or inner whorl rudimentary or absent, free or connate at the base. Stamens are with a truncate dilated, rarely with a apiculate or hemispherical apex. Carpels are numerous. One ovule is basal. The characteristic feature of the genus is their syncarpium fruit, formed by amalgation of many pistils and the fleshy receptacle.

Cherimoya
(*Annona cherimola* Mill. syn. *A. tripetala* Ait.) (2n=14)

It is a native of highlands of Ecuador and Peru (Paull and Duarte, 2011). The plants are tender, evergreen but are frost resistant. It is a fruit tree of tropical highlands unlike the other *Annona* species. It is a deciduous to semi-deciduous, small, erect or somewhat shrubby or spreading tree growing rarely over 7.5 m in height. The bark is grayish and young shoots are pubescent. The leaves are ovate to ovate lanceolate, sometimes obovate or elliptical, 12-20 x 8 cm in size, persistently brownish, sparsely pubescent on the upper surface and are velvety tomentose on the lower side with minutely hairy petioles. The pubescence persists.

The inconspicuous, hermaphrodite, protogynous flowers are often opposite a leaf at the base of a branchlet, usually solitary but sometimes 2 or 3 on short tomentose peduncles, borne axillary on both young and old growth. Three outer petals are fleshy, oblong linear, up to 3 cm long, their outer surface being green and the inner surface whitish or yellowish, sometimes with purple dots at the base. Inner 3 petals are very small, scale-like and reddish to purplish. The androecium comprises numerous free fleshy stamens, arranged spirally on the basal part of the conical receptacle. The gynoecium comprises numerous free pistils on the upper part of the receptacle. Hand pollination results in higher fruit yield. The fruits ripen in December-January.

The fruit is easily broken or cut open, exposing the snow white, juicy flesh of pleasing aroma and delicious subacid flavour and containing numerous hard, brown or black bean-like, glossy 1.25 to 2 cm long seeds (Morton, 1987). (Gardiazabal & Rosenberg, 1993). The diploid chromosome number of cherimoya is 2n=14 (Ronning *et al.*, 1995) although 2n = 16 has also been reported (Pascual *et al.*, 1993).

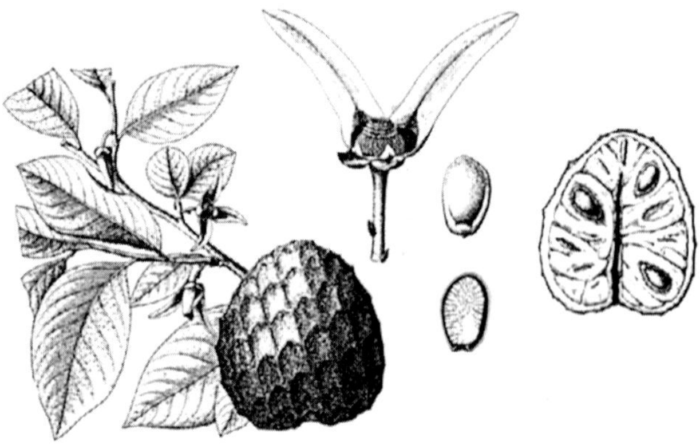

Fig. 9.1. *Annona cherimola* Mill.: leaf, flower, fruit and seed (Van Damme, 1992).

The fruit is a pseudocarp formed by the fusion of carpels and receptacle into a fleshy mass (Fig. 9.1). It is variable in shape (conical or somewhat heart shaped) with protuberances on surface to spheroid or ovoid with the surface covered with U-shaped areoles, which are rather smooth. The fruit is large in size as compared to custard apple having 0.1-1 kg weight and 10-15 cm diameter. The fruit is composed of 15-25% exocarp (fruit skin), 65 and 80% edible mesocarp (pulp and thalamus), and 3-10% seeds. The pulp is white, creamy, buttery and slightly acidic, soft and juicy with a mix of pineapple and banana flavour. The yield is poor (25/ tree) but the fruits do not crack. These are not as sweet as custard apple. From quality point of view, the fruit is considered as the best among the genus *Annona.* The seeds are large, hard, horny, brownish, obovate, obliquely truncate and compressed with thin membranous wrinkled testa (IBPGR, 1986b; Morton, 1987; Verheij and Coronel,

1991). Endosperm is white and wrinkled. The embryo is small and buried in one end of the seed. The seeds retain viability for 7 years.

Five typical fruit forms based on the nature of the tubercles or areoles on fruit skin are:

a. forma '*laevis*' (lisa) having smooth skin, difficult to discern areoles, often mistaken for *A. glabra*, producing heart shaped fruits, e.g. in Lisa.
b. forma '*impressa*' (fingerprint) having areoles with U-shaped depressions producing conoid or subglobose fruits with juicy pulp, good flavour and relatively fewer seeds, e.g. in Bays, Booth and Mc Pherson.
c. forma '*umbonata*' having thick skin with protuberances (small points at the apex of each areole) producing oblong conical fruits with pineapple flavour, e.g. in Horton.
d. forma '*tuberculata*' having large sharp points at the apex of each wood-like areole produceing heart shaped fruits, e.g. in Golden Russet.
e. forma '*mamillata*' having areoles with large blunt protuberances as are found on the Nilgiris in south India.

Cultivars

Some of the most common cultivars are Fino de Jete, which occupies 95% of the Spanish cherimoya area, Bays, Booth, White and Pierce in USA and Australia, Reretai and Bronceada in New Zealand, Bronceada and Concha Lisa in Chile and Cumbe in Peru. The recommended cultivars are Bays and White (California), and Basta, Pinchua, Fino de Jete (Spain) that yield 100-150 kg fruits per tree. Cumbe is a favoured cherimoya cultivar of Peru. The cultivars like Burton Wonder, Burton, Chaffey, Spanish, Madeira, Smoothys and Reretai have been recommended for cultivation in New Zealand as these are regular bearing and produce sweet flavoured and juicy fruits. Chilean cultivars Bronceada and Concha Lisa have performed well in Australia. Andrews, Kempsey and Mossman are the important cultivars of Australia (Nakasone and Paull, 1998). Madeira, Mateus 1, Perry Vidal and Funchal are important cultivars grown on Madeira Islands. Gangemi and Leone are the cultivars of Italy (Pinto *et al*., 2005).

The criteria to select elite plant types from the seedling population should be regularity in bearing heavy yields of uniform size fruits having smooth green skin, juicy sweet flesh of pleasant flavour and low seed content besides good keeping quality and freedom from grittiness and browning near the skin (Morton, 1987; Verheij and Coronel, 1991; Smith *et al*., 1992).

Sweet sop
(***Annona squamosa*** L.; sugar apple or sharifa) (2n=14)

It probably originated in the Caribbean region (Janick and Paull, 2008). It is the most important *Annona* species in India. It grows wild in Andhra Pradesh and Rajasthan in rocky habitats. The trees are small, bushy, hardy and evergreen. The tree grows up to 3-6 m in height with an open crown consisting of irregular spreading branches and somewhat zigzag twigs. The small aromatic leaves are alternately arranged on short hairy petioles and are lanceolate or oblong, blunt-tipped, 5-15 x 2-5 cm in size, dull green and glabrous on the upper side and pale with a bloom below. Flowers are fragrant, hermaphrodite, borne singly or in groups of 2 to 4 along the branch tips opposite the leaves. The flower is oblong, 2.5-3.8 cm long, never fully open, borne on 2.5 cm long and drooping stalk and has 3 fleshy outer petals, yellow green on the outside and pale yellow inside with purple or dark red spots at the base. The inner petals are merely tiny scales. Flower has numerous stamens and carpels. The plants are cross fertile and rarely self fertile. Dichogamy is found. The fruit ripens in September-October. The fruit is smaller as compared to that of cherimoya. It is globose or conical pseudocarp, 5-10 cm in diameter, formed of loosely cohering or almost free carpels, the rounded ends projecting to render the surface tuberculate (Fig. 9.2). Surface is greenish yellow or red having a powdery bloom. The pulp is white tinged yellow and very sweet. Seeds are dark brown or black and 1.25 cm long. There may be as many as 60-80 seeds per fruit but are usually 20 to 38. Some trees, however, bear seedless fruits (Morton, 1987; Brücher , 1989). Fruit cracking is a problem.

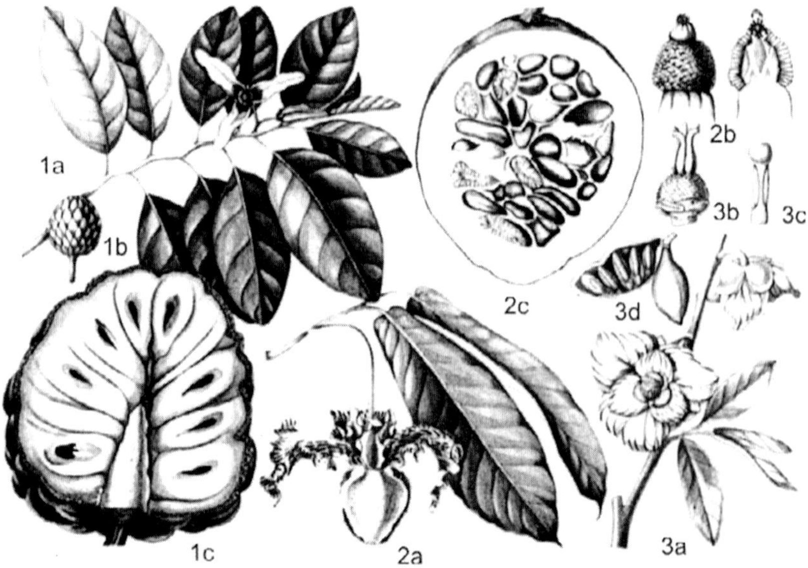

Fig. 9.2 *Annona squamosa* (a) shoot with leaves in two ranks and axillary flower; (b) young fruit; (c) vertical section of fruit comprising an aggregate of numerous berries with the fleshy receptacle; 2. *Monodora myristica* (a) leafy shoot and flower; (b) androecium of numerous short-stalked stamens and gynoecium comprising united carpels; (c) vertical section of fruit with many seeds; 3. *Asimina triloba* (a) flowering shoot; (b) gynoecium of five free carpels; (c) stamen with anther surmounted by swollen extension of connective; (d) young fruit (Heywood, 1985).

Cultivars

Balanagar: This is a selection made from the groves in Mahboobnagar district of Andhra Pradesh (India). It yields 50-60 fruits per tree. The fruit shape is pyramidal or cordate with very rough and pitted areoles and usually remains green when ripe. The flakes are crisp and slightly leathery. The pulp is bright white, very sweet and juicy with medium granular mesocarp and excellent flavour. Average seed content is 25 per fruit.

Washington P1107-005: The cultivar is from Australia. Tree is vigorous with broad and large leaves. It bears 70- 80 fruits per tree. Fruits are medium to big in size and spherical to short conical in shape. The rind is grayish green having a fine bloom. The flakes are soft, moderately adhere to the seed. The pulp is bright white, sweet and buttery.

Red Sitaphal: It was located as a chance seedling. Fruits are pink coloured and contain large number of seeds and erythrite red pulp.

Island Gem: This cultivar is from Australia. The fruits are of medium to large size. The pulp is very sweet.

Mammoth: The plants are dwarf compared to those of other cultivars. The leaves are slightly folded. The fruits have smooth, prominent and round areoles and better keeping quality. The pulp is bright white and sweet.

In India, the recommended cultivars are Washington, Barbados, British Guiana, Balanagar, Local Sitaphal, Mammoth and Red Sitaphal. In the Philippines, three types are grown that bear (a) green and seeded fruits (common), (b) purple fruits, and (c) green seedless fruits. In Thailand, the common cultivars are green "Fai" and yellow easy to peel "Nahang". In Florida, the important cultivar is Seedless Cuban that produces malformed fruits with mere vestiges of underdeveloped seeds. Its flavour is not appealing as that of the normal fruit. The important cultivars of Egypt are Beni Mazar having large (150-180 g), round fruits with 56-60 per cent flesh and 15-30 seeds, and Abd El Razik having large (236 g) and nearly round fruits with light green or reddish rind, 69.5 per cent flesh and 14 seeds. Cuban Seedless developed in Cuba has medium-sized seedless fruits. The other Cuban cultivar has low fibre content (Nakasone and Paull, 1998).

Hanuman phal

(***Annona atemoya*** Hort. ex Wester; *A. squamosa* L. x *A. Cherimola* Mill.)
(2n=14)

The hybrid is believed to have been developed in Florida (USA) by P.J. Wester in 1908 who called it "atemoya", after the Brazilian name "ate" for sweetsop and "moya" for cherimoya (Nakasone and Paull, 1998). It combines the best qualities of both the parents and is adapted to a wider range of environmental conditions than either parents. The fruit is well known in Australia, Central America, Florida, India, Israel, New Zealand, the Philippines, South America and South Africa (Morton, 1987)

The tree is small, deciduous and grows up to a height of 6-10 m. The leaves are alternate, glabrous, 10-20 x 4-8 cm in size and are lanceolate, elliptic or ovate in shape. These are broad like those of cherimoya but are glabrous like those of sugar apple The tree loses leaves every year for a brief period depending upon climatic conditions. The three sided and fragrant flower buds vary in size. Flowers of 3-4 cm size with 3 fleshy, pale yellowish green petals, are borne single or in clusters of 2-3 in the axils of leaves on one year old or new shoots. The flower has numerous unicarpellate pistils on a common receptacle. The fruit is spherical, conical or ovate, 8-15 cm in diameter and 250-600 g in weight. It is like that of cherimoya. The shape and surface texture of the fruit vary greatly. The fruit surface may be relatively smooth with rounded protuberances and glaucous bloom. Its rind is thin and green that becomes yellowish green on ripening. The flesh is very sweet, buttery with a pleasant flavour and is soft when ripe. The fusion of the carpels and sourness of pulp are between those of the two parents. Seeds are few. Each fruit contains 15-40 hard, black and 10-15 mm long seeds. The seeds are larger than those of sugar apple and much darker than those of cherimoya. These are oblong, obliquely truncate at the micropylar end with a dark brown testa (Morton, 1987; Martin *et al*, 1987).

Cultivars

The important cultivars are Mammoth, Pink's Prolific and Island Gem in Australia; Bernitski, Gefner, Hette, Kabri, Kaller and Malamud in Israel; and African Pride, Bradley and Page in Florida. Some atemoyas developed at the Fruit Research Station, Sangareddy (Andhra Pradesh) in India are also promising (Martin *et al*, 1987; Morton, 1987).

Arka Sahan: It is a hybrid of Island Gem (*A. atemoya*) x Mammoth (*A. squamosa*). The fruits mature during September-October and the mature fruits (210 g) take about 6-7 days to ripen. The fruit skin is light green, moderately thick (0.5 cm) and has a waxy bloom. The eyes are large and flat. The creamy white flesh is juicy, tender and remarkably sweet with 22.8 per cent total sugars and mild pleasant aroma. The fruit has few seeds (9/100 g) and large segments. The edible pulp is more than in Mammoth. Its pulp contains 2.49 g crude protein, 42.29 mg P and 225 mg Ca per 100 g compared to only 1.33 g, 17.05 mg and 159 mg respectively in that of cultivar Mammoth. About 12 tonnes of fruits can be obtained per hectare. The fruits have long shelf life.

Bullock's Heart

(***Annona reticulata*** L.; Ram phal) (2n=14)

It is native of West Indies and tropical Central America. The tree is semi-deciduous. It grows erect up to 7 m in height with a rounded or spreading crown. It is less resistant to cold and heat as compared to sugar apple. The young shoots are reddish brown and downy. The leaves are large (10-20 x 2-5 cm in size), alternate, oblong or narrow lanceolate with conspicuous veins, dark green and glabrous or pubescent on the veins only. The petiole is curved up in the bud stage. Flowers are fragrant, slender with 3 outer fleshy and narrow petals, 2-3 cm long, light green externally and pale yellow with dark red or purple spots on the inside at the base. The fruit ripens in April-May. The fruit is slightly larger than that of sugar apple. The fruit is 8-16 cm in diameter, heart shaped, lopsided or irregular or nearly round or oblate with a deep or shallow depression at the base with yellowish red carpels fused to form the hexagonal areoles, which provide the reticulated fruit surface (Fig. 9.3). Fruit skin is thin but tough, yellow or brownish when ripe with a pink reddish or brownish red blush and faintly or distinctly reticulated. The fruit of ram phal is of two types: i) heart-shaped like that of sugar apple, and ii) reticulate form having fingerprints on the surface. The tree of the reticulate form is more prolific giving 20 to 25 fruits per tree. Fruit pulp is thick, creamy white, custard-like, granular surrounding the moderately juicy segments, each of which contains a single, hard, dark brown or black, glossy, oblong, smooth, less than 1.25 cm long seed. A single fruit contains 55-76 seeds (IBPGR, 1986b; Morton, 1987; Brücher, 1989).

Fig. 9.3. ***Annona reticulata*** **fruit** (Source: León, 1987; Calzada Benza, 1993).

Cultivars

APK (Ca) 1: It is a clonal selection from a high yielding type in Courtallam, Tamil Nadu. It is drought tolerant and is suitable for black soils under both irrigated and rainfed conditions. Fruit yield is 14.9 kg/ tree.

Sour sop
(*Annona muricata* L.; guanabana)

It originated in tropical America (Morton, 1987; Verheij and Coronel, 1991) and grows wild from sea level to 1065 m altitudes spread over southern Mexico to Brazil and the West Indies. It has been introduced in the Old World tropics and is now distributed from southeastern China to Australia, the warm lowlands of eastern and western Africa and the Pacific Islands. Sour sop fruit is the largest among the *Annonas* and has unique aroma and flavour. It is grown commercially for its juice in the Philippines, Puerto Rico and Venezuela (Morton, 1987). It is commonly found in subsistence farms in South East Asia and became established very early in the pacific islands. It is grown extensively in Brazil, Colombia, Costa Rica, Cuba, Jamaica, Panama, Peru and Mexico and from Culiacan to Chiapas and from Veracruz to the Yucatan Peninsula in the Gulf region (Nakasone and Paull, 1998). At present it is largely confined to home gardens because of short shelf life and erratic yield of fruits but appears to have excellent potential for production of good quality juice and other products (FAO, 1986; Martin *et al.,* 1987).

The tree is small, evergreen and low branching usually growing 5 to 10 m in height. The leaves are glossy, leathery and oval or rectangular and dark green, 1.5 to 2.5 cm in length and give a characteristic smell when crushed. The flowers are solitary, yellow, hermaphrodite, thick and fleshy, almost globular, up to 3 cm in diameter borne on small axillary shoots or directly on trunk of the tree. The flower has 3 green, almost free sepals, 6 petals in two rings enclosing a central torus bearing numerous short and thick filaments. The fruit is a syncarpium, rounded or elongated,

30 cm long and up to 1-5 kg in weight. The fruit skin is green having numerous more or less woody spines (Fig. 9.4). The flesh is white and juicy and has a unique musky rather subacid flavour and smells somewhat like pineapple. It contains numerous black seeds of 2 x 1 cm size, which are poisonous and can be readily separated from the flesh (Morton, 1987; Brücher, 1989, Verheij and Coronel, 1991).

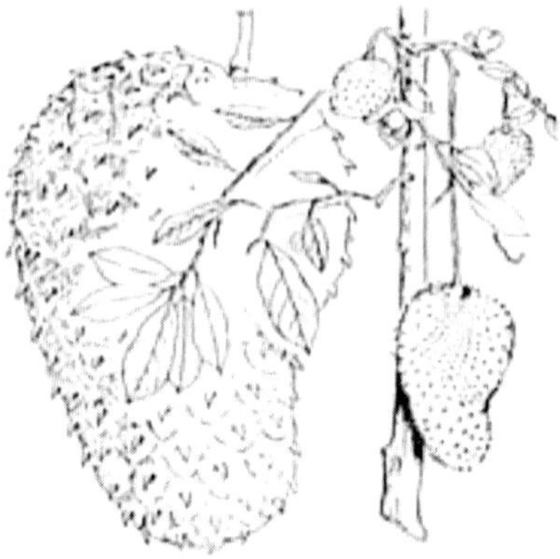

Fig. 9.4. A*nnona muricata* fruit (Source: Source: León, 1987; Calzada Benza, 1993).

Cultivars

In Puerto Rico, the forms and types of seedling sour sops are divided into 3 general classes: sweet, subacid and acid. Nakasone and Paull (1998) have separated sour sop clones into groups such as acid and low acid or juicy and non-juicy. Fourteen different types are known in Puerto Rico. In Cuba, guanabana sin fibre (fibreless) type is grown. Guanabana dulce (sweet) is an important type of Dominican Republic. In El Salvador, two types are distinguished, the guanabana azucaron and the guanabana acida. The acid type is very sour and is used only for the preparation of drinks. In Indonesia and the Philippines, sweet and sour fruited types are known. A sweet type in Indonesia is Sirsak Ratu having small and few seeded fruits with subacid flavour. Attempts have been made to develop hybrids with mountain sour sop, *A. montana* Macfad, to induce cold resistance (Morton, 1987; Verheij and Coronel, 1991).

Soncoya
(*Annona purpurea* Moc. and Sesse ex Dunal syn. *S. manirote* Kunth., *A. involucrate* Baill.; cabeza de negro; cabeca de negro)

It is native of southern Mexico and central America (Martin *et al.*, 1987) and is found growing on the coastal lowlands from southern Mexico to Panama, Colombia and Venezuela. It has been introduced into Philippines, Puerto Rico and other parts of tropical America (Morton, 1987; Brücher, 1989).

The tree is deciduous, small to medium in height (6-10 m) with short trunk of 45 cm diameter and spreading branches that are rusty woolly when young. The leaves are alternate, simple, short petioled, oblong elliptic or oblong lanceolate,

20-30 x 10-14 cm in size, acuminate, brown and hairy on both surfaces with prominent veins beneath. Strong scented flowers emerge with the new leaves which are solitary, fleshy, large, conical, held at the base by a rusty, hairy, 3-parted calyx and have 3, very thick outer petals, brown hairy outside and yellowish and purple mottled within, and 3 smaller, thinner inner petals, creamy white outside and purple inside. The fruit is thick stalked having protuberances, each tipped with a curved hook and coated all over with fibres (Fig. 9.5) and is of mild agreeable flavour. Seeds are numerous, obovate, 2.5-3 cm long, dark brown each enclosed in a thin close fitting membrane. The fruit carpels separate easily when ripe (Morton, 1987; Brücher, 1989).

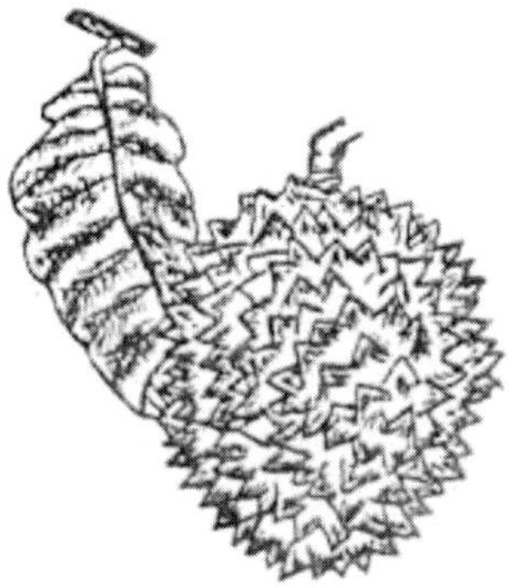

Fig. 9.5. ***Annona purpurea*** **fruit** (Source: León, 1987; Calzada Benza, 1993).

The ilama

(***Annona diversifolia*** Safford; White annona; papauce; annona blanca)

It is native of central America and Mexico (Martin *et al.*, 1987). It grows in the foothills from the south-west coast of Mexico to the Pacific coast of Guatemala and El Salvador. Its distribution is very limited because of its poor adaptability (Nakasone and Paull, 1998). It has been introduced in USA (Florida), Puerto Rico, St. Croix and various parts of tropical America, Asia and Philippines (Morton, 1987).

It is a tender tropical plant. The tree is spreading or erect growing up to a height of 7.5 m, often branching from the ground and has pale, brownish gray and furrowed bark. Leaves are glossy, thin, elliptic to obovate or oblanceolate and 5-15 cm long. There are 1 or 2 leaf-like, nearly circular, glabrous 2.5-3.5 cm long bracts clasping the base of the flowering branchlets. Flowers are solitary, long stalked and maroon which open to the base and have small rusty, hairy sepals and narrow, blunt, minutely hairy 3 outer petals. The fruit is conical, heart shaped or ovoid globose, 12-15 cm long and 450-900 g in weight (Fig. 9.6). The pulp is white, pink or reddish with a typical aroma and an exquisite flavour. The fruits of some cultivars are similar to those of sugar apple. The fruit is studded with more or less pronounced, triangular protuberances. The rind is pale green to deep pink or purplish, coated with a dense, velvety gray white bloom, which is about 6 mm thick, leathery, fairly soft and granular. Seeds are 25 to 80, hard, smooth, brown and cylindrical, 2 x 1 cm in size, enclosed in close fitting membranes which easily slip off when split (Morton, 1987).

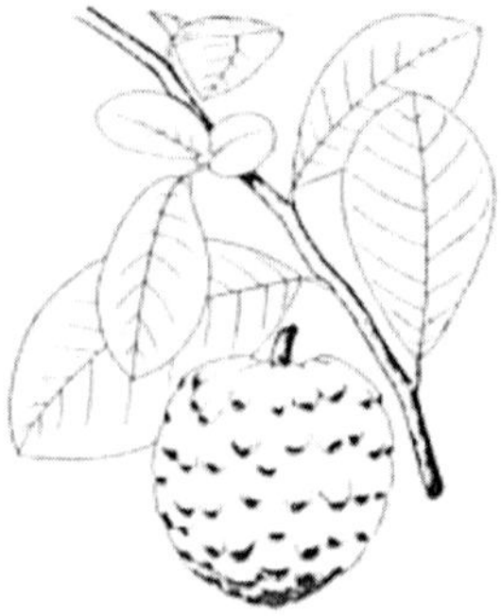

Fig. 9.6. ***Annona diversifolia*** **fruit** (Source: León, 1987; Calzada Benza, 1993).

Cultivars

There are generally two types, green and pink. The green type has white and sweet flesh. The pink type has pink tinge near the rind and around the seed, all pink or even deep rose and tart in flavour. Important cultivars of ilama are Fairchild, Rosendo Perez, Guillermo and Gramajo (thick skinned, grayish green fruit); Imery (big fruit with thinner skin), Pajapita (pink surface), Nilito (irregular surface), Romen (small fruit with hard skin), Genova White (smooth, white green skin) and Efrain (Bermejo and Leon, 1994). The cultivar Imery has been released from El Salvador, which has large and pink fleshed fruit but not as flavourful as the white fleshed type from Guatemala (Morton, 1987).

Wild custard apple

(***Annona senegalensis*** Auct. non Pers. syn. ***A. chrysophylla*** Boj.; abo; wild sour sop)

It is native of East and West Africa (Martin *et al.*, 1987; Pinto *et al.*, 2005). This species is common throughout the tropical Africa from the Cape Verde Islands and the Nile and upper Guinea to the Transvaal and Zulu land (Martin *et al.,* 1987; Morton, 1987). Wild custard apple is widespread in sub-Sahelian tropical Africa.

It is a deciduous sprawling shrub or tree of 6-11 m height having smooth silvery bark. The leaves are aromatic, simple, alternate, blue green, broad elliptic or broad ovate, 7.5-17.5 x 4-10 cm in size, blue green above and downy and prominently veined beneath. The flowers are borne singly or in pairs in leaf axils on 2.5-4 cm long stalks, clasped by a 3-parted calyx and have 3 triangular, thick, waxy, velvety and whitish outer petals, 3 pale yellow inner petals and numerous stamens. The fruit is rounded oval, 2.5 to 10 cm long, fleshy, yellow or orange when ripe and is seedy (FAO, 1983, 1988; Morton, 1987).

Pond apple

(***Annona glabra*** L.) (2n=28)

The plants has glabrous, very smooth and glossy leaves. The fruit is smooth and reddish yellow and is not edible. It is used as a rootstock. The most common botanical variety in Ghana is *deltoides*. It has elliptic to oblong elliptic leaves, which are rounded to broadly deltoid at the base. Cultivar Porpetac of Uganda has oblong elliptic, oval elliptic or elliptic leaves which are rounded obtuse or broadly cuneate at the base. In a dwarf form, the fruits are borne so low that they touch the ground and are of better quality than those of the taller types (Morton, 1987; Pinto *et al.*, 2005).

The species *A. scleroderma* Saff. (Poshte) is edible and is grown in southwestern Guatemala which is notable for its tough skin useful to allow handling and for resistance to insect attack (Bermejo and Leon, 1994). Another species *A. stenophylla* Engles and Diels occurs in Botswana, Namibia, Zimbabwe and Malawi and is used as seasonal staple for bushmen (FAO, 1983).

***A. cutemoya* (Atemoya x *A. reticulata* or *A. glabra*)**

Genus *Rollinia* A. St. Hil (2n=48)

The plants are trees or shrubs with simple or rarely stellate hairs. Flowers are bisexual borne in leaf-opposed or super axillary fascicles. Sepals are 3, valvate. Petals are 6, valvate in 2 whorls, connate at the base, outer 3 with a spur or a wing or the back and inner much shorter than the outer ones. Stamens and carpels are numerous with one basal ovule. Compound fruit is formed by the united monocarps. It has about 65 species in Central America, West Indies to South Brazil, Paraguay and North Argentina.

Biriba

(***Rollinia mucosa*** (Jacq.) Baill., syn. ***R. orthopetala*** A. DC., ***R. sieberi*** A. DC., ***R. deliciosa*** Saff., ***A. mucosa*** Jacq.; wild sweetsop; wild sugar apple; anon Cimarron; cachiman crème; condessa)

It is native of Central and South America and the West Indies (Martin *et al.*, 1987). It is found growing wild from Peru and northern Argentina, Paraguay and Brazil and northward to Guiana, Venezuela, Colombia and southern Mexico, Trinidad, the lesser Antilles including Guadeloupe, Martinique and St.Vincent and Puerto Rico. It is a favourite fruit in western Amazonia.

It is a fast growing, deciduous tree, 4-15 m in height. Leaves are alternate, 10-25 cm long, oblong elliptic or ovate oblong, pointed at the apex, rounded at the base, and leathery and hairy on the underside. Flowers, borne 1 or 3 or occasionally more together in the leaf axils, are hermaphrodite, 2-3.5 cm wide, triangular with 3 hairy sepals, 3 large, fleshy outer petals with upturned or horizontal wings and 3 rudimentary inner petals. The fruit is conical to heart shaped or oblate, 15 cm in diameter having yellow rind composed of more or less hexagonal and conical segments, each tipped with a wart-like, 3 mm thick, leathery, tough and indehiscent protrusion. The pulp is white, mucilaginous, translucent, juicy and subacid or sweet. Seeds are numerous, dark brown, elliptic or obovate and 1.6-2 cm long (FAO, 1986; Morton, 1987).

The only named selection is Regnard (P. J. Wester, 1917 reported by Morton 1987). A form found in the western Amazon region has fruit weighing up to 4 kg with very pronounced points.

Genus *Stelechocarpus* (Blume) Hook. f. & Thom. (2n=18)

Trees are with simple hairs. Flowers are dioecious, fasciculate on the wood having 3 imbricate sepals, 6 imbricate petals in 2 whorls. Stamens are numerous. Fruit is globose. It has 5 species in East India to New Guinea.

Burahol
(***Stelechocarpus burahol*** (Blume) Hook. f.; Thomson kepel)

It is native of western Malaysia. It is found in South East Asia throughout Malaysia as far as the Solomon Island but its cultivation is limited to Java. It has also been introduced in Philippines and Australia (Verheij and Coronel, 1991).

It is an erect, evergreen tree and grows up to 25 m tall. The dark gray brown to black trunk is up to 40 cm in diameter, characteristically covered with numerous thick tubercles. The dark green, thin and leathery leaves are elliptic oblong to ovate lanceolate, glabrous and 12-27 x 5-9 cm in size with 1.5 cm long petioles. The flowers are unisexual, green turning whitish and are fascicled on tubercles. The male flowers are borne on upper trunk and older branches in groups of 8-16 and are up to 1 cm in diameter. The female flowers emerge only on the lower part of the trunk and are up to 3 cm in diameter. The fruit has 1-13 berry-like ripe carpels, which are almost globose, brownish, 5-6 cm in diameter with brown, juicy and edible pericarp and contains 4-6 ellipsoid and 3 cm long seeds (Verheij and Coronel, 1991).

Genus *Asimina* Adans (3n = 27)

The plants are shrubs or small trees with simple hairs. Flowers are bisexual, axillary, solitary having 3 or rarely 4 valvate sepals; 6 or rarely 8 imbricate petals in 2 whorls, the outer longer than the inner; numerous stamens, connective with a capitate apex; 3-15 carpels; numerous biseriate ovules, the monocarps oblong, stipitate or sessile. It contains about 8 species spread in North America, especially Florida.

Pawpaw
(***Asimina triloba*** (L.) Dunal; Michigan banana; Nebraska banana; Prairie banana) x = 9; 2n = 18

It is native to the eastern USA (Darrow, 1975) particularly important in Kentucky State. It is found in the region from the Gulf of Mexico to the Atlantic, westwards to Oklahoma and as far north as New York and Michigan. It has been introduced in the former USSR, Argentina, Chile, India, Australia and New Zealand. It is planted from New Jersey, New York to South Canada (Kubitzki *et al.*, 1993) for its edible fruit.

The tree is small of 1.5-11 m height, deciduous and aromatic. The branchlets are fulvous pubescent when young and later turn glabrous and brown. The leaves are alternate, membranous, and obovate to oblanceolate, 15-30 cm long with acuminate to acute apex and 5-10 mm long petiole. The solitary flowers are borne axillary on previous season growth. The purple flowers are cup-shaped and are 2-5 cm in diameter having 3 ovate, acute, greenish and pubescent sepals free from each other; 6

broad ovate and rounded petals, later reflexed at apex in 2 whorls of 3; 1.5-3 cm in length, numerous stamens and gynoecium composed of 3-7 carpels. The fruit is a cylindrical, multi-seeded berry, 5-15 cm long and 25-300 g in weight. Fruits may be borne singly or in clusters that resemble the "londs" of a banana plant.

Important cultivars are Middletown, PA-Golden, Wells, Prolific, Wilson, Sweet Alice, Mason/WLW, G-2, M-1, Overleese, Glaser, Little Rosie, Silver Creek, Zimmerman, Davis, Taylor, Taytoo, Mary Foos, Johnson, Sunflower, Mango, NC-1, and Mitchell. Overleese and Sunflower are most widely grown cultivars. Fruit of Overleese is 350 g in weight compared to 250 g in Sunflower (Callaway, 1992; CRFG, 1999).

⑧ ⑧ ⑧

Chapter 10

LAURALES

The plants are trees or shrubs, sometimes woody lianas, rarely twining parasitic herbs (*Cassytha*), usually with oil or mucilage cells in the parenchymatous tissues. Nodes are unilacunar with 1-7 traces. Xylem is usually with well developed vessels. Vessels are with scalariform or simple perforations; lateral pitting is scalariform to alternate or mostly alternate. Fibres range from tracheids through fibre-tracheids to libriform. Rays are mostly heterogeneous. Axial parenchyma is apotracheal or paratracheal, rarely absent. Sieve element plastids are of S-, Psc- or Pest-type. Leaves are alternate or opposite, sometimes verticillate, simple, entire or sometimes lobed or dentate, pinnately or rarely palmately compound, without stipules. Stomata are paracytic or less often anomocytic.

Flowers are usually in cymose or racemose inflorescences, rarely solitary, actinomorphic or very rarely oblique, spiral, spirocyclic or more often cyclic, bisexual or unisexual, mostly with more or less developed and usually cup-shaped hypanthium (floral cup) of receptacular origin. Perianth is spiral or cyclic (often 3-merous), usually not differentiated into sepals and petals. Androecium consists of (3-) 5 to many stamens, cyclic or spiral; stamens more or less ribbon-shaped or more often differentiated into filament and anther; filaments are frequently with two lateral glands; anthers tetrasporangiate or disporangiate, opening longitudinally or more often by valves, rarely by pores or very rarely circumscissile (*Hennecartia*). Tapetum is secretory or amoeboid. Microsporogenesis is successive or simultaneous (Calycanthaceae). Pollen grains are 2-celled or rarely 3-celled, mostly inaperturate, frequently 2-colpate, rarely with 2-12 slightly irregular porate apertures, mostly tectate. Gynoecium is apocarpous, spiral (Gomortegaceae, Calycanthaceae and some Monimiaceae) or whorled (polymerous or more often monomerous) or less frequently syncarpous; carpels are 1-2,000, glabrous or rarely hairy, fully sealed and with a localized stigma on a distinct stylodium or rarely unsealed above and with shortly decurrent stigma. Ovule is solitary in each carpel or in each locule, anatropous, rarely orthotropous or hemitropous, bitegmic or rarely unitegmic, crassinucellate. Female gametophyte is usually of *Polygonum*-type. Endosperm is cellular or nuclear (Lauraceae-Lauroideae). Fruits are of various types. Seeds are with endotestal seed coat, small to large embryo and well developed, scanty or no endosperm. It produces proanthocyanins but not ellagic acid, and very often with benzyl isoquinoline or aporphine alkaloids (Takhtajan, 2009). It contains seven families.

Family Lauraceae (Avocado, Cinnamon)

It contains 50 genera and 2500-2750 species, mainly in the tropics and subtropics (Heywood *et al.*, 2007). The plants are trees, shrubs or twining parasitic vines. Nodes are unilacunar with scattered spherical cells containing aromatic terpenoids, usually with tannins and with benzylisoquinoline and aporphine alkaloids. The leaves are alternate and spiral, nearly opposite but never two-ranked, simple, entire, rarely lobed, usually leathery and evergreen. The stipules are absent. The inflorescence varies but is usually cymose (determinate) or racemose (indeterminate). The flowers are small, greenish or yellowish, perigynous or epigynous, regular, bisexual or unisexual. Perianth is undifferentiated (corolla none). Stamens are in three or four whorls of 3 each, often some are reduced to staminodes. Anthers open by uplifting of the valves. The ovary is usually superior and free, 1-celled, 1-ovuled, style is filiform or short. The fruit is a drupe or a 1-seeded berry, commonly seated in the impersistent cup-shaped hypanthium or enveloped by the persistent base of the perianth. The seeds are pendulous, without endosperm, completely filled by the large fleshy cotyledons of the embryo. The important plants are avocado, cinnamon (*Cinnamomum zeylanicum*), camphor (*C. camphora*) and some well known ornamentals like laurel (*Laurus nobilis*), Californian laurel (*Umbellularia californica*) and sassafras (*Sassafras varifolium*).

Genus *Persea* Mill.

It contains about 200 species, almost equally represented in tropical to warm temperate America and Asia, but absent from Africa and Australia. The species, *P. indica* (L.) Spreng. in the Canary Islands, is possibly misplaced in this genus. It has 3 subgenera: subgen. *Persea* with equal tepals in deciduous fruit, including *P. americana* Mill., the avocado in America; subgen. *Eriodaphne* with unequal tepals in persistent fruit, spread in America; and subgen. *Machilus* with equal tepals, persistent and reflexed fruit and native to Asia (Kubitzki *et al.*, 1993).

The plants are trees and shrubs having fragrant bark. Leaves are alternate, less often subverticillate, penninerved. The fruit buds are terminal or subterminal and are mixed as in mango. The buds differentiate shortly before blossoming. Inflorescences are thyrso-paniculate, often originating from the terminal vegetative bud. The flowers are small, yellowish green and profuse, trimerous, bisexual, tepals equal to strongly unequal (outer whorl smaller). Corolla is missing. Stamens are 12 in 4 whorls and 3 of these are staminodes. Staminodes are conspicuous, sagittate, and stipitate with very small and flat receptacle. In the 3 functional whorls, anthers are mostly 4-locular where the pollen is arranged in two pairs above each other or in a very narrow arc, the inner first and second whorl ±introrse, the third whorl mostly extrorse to ±latrorse. Filaments are usually longer than the anthers. The solitary pistil is simple and bulbous. The ovary is hypogynous. The fruit is a one-seeded berry, free on a scarcely enlarged pedicel. The tepals are deciduous or persistent.

Avocado

(***Persea americana*** Mill. syn. ***P. gratissima*** C. F. Gaertn., ***P. leiogyna*** S. F. Blake; Guatemalan and West Indian avocado; aguacate; alligator pear) (2n=24, 36, 48)

Avocado is an evergreen and erect tree growing up to 20 m in height. Leaves are simple, elliptic or ovate oblong, 5-30 x 3-15 cm in size and are spirally arranged. Flowers are small, bisexual, fragrant, greenish yellow, apetalous, borne on compact axillary panicles crowded at the ends of the branches. Flower has 6 perianth segments, 9 stamens, arranged in three series, the innermost whorl of 3 staminodes, surrounding a one celled superior ovary having single ovule. The fruit is large (7-20 cm long, 200-2000 g weight), pyriform or globose, fleshy and single seeded berry having yellow green to purple and leathery skin, yellow or yellowish green or purple or red mesocarp of a butter-like consistency and nutty flavour. The fruit has a single seed, which is large, globose having two seed coats and two large fleshy cotyledons enclosing a small embryo (Bergh, 1976; Brücher, 1989; Morton, 1987; Verheij and Coronel, 1991).

Horticultural races

There are three races of *P. americana,* namely Mexican, Guatemalan and West Indian, which differ mainly in tolerance to cold and soil salinity, time of fruit maturity, skin thickness and oil content in fruit. West Indian cultivars have large, smooth, shiny-skinned fruits containing more water and less fat (monounsaturated oil) than the other groups. They are sometimes marketed as "lite" (diet food) avocados with fewer calories. These are grown in warm, tropical climates. The Guatemalan group is originally from the highlands of Guatemala. Cultivars of this group can be grown in more temperate climates than those of the West Indian group. A popular Guatemalan cultivar is Hass, easily recognizable by its thick, black, rough skinned fruit. The Mexican group includes some of the hardiest and most commonly grown cultivars including Duke, Mexicola, and Zutano. Some of the characteristics of the three avocado races are given in Table 10.1.

Table 10.1. Characteristics of horticultural races of avocado.

Trait/ Particulars	West Indian	Guatemalan	Mexican
Native to	Lowlands of Central and South America, introduced into West Indies	Highlands (800-2400 m) of Central America to Ecuador and Mexico	Highlands (2400-2800 m) of Mexico, Andes to Chile
Climate	Tropical	Subtropical	Semi-tropical, rarely does well in coastal environment
Cold tolerance	Least	Intermediate	Most
Salt tolerance	Most	Intermediate	Least
Heat resistance	-	-	Resistant to heat and low humidity
Leaf anise	Absent	Absent	Present

Leaf colour	Pale yellow	Green with red tinge, usually young foliage reddish	Green
Bloom to fruit maturity	Early maturing, 6 to 9 months (summer cultivar)	9 to 14 months, winter cultivar	6-8 months (rapid development)
Fruit size	Variable	Variable, usually large	Small
Colour of fruit	Green or reddish	Green	Often dark
Skin thickness	Medium	Thick, sometimes over 6 mm	Very thin, rarely over 0.75 mm
Skin surface	Shiny, smooth leathery	Rough, usually thick and leathery to woody	Waxy bloom
Seed size	Variable; cotyledons are rough	Small	Large to very large
Seed cavity	Variable, usually loose, seed can shake in fruit	Tight	Loose
Oil content	Low, 5 - 7%	High, 7.5 to 18%	Highest, up to 30%
Pulp fibre	Less common	Less common	Common
Pulp flavour	Sweet, mild, milky to watery	Rich	Anise aroma, rich
Others	At point of fruit attachment, pedicels have unique nailhead configuration. Cotyledons are rough	Commercially important, its hybrids are useful	Bloom earliest; flowers more pubescent; leaf under-surface more glaucous (white with bloom)

Source: Bergh, 1975; Bergh and Ellstrand, 1986.

Cultivar groups

As the flowering behavior in cultivars of avocado is unique, these have also been classified into two complementary groups designated as A and B, based on the flower type, irrespective of the horticultural races (Table 10.2).

Table 10.2. Cultivars of the designated avocado groups A and B based on flowering behaviour.

Type A	Type B
Hass	Bacon
Simmonds	Fuerte
Guatemala	Zutano
Ruehle	Gwen
Nadir	Nabal
Lula	Regina
Rincon	Ruehle
Choquette	Hardee
Rodringues	Sharwil

Nakasone and Paull, 1998

Cultivars

There are several hundred cultivars of avocado but only a few are commercially important. The important ones are Sharwil, Pinkerton (Guatemalan and Mexican), Fuerte, Rincon, Zutano, Bacon, Jim and Santana (Mexican and Guatemalan). Cultivars of the tropical area are Cardinal, De Leon No.1, Calma, Booth 8, Lula, Peterson and Waldin. The cultivars Duke and G 6 are moderately resistant to blight. Selection within open pollinated seedlings has resulted in producing many valuable rootstock cultivars, e.g. GA-13 and Maoz highly tolerant to saline conditions and Duke-7 tolerant to *Phytophthora cinnamomi* (IBPGR, 1986b; Morton, 1987; Verheij and Coronel, 1991).

The cultivars grown in different parts of the world are:

California, USA: Fuerte, Hass, Zutano, Bacon. Reed, Pinkerton, Gwen.

Florida, USA: Pollock, Simmonds, Nadir, Booth 8, Lula, Hardee, Ruehle.

Australia: Zutano, Sharwil, Bacon, Fuerte, Hass.

Israel: Fuerte, Hass, Nabal, Ettinger, Hordhim,Wurtz, Fuerte, Reed, Pinkerton.

South Africa: Fuerte, Hass, Edranol, Ryan.

Mexico: Fuerte, Hass, Bacon, Reed, Criolla (Local), Zutano.

Spain: Hass, Bacon, Fuerte, Reed, Zutano, Gwen.

Philippines: Cardinal, Calma, Uno, 240, 227, Parker, RCF Purple, Capillo Green.

Indonesia: Ijo Panjang, Ijo Bundar, Tawangmangu, Batu, Lembang.

The cultivars belonging to the three horticultural races and hybrids between them are as follows:

A. West Indian (*P. americana* Mill. var. *americana*): The trees are most tender. These are susceptible to cold. The foliage is pale in colour. Mature leaves are of yellow green colour. The fruit ripens during summer to autumn. The fruit is smooth and large in size. The skin is leathery and not more than 1.56 mm in thickness. The thick-skinned cultivars are Lula, Booth Pollack, Waldin, Butler, Fuchs, Ruehle and Choquette.

Purple: The fruit is large, pear-shaped having distinct and long neck, shiny, smooth and leathery skin of dark red to maroon colour that peels off easily from the pulp. The flesh is 2 cm thick, smooth and deep yellow near the seed and yellowish green below the skin (periphery) having rich and nutty flavour. The seed lies loosely in it.

Lula: The cultivar originated in Guatemala. It is more suitable for cultivation under tropical climatic conditions. Tree is dense, broad and prolific. The fruit is very large, pyriform in shape with slightly rough glossy green skin and weighs from 400 to 700 g and contains about 15 per cent oil.

B. Guatemalan (*P. nubigena* var. *guatemalensis* L. O. Willams): The trees are intermediate in hardiness. These are susceptible to cold. The new growth has purplish red colour. The foliage is deep green. The fruit ripens during winter to spring. The fruit is medium to large with a long stalk. Thickness of the skin is 1.56-6.25 mm and is hard and warty. It has cultivars such as Anaheim, Nobel, Reed, Hazzard, Edranol, Wurtz, and Haas.

Hass: It is a selection made in California from seedlings of Lyon of Guatemalan race. It is suitable for cultivation in subtropical conditions. The tree is upright, rather open and not tall and vigorous with an A-flower type. The fruits mature earlier than those of Fuerte. The fruits are round, medium in size, 340 g with bumpy pebbled thick but pliable skin. It is initially green and turns dark purplish black when ripe, while that of "green" cultivars remains green. Fruit size tends to be small in the warmer areas. Flesh is good having fairly small seed with 19% oil. It is late maturing with some tolerance to diseases and pests. When ripe, it yields to gentle pressure. Soft avocados are generally considered over-ripe and possibly rancid. Crops are heavy and reliable as long as fruits do not remain hung too long.

Adrith: It is a Californian cultivar and produces high yields regularly. The fruit is of medium size, around 250 g in weight, green in colour and of good flavour.

Green: The fruit is large (452-680 g), oval and has thick and stout neck, thin (2-2.5 cm in thickness), warty and yellowish green skin and rough surface. The flesh has nutty flavour and is greenish yellow that later turns green. The seed is lightly placed in the cavity.

Anaheim: Tree is columnar and productive. Fruit is very large, up to 680 g, elongated and glossy green having small seed with 15% oil.

Frazer: It has large fruit size of 312 g and up to 482 g, lemon shaped having a thick and pebbly black skin.

Gem: It originated from open pollinated Gwen seedlings. Average fruit weight is 275 g. Skin thickness is average (1.6 mm). It seems to set fruit every year. The tree is spreading but is like Gwen.

Gwen: It is a seedling of Hass. Tree is dwarf and open up to 4.2 m, has low vigour. Fruit is small, 227 g, looks like Hass, elongated and green. Flesh is good. It is the most productive of dwarf avocados and is best for outdoor use, for containers and greenhouse. Average fruit weight is 255 g, average skin thickness is 1.7 mm. It has a strong tendency to alternate bearing.

Marvel: It originated from open pollinated Gwen seedlings. The tree is upright and compact and hides the fruit well. Average fruit weight is 213 g and average skin thickness is 1.2 mm.

Nobel: It originated from open pollinated Gwen seedlings. The tree is weeping but is more or less compact and upright. The cultivar does not produce much bud wood. Average fruit weight is 249 g. Average skin thickness is 1.4 mm.

Queen: Tree is broad. Fruit is exceptionally large, 680 g, elongated having excellent purple flesh with 13% oil content. It is fairly hardy.

Lyon: Tree is columnar, slow growing, difficult to propagate and is often scion incompatible. Fruit is pyriform, commonly over 680 g having dark glossy green and rough skin and 21% oil of high quality.

C. Mexican (*P. americana* var. *drymifolia* Blake): The trees are hardier with light green bark and smaller than those of *P. americana* including the leaves and fruits. These are resistant to cold. It is self fertile. The young leaves are light green in colour The leaves are more pubescent. Crushed leaves give strong aniseed aroma. The flowers are also more pubescent. Dichogamy is observed and thus cross pollination is the rule. It develops seedless fruits owing to parthenocarpy. The fruit is a small berry having one seed that is large and has more oil content. The skin is very thin and membranous, thickness not more than 0.78 mm. The important cultivars of Mexican race are Mexicola, Topa Topa, Zutano, Duke, Ganter and Gottfried.

Topa Topa: The tree is columnar and vigorous. Fruit is handsome, elongated pyriform, small to medium, 227 g, smooth and dark purple with white waxy bloom. Skin is paper thin. Flesh is rather poor with 15% oil. The seed is elongated. Seedlings are commonly used for rootstock because of hardiness.

Puebla: The tree is broad and high branching. Fruit is beautiful, medium to large, 227 g, having ovoid, lacquered and maroon purple thin skin. Flesh is excellent with 20% oil. It is least hardy to temperatures below 0°C.

Mexicola Grande: It is a seedling selection of Mexicola. The tree is tall and spreading similar to Mexicola. Fruit is 15-25% larger than that of Mexicola and somewhat rounder in shape with better seed/flesh ratio. Skin is paper thin and purple black. The flesh is of high quality with high oil content.

Mexicola: Tree is tall, spreading and vigorous. Fruit is small, 141 g, round pyriform having paper thin, purplish black skin with waxy bloom. Flesh is of high quality. Seed is very large. It is the hardiest of the known cultivars, recovers rapidly from freeze and its seedlings are useful as rootstock.

Duke: Tree is vigorous and open and resists wind. Fruit is small, 340 g, elongated pyriform and waxy green having paper thin skin. Flesh is excellent having 21% oil. Seeds are commonly used for rootstocks. It resists root rot and is extraordinarily hardy and recovers quickly from freeze up to -5.5°C. Fruiting season is October.

Ganter: Tree is tall, spreading and open. Fruit is small, up to 227 g, long pyriform having paper thin and pale waxy green skin. Flesh is good with 18% oil.

D. Mexican-Guatemalan hybrids: These are resistant to cold. The trees have dark green leaves.

Fuerte: The cultivar is from California. The hybrid is a very popular cultivar grown all over the world. It has a green-skinned, pear-shaped fruit maturing shortly after Shepard. Fruits are large, pyriform with 20-26 per cent oil. It performs better in subtropics than in the tropics but withstands some cold. It has a B-type flower and its cropping is more reliable in warmer climates.

Pinkerton: The hybrid was bred in California and crops heavily and reliably in most districts in Australia. It has an A-type flower and the tree is semi-dwarf in habit. Fruits are variable in size, 198 to 340 g having thick green skin with a slight pebbly texture and a long neck.

Zutano: The tree is columnar. The fruit is picked from October to February. It is small to medium, elongated smooth green and resembles Fuerte but is inferior because it has fibres. It is considered of medium quality.

Wurtz (Littlecado): The semi-dwarf tree is densely foliaged and prostrate. It has weeping habit and low vigour and is difficult to train. It is a late maturing cultivar. Fruit is pear-shaped and dark green of medium size, 283.5 g. Cropping can be strongly biennial.

Whitsell: Tree is dwarf with low vigour growing to 3.6 m and is not hardy. Fruit is small, 170g, elongated and appears like Hass. Flesh is good. It bears fruits in alternate years. It is suitable for growing in containers and greenhouse.

Ryan: The tree is low and spreading. Fruit is medium, 397g, elongated, otherwise resembles Hass. The skin is thick, pebbled and purple. Flesh is good with 25% oil.

Rincon: The tree is small. Fruit is small to medium, 283g, green resembling Fuerte. Flesh is good having dark areas in the flesh which are "strings" (fibres). The fruit is of medium quality and has large seed.

Reed: It is a cross between Anaheim and Nabal. The trees are columnar, upright and semi-vigorous. Its fruits ripen in summer. It is a late and prolific cropping cultivar bearing large, 425g, round, fruits of excellent quality having pebbled, green and thick skin and small seed. Flesh is good.

Murrieta Green: Tree is slow growing and can be easily trained. It is readily adaptable to espalier. Fruit is large, 510g, oblate, green resembling Fuerte. Flesh is exceptional with 18% oil.

Jim: Tree is upright. Fruit is small to medium, 284g, olive green with long neck and 12% oil.

Fuerte: This is the most popular cultivar for general planting and upon which the avocado industry was built. Tree is open, spreading and tall. Fruit is large to very large, 454 g, elongated pyriform having dark green skin, numerous small raised pale spots, waxy bloom and thin skin. Flesh is good with medium seed, 18% oil, excellent flavour, texture and shipping qualities. It tends to bear in alternate years and is unproductive near the coast.

Creamhart: It is a seedling of Reed. Tree is open and upright branching. Fruit is medium, up to 397 g having green skin and extraordinarily pale, buttery and nearly fibreless flesh. It is not alternate bearing.

Bacon: Tree is broad and productive. Fruit is small to medium, up to 40g, round ovoid and smooth green. Flesh is only fair, almost colourless with seed cavity that moulds rapidly.

Nabal: The tree is dense and columnar. Young trees require pinching to force low branching. Trees tend to bear in alternate years. Fruit is handsome, pyriform, large, 482g, green with skin resembling Fuerte. Flesh is of exceptionally high quality with 16% oil.

Philippine cultivars

Cardinal: The fruit is bottle-necked with an average weight of 400g. The skin is reddish purple and thick (1.3 mm). The seed is small (40g) and is loose to tight in the cavity. The flesh is yellow, moderately fibrous and constitutes 80% of the whole fruit by weight.

Calma: The fruit is ovoid and weighs 600 g. The skin is reddish purple and intermediate in thickness (1 mm). The seed is small (80 g) and is loose in the cavity. The flesh is yellow and is 80% of the whole fruit by weight.

Uno: The fruit is ovoid and weighs 400 g. The skin is purple and is rather thick (2 mm). The seed is small (80 g) and is loose to tight in the cavity. The flesh is creamy yellow and is 80% of the whole fruit by weight.

240: The fruit is ovoid and weighs 600g. The skin is green and thick (1.26 mm). The seed is intermediate in size (90 g) and is rather loose in the cavity. The flesh is creamy yellow and is 80% of the whole fruit by weight.

227: The fruit is bottle-necked and weighs 500 g. The skin is purple and thick (1.3 mm). The seed is small (50 g) and is loose in the cavity. The flesh is dark yellow and is 80% of the whole fruit by weight.

Parker: The fruit is ovoid having an average weight of 600 g. The skin is purple and thick (1.1 mm). The seed is small in size (70 g) and is tight in the cavity. The flesh is creamy yellow and is 80% of the whole fruit by weight.

RCF Purple: The fruit is ovoid weighing 400 g. The skin is reddish purple and thick (1.2 mm). The seed is small (40 g) and is loose in the cavity. The flesh is creamy yellow and is 80% of the whole fruit by weight.

Cepillo Green: The fruit is pyriform weighing 700 g. The skin is green and intermediate in thickness (0.9 mm). The seed is intermediate in size (90 g). The flesh is dark yellow and is 80% of the whole fruit by weight.

Indonesian cultivars

Two types of cultivars are grown; one having big fruits supposedly derived from the West Indian race and the other having smaller fruits derived from Mexican and its natural hybrids. In general, the avocado is differentiated into two groups; the butter type (or mentega) having fruits rich in nutrients and having high contents of fat and vitamin A, and the milk type (or susu) having fruits with low fat content and rather thin flesh. There are also the Ijo Panjang and Ijo Bundar types which are long and round with green skin colour with relatively small seeds. The Gontor type has medium-sized, round, purple fruits having rather rough skin. Besides, there are cultivars such as Tawangmangu, Batu and Lembang.

Cultivars in India

Although avocado is not a commercial fruit crop but as a result of introductions from Sri Lanka scattered plants are grown in Tamil Nadu, Kerala, Maharashtra, Karnataka in the south central India and in Sikkim. The cultivars of West Indian race are grown in localized pockets in Maharashtra, Tamil Nadu and Karnataka. In tropical and near tropical areas, only West Indian race is well adapted but its hybrids with Guatemalan (e.g. Booth selection) perform well and are considered valuable for extending the harvest season. In less tropical regions, hybrids of Guatemalan with Mexican race predominate since they combine the cold hardiness of the latter with the superior horticultural traits of both and also bridge the two seasons of maturity. In Sikkim, both the Mexican and Gautemalan races successfully grow in hill ranges at altitudes of 800-1,600 m at temperatures from 12 to 30°C with an average annual rainfall of 2,000 mm. The Mexican race is cultivated on mid-altitude hills (pH 5-6). In Coorg, Karnataka avocado has been planted as a mixed crop in coffee based cropping system.

TKD 1 (PA 2): It is a selection and recommended for growing in irrigated and rainfed areas of Pulneys, Shevroys and other hills of Tamil Nadu. The trees are semi-spreading, suitable for high density planting. The fruits mature early. Fruit is dark green, round and medium-sized. Fruit yield is 264 kg/tree or 28.4 tonnes/ha.

CHES A-1: It is a selection from seedlings of unknown origin. The tree is medium, 45-50 cm tall and spreading. The leaf is 20-22 cm long and 8-10 cm wide. It flowers in February-March and the fruits mature in October-November. The fruits are borne in clusters of 3 to 5. The fruit is medium in size, green, round and weighs 200-250 g with pale yellow pulp and recovery of 60 per cent having 10.5°Brix TSS. A tree yields 300-500 fruits.

Cultivars from Israel

Ettinger: It is of unknown parentage, but it contains certain traits of the Mexican race such as tolerance to low temperatures (4 hours of -6°C in mature tree) and thin skin. Harvest season is early but short, mainly October through November. The fruits are bright green skinned with good size having high internal quality. The yields are good to medium. It is also a potent pollinizer for Hass and Pinkerton.

Ardith: It is a local selection of a chance seedling from Ettinger.

Australian cultivars

Shepard: It is a cultivar from California. The tree is precocious, heavy cropping, semi-dwarf producing green pear-shaped fruits. The flesh is pale yellow when ripe with a smooth, buttery texture. It has a B-type flower pattern and is sensitive to the environment during flowering with a requirement that night temperatures do not fall below 12°C. The fruit has moderate disease and pest resistance and it is the earliest maturing cultivar. Its major disadvantage is the large seed size.

Sharwil: The cultivar was selected in Queensland and thought to be predominantly Gutemalan with some Mexican genes. The tree is vigorous with the potential to set heavy crops of smooth, green, pear-shaped fruit. Flesh quality is excellent and seed size is typically 13-15% of the fruit. The cultivar has a B-type flower pattern dependent on temperature conditions. It is a mid season cultivar maturing after Fuerte. It has become the most important cultivar of Hawaii and is more disease and pest resistant than Fuerte.

⑧ ⑧ ⑧

LILIOPSIDA (MONOCOTYLEDONS; MONOCOTS; MONOCOTYLEDONAE)

The Liliopsids most probably originated from some very ancient vessel-less herbaceous member of Magnoliopsida that had a tactostelic vascular system, P-type sieve element plastids, 3-merous flowers, apocarpous gynoecium with laminar diffuse (scattered) placentation, bitegmic and crassinucellate ovules (with parietal tissue between the female gametophyte) and the nuclear epidermis, and primitive 2-celled and l-colpate pollen grains. The monocots are considered monophyletic based on their herbaceous habit, parallel-veined leaves with a sheathing base, embryo with a single cotyledon, sieve cell plastids with several cuneate protein crystals, stem with scattered vascular bundles, adventitious root system and sympodial branching with no secondary thickening.

The plants are usually herbs, but often secondarily arborescent. Primary woody plants are absent among the monocots. The primary root is usually ephemeral, dries out in the early growth of the plant and is replaced by an adventitious root system that develops from the stem or as in grasses directly from the hypocotyl. Ontogenetically root cap and root epidermis are of different origin.

The leaves are formed almost entirely from the apical (not basal) end of the primordium. Leaves are entire with no glandular teeth, if any, these are more or less spiny. Leaf venation is striate or of derived types, mostly arcuate striate or longitudinally striate (parallel), less often palmate striate or pinnate striate, almost always more or less closed at the apex (the veins emerging from the leaf base usually run together again at their apices). Leaves are usually not clearly divided into petiole and lamina, less often more or less differentiated, but in these cases the "petiole" and the "lamina" are not homologous to those of magnoliopsids (of secondary origin), often with sheathing base. Leaf traces are usually numerous.

Prophylls (including bracteoles) are usually solitary and nearly always adaxial. Vascular bundles are usually without cambium or rarely with vestigial cambium only. Vascular system of the stem usually consists of many separate scattered bundles or sometimes of two or more rings of vascular bundles, and the axis mostly attains its full diameter early, after which no increase in thickness takes place. Only in some groups does thickening of the axis occurs by means of division and enlargement of ground parenchyma cells (so called diffused secondary growth), as in palms, or by means of special kind of cambium that arises in the parenchyma outside the primary vascular system, as in some herbaceous and woody Lilianae. Sieve element plastids are of P-type with several to numerous cuneate (triangular) crystalloid bodies (lacking in all magnoliopsids except *Saruma* and *Asarum* in Aristolochiaceae). Phloem is without parenchyma, usually without clearly differentiated bark and pith.

Flowers are pentacyclic usually 3-merous, sometimes 4- or 2-merous, and very rarely 5-merous with androecium opposite the petals. Filaments are narrow and anthers are broadly attached. Nectaries are predominantly septal. Pollen grains are mostly monosulcate (1-colpate) or of derived types, often uniporate. Embryo, when differentiated, is always with one cotyledon. The cotyledon is usually with two main vascular bundles. The class Liliopsida includes 4 subclasses, 31 orders, 120 families, more than 3,000 genera and about 65,000 species.

⑧ ⑧ ⑧

Chapter 11

ALISMATALES

The plants are aquatic or marsh herbs, rhizomatous, hydrophilous, without raphides. The stems are with small scales or glandular multiseriate hairs within the sheathing leaf bases (axillary trichomes) at the nodes (lacking in Limnocharitaceae but replaced by uniseriate hairs in *Scheuchzeria*). Flowers with subtending bracts, choricarpous or syncarpous (pseudomonomerous) gynoecium, extrorse anthers and a large green embryo. Endosperm development is helobial or nuclear. Mature seeds are nearly always without endosperm. The tissues contain oxalates. It contains 13 families and 3320 species.

Family Araceae (aroids and duckweeds)

Most species occur in tropical South East Asia, Africa, and America and fewer in temperate and boreal zones. It contains about 110 genera and 3200 species (Heywood *et al.*, 2007).

The plants are perennial, mainly terrestrial herbs with a variety of life forms, including geophytes, epiphytes and climbers. These have flowers in a spadix (aroids) and minute floating aquatic herbs have reduced flowers (duckweeds), often with rhizomes or corms, vines with aerial roots, epiphytes or floating aquatics. Grooved raphide crystals of calcium oxalate are present in specialized cells and associated chemicals causing irritation of mouth and throat. Cyanogenic compounds are often present sometimes with alkaloids often with laticifers, with a milky or watery sap (latex), mucilage canals or resin canals.

The roots are adventitious, often thickened rhizomes or subglobose tubers. Climbers and epiphytes have root dimorphism, e.g. some roots are absorbent, growing downward toward the soil while the others, not influenced by gravity, grow away from light and clasp firmly as they grow into crevices in the branches of the supporting tree. Many aerial roots develop an outer water absorbing tissue similar to the velamen of orchids. A few genera, e.g. *Anthurium* and *Philodendron*, include species that are truly epiphytic and collect water and mineral salts in their leaf rosettes. The aquatics either lack roots (*Pistia, Wolffia*) or develop simple roots (*Lemna*). The leaves are usually differentiated in petiole sheath, petiole and an expanded leaf blade of variable shape. Some species, e.g. the Swiss Cheese plant (*Monstera deliciosa*) develop fenestrated or holed leaves during development.

The inflorescence is indeterminate, usually consists of a dense spadix with numerous ebracteate flowers and is usually subtended by a conspicuous spathe that is often green but sometimes elaborately coloured. In the aquatics (*Lemna*), the inflorescence is reduced to a single flower, more or less hidden in a cavity of the fronds. The flowers are sessile and bisexual or unisexual. With a few exceptions (*Arisaema*), the inflorescence is bisexual with male flowers borne above female flowers. The tepals are often more or less connate in bisexual flowers and absent in the unisexual flowers. There are usually 2 whorls of 2 or 3 stamens more or less opposite the tepals, if present. The ovary is superior or embedded in the spadix and generally composed of 1 to 3, rarely more, carpels with a comparable number of locules with 1 to numerous anatropous, amphitropous or atropous ovules on basal, apical, axile or parietal placenta. The style is usually inconspicuous with lobed stigma. The fruit is a berry, sometimes an utricle, a drupe, or nut-like with 1 to many seeds, which usually have endosperm. The embryo is generally straight, although some species have a curved embryo with or without endosperm.

Nearly all species, except some of the aquatics (*Lemna*), are insect pollinated. The inflorescence of many species emits a nauseous, foetid odour that attracts carrion flies to effect pollination, but some have less offensive odours (*Spathiphyllum* and *Philodendron* spp.).

Genus *Monstera* Adanson [2n = 60 (24, 48, 56, 58, 70)]

It has about 40 species in tropical America from Mexico to South Brazil (Kubitzki *et al.*, 1998). The plants are climbers, hemi-epiphytes in humid forest. Leaf blade is entire or perforated and/or pinnatifid having fine venation parallel pinnate or ±reticulated. The inflorescences are 1 to several having sessile spadix, 2-locular ovary with 2 ovules per locule, anatropous and placenta at base of septum. The seed is obovoid or subcordate, a little compressed having S-shaped raphe, smooth and thick testa, no endosperm and large embryo.

Ceriman

(***Monstera deliciosa*** Liebm.; split leaf philodendron)

It is native of South Mexico and Guatemala (Martin *et al.*, 1987). The related edible species *M. perusa* (L.) de Vries that grows in rain forests of Panama and produces sweet acid fruits (Brücher, 1989). It is grown chiefly for its ornamental foliage and edible fruits. It is planted on rockeries along pillars or tree trunks and in pots to display its elegant foliage. The variegated juvenile leaves of *M. dubia* (H.B.K.) Engler & Krause, adpressed to tree boles in Amazonian forests, frequently attract the attention of travelers.

It is a stout, woody stemmed, close jointed, deciduous and 10 m long climber, forming cord-like hanging aerial roots. The leaves are often very large (1 m), orbicular ovate and broad, entire, pinnately cut and perforated or pinnatifid, thick, leathery, elliptic to oblong having lobes in 1-4 series on each side of the midrib. The petioles are prominent and sheathing. The leaves make one of the world's most ubiquitous ornamental foliage. Peduncles are terminal, solitary or fascicled bearing ovate or oblong, boat shaped, creamy spathe, which opens wide after flowering. The spadix is bisexual, shorter than the spathe, cylindrical or nearly so, densely flowered with perfect flowers above and sterile below. Perfect flowers are without perianth having 4 stamens and 2-celled ovary with 2 ovules in each cell. Berries are very small, crowded or formed into a multiple fruit, which is cone-like, 25 cm long and 5-6 cm in diameter. The fruit ripens gradually from base upwards and takes about one year to mature after flowering. The fruit becomes ready for consumption when all the scales fall off in about a week or more after picking (Morton, 1987; Brücher, 1989). The pulp surrounding the seeds is delicious and is used in Mexico to make ice cream and soft drinks (Kubitzki *et al.*, 1998).

⑧ ⑧ ⑧

Chapter 12

PANDANALES

The plants are herbs, trees or climbers. Raphides are mostly present and lack silica bodies. Vessels in roots and mostly also in stems and leaves are with scalariform perforations. Stomata are tetracytic, rarely anomocytic. Flowers are epigynous to hypogynous. Gynoecium is syncarpous. Microsporogenesis is successive. Endosperm development is nuclear or helobial. The order contains 5 families.

Family Pandanaceae (screwpine family)

It is a small tropical family of woody plants with long, spiny, ensiform leaves and usually naked, unisexual flowers. The plants are tall, usually branched trees, shrubs or climbers with stems that are annulated by leaf scars and often supported by adventitious roots, which serve as prop or clasp roots. The long, narrow, sometimes stiff and ensiform leaves are tristichous or arranged in 4 rows, which may be spirally twisted due to the spiral growth of the stems and are often aggregated at the end of the stems. The leaves are usually armed on the margins and occasionally on the upper or both sides of the lamina. The inflorescences are unisexual, terminal or less frequently lateral, initially erect but later nodding, consisting of racemes or spikes, which are gathered into large spikes or umbel-like inflorescences, or into repeatedly branched panicles, often with green lower bracts and coloured upper bracts. The flowers are naked or with a vestigial perianth, unisexual (plants dioecious), occasionally with remnants of the other sex. The flowers are distinct (*Sararanga*) or more or less indistinct (*Freycinetia, Pandanus*). The staminate flowers have a few to several hundred, sometimes basally fused stamens. The female flowers are composed of 1 to several, superior carpels that are partially or completely fused with 1 to many locules, depending on the degree of fusion between the carpels, and 1 to numerous anatropous ovules per locule, on basal or parietal placentas. The fruit is a multilocular drupe or a berry with small seeds, a minute straight embryo and a starchy or oily endosperm. It contains about 3 genera and 800-900 species (Heywood *et al.*, 2007).

Genus *Pandanus* Parkinson

The plants are trees or shrubs, with or without prop roots, rarely epiphytes. Leaves in three spiral rows, are amplexicaul, sometimes semi-amplexicaul at base; auricles are sometimes well differentiated (*P.* sect. *Dauphinensia*). Inflorescences are variable with sexes as to number of spikes, pistillate spikes being generally less numerous than staminate spikes. Flowers are usually unisexual. Staminate flowers are generally distinct with stamens very variable in numbers, free on spikes or aggregated into phalanges of various forms. Pistillate flowers are with 1 several, generally 1-ovulate carpels. Fruit is a monodrupe or polydrupe (phalange). Seeds are fusiform or obovoid having thin and membranous seed coat. It has about 700 species in tropical zones from Africa to Asia and various archipelagos in the Pacific (Kubitzki *et al.*, 1998). The important species that produce edible fruits are *P. brosimos* Merr. and Perry., *P. conoideus* Lam., *P. leram* Jones ex Fontana, *P. dubius* Spreng (pandanus), *P. julianetti* Martelli (highland pandanus) and *P. tectorius* Sol. ex Balf. f. (screwpine) (Verheij and Coronel, 1991). *Pandanus julianetti* is found in the highlands of New Guinea between 1450 and 2800 m altitudes (Walter and Sam, 2002). Pandanus is grown for domestic uses. Developing new uses of fruits, seeds and other plant parts can enhance its value.

Karuka
(*Pandanus brosimus* Merr. and Perry.)

It is an evergreen and woody plant with an erect to decumbent branched stem, usually forming rigid prop roots from the leaf axils. It can be developed as fruit cum nut crop particularly in highlands above 2000 m (Verheij and Coronel, 1991). Stems are often knobby or prickly showing leaf scars. The bark is thin, often green just below the epidermis. The leaves, spiralled in three series, are linear and undivided, usually M-shaped in cross section and with prickles along the margins. The plants are dioecious and strictly unisexual. Staminate inflorescences are ephemeral, bracteate, usually spicate consisting of perianthless flowers. Flower is a cluster of stamens having mostly white to yellowish and often scented pollen. Bracts are mostly white to cream or yellow and sometimes orange to purplish. The inflorescence gets depleted of pollen and decay within 3-4 days. Pistillate inflorescence is either a globose to cylindrical head or a spike. The upper bracts in the head are early caducous. Each head consists of either massed unilocular carpels ripening as drupes or of 2 to many seed chambers. Stigmas are always distinct on the apex of each carpel. The fruit is syncarpous and becomes yellow, orange, red or occasionally purplish red on ripening. Fruit can grow up to 30 cm in diameter and 15 kg in weight. It contains 50 or more fibrous segments each with 2 to 4 edible seeds. The exocarp of each carpel is firm to fleshy. The mesocarp is always fibrous towards the base and the endocarp is bony. Seeds are endospermous, contain between 10-60% oil depending upon species that retain oil within the thin to massively thick and bony endocarp (Verheij and Coronel, 1991).

[COMMELINIDS]

The plants have UV-fluorescing cell walls (ferulic/coumaric acids), silicic acid in leaves, cuticular waxes, often in rodlets aggregated into scallops.

Chapter 13

ARECALES (PALMALES)

Plants are prevalent in tropical to subtropical region. Stem is woody, monopodial, tall, sometimes climbing and armed with hooks, generally covered by persistent leaf bases. Leaves are palmate (pleated). Leaves are often very large, entire or pinnately or flabellately divided and nerved with rachis often extended at the base into a fibrous sheath. Plants are dioecious to bisexual. Inflorescence is a spadix. Flowers are unisexual, regular, small, actinomorphic and borne in long panicle, in large spathe-like bracts, double perianth. Stamens are usually six. Carpels are one or more and are usually distinct having one ovule each. Ovary is superior with free ovary or locules. Fruit is a drupe or berry and seed is endospermic. The order contains the single family Arecaceae.

Family Arecaceae (Palmae/ Palmaceae; palm family)

It is a family of 190 genera and 2000 species (Heywood *et al.*, 2007). Uhl and Dransfield (1988) classified the family into six subfamilies and 200 genera. In India, 25 genera and 225 species are found.

Palms are mainly distributed in the tropics, with many species in Central America, northern South America and East Asia. Palms occur in many habitats, from mangrove swamps to lowland rain forest. With the exception of East Asian mangrove swamps (*Nypa*) and wetlands (*Mauritia*, *Copernicia*) in northern South America, palms are rarely the dominant or most conspicuous part of any vegetation type. There are a few subtropical and temperate outliers, including the European *Chamaerops humilis*, which occurs at latitude 44°N. Few species have overcome this limitation. *Trachycarpus* reaches 2400 m altitude at 32°N in the Himalayas, where the land remains under snow from November to March and *Serenoa* reaches 30°N in North America. In Borneo, *Calamus gibbianus* reaches an elevation of more than 3000 m but *Ceroxylon utile* has been recorded at more than 4000 m in Colombia.

The life form of palms is highly variable. Some are tree or shrub-like, others are nearly stemless or climbing, but all have woody stems that terminate in a crown of leaves. The stems are solitary or clustered, rarely branched, armed or unarmed, often covered with leaf scars. All palms have a single apical bud and if killed by frost the stem dies. Branching, if occurs, is dichotomous (*Hyphaene, Nypa*). Some species (e.g. *Metroxylon sagu*) store huge amounts of starch in the stem and utilize it in one gigantic burst of reproduction after which they die back. The unbranched stem is 50-

60 m in height. Despite the massive size of the stem, the diameter increases solely by primary growth. Once fully formed its width is maintained. The leaves are often large, tough and plicate, usually spirally arranged, only rarely di- or tristichous, initially with a tubular sheath, which may later split open and be armed with spines or prickles, and generally have a distinct petiole, which is unarmed or armed with spines or teeth. The blade is palmate, pinnate and rarely bipinnate (*Caryota*), bifid (*Asterogyne*) or entire, tough and usually plicate (folded like a fan). The folds are either arranged on either side of an elongated central rachis (feather palms), or arise crowded from very short central rachis or costa (fan palm). Large fan leaves are intermediate between the feather and fan types and have a massive central costa (costapalmate). The folds develop as the leaf grows in bud before it is unfurled and, as it expands from the bud, swellings (pulvini) develop that push the folded leaflets out to their mature position. The leaves may be undivided or frequently split along the folds such that the folds are V-shaped (induplicate as in *Phoenix*) or A-shaped (reduplicate as in *Butia*). The former possesses an apical leaflet and the latter does not, a distinction that arises early during development. The "leaflets" may contain one to several folds, the linear, fishtail-shaped, acute or praemorse (looking as if bitten off). Before final expansion of the leaf, superficial cells often divide to form hairs or scales that are often of great complexity and beauty. The loose surface layer so formed acts as a lubricant during the opening of the leaf. The leaves form crown at the top of tree. Rachis is often expanded at the base into a fibrous sheath. Petiole base is broad. Palm leaves vary in size.

The plants are monoecious or dioecious. Palm inflorescences are axillary, simple or huge panicles with up to 6 orders of branching, often emerging among the leaves, but sometimes below or above the crown (*Corypha, Metroxylon*), usually solitary, but occasionally several appear together. The inflorescence invariably has a more or less prominent prophyll. Species of *Corypha* have tree-like inflorescences that carry up to 10 million flowers. The flowers occur individually or 2 to 3 together in cincinnate clusters or are 2-ranked. Sometimes the flowers are borne in pits in the inflorescence branches. The flowers are small, sessile, very rarely bisexual, actinomorphic, hypogynous and regular; usually unisexual (the plants then monoecious, andromonoecious). Unisexual flowers often develop by abortion. Leathery and fleshy perianth may be persistent. The perianth is 6-parted (6 segments) arranged in two whorls of 3 each. Male flowers occasionally have both 4 sepals and petals. Stamens are 6, rarely numerous, in two series. More than 6 stamens per flower are not uncommon and more than 1000 occur in *Ammandra*. Their filaments may be connate or free. The anthers are versatile, dehiscing by vertical slit. Palms are wind- or animal-pollinated (by ants, bees, beetles or flies) or both. Gynoecium is tricarpellary with apocarpous, syncarpous superior ovary. Ovary is 1 to 3- celled. The flower may have up to 10 carpels that are either free (apocarpous) or wholly or partly fused (syncarpous). Each carpel has a single ovule and the ovules are erect or pendulous anatropous (rarely semi-anatropous or atropous). Fruiting carpel is distinct. The style is filiform and often expanded at the apex. Placentation is axile in trilocular ovary. One ovule is borne in each cell. Ovary is vestigial or absent in male flowers.

The fruits are mostly one seeded berries or drupes with a single seed, or rarely 2 to 10. They vary in size from 4.5 mm in diameter to a length of 50 cm and a weight of 18 kg found in *Lodoicea maldivica* (double coconut- the world's largest fruit or seed). The fruit surface is most often smooth but may be covered with exquisite, geometrically arranged scales, prickles, hairs or warts. The mesocarp is fleshy or dry and variously fibrous. The endocarp if distinct is mostly thin. Many fruits are brightly coloured and virtually all are indehiscent. The storage tissue is endosperm, which is oily or fatty rather than starchy. It is sometimes extremely hard, in which case it is known as vegetable ivory (*Phytelephas*) and used for carvings or buttons. The fruit is a fleshy berry containing numerous stony seeds. The fruits finally form compact infructescences. In *Cocos nucifera,* two carpels abort and mature fruit can only be easily identified by presence of three longitudinal sutures and also by the presence of three round scars on the hard endocarp of fruit. The seed has copious, starchy endosperm and a straight embryo. Exocarp is often fibrous, sometimes covered by reflexed scales. The seed is hollow. Upon germination, the cotyledon remains as a haustorium within the testa and axile placenta.

The important fruit species are *Cocos nucifera, Metroxylon rumphii (*sago palm*), Areca catechu, Elaeis guinensis, Phoenix dactylifera, Phoenix sylvestris (*wild date palm*)* and *Borassus flabellifer* (fan palm or *tad*).

Taxonomy and classification of palms

Moore (1973) recognized 25 natural groups of genera but without giving any formal taxonomic rank. Uhl and Dransfield (1988) collected information on each group of the palms from the extensive field work of Moore to formalize Moore's classification. Six subfamilies were recognized dividing them further into tribes and in some cases into subtribes. These are: Coryphoideae (three tribes), Calamoideae (two tribes), Nypoideae (one species), Ceroxyloideae (three tribes), Arecoideae (six tribes) and Phytelephantoideae. These subfamilies represent six major lines of evolution. Four characters used in delimiting the subfamilies were (i) leaf palmate, costapalmate or pinnate and induplicate or reduplicate, (ii) the number of peduncular bracts on the inflorescence, (iii) arrangement of flowers on the rachillae, and (iv) structure of the gynoecium.

Coryphoideae

The Coryphoideae is the most diverse as well as the most unspecialized (primitive) subfamily of the palms. With the exception of the Nypoideae, all apocarpous palms (with free carpels) are included in this subfamily. The leaves are palmate, costapalmate, rarely entire or pinnate and induplicate. The flowers are solitary or clustered, 3-merous in all whorls or apocarpous or more or less syncarpous. Palms in this subfamily are never strictly monoecious. Many coryphoid palms are valuable ornamentals, and the hardiest palms belong to this subfamily including the date palm (*Phoenix*) and the allied induplicate leaved, pinnate or bipinnate tribe Caryotoeae (fishtail palm).

Calamoideae

The Calamoideae, the rattans, contain only 22 genera, but represents a quarter of all palm species because of the sizable number of rattan species in the Asian tropics. The subfamily is the most abundant in eastern Old World tropics, often in high rainfall or swampy areas. Only four genera occur in the New World. *Raphia* occurs in both the hemispheres. Many of the species are conspicuously spiny.

Nypoideae

This subfamily consists of a single monotypic genus *Nypa. Nypa fruticans* is the mangrove palm of Asia and the West Pacific, very different from the other palms. It grows from a prostrate, dichotomously branched stem and bears reduplicate, pinnate leaves and erect inflorescences with a terminal head of male flowers and branched lateral spikes of staminate flowers.

Ceroxyloideae

The Ceroxyloideae contains mostly New World palms but two genera occur in Madagascar, one in the Mascarene Island and the other in Australia. The subfamily is distinguished by reduplicate leaves that are regularly or irregularly pinnate, bifid or entire, numerous peduncular (empty) bracts on the inflorescence and flowers arranged singly in rows (acervuli).

Arecoideae

This pantropical subfamily is the largest in the palm family and contains the greatest number of important species such as coconut and African oil palm. The Arecoideae consists approximately of 113 genera in six tribes. All are reduplicate and monoecious. The basic flower cluster of the Arecoideae is the triad, but it is reduced to a single flower along some portions of the rachillae in many genera.

Phytelephantoideae

This morphologically isolated subfamily comprises three genera (*Ammandra, Phytelephus* and *Aphandra*) in north west South America and Panama. Male flowers contain a large number of stamens and female flowers are clustered in a head-like structure. The fruits are many seeded. The hardened endosperm of the phytelephantoid palm is called tagua or vegetable ivory.

Genus *Borassus* L.

The trees are armed. Leaves are costapalmate with large adaxial hastula abaxial low; blade suborbicular to flabellate, divided to 1/2 into single fold bifid segments. Leaflets are folded in young stage. Plants are dioecious. Spathes are numerous. Staminate inflorescence is branched to 2 orders having pits with reflexed cincinnus of 30 flowers, 6 stamens, elliptic, sulcate pollen with verrucate, tectate exine, finely reticulate between the warts. Pistillate inflorescence has 0-1 branch and atropous ovule. Fruit is 1-3-seeded with endocarp internally ridged. Seed is bilobed with homogeneous endosperm. Eophyll is undivided. Seven species are recognized, but only 3 or 4 are found in Africa, Madagascar, northeastern Arabia through India and SE Asia to New Guinea and Australia (Kubitzki *et al.*, 1998).

Palmyra palm
(*Borassus flabellifer* L. syn. *B. flabelliformis* Roxb.; toddy palm; wine palm; fan palm)

It is native of tropical Asia. The palm is solitary, unarmed and pleonanthic. The stem is tall, usually unbranched and grows to a height of 20-30 m and attains 60-90 cm diameter having scars of leaves. The stem is topped by a crown of 20-30 large leaves, each having a stout, long (0.9-1.5 m) petiole, and a rachis with lamina. The petiole base is broad having a vertical split and is persistent. It clasps the stem almost half the circumference and is surrounded by a fibrous network of spikelets. Leaf petiole is adaxially grooved with sclerotic serrated margin. Leaf lamina is palmate, 1.0-1.5 m long with 60-80 compound segments. The lamina is plicate with ribs, extending along adaxial folds. The segments are induplicate. Foliar spirals have alternate phyllotaxy.

The palm is dioecious. The palm starts bearing 12-15 years after seed germination. Flowering is seasonal. Inflorescences (spathes) develop from November to March. The inflorescence is interfoliar branched spadix sheathed by many imbricate, fibrous, coriaceous spathes. The male inflorescence appears to be finger-like projection while the female inflorescence looks like a bunch of small dark green fruits. The outermost spathe is the smallest while the innermost spathe is the longest. A palm produces 5-8 spathes annually. Male spadix has 5-10 branches each ensheathed by a spathe. Each branch has 2-3 branchlets or spikes. The spike is stout, 30-40 cm long and 2.5-4.0 cm wide, the width decreasing from base to the apex. The spike is imbricated by numerous bracts that are wedge shaped, cuneate, and retuse and adhere by their lateral margins to the keel or back next one above, to form a cavity enclosing small scorpioid spikelets. There are 800-1000 spikelets per spike each having 15-20 sessile, small florets. Each flower is subtended by a small semi-transparent cuneate bracteole. The flowers in spikelet are arranged in two vertically opposite rows, serrated into each other, each spikelet forming an arch. These are arranged in parallel or nearly straight rows running around the spike. A single spadix may contain 200,000-250,000 florets. The flowers are sessile having 3 imbricate sepals, cuneate with truncate tips, 3 short, ovate and imbricate petals, 6 stamens, filaments connate into a stalk with corolla, large, sessile, oblong and bilocular anthers that split longitudinally. Filaments are dark and dorsifixed.

Female spadix has 2-4 branches or spikes, sheathed by spathes. The upper half of the spike is imbricated by bracts while the lower end is a smooth peduncle. A barren bract ensheaths the spike, from where the flowers rise and the terminal of the spike extending to 5-8 cm beyond the flower is also ensheathed by barren bract. A female spadix has 30-75 flowers. The flower is large, globose having 6-lobed, fleshy, imbricate, reniform and accrescent perianth, 6 staminodes, globose, 3-4 celled ovary, 3-4 syncarpous pistils and 3 sessile and recurved stigma. Ovules are basal and erect.

Flowers bloom throughout the day and most of them open between 8 and 11 AM. Pollination is by insects and wind. It takes 120-130 days for the fertilized flower to mature into a fruit. The fruit is a fleshy drupe weighing 1-3 kg, 12 to 15 cm in diameter, nearly spherical with flat bottom and dark purplish black colour. Six reniform perianth lobes are arranged at the stalk end in two whorls of 3 each. The epicarp is thin, fibrous and brittle. It is creamy when young and turns black or pinkish yellow on maturity. The mesocarp is fleshy and fibrous. The number of nut-like pyrenes within mesocarp is 1-3, each of which contains a seed. The endocarp is hard and covers each seed having a brown testa. The endosperm is gelatinous when the seed is young, filling the interior cavity after 60-70 days of fertilization. The endosperm hardens as the fruit matures forming a cavity at the centre. The embryo is positioned below the germ pore embedded within endosperm. The germ pore is situated at the stigmatic end of the fruit. A large quantity of sugary sap exudes when inflorescence axis is tapped.

A selection, SVPR 1, has been made at Palmyra Research Station, Srivilliputhur, Tamil Nadu in India. It gives annual yield of 140-150 fruits. Its female palm has produced as much as 298 litres of neera in a tapping duration of 90 days.

African fan palm
(***Borassus aethiopum*** C. Mart. syn. ***B. flabellifer*** (Mart.) Warb. var. ***aethiopum****;* ron palm; deleb palm; black rum palm)

It is native of Africa. It is distributed throughout the Savannas of the semi-arid and sub-humid tropics in western Africa from Senegal to Nigeria and in a belt southwards from Sudan to Mozambique and Transvaal (FAO, 1988).

The palm has a crown up to 8 m wide formed by 15-30 fan-shaped leaves. The leaves including the leaf stalk are up to 4 m long. The leaf blade is divided about the middle into numerous linear lanceolate folded segments about 3 cm at the base. The palm is dioecious. The inflorescences bear yellowish flowers. Male flowers are clustered in a branched spadix up to 1.5 m in length. Female flowers are borne on unbranched short spadix. The fruit weighing up to 1 kg is a round ovoid drupe, 15 x 12.5 cm in size, greenish yellow to orange in colour with the base enclosed in 6-7 cup-shaped bracts and contains 3 hard coated seeds surrounded by fibrous deep yellow pulp. Seeds are creamy brown, segment shaped, weighing about 100 g (FAO, 1988; Herzog *et al.,* 1996).

Genus *Cocos* L.

The palms are low or tall solitary trees. The trunk gives a ring appearance and is spineless. No suckers are produced. The leaves are large and palmately veined. The leaf bases tend to adhere. Petiole is unarmed. Leaflet tips are asymmetrical. The palms are monoecious. The male and female flowers are in the same spadix. Inflorescence is branched to 1 order and the peduncular bract is shallowly grooved. The flowers are small in erect spadix. Staminate flowers are sessile, asymmetrical having 3 distinct sepals, 3 distinct petals, 6 stamens, not inflexed filaments, linear, medifixed and latrorse anthers, sulcate or trichotomosulcate, exine tectate and reticulate pollen. Pistillate flower is very large with unlobed staminodal ring. Protandry exists and thus cross pollination takes place. Only one of the carpels develops to give rise to seed. The fruit is a fibrous 1-seeded drupe, not beaked having smooth epicarp, very thick, fibrous mesocarp and endocarp with 3 longitudinal ridges and basal pores. Endosperm is homogeneous and hollow, partially filled with fluid. It constitutes the edible portion and goes through two developmental phases – liquid and meaty. Of the three micropylar eyes on the seed, each representing a carpel, only the largest one has the embryo. Corresponding to the three carpels, there are 3 ridges on the endosperm. Propagation is usually by seeds. Germination is adjacent-ligular and eophyll is entire.

Coconut
(*Cocos nucifera* L.)

It is from western Pacific and is widely cultivated throughout the tropics. The originally considered two centres of origin were South East Asia (Melanesia) and Central and South America (Paull and Duarte, 2012). The trees are typical single-trunked palms. The stem is hard stout and may reach up to 30 m in height, usually 6 to 15 m. The leaves are up to 6 m long, pinnately compound with 200 or more leaflets and borne in a spiral arrangement at the apex of the trunk. The life span of a leaf may be 3 years. Mature palm has up to 30 leaves. Usually a new leaf develops each month while the oldest one drops. The palm is monoecious. Each leaf axis produces an inflorescence. Inflorescence is a compound spadix arising from the leaf axis. The spathe is 1.0-1.5 m long and 15 cm wide at the widest part and has 40 spikelets each having 200-300 male flowers at the top and 1 or more female flowers at the base. The inconspicuous and protandrous flowers are off-white to gray or yellow. Pollination is by insects and wind. About 25-40% female flowers reach maturity. The fruit is a drupe (not a true nut), ovoid in shape, up to 35 cm long and 30 cm in width weighing 1.2 to 2 kg. The exocarp or skin is green, yellow or bronze gold turning to brown and together with mesocarp make up the husk. The mesocarp is composed of fibre called coir. The endocarp or shell is hard. Within the shell is a single seed. The endosperm or meat is the white fleshy edible part and forms copra on drying. The palm cultivars are of two types, dwarf and tall. Their main characteristics are presented in Table 13.1.

Table 13.1. The characteristics of tall and dwarf types of coconut.

Characteristics	**Dwarf type (*Cocos nucifera* var. *nana*)**	**Tall type *C. nucifera* var. *typica*)**
Height	8 m	25 m
Leaf production per year	16-18	About 12
Juvenile period	1.5-3 years	6-8 years
Flowering time	Early	Late
Economic life	30-35 years	60 years
Pollination	Autogamous, Self-pollinate	Allogamous, Outcross
Fruit	Small	Medium to large
Disease resistance	Some resistance to lethal yellowing	Susceptible
Undesirable characters	Periodicity in bearing, Less adaptable, Weaker leaf and bunch attachment, Smaller nuts, Lower copra production, More water	Difficult harvesting due to height
Populations	Green Catigan-Davao Philippines Tacunan-Davao Philippines	Laguna-Philippines Macapuno-Philippines

	Aromatic -Thailand	Tahiti-Tahiti
	Yellow Malayan-Malaysia/Ivory Coast	West African Tall-Ivory Coast
	Red Malayan-Malaysia-Ivory Coast	
	Cameroon-Cameroon, West Africa	Rennel- Solomon Islands
Cultivars	Chowghat Green Dwarf (CGD), Chowghat Orange Dwarf (COD), Ganga Bondam	West Coast Tall, East Coast Tall, Lanka Tall, San Ramon

Leaf is pinnate pinnatisect. Leaf segments are reduplicate having leaf base without split, slender, long and nonspinous petiole. Foliar spirals are 5. Flowering occurs throughout the year. The spadix is interfoliar, short and less branched. Male flower is bigger, often paired, shortly pedicellate having 6 stamens and 6 thin perianth. Male flowers are 8000-10000 in a spadix. Female flower is globose, smaller with 6 accrescent perianths. Pollination is allogamous, autogamous. Fruit matures 11-12 months after pollination. The fruit is an ovoid drupe with thin green epicarp. Mesocarp is fibrous. The drupe has one hard pyrene. The germ pore is at the stalk end of the fruit. The endosperm of the ripe fruit is edible. Endosperm separates from the endocarp on maturity and yields copra. The copra yields valuable oil. The mesocarp is fibrous and yields coir.

As there is no crossing barrier between the tall and dwarf types, natural crossing has resulted in genetically heterozygous forms that widely differ. Most commercial plantings use its own high yielding tall selection in each region, e.g. Ceylon Tall, Indian Tall, Jamaica Tall (syn. Atlantic Tall), Panama Tall (syn. Pacific Tall).

Tall cultivars

West Coast Tall: It is a very popular cultivar grown extensively along the west coast of India. Bearing starts early, 6-8 years after plantation. Nuts are round to oblong, initially green turning yellowish orange to brown at maturity. The palm produces nearly 70-80 nuts/tree/year. Meat or copra is 150-165 g per nut having nearly 70-73% oil content.

Lakshadweep Micro: The cultivar is native of Lakshdweep Island and bears 175-180 nuts/tree/year, which are small in size. The flowers are solitary or clustered. Copra content is nearly 70-75% and oil content is around 75%.

Kappadam: The palms take nearly 10 years to start bearing. Nuts are large and ellipsoid in shape. The palm is shy bearer (60 nuts) but has very high copra content (285 g per nut).

Macapuno: It is grown extensively in Philippines. In some nuts the whole endocarp is full of jelly-like endosperm which is soft and is considered a delicacy. This is a special trait of this cultivar.

Kalpa Dhenu: It commences flowering 67 months after planting. The cultivar has potential to produce 22794 nuts per hectare. The quantity of water is 290 ml per tender nut.

Kalpa Pratibha: The cultivar has potential to produce 23275 nuts per hectare. The quantity of tender nut water is 448 ml per nut.

Kalpa Mitra: The cultivar has potential to produce 80 nuts per palm. The quantity of tender nut water is 495 ml per nut.

Chandra Kalpa: The cultivar can withstand moisture stress and can grow in all types of soils. The annual production is 100 nuts per palm.

Kera Chandra: The annual production is 110 (90-200) nuts per palm.

Dwarf cultivars

Kalpa Raksha: This is a semi-tall cultivar with resistance to diseases like root wilt. It is a tender nut cultivar for wilt affected lands. The plants come to flowering 54 months after planting. The tender nut water is sweet. Per palm yield is 87 nuts (65 nuts in wilt affected land), 16.38 kg copra and 10.65 kg oil. Tender nut gives 290 ml sweet water.

Chowghat Orange Dwarf (COD): This is a early flowering tender nut cultivar. It takes about 3-4 years to come to flowering after planting. Annual yield is 63 nuts per palm.

Kalpa Sree: This is a very early flowering cultivar and comes to flowering 2.5-3 years after planting. The annual yield is 90 nuts per palm with copra yield of 96.3 g. The tender nut water is very sweet and the oil quality is superior.

Dwarf Green: The petioles and nuts are markedly dark green. Trunk is thin. The crown has nearly 20-25 leaves. The palms flower early (3rd year) and each tree produces 110-120 nuts. The nuts are small, oblong and beak-like at distal end. Copra is leather-like giving 90 g per nut and 74% oil.

Dwarf Orange. It is similar to Dwarf Green except that the petioles, spathes and nuts are orange in colour. Trunk is thin, the crown is compact and the leaf blades are narrow. Bearing starts in third year. The nuts are small to medium, spherical and low in oil. Copra is nearly 100 g/nut The nut yield is better than in Dwarf Green.

Ganga Bondam: It is a semi-tall type. Palm starts flowering in fourth year and produces nearly 65-70 nuts per year. The nuts are medium sized. The copra is of high quality with oil content around 70%.

Coconino: It is a dwarf cultivar from Philippines. Flowering commences in 3-4 years. The palm produces about 100 nuts per year. Copra content per nut is high (about 260 g).

Hybrid cultivars

VHC 1 (ECT x Malayan Dwarf Green): It is an early bearer. Its pre-bearing age is 4 years giving 98 (80-145) nuts/palm/year. Copra content is 135 g per nut and oil content is 70%.

VHC 2 (ECT x MYD): It yields 8% more nuts (107 nuts/palm/year) and 11% higher oil content (69%) than VHC1 and as much copra as VHC 1. The buckling of leaves and bunches is negligible with a higher degree of stability.

VHC 3 (ECT x MOD): It yields 156 nuts and 25.2 kg copra per palm with 70% oil content. Copra yield is 162 g per nut as against 146 g in VHC 2.

Godavari Ganga (ECT x GBGD): The cultivar is high yielder giving 140 nuts/palm/year.

Kahikuchi Coconut Hybrid (MYD x WCT): It is a semi-tall hybrid with circular canopy and starts bearing at 64 months age with oval nuts of yellowish green colour.

Konkan Bhatye Coconut hybrid 1 (GBGD x ECT): It is a tall palm with semi-circular canopy bearing at 66 months age with green coloured oval fruits.

Chandra Sankara (COD x WCT): It is a high yielding hybrid giving 116 nuts (100-150) per palm with copra content of 160-230 g and 68% oil in copra. Palms come to flowering earlier than the tall cultivars. It is susceptible to drought and requires irrigation during summer months.

Chandra Laksha (Laccadive Ordinary Tall x Chowghat Orange Dwarf): The palm comes to flowering in about 3-4 years after planting. The palm has high nut, oil and copra yield giving annual yield of 109 nuts and 21 kg copra per palm with 69% oil in copra. It is relatively tolerant to drought.

Kera Sankara (WCT x COD): The palm comes to flowering by the fourth year after planting. The yield is 108 (70-130) nuts and 21 kg copra per palm with copra content of 187 g per nut and 68% oil in copra. Under rainfed conditions, annual yield is106 nuts/palm.

Kalpa Samrudhi (MYD x WCT): It is a tender nut cultivar. The nut yield is 117 per palm. The copra yield is 4.38 tons/ha and oil yield is 3.04 tons/ha.

Kalpa Sankara (CGD x WCT): The cultivar is resistant to root wilt. The nut yield is 85 per palm. The copra yield is 2.5 tons/ha and oil yield is 1.69 tons/ha.

Kalpa Tharu: The annual production is 116 nuts per palm with copra content of 176 g under rainfed conditions.

VPM 3: It yields 72-92 nuts and 15 kg copra per palm. The age duration of palms is 100 years.

ALR (CN) 1: It is a single line selection from Arasampatti Tall. The palms come to bearing in 5 years after planting and continue to bear until 80 years. It is drought tolerant and also tolerates insect pest damage. It is high yielding (7645 nuts giving one ton copra).

Laksha Ganga (Laccadive Ordinary Tall x Gangabondam Green Dwarf): The mean yield is 108 nuts/palm/year, annual per palm copra yield is 21 kg and oil content in copra is 69%.

Kera Ganga (West Coast Tall x Gangabondam Green Dwarf): The average annual yield is 100 nuts/palm, annual copra yield is 20 kg/palm and oil content in copra is 69%.

Anada Ganga (Andaman Ordinary x Gangabondam Green Dwarf): The average annual yield is 95 nuts/palm, annual copra yield is 21 kg/palm and oil content in copra is 68%.

Kera Sree (West Coast Tall x Malayan Yellow Dwarf): The average annual yield is 112 nuts/palm with copra content of 216 g/nuts and 66% oil content in copra.

Kera Sowbhagya (West Coast Tall x Strait Settlement Apricot): The average annual yield is 130 nuts/palm with copra content of 195 g/nuts with 65% oil in copra.

Cultivars have been classified on the basis of characters of the nut (Hunger, 1920):

i. Viridis (green nut)
ii. Rubescence (gray brown nut)
iii. Macrocarpa (very big nut)
iv. Rutila (very thick husk and little endosperm)
v. Euberna (albino/ornamental)
vi. Pumilla (green dwarf early bearing)
vii. Regia (yellow/orange/red, dwarf)

Genus *Phoenix* L.

It originated in Asia and Africa. Twelve species occur in Atlantic islands through Africa, Crete, the Middle East and India to Hong Kong, Taiwan, Philippines, Sumatra and Malaya (Kubitzki *et al.*, 1998). *Phoenix dactylifera* is the most important species.

The palms are solitary or clustered, pleonanthic, dioecious and have erect or inclined stems that are spineless and generally have the scars of fallen dry leaves. Leaves are terminal forming a crown and are induplicate, pinnate having fibrous sheath, single-fold, acute, regularly arranged or grouped leaflets, proximal ones modified as spines (acanthophylls). These are unequally pinnate (pinnatisect). Inflorescences are with interfoliar branching. The spadix has two edges that are laterally compressed. The staminate and pistillate are similar. Peduncular bracts are absent. Flowers are solitary. The flowers are small, yellow or white and unisexual. Staminate flower has connate sepals, 3 valvate petals, usually 6 stamens (rarely 3 or 9), elliptic or circular, sulcate pollen, reticulate, tectate exine. Pistillate flowers are globose having connate sepals, imbricate petals and 6 staminodes. Ovary consists of 3 carpels of which 2 have aborted, distinct, follicular and anatropous ovule. Endosperm is homogeneous with lateral or sub-basal embryo. The seed has deep longitudinal groove on the ventral side. Germination is remote tubular and eophyll is undivided.

Date palm
(*Phoenix dactylifera* L.)

It is a native of the regions around Persia. The palm is subtropical, hardy, evergreen and is very drought resistant having high heat requirement for maturity of fruits. The height of the palm may range from 9 to 30 m. The leaves are 3 to 3.6 m long, pinnately divided and last for 3 to 7 years. The leaf bases are persistent. The leaflets are more pointed forwards. The inflorescence arises from the axil of the previous year's leaf and is about 90 cm in length. It is branched containing 25 to 100 sessile spikes. It contains up to 10000 flowers in one spadix. The pistillate flowers are rounded and triangular. The staminate flowers have 6 stamens and are more showy. Pollination takes place by wind. Hand pollination is practiced. Parthenocarpy is also found but the fruits are smaller and commercially not viable. The phenomenon of metaxenia is observed wherein the pollen of the male parent affects the quality of the fruit with respect to shape, size, colour and the period required for maturity. The fruit is a one seeded berry in which the two ovules have aborted. It is 2.5 cm or more in length and has a thick edible flesh. The seed is acute and pointed at both the ends. The seeds are imperfect.

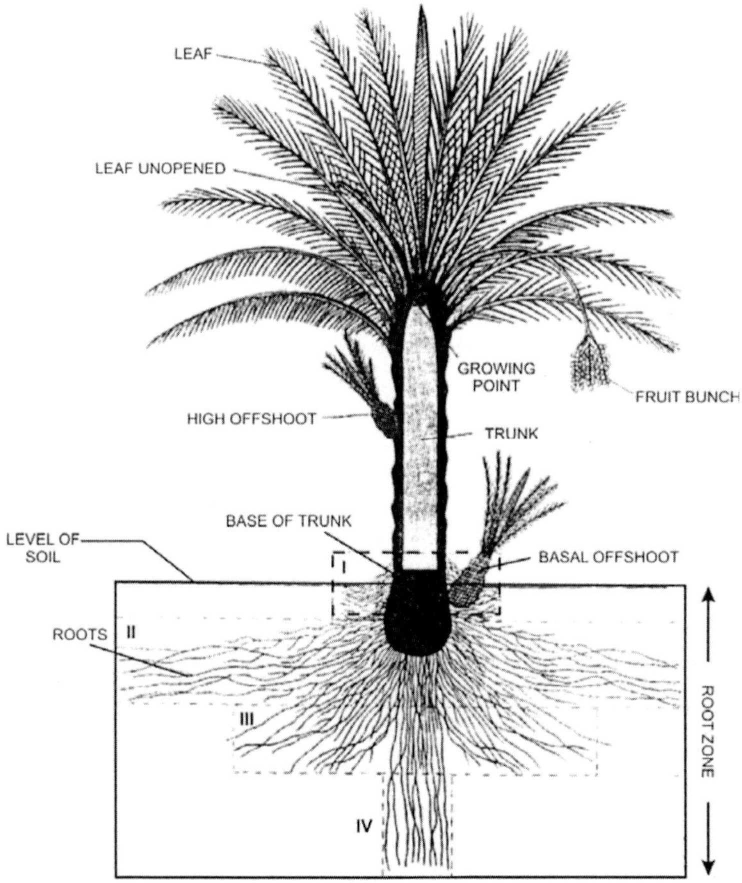

Fig. 13.1. Offshoot attachment in date palm.

Cultivars

Although the number of date cultivars is around 1000, but only a few are cultivated commercially. These can be classified on the following bases:-

I. Nature or kind of sugar:

   i. Invert sugar dates, and

   ii. Cane sugar dates (e.g. Deglet Noor)

II. Texture (consistency of flesh) of fruit at maturity:

i. Soft dates: In these cane sugar is converted to reducing sugar (also called as invert sugar dates) at ripening time, e.g. Halawy, Khadrawy, Shamran, Saidy, Barhee.

ii. Semi-dry dates: These retain much of the sucrose on full ripeness and hence called 'cane sugar' dates. Nearly one third of the total sugar in these dates could be sucrose, e.g. Deglet Noor.

iii. Dry or bread dates (e.g. Thoory)

III. Place of origin:

i. Arabian: These have very high heat requirement and are moderately resistant to rain damage. Most of these belong to invert sugar group and their quality is excellent.

ii. North African: These have high heat requirement and have low resistance to rain damage. These are mostly soft invert sugar dates of good quality.

Halawy: It is an important Iraqi cultivar. The trees are tall and vigorous. It is an early cultivar. The fruits are yellow, extremely sweet (not astringent) at *doka* or khalal (hard ripe) stage of maturity and is one of the most successful cultivars in India. The fruits reach *doka* stage by second fortnight of July in western Rajasthan in India. On ripening to pind or tamar stage, the fruits darken to a deep translucent golden brown colour. The fruit is of small to medium size (7-10 g), oblong elliptic with obtuse apex and almost horizontal base, thin skinned with soft flesh and a distinctive rich flavour. The skin of the fruit adheres to the flesh strongly. Fruit yield at *doka* stage ranges from 70 to 100 kg per palm at Bikaner in India. The TSS of *doka* fruits is 27-43°B and can be eaten or processed.

Khadrawy: It is another cultivar from Basra, Iraq. The growth of palms is very slow and thus mature palms are considerably shorter than those of other cultivars. The fruits reach *doka* stage by the end of July in western Rajasthan. The fruit is of medium size, oblong ovate with broad apex and a bit slanting base. The fruit skin is thin but adheres only moderately to the flesh. The fruit is greenish yellow to yellow at khalal, turning amber at rutab and reddish brown and soft at tamar. The fruits are highly astringent at full *doka* stage when the TSS is about 30°B.

Zahidi or Zahedi: The cultivar originated in northern Iraq. It is a widely grown cultivar in Iraq. The palms are semi-vigorous, fast growing and heavy bearing. The palm has a compact crown. The fruit ripens in mid season and has a distinctive obovate to ovate shape. The fruit is small to medium in size, 7-10 g, with the broader end towards the apex. The fruit surface is smooth and hard and hence resists damage from humidity and rain. The fruits reach *doka* stage by the middle of August in western Rajasthan. These are ovate, yellow and astringent at *doka* stage and have a TSS of about 30°B. Later the softer portions turn light brown and the drier basal portion fades to yellow or straw colour at rutab. The sugary fruit is consumed at tamar stage when the softer portion turns reddish brown and the drier portions light brown. The thick and tough skin adheres to the flesh. It is a mid season and semi-dry date with no special flavour. The seed is large and grayish brown. Average yield of 125 kg *doka* fruits per palm has been obtained in western Rajasthan.

Barhee or Barhi: The palms are robust with semi-vigorous growth and stout trunks and medium height having a good canopy spread but produce fewer offshoots. It is a mid season and soft date of high quality. It reaches *doka* stage by middle of August in western Rajasthan. The fruit skin is thin and lacks tannin and thus has no astringency even at green unripe stage (*gandora*). The fruits are golden yellow at khalal stage having 32°B TSS. These are marketed and consumed as fresh fruit at khalal stage. Average yield per palm is 100 kg *doka* fruits. The fruits are small to medium in size, 3-4 cm (15-20 g) and oval in shape. These turn amber at rutab and reddish brown at tamar.

Deglet Noor or **Deglet Nour** or **Deglet Nur** (meaning "date of the light" in Arabic): It is believed to have originated near Touggourt in the Algerian Sahara during the 17th century. It is commonly produced in Algeria and Tunisia and is popular in European and US markets. Weather requirements limit its production in other areas. It is not considered suitable for growing in the hot and humid Persian Gulf region. It performs the best in a relatively hot and dry environment having light soil underlain by loam or silt. Being a cane sugar and dry or semi-dry type, it is not considered to be a typical representative of North African group. The berry is large, oblong ovate, of very attractive appearance turning light red at khalal, amber brown at rutab and light brown at tamar and has a distinctive quality and delicate flavour. Fruit size is 40-50 x 20-25 mm, with medium thick skin adhering to the 4-5 mm thick flesh, and with a medium brown seed. It is a high yielding cultivar but is susceptible to rain damage and has a tendency to shrivel.

Thoory: It is considered to be the dry or bread type date. The fruits are oblong with a firm and hard flesh.

Medjool: It originated in North Africa and is commercially cultivated in Morocco, Algeria and other countries in that region. In Morocco, bayoud disease in the early 1900 nearly wiped it out. Now its major producers are USA and Israel. The trees are vigorous and tall with erect growth habit. It is a late ripening cultivar. It is a large fruited soft date. The fruits are more firm than those of Barhee and Khadrawy. The irregularities in fruit shape are common and are associated with ridges on the seed. The fruits at *doka* stage are highly astringent. The fruit has orange yellow colour with a fine reddish brown 'stippling' at khalal, ripening to an amber colour turning into reddish brown, and more or less translucent at tamar. In western Rajasthan, *doka* stage reaches in mid August giving average yield per palm of 75 kg *doka* fruits. Its fruits having thick pulp are considered suitable for dehydration to prepare *chhuhara* (khalal matbukh). It has some tolerance to damage from rain and high humidity conditions.

Sewi: The trees are tall, vigorous in growth and erect with moderate canopy. It is a late ripening cultivar. Fruits reach *doka* stage by the first fortnight of August in western Rajasthan. The fruits are oblong in shape and yellowish green in colour and are sweet at *doka* stage and can be eaten as fresh fruit.

Deglet Belda or Daglia Beida or Daqlash Baydahi: It originated in Algeria. The tree is of medium vigour with a medium heavy trunk and is said to be quite salt tolerant. The fruit ripens early in the season. It has a dry type fruit with firm flesh and good flavour. The fruits are medium sized, 3.7-4.5 x 2.0-2.3 cm, oblong or narrowly oblong with moderately thick and relatively smooth skin. These are light pale brown when immature and very light pale brown or buff at maturity and when cured.

Hayany (Hayani): The cultivar is from Egypt. Trees are of medium vigour with a slender trunk and moderately arched leaves and give prolific offshoot production. It is an early ripening cultivar. The fruit is large, 12-20 g, oblong elliptical, 4.5-5.5 x 2.2-2.8 cm, with medium thick skin that is deep red when immature, but almost black at maturity (rutab). The flesh is soft and watery (about 72%) with a mild flavour lacking distinct quality. It produces good yields (110-140 kg/tree).

Khalas: It is an Arabian cultivar. The tree is semi-vigorous in growth and the trunk is medium heavy. The fruit is semi-dry type, 3.0-4.0 x 1.9-2.3 cm, oblong oval, with a thin skin that is yellow when immature, and amber to reddish brown at *pind* stage maturity. The flesh is very tender and melting and has rich and delicate flavour. The cultivar is early to mid season. *Doka* stage reaches during the second fortnight of July in western Rajasthan. The fruits are sweet at *doka* stage and are suitable for raw eating as fresh fruit. Average yield is 75 kg *doka* fruits per tree.

Rhars or Ghars: It originated in Algeria. It is a very early ripening cultivar. The soft type fruit is large, 4.5-5.5 x 2.0-2.4 cm and oblong ovate. The skin is medium thick and medium tough, yellow when immature and amber to reddish brown at maturity. The flesh has rich flavour and is sweet, soft and melting. The fruit has good quality but is susceptible to checking from rain or high humidity. It yields 90-115 kg fruits per tree.

Samany or Samani or Samian (Rashedi): It orginated in Egypt. It is a mid season cultivar. The fruit is soft, very large, 5.0-6.0 x 2.5-3.3 cm and oblong ovate. The skin is thin and tender, yellow when immature and dull amber to brown at maturity. The flesh is soft but is rather coarse with a mildly sweet flavour initially but becoming rather insipid later. Fruit quality is good.

Shamran (Sayer): The trees are semi-vigorous. It is a mid season cultivar. The fruits at *doka* stage are astringent, yellow in colour with slightly pink shaded base, medium in size and oblong in shape with obtuse apex. The average fruit weight is 6.5 g and fruit size of 3.50 x 2.18 cm. It has pulp thickness of 0.56 cm at *doka* stage. The fruits reach *doka* stage (41°B TSS) by the end of July in western Rajasthan. It is a prolific bearer and yields about 100 kg *doka* fruits per palm. It is somewhat tolerant to high humidity.

Khuneizi: The trees are semi-vigorous having spreading growth habit. It is an early ripening cultivar. The fruit is dark red in colour, oval in shape with pointed apex at *doka* stage with crispy and sweet pulp and is thus suitable for raw eating as fresh fruit. *Doka* stage (43°B TSS) reaches by the middle of July in western Rajasthan. At *pind* (tamar) stage, the fruit becomes dark brown. Average yield is 40 kg *doka* fruits per tree.

Zagloul: The trees are vigorous and erect in growth habit. It is a mid season cultivar. The fruits are astringent and red in colour at *doka* stage. These are large in size, oblong oblique and asymmetrical in shape. The calyx is small in size and is slightly depressed at the base. *Doka* stage reaches by the middle of July in western

Rajasthan. The fruit bunches are large. It is a prolific bearer and average yield is 150 kg *doka* fruits per palm.

Bentaisha: Berry is dark red, globular, 2-3 cm, 15-20 g, sweeter in taste than Hayani having a high moisture content (about 89%). It is a less common cultivar than Hayani and is harvested when either red or black (rutab).

Ameri: Berry is reddish yellow, oblong 4-5 cm, 15-23 g having moderate moisture (about 62%) and high fibre content. The fruits are eaten dried.

Date sugar palm
(***Phoenix sylvestris*** Roxb.; wild date palm)

The species is indigenous to India and is widespread throughout India and Pakistan up to an altitude of 1500 m. About 29 million palms are reported to exist in India. It is a close relative of *P. dactylifera* L. Probably *P. dactylifera* might have originated from it. There are no clear-cut distinctive features to separate it from *P. dactylifera*. It is distinguished from *P. dactylifera* by the absence of offshoots or root suckers, smaller leaves, less fleshy and less sweet fruits. It has a stout trunk with rough surface owing to the persistent bases of leaf stalks and the crown is large and hemispherical. The grayish green, glabrous and pinnate leaves are 30 to 60 cm long, in 2-4 rows, having spinous petioles and persistent leaf bases with compressed axis towards the apex, bearing channelled, triangular, 10 cm long spines at their bases. The leaflets tend to be arising at right angles. The numerous, 15-45 cm long, rigid, sword shaped leaflets are covered with a fine bloom. The fruiting peduncle is short (about15 cm or a little longer). Male and female flowers are borne on different palms. The small, white and scented male flowers are borne in a 60-90 cm long and erect spadix. The stalk of the spadix is highly compressed and short. Spathes are leathery and almost woody. The greenish female flowers are present on 30-60 cm long spikes arranged in distinct groups. Fruit cluster is 90 cm long. The fruit is an oblong ellipsoid berry scattered on long and pendulous spikes. It is not longer than 2.5 cm and is terete (cylindrical and tapering towards one end) and has sweet and scanty flesh. The colour of the berry is reddish yellow. The seed is rounded at both the ends.

Jangli khajur
(***Phoenix acaulis*** Buch-Ham. ex Roxb.; Thhal)

It is a pigmy palm found in sub-Himalayan tract, northeastern and peninsular region in hills. It flowers in cold season and fruit ripens in April-May. Drupes are sweet.

Dwarf date palm or hill date palm
(***Phoenix loureiroi*** var. ***pedunculata*** (Griff.) Govaerts
syn. ***P. humilis*** Royle var. ***pedunculata*** Becc.)

It is found growing in hilly green of India (submontainous Kumaon) and also in Indochina, China and Myanmar. The palm contains solitary and clustering plants with trunks of 1–4 m height and 25 cm width, usually covered in old leaf bases. The leaves vary in length but usually reach 2 m with leaflets with wide bases and sharply pointed apices. The leaflets emerge from the rachis at varying angles forming a stiff, plumose leaf. The fruit is produced on erect, yellow inflorescences, usually hidden within the leaf crown. It is a single seeded drupe, sweet and bluish black when ripe. Based on the presence or absence of sclerotic, tannin filled cells along the midribs and margins of leaflets, there are two varieties, *P. loureiroi* var. *loureiroi* and *P. loureiroi* var. *pedunculata* (Griff.) Govaerts syn. *P. loureiroi* var. *humilis* S.C. Barrow.

Palawat
(***Phoenix pusilla*** Gaertn syn. ***Phoenix farinifera*** Roxb.)

Fruit is edible, sweet and mealy of chestnut flavour and used to made sugar and intoxicating drink.

Shelu (***Phoenix robusta*** Hook. f.)

The palm is found growing in Bihar and Deccan Peninsula. Drupes are edible.

False date (***Phoenix atlantica*** A. Chev.)

The palm is found growing in Atlantic part of North Africa. Fruits are edible. Its cultivar Morocan is grown in Morocco.

Canary Island date palm
(***Phoenix canariensis*** Hort. ex. Chabaud)

It is very quick growing and handsome ornamental palm. It does not produce any suckers. It is grown as ornamental palm. Fruits are edible.

Dwarf date palm
(***Phoenix reclinata*** Jacq.; Senegal date palm)

It is found growing throughout the pantropics. Pulp is eaten. Trunk is tapped for sap to prepare wine.

Phoenix rupicola T. Anders.

It is found in Sikkim. Fruit is edible. It is also grown as ornamental palm.

Genus *Euterpe* Mart.

The palms are tall, solitary or clustered. Crowns are usually prominent. Inflorescences are branched to 1 order; peduncle dorsiventrally compressed having peduncular bract and prophyll equal or subequal; rachillae pendulous, hairy. Staminate flowers are paired or single distally having 3 valvate petals, 6 stamens, elliptic, sulcate or sometimes trichotomosulcate pollen with tectate, finely reticulate or foveolate exine and 3-lobed pistillode. Ovule is hemi-anatropous. Stigmatic remains are lateral to subapical. Endosperm is ruminate or homogeneous and embryo is sub-basal. Germination is adjacent ligular and eophyll is bifid or pinnate. Seven species are found in Central through tropical South America extending into Trinidad and the Lesser Antilles (Kubitzki *et al.*, 1998).

Acai palm

(***Euterpe oleracea*** C. Mart.; assai; asai; pina palm; cabbage palm; para palm; palmit; acai-do-para; manicola)

It is native to Amazon region of Brazil and is found growing in Colombia, Ecuador, Venezuela and Brazil. It has been introduced into India, Sri Lanka and Malaysia. The other related species, *Euterpe edulis* C. Mart., is distributed along the southern seacoast of Brazil and *E. precatoria* Mart. occurs on Peruvian-Brazilian-Colombian borders (Martin *et al.*, 1987; Tabora *et al.*, 1993).

Acai is a monoecious, clustered and unarmed feather palm. It grows up to a height of 25 m. The palm is easily recognized by its long (20-30 m), thin and elegant stem having a basal diameter of 15-20 cm. The long pinnate leaves have pendulous segments. The leaves are 2-3 m long, inserted mainly on top of the palm. The inflorescence is a 50-80 cm long panicle bearing yellow, unisexual flowers. The fruit is a small, round, black violet drupe, 12-15 mm in diameter with single seed. The fruits are borne in large cluster (Anderson, 1988; Brücher, 1989; Verheij and Coronel, 1991).

Genus *Attalea* Kunth

The palms are small to massive, solitary, acaulescent or erect. Leaflets are single-fold with irregularly lobed tips. Staminate flowers are asymmetrical, sessile or stalked having 3 distinct, imbricate or briefly connate sepals, (2)3(-5) petals equaling or longer than the sepals. Occasionally basally connate, variously membranous or terete, fleshy, 3-75 stamens, shorter to much longer than petals and varied in shape, straight or spirally twisted, dorsifixed to medifixed anthers, sometimes separate or joined and coiled around each other, latrorse or introrse. Pistillode is inconspicuous or absent. Twenty nine or more species are found in South and Central America and the Caribbean (Kubitzki *et al.*, 1998).

Babassu

(***Attalea speciosa*** C. Mart. ex. Spreng. syn. ***Orbignya phalerata*** Mart., ***O. martiana*** Barb.-Rodr., ***O. speciosa*** (Mart.) Barb.-Rodr.; babacu palm; aguassu)

It is native of southern and eastern fringe of Brazilian Amazonia. It is distributed throughout South America. It grows wild in more than 150,000 km^2 area from the Atlantic Ocean to Bolivia especially in Maranhao, Bahia and northern Minas Gerals and Mato Grosso. The related edible species are *A. cohune* C. Mart. (cohune palm), *A. colenda* (O. F. Cook) Balslev and Ardr. Hend.

It is an erect, smooth, pleonanthic, single stemmed feather palm growing up to 20 m in height. Leaves are elegant, large and pinnate with long, rigid, oblique acuminate having 10-25 leaflets disposed in a vertical plane. The palm is monoecious. The spadix has large racemose and pendant branches, which are rigid, bracted and dense. Female spadix has many sessile flowers on branches with abortive male flowers at the apices. Male spadix has flowers with small calyx, two or rarely three overlapped petals, 24 stamens, aggregate in groups of eight. Female flowers are much larger, ovoid oblong with broadly oblong sepals, slightly smaller, oblong petals with irregularly serrated margins and 3 to 6 stigmas. Fruit is an oblong, conical, pointed drupe with persistent calyx. Epicarp is fibrous, 1-4 mm thick, mesocarp is mealy, dry, 2-12 mm thick and the endocarp is woody, 100-200 g in weight enveloped almost half way and has 3 to 6 seeds. Seeds are ellipsoid in shape, flattened and 2-6 x 1-2 cm in size (FAO, 1986; Clay and Clement, 1993; Wickens, 1995).

Cultivars

There is plenty of scope to develop cultivable types using the rich variability occurring in Brazil. Search for genotypes having precocity and high kernel content besides the ability to grow on poor soils and degraded pastures in areas considered too dry for African palm, peach palm, tucumas is required for future development (FAO, 1986).

Genus *Mauritia* L.f.

The palms are massive, solitary and unarmed. Staminate rachilla is catkin-like, bearing crowded, spirally inserted bracts, each subtending a pair of flowers and each with a bracteole. Pistillate rachilla is very short, not catkin-like bearing solitary pistillate flowers. Staminate flowers have tubular, 3-lobed calyx, 3 elongated petals, free filaments, elongate and latrorse anthers, sulcate or monoporate pollen with intectate exine with spines and minute pistillode. Pistillate flowers are larger than the staminate. Fruit is rounded and large. Seed has a blunt beak and basal embryo. Eophyll is with 2 divergent leaflets. Two species are found in wetter parts of tropical South America (Kubitzki *et al.*, 1998).

Buriti palm
(***Mauritia flexuosa*** L. f. syn. ***M. vinifera*** C. Mart.; moriche palm; muriti; miriti palm)

It is native of northeastern South America. It is found growing in the Amazon basin, Venezuela, Colombia, Peru, Bolivia, Brazil and Guiana. It is one of the most majestic trees of the Amazon basin.

It is a massive, solitary, unarmed, pleonanthic, dioecious fan palm and grows up to 20-30 m in height with a thick trunk of 30-60 cm diameter. The crown consists of 15 to 20 feathery, reduplicately palmate, fan-shaped open leaves. The 3 m long leaves are so heavy that two persons are needed to carry a leaf. These fall to the ground as they age. The inflorescences are large (2 m long) and pendant. Male catkins are 6 cm long, bearing spirally arranged pairs of small flowers. Female catkin is very short, 1 cm long, bearing 1 or 2 flowers. Five to eight fruit bunches, at various stages of maturity, can be found on a tree. The fruits are globose or spherical (5-6 cm diameter) covered with rhomboidal, shiny brown scales. The mesocarp is thin and is composed of a cap of sponge-like orange pulp around the large and hard seed. The seed is rather easy to crack (FAO, 1986; Brücher, 1989; Wickens, 1995).

Genus *Oenocarpus* Mart. or *Jessenia* Burret

The palms are solitary or clustered. Crownshafts are partial. Inflorescences, becoming infrafoliar, are branched to 1 order laterally and abaxially (hippuriform). Adaxial branches are absent, rarely bifurcate or spicate. Peduncle is flattened with peduncular bract longer than prophyll. Staminate flowers are paired or single distally having 3 valvate petals, 6 (7-20) stamens, elliptic and sulcate pollen having tectate, scabrate or reticulate exine. Pistillode is bifid or trifid. Stigmatic remains are apical to eccentric. Endosperm is homogeneous and embryo is very large. Germination is adjacent ligular and eophyll is bifid. Nine species are found in the region from Costa Rica and Panama to the Amazon and Orinoco Valleys in South America (Kubitzki *et al*., 1998).

Pataua

(***Oenocarpus bataua*** Martius syn. ***Jessenia bataua*** (Mart.) Burret.; ***J. polycarpa*** Karst.; Seje, Mil Peros; Jagua; Ungurahui)

It is a native of tropical South America and is distributed in Colombia, Venezuela, Guyana, Surinam, French Guiana, Ecuador, Peru and Brazil. It is found growing in tropical rain forest and also in inland forest up to 1000 m altitude. The palm needs to be domesticated and commercially exploited (FAO, 1986). The related species *O. bacaba* has very small seeded and thick fleshed parthenocarpic fruits and *O. multicaulis* has faster growth and precocity (FAO, 1986; Wickens, 1998).

The plant grows as a solitary, unarmed, pleonanthic feather palm with a diameter of 25-45 cm and has spineless trunk. Leaves are pinnate, 6-8 m long with 4-6 m long rachis. Leaflets are alternate, lanceolate, acute and 40 to 75 mm wide. The palm is monoecious. Spathe is 1 m long and woody. The cream coloured flowers are borne in triads, one inner pistillate and two outer staminate, on the proximal 1/3-1/4 of the rachillae, distal to which are found only staminate flowers and rachillae attenuate towards the apex. Staminate flowers are 5-6 mm long having 3 sepals, 3 petals and 8-16 stamens and owl shaped filaments. Pistillate flowers have three imbricated sepals and petals and no stamens. Panicles may contain 1000 fruits each weighing 10-15 g. The fruit is an ovoid to ellipsoid drupe, 2.5 to 4 cm long, deep purple when ripe with ruminate endosperm (Brücher, 1989). Two types are known, one with whitish mesocarp and the other having purplish or pinkish mesocarp. A variant with reddish inner skin tissue has also been recognized. A field gene bank has been established at EMBRAPA, Belem, Brazil.

Genus *Bactris* Jacq. ex Scolopi

The palms are solitary or caespitose, acaulescent to erect. Lamina is undivided or leaflets are single or multifold and tips are acute, rarely praemorse, concolorous or discolorous. Inflorescence is protogynous, spicate or branching to 1 order, peduncular bract is persistent or disintegrating having rachillae bearing triads throughout or basally with staminate flowers distally or few triads scattered among staminate flowers. Stamens are 6 (-12) and distinct, anthers are dorsifixed, pollen is sulcate or trichotomosulcate having tectate exine. In pistillate flowers, sepals and petals are connate with 6-toothed and free staminodal ring. Fruit is 1-seeded having smooth or spiny epicarp with equatorial pores and lateral embryo. Eophyll is bifid. Sixty four species recognized by Henderson *et al.* (1995) are distributed in the region from Central to South America and the Antilles (Kubitzki *et al.*, 1998).

Pejibaye

(***Bactris gasipaes*** Kunth syn. ***Guilielma gasipaes*** (HBK) L. H. Bailey, ***Gasipaes chantadura*** Triana., ***G. microcarpa*** Hub., ***G. utilis*** Oersted. ***G. macana*** Mart. and ***G. ciliata*** (R. and P.) Wendl.; peach palm)

It is native of Amazonia, Peru. Pejibaye may have originated from wild relatives, possibly as hybrid, in the south west portion of Amazon Basin and has been widely dispersed by humans in South and Central America (Clement, 1988, 1989b; Mora-Urpi, 1996). It probably evolved from pupunha (*Bactris microcarpa)* of eastern Peru. The pejibaye grows in virgin forests in Peru and Ecuador on slopes too steep for agriculture. It is rarely cultivated outside the central and northern South America and the West Indies. The related edible species are *B. maraja* Mart., *B. guineensis* H. E. Moore and *B. major* Jacquin.

Pejibaye palm is a tropical species and requires hot and wet tropical lands. The palm grows well up to 700 m altitude and is occasionally found even at 1,500 m elevation. For its optimum growth, temperature of 18-24°C and an evenly distributed annual rainfall of 3000 to 4000 mm are required. Drought is deleterious as most of the roots are produced near the soil surface.

Peach palm is a multistemmed, unarmed, pleonanthic and monoecious feather palm. It develops a straight, slender, 13 m tall stem after 10-15 or more years. The circular leaf sheath is normally covered with black spines. A new leaf (frond) is formed after every 2-4 weeks depending on the vigour of the palm. Fronds are 2.4-3.6 m long and spirally arranged around the trunk with a phyllotaxy of 110°. The leaflets (pinnae) are linear lanceolate with a bristly or prickly margin. The petiole normally has short and firm spines in 3 longitudinal strips on its lower surface, especially near the basal attachment. Typically, there are 10-13 fronds per palm. Suckers emerge during the first 5 years. Old palms may also produce suckers from the stump after felling. Usually about 8 offshoots are produced on a palm with a maximum of 18 of which 2-4 are normally allowed to develop.

The inflorescences develop in the leaf axils of older fronds or very occasionally above the leaf scars just below the crown. The inflorescence is about 50 cm long with a central stalk (rachis) to which branchlets (rachillae) are attached. The small, sessile, cream coloured flowers are borne on the rachillae with female flowers scattered between the more abundant male flowers. They have an annular and leathery calyx, a small, round, 3-toothed corolla and a trilocular ovary with 3 sessile stigmas. Male flowers are light cream yellow, 2-6 mm in length and width with six stamens arranged in pairs on the side of corolla. Female flowers are irregularly arranged among male flowers. Female flowers are usually yellow or rarely green, 3-13 mm long and 4-12 mm wide. The gynoecium is syncarpous and trilocular. The male flowers normally drop within 24 hours of releasing the pollen. Pollination is carried out by small weevils. The bunch of 50-100 fruits weighs 10-15 kg. The fruit is a cylindrical drupe, 2-6 cm in diameter, usually of orange colour but may be green, yellow, orange red to brown. Average weight of fruit varies from 29 to 100 g. The base of the fruit is nearly covered by the green leathery calyx. The fruit pulp is edible when cooked. The nut is conical, about 2 cm long and has a 1-2 mm thick, hard and black shell enclosing a white kernel. Average weight of the nut is around 3 g. The seed kernels may have oil rich endosperm. Seedless fruits (pejibaye macho) are produced in some palms (FAO, 1986, IBPGR, 1986, Morton, 1987, Brücher. 1989; Verheij and Coronel, 1991).

Cultivars

Since pejibaye has been in cultivation for more than 500 years, numerous cultivars exist particularly in Costa Rica but have not been described. These have variations in pericarp colour, fruit size, flesh thickness and texture. Mora-Urpi (1984) divided the known landraces into two subcomplexes: the occidental group including the landraces found north and west of the Andes Mountains and the oriental group including landraces from the Amazon and Orinoco Basins. Landraces of the occidental group have stouter and harder stems, more and stronger spines, larger leaves and better anchorage in the soil when young compared with those of the oriental group. The oriental and occidental subcomplexes are further divided on the basis of fruit size into microcarpa, mesocarpa and macrocarpa landraces. Macrocarpa landraces have larger fruit size (Mora-Urpi *et al.,* 1997). Seedlessness and spinlessness are partly heritable. It can hybridize with other *Bactris* species (Morton, 1987).

Genus *Salacca* Reinw

The palms are acaulescent, caespitose, pleonanthic. Leaves are pinnate or entire bifid having single-fold except for compound terminal segments, concolorous or discolorous, entire and acuminate leaflets. Inflorescences are axillary, emerging from a cleft in abaxial surface of subtending petiole, spicate or branched to 1 or 2 orders and catkin-like rachillae. Staminate flowers are paired having 6 epipetalous stamens, short, introrse anthers, elliptic, meridionosulcate pollen with tectate, perforate exine and supratectal spinules. Pistillate flower is larger than the staminate. Fruit is irregular, epicarp scales are smooth or with recurved spine-like tips, homogeneous endosperm and basal embryo and bifid eophyll. About 20 species are found from Burma and China to Borneo and Java and several of these are cultivated for their fruit (Kubitzki *et al*., 1998).

Rakum palm
(*Salacca wallichiana* C. Martius; sala)

It is native of the lowlands of southern Myanmar, peninsular Malaysia and the coastal provinces in Thailand from Bangkok eastwards. In Thailand, it grows wild and is cultivated in hot and humid areas (Verheij and Coronel, 1991).

It is a creeping and tillering palm, growing in clumps with very spiny leaves. The creeping stem can reach 3-4 m height with an erect terminal, 1 m tall leaf bearing part and many adventitious roots. The leaves are 3-7 m long, pinnate, bearing flat spines almost perpendicular to the leaf sheaths. Leaflets are 60-75 x 6-8 cm in size. The palm is dioecious. Male inflorescences are about 1 m long, branching into many reddish spadices. The flower has 3 sepals, 3 petals and 5 stamens with anthers containing yellowish functional pollen. Female inflorescences are 1-2 m long with 3-8 reddish spadices each having staminate and hermaphrodite flowers in 1:1 ratio, both without functional pollen. Staminate flowers have a reddish, tubular corolla and 5 staminodes borne on the corolla throat. Hermaphrodite flower has 3 pink sepals fused at the base, trilocular hairy ovary with a short, trifid, dark red stigma and 5-6 staminodes borne on the corolla throat. Fruit is an obovoid, 2.5 cm long drupe occurring in dense heads. The fruit skin (epicarp) consists of orange brown scales with reflexed, brittle points and the endocarp is not differentiated. Seeds are 1-3, covered with a fleshy sarcotesta (Verheij and Coronel, 1991).

Cultivars

The important cultivars are Sala Mor, Sala Sane, Sala Noenwong and the spineless Sakum. Sala Mor and Sala Sane originated from rakum palm grown near Bangkok.

Salak palm

(***Salacca zalacca*** (Gaertner) Voss syn. ***S. edulis*** Reinw.; salak; snake fruit) (2n=28)

It is native of South East Asia. It grows wild in southwestern Java and southern Sumatra but its place of origin is not known. It is found growing as under-storey palm in tropical rain forest. It is cultivated throughout Malaysia and Indonesia as far as the Moluccas and has been introduced into New Guinea, the Philippines, Ponapa Island and is also reported to occur in the Fiji Islands (Martin *et al.*, 1987; Verheij and Coronel, 1991).

The palm is relatively small, compact, very spiny, creeping and tillering, growing in compact clumps resulting from successive branching at the base. Roots are not deep. The leaves are pinnate having 3-7 m long leaf sheaths. Petioles and leaflets are armed with numerous, long, thin, gray to blackish spines. Leaflets are 20-70 x 2-7.5 cm in size. The palm is dioecious. Inflorescence is an axillary compound spadix, stalked and enclosed by spathes. Male inflorescence is 50-100 cm long, consisting of 4-12 spadices, each of 7-15 x 0.72 cm size. The female inflorescence is 20-30 cm long, composed of 1-3 spadices, each 7-10 cm long. The flowers emerge in pairs in the axils of scales. The staminate flower has reddish, tubular corolla and 6 stamens borne on the corolla throat besides a minute pistillode. The pistillate flower has tubular corolla, which is yellow green outside and dark red inside, a trilocular ovary with a short trifid red style and 6 staminodes borne on the corolla throat. Each spadix has 15-40 fruits, which are globose to ellipsoid, 5-7 x 5 cm in size, tapering towards base and rounded at the top. The epicarp comprises numerous yellow to brown, united, imbricate scales, each ending in a fragile prickle. Usually, there are 3 seeds per fruit, with 2-8 mm thick, fleshy, cream coloured sarcotesta and a smooth, stony inner part of 23-29 x 15-27 mm size, which are blackish brown and trigonous having two flat and one curved surface. Endosperm is homogenous and white (Verheij and Coronel, 1991).

Cultivars

The salak palm grown in northern Sumatra is a distinct species, *S. sumatrana* Becc. *S. zalacca*, cultivated in Indonesia, has two botanical varieties, *zalacca* from Java and *amboinensis* (Becc.) Mogea from Bali and Ambon. In Indonesia, at least 20 types are distinguished according to their place of origin and cultivation, e.g. Condet, Pondoh, Bali and Suwaru, which may develop into distinct cultivars in due course (Verheij and Coronel, 1991).

Genus *Arenga* Labill.

The palms are dwarf to large, solitary or clustered, acropetally pleonanthic or basipetally hapaxanthic, monoecious or dioecious. Leaves are pinnate having usually discolorous leaflets. Inflorescences are bisexual or unisexual, sometimes multiple, spicate or branched to 1-2 orders. Staminate flower has 3 imbricate, distinct or briefly connate sepals, valvate corolla, 6, 9-numerous stamens, elongated latrorse anthers, sulcate pollen with intectate spiny exine. Pistillate flower is globose having 3 distinct, imbricate sepals, 3 basally connate, valvate petals and 3 or no staminodes. Fruit is 1-3-seeded having homogeneous endosperm, lateral embryo, flabellate or bifid eophyll. About 17 species are found in the region from India to South China, Ryukyus and Taiwan, through SE Asia, Malesia including Christmas Islands (Indian Ocean) to north Australia, the greatest diversity occurring on the Sunda Shelf (Kubitzki *et al.*, 1998).

Sugar palm

(***Arenga pinnata*** (Wurmb.) Merr., syn. ***A. saccharifera*** Labill. ex DC.; areng palm)

It is thought to be indigenous to South East Asia where its occurrence is the most common. It is also known as ejow, kaong, black sugar palm, gomuti and toddy palm. It is distributed throughout South and South East Asia.

It is a moderate to tall, unbranched, pleonanthic and solitary feather palm without root suckers. The roots are black, very strong, extending more than 10 m from the trunk and going as deep as 3 m. The trunk is 10-20 m high and 30-65 cm in diameter covered by bases of broken leaves and long black gray fibres. Its crown is dense having 12-20 erect to spreading leaves that are 6-10 m long and pinnate with 1-1.5 m long petioles and sheaths at the base. The leaflets are 80-130, strap-like, 140-180 x 8-11 cm in size, crowded along the rachis and held in several planes with auricles at base. The palm is monoecious. The inflorescences are usually unisexual, pendulous, often more than 2 m long arising from leaf axils and peduncle breaking up into a number of flower bearing spikes. Female inflorescences are 3-7, formed at the top and male ones are 7-15 appearing later on the lower portion of the stem. The flower has 3 coriaceous sepals and a tubular, 3-lobed corolla. The number of male flowers is up to 11500 per inflorescence with many stamens that are greenish to bronze when still closed and yellowish when open. Female flowers are up to 15000 per inflorescence and have globose trilocular ovary. The fruit is globular, 5-8 cm long, fleshy, turning from green to yellow and black after falling and contain 2-3 black seeds (FAO, 1984).

Genus *Astrocaryum* G.F.W. Meyer

The palms are acaulescent to erect, solitary or clustered. Leaflets are single-fold having acute or bifid tips. Inflorescence is protandrous, branching to 1 order with persistent peduncular bract rachillae and with or without basal bare portion and 1 to several triads, distally bearing spirals of solitary staminate flowers in pits. Stamens are 3-12 with dorsifixed rectangular, latrorse anthers, sulcate or trichotomosulcate pollen and tectate exine. Pistillate flowers have free sepals, connate petals, 6-toothed staminodal ring, free or briefly adnate to petals with sterile anthers. Fruit is 1(-2) seeded having smooth or bristly epicarp, thick endocarp, subterminal pores, hollow endosperm and subterminal embryo. Eighteen or more species are found from Caribbean and Mexico southwards to Argentina (Kubitzki *et al*., 1998).

Tucuma
(*Astrocaryum aculeatum* G. F. W. Meyer; star nut palm)

It is native of Amazonia. The other related species are *A. jauari* Mart., *A. murumuru* Mart., *A. vulgare* Mart. and *A. auri* Mart. (FAO, 1986). It has spread throughout the whole of Amazonia, Guyana, Peru and Colombia. The plants are abundant especially in disturbed areas (Leaky and Newton, 1994). The species is important as a source of fruit and fibre from the leaf epidermis. It is exceptionally tolerant to poor degraded soils and can withstand drought periods for a few months. It requires tropical climatic conditions and is grown in areas receiving over 1600 mm annual rainfall (FAO, 1986; Brücher, 1989).

Tucuma is a tall, single stemmed, pleonanthic feather palm growing up to 20 m. The younger part of the stem is armed with whorls of black and 1-10 cm long spines. The leaves are usually 10-15 in the crown, reduplicately pinnate and 4-5 m long having 100 pairs of leaflets grouped and held in different planes that are linear, 60-100 x 3-4 cm in size, dark green on upper surface. The palm is monoecious. Inflorescence is 2 m long bearing 200-300, 30-40 cm long rachillae. The rachillae bear 1-5 female flowers in the basal 10 cm and densely packed male flowers along the remaining length. Male flower is 4 mm long with cream coloured sepals and petals and 6 stamens with purple filaments and white anthers. Female flower is cream coloured, 15 mm long. The fruit is usually 1-seeded, globose or broadly ellipsoid, 4-6 cm long, 3-5 cm in diameter, green in colour turning yellow brown, often 200-400, even up to 700, in the infructescence, 70 to 90 g in weight and hard having smooth epicarp, 2-5 mm thick, fibrous, oily and orange yellow mesocarp, very hard, woody, black, 2-3 mm thick endocarp with star-like pores, homogenous endosperm with a central hallow filled with fluid (FAO, 1986; Brücher, 1989).

Cultivars

No standard cultivar is available. There is lot of variability available with regard to fruit size, weight, quality, pulp thickness and yield. Selections should aim at oily types with thicker pulp, longer harvest period, faster growth and precocity. There is also need to select better types having spineless stem, sweet nutty flavour, medium oil and low fibre contents and thick pulp (FAO, 1986; Brücher, 1989).

Genus *Hyphaene* J. Gaertn

The palm stems are dichotomously branched, rarely unbranched. Leaves are costapalmate having spiny petioles. Stigma is pyramidal with 3 glandular angles. Pericarp is with numerous irregular scales. Mesocarp is corky and fibrous at maturity, endocarp developing from a layer external to the dark brown to blackish and thick locule wall with 3 + 3 or 3 + 3 +6 flanges penetrating the fruit cavity, forming symmetrical, incomplete partitions. Germination is remote.

The single genus has no obvious close relative. The dyad of a hermaphroditic and a staminate flower is found elsewhere only in *Metroxylon* but there is almost nothing to link the two genera. *Eugeissona* is regarded to have arisen probably early in the differentiation of the Calamoideae. The flowers are among the largest among the palms (Kubitzki *et al.*, 1998).

Doum palm
(***Hyphaene thebaica*** (L.) Mart.; ginger bread palm)

It is native of northern and western Africa and is found growing in dense stands along the rivers in hot and dry valleys of tropical Africa, in the Middle East and in western India. It is very common in the coastal regions of East Africa and Eritrea. The related edible species are *H. coriacea* Gaertn., *H. compressa* Wendl. and *H. petersiana* Mart. These species are found growing in East Africa (FAO, 1988).

The palm is pleonanthic, 10 m tall and dichotomously branched, 1 or 2 or more times. The leaves are large, flabellate with linear lanceolate lobes and numerous upward curved hooks on the petioles. The palm is monoecious. Pointed bracts surround the male spadices. Branches of female spadix are stouter. Flowers are small and whitish. Fruits are yellowish brown, globose, 5 x 5 cm in size with a strong fibre surrounding the hard seeds (FAO, 1988; Duke, 1989).

Chapter 14

ZINGIBERALES (CANNALES)

The plants are large herbs with rhizomes and fibrous roots, pseudostem often very short, formed by spirally arranged imbricate leaf sheaths. The sheaths are open or rarely closed. If woody, the leaves are never compound. The vessels are more or less limited to the roots. Silica cells are present in the bundle sheaths. Leaves are clearly differentiated into a petiole and blade with pinnate venation, often tearing between the secondary veins, with blade rolled into a tube in bud, and the petiole and midvein with enlarged air canals. The inflorescence is central. The flowers are normally bisexual and irregular/monosymmetric. Perianth is corolla-like. Calyx and corolla are in separate whorls. Carpels are fused. Septal nectaries are present. Androecium is often strongly modified/reduced. Number of stamens is 5-6 or reduced to one and the remaining transformed into petaloid staminodes. Pollen usually lack exine. Ovary is inferior. Fruit is capsule or fleshy and indehiscent. Seeds are arillate and endospermic. The endosperm is mealy, horny or fleshy or cotyledonous. The tissues contain silicic acid.

The order contains 8 families including many familiar plants like ginger, cardamom and turmeric of Zingiberaceae, banana and plantain of Musaceae and the arrowroot of Marantaceae. The other members are Cannaceae, Strelitziaceae and Lowiaceae. Strelitziaceae has often been combined with Musaceae as a single family and Lane (1955) considered this as the best treatment. On anatomical grounds, Tomlinson (1959) suggested the natural groupings *Musa-Ensete*, *Ravenala-Strelitzia* and *Heliconia.* Tomlinson (1962) gave a general discussion of the phylogeny of the group. Relationships seem to be reticulate and thus family limits will probably be rather arbitrary. One view is represented in the following key:

Androecium not petaloid, stamens 5-6

Leaves and bracts spirally arranged; male and female (or hermaphrodite) flowers separated within one inflorescence; fruit is a many-seeded berry - Musaceae (2 genera–*Musa, Ensete*)

Leaves and bracts distichous, the latter occur spiral by twisting; flowers hermaphrodite, fruit is a capsule or, if fleshy, only 1-3 seeded

Main veins parallel. Transverse venation absent or inconspicuous; sepals not united into a long tube, median petal not markedly larger than the laterals -Strelitziaceae (genera - *Strelitzia, Ravenala, Phenakospermum)*

Main veins parallel, joined by conspicuous transverse minor veins; sepals united into a long tube; median petal conspicuously enlarged into a coloured labellum -Lowiaceae (genus-*Orchidantha*)

Androecium petaloid, stamen solitary

Aromatic plants with ligulate leaves, spirally or distichously arranged; stamen 2-celled -Zingiberaceae (45 genera, *Zingiber, Costus, Curcuma, Alpinia, Hedychium*)

Plants not aromatic; leaves not ligulate, always distichous. stamen 1-celled, i.e. it is a half-stamen, borne on the edge a petaloid segment

Leaves pulvinate, flowers rarely (? never) large, showy and red; ovules solitary in each cell -Marantaceae (25 genera, *Maranta, Calathea*)

Leaves not pulvinate; flowers large and showy, often red; ovules numerous in each cell -Cannaceae (genus-*Canna*)

Family Musaceae (banana family)

It contains two genera *Ensete and Musa* and 40 species. The plants are large to gigantic monocarpic or suckering perennial tropical herbs with pseudostems formed by overlapping sheaths of very large, simple, entire leaves and huge pendant, bracteate inflorescences. These are sometimes partially woody. *Musa* has lacticifers sprouting from the rhizome, whereas *Ensete* lacks lacticifers. It is unbranched and monocarpic. The above ground growth forms a rhizome or a bulbous base. The very large leaves are spirally arranged, entire, pinnately veined and sheathing with distinct petiole having a thick midrib with an axile placenta. The petioles are almost entirely free or clasping (concentric) to form a pseudostem as in banana. The plants are monoecious. The flowers are borne in axils of large, often coloured bracts, on large spikes; irregular perfect or unisexual. Male flowers are in upper and female flowers in lower bracts. Perianth is usually differentiated. The petals are 3 or less, free or united. Stamens are 6, one is usually a staminode. The ovary is inferior, 3-celled and ovules are usually numerous and axillary, sometimes also solitary and basal. The style is filiform and often expanded at the apex. The stigma is often 3-lobed. The fruit is a fleshy berry containing numerous stony seeds and finally form compact infructescences. The seeds are minute having copious starchy endosperm and straight embryo (Heywood *et al*., 2007).

Genus *Musa* L. (x = 7, 9, 10, 11; 2n=22, 33, 44)

The genus name *Musa* is thought to be derived from the Arabic name for the plant (*mouz*) which, in turn, may have been applied in honour of Antonius Musa (63–14 BC), physician to Octavius Augustus, first emperor of Rome (Hyam and Pankhurst, 1995). There are inconsistencies in the number of sections and number of species proposed for inclusion in the genus *Musa.* This has largely been brought about by the domestication of the fruit bearing cultivars and the subsequent temporal and genetic separation from the original species, as well as the widespread vegetative reproduction in the genus and natural occurrence of many hybrids (Heslop-Harrison and Schwarzacher, 2007). The number of sections within *Musa* is between 3 and 5 and the number of species is between 35 and 50 (Constantine and Rossel, 2001). According to Häkkinen and De Langhe (2001), the genus contains 70 species and all the wild species are diploids (2n = 2x = 14, 18, 20, 22) and native to South East Asia and occur from the Himalayas and South China to North Australia and the Philippines and further east into the Pacific (Pemba, Samoa and Hawaii) supposed to be as a result of introductions.

It is a tropical genus of tree-like suckering herbs that are bulbous or with perennial rhizomes, often growing in dense clumps with leaf-opposed lateral buds. The roots are in two sets – one extends horizontally in the top 60 cm soil while the other set goes down vertically up to 180 cm deep. The main roots are uniform in thickness and bear several small roots. The leaves are very large, entire, oblong elliptic, smooth and glabrous with a waxy coat and a gray or glaucous covering on lower surface. Stomates are also on the upper surface. The leaves have reddish edges. Tepal lamina is 5-toothed and not deeply divided. Flowers are borne in terminal spikes that are usually hanging down. In some species, these are erect, but these are few and not edible. The flower emerges from the pseudostem. The lower clusters are of pistillate flowers and the upper are staminate and neutral. The flowers are borne in the axils of bracts in two rows each. Flowers and bracts are separately inserted on the axis. Bracts are caducous. The calyx is tubular, splitting on one side and has 3-5 teeth. The corolla consists of one petal that is simple or sometimes three lobed. Flowers of proximal cymes are usually functionally female. Stamens are 6 of which 1 is a staminode. Pollination is not required in edible cultivars as the fruits develop from non-stimulated parthenocarpy. The inflorescence develops into a bunch. Occasionally there are 2 bunches per shoot. The bunch carries many hangs (the fingers in two rows between a bract). There are 6-12 hangs in a bunch. The finger is an individual fruit. The fruit is a berry. Carpellary wall (wall of the ovary) constitutes the fleshy edible portion of the fruit. Seeds are numerous and small. Triploidy is common but it is not necessary for seedlessness of fruits.

In 1887, the French botanist Paul Sagot published an article in which he subdivided the genus into three unnamed sections: i) the edible bananas, ii) the ornamental bananas with upright inflorescences and brightly coloured bracts, and iii) the giant *Ensete* species, which was later given as a genus. Baker (1893) gave the first classification of the genus *Musa* and divided the genus into 3 subgenera:

i. Physocaulis– It is native of Africa (Abyssinia). Chromosome number is 2n=18. The stem bark is bottle shaped. No stolons are produced. The leaves are large (540 x 90 cm). The midrib is red. Inflorescence is globose. The petals are 3-lobed (tricuspidate). The fruit is dry and leathery and is not edible. It contains the species *Musa superba*.

ii. Rhodochlamys– the flowers are fused to a bract. The bracts are light coloured. Petals are linear. The fruit is not edible.

iii. Eumusa– It contains the edible species.

The classification was revised by Cheesman (1947). He gave emphasis on chromosome number, pseudostem stature, inflorescence characters and seed characters in his classification and did not take into account the edibility of the fruit. Thus he removed Physocaulis (chromosome number 2n=18) from genus *Musa* and put it under a separate genus *Ensete* having 7-8 species including *E. superba* distributed from West Africa to New Guinea. The genus differs from *Musa* by being monocarpic, non-suckering with a distinctively swollen base and large sized smooth seeds. It is used for fibre and vegetable. He divided the genus *Musa* into two groups (A and B) each with two sections (series) and thus recognized four sections mainly based on basic chromosome numbers and orientation and arrangement of flowers in the inflorescence. The members are of both seeded and parthenocarpic types.

Group A – Chromosome number 2n=22 or 33 (x=11). The bracts are imbricate in bud stage. These are glaucous and convolute. The group has 2 sections:

1. Section *Eumusa (*x=11): The plants are robust with pseudostem over 3 m in height. The inflorescence is pendant or semi-pendant having dull and waxy bracts. The flowers are many to a bract and are found in two rows. The fruit is reflexed (bent) and is never orange red. The seeds are compressed. It is predominantly used as fruit and vegetable and also for fibre and as ornamental. The section has 13-15 species distributed from South India to Japan and Samoa (Stover and Simmonds, 1987). Häkkinen and Wallace (2011) have described following 15 species:

i. *Musa accuminata* Colla (Colla, 1820; Cheesman, 1948; Simmonds, 1956; Häkkinen and De Langhe, 2001)

ii. *M. balbisiana* Colla (Colla, 1820; Cheesman, 1948; Simmonds, 1956; Argent, 1976)

iii. *M. banksii* F.Muell. (Mueller, 1864)

iv. *M. basjoo* Iinuma (Iinuma, 1874)

v. *M. celebica* Warb. (Warburg, 1900)

vi. *M. cheesmanii* N.W. Simmonds (Simmonds, 1956)

vii. *M. griersonii* Noltie (Noltie, 1994)

viii. *M. itinerans* Cheesman (Cheesman, 1949a,b; Häkkinen *et al.*, 2008)

ix. *M. lanceolata* Warb. (Warburg, 1900)

x. *M. nagenisum* Prain (Prain, 1904; Häkkinen and Väre, 2008)

xi. *M. ochracea* K. Sheph. (Shepherd, 1964)

xii. *M. schizocarpa* N. W. Simmonds (Simmonds, 1956)

xiii *M. sikkimensis* Kurz (Kurz, 1877)

xiv. *M. thomsonii* (King) Baker (Baker, 1893; Cheesman, 1948; Cowman and Cowman, 1929)

xv. *M. yunnanensis* Häkkinen and H. Wang (Häkkinen and Wang, 2007, 2008)

2. Section *Rhodochlamys* (x=11) has 5-7 species important only as ornamentals, distributed from India to Indochina (Stover and Simmonds, 1987). The plants are slender with pseudostem always less than 3 m in height. The inflorescence is erect having opaque and mostly waxy, brightly coloured bracts. The flowers are few to a bract and are usually in a single row. The fruits are non-parthenocarpic with no nutritional value and do not reflex.

Group B – Chromosome number x=10. The bracts are imbricate in bud stage. These are firm and highly polished on the outside. The group has 2 sections:

3. Section *Australimusa* (x=10) has 5-7 species distributed from Queensland to the Philippines and yield fruits and fibre. The inflorescence is erect and usually having shiny bracts. Red sap is present in stem. The seeds are subglobose to lenticular.

Fehi banana is distinguished by the erect bunches and the purplish red or reddish-yellow sap of the plants which has been used as ink and for dyeing. The plants may be 10.9 m in height and the leaves are 50-75 cm wide. The fruit bunches have about 6 hands bearing orange or copper coloured thick skinned fruits which are starchy, sometimes seedy and of good flavour when boiled or roasted.

4. Section *Callimusa* (x=10) has 6-10 species important only as ornamentals distributed in Indochina and Indonesia. The plants are ornamental, dwarf and short. The inflorescence is usually erect and showy having shiny bracts. The fruits are non-parthenocarpic with no nutritional value. The seeds are barrel or top-shaped. One of the species, *M. coccinea,* has been crossed with Monthan.

Argent (1976) from Papua New Guinea enacted a section *Igentimusa* (n=7, 9 or 10) including the species *M. ingens* Simmonds. The plants are tall and have pendant inflorescence and dull cream bracts. The results of a further study by Simmonds and Weatherup (1990a) using principal coordinate and clustering techniques did not support Argent's proposal since *M. ingens* was found to be more closely allied to several members of the *Musa* section. Daniells *et al.* (2001) place *M. ingens* in *Incertae sedis.* According to Horry *et al.* (1997), relevant section has to be determined for 3 species, *M. ingens* (2n=14), *M. lasiocarpa* (2n=?) and *M. boman* (2n=20?).

Based on several molecular analyses, Häkkinen (2013) supports acceptance of only two *Musa* sections, *M.* sect. *Musa* and *M.* sect. *Callimusa. Musa* sect. *Rhodochlamys* is synonymized with *M.* sect. *Musa* and *M.* sect. *Australimusa* and *M.* sect. *Ingentimusa* are treated as synonyms of *M.* sect. *Callimusa*. Thus, 33 species are assigned to *Musa* L. sect. *Musa* and 37 to *Musa* sect. *Callimusa* (Table 14.1).

Table 14.1. Species of *M.* sect. *Musa* and *M.* sect. *Callimusa* (Häkkinen, Markku (2013).

M. sect. *Musa* = *Musa* sect. *Rhodochlamys* (Baker) Cheesman	*M.* sect. *Callimusa* Cheesman = *Musa* sect. *Australimusa* Cheesman = *Musa* sect. *Ingentimusa* Argent
Musa acuminata Colla, *M. aurantiaca* G. Mann ex Baker, *M. balbisiana* Colla, *M. basjoo* Iinuma, *M. celebica* Warb. ex K. Schum., *M. cheesmanii* N.W. Simmonds, *M. chunii* Häkkinen, *M. flaviflora* N.W. Simmonds, *M. griersonii* Noltie, *M. insularimontana* Hayata, *M. itinerans* Cheesman, *M. kattuvazhana* K.C. Jacob, *M. lanceolata* Warb. ex K. Schum., *M. laterita* Cheesman, *M. mannii* H. Wendl. ex Baker, *M. nagensium* Prain, *M. ochracea* K. Sheph., *M. ornata* Roxb., *M. rosea* Baker,	*M. arfakiana* Argent, *M. azizii* Häkkinen, *M. barioensis* Häkkinen, *M. bauensis* Häkkinen & Meekiong, *M. beccarii* N.W. Simmonds, *M. boman* Argent, *M. borneensis* Becc., *M. bukensis* Argent, *M. campestris* Becc., *M. coccinea* Andrews, *M. exotica* R.V. Valmayor, *M. fitzalanii* F. Muell., *M. gracilis* Holttum, *M. haekkinenii* N.S. Lý & Haev., *M. hirta* Becc., *M. ingens* N.W. Simmonds, *M. jackeyi* W. Hill, *M. johnsii* Argent, *M. juwiniana* Meekiong, *M. lawitiensis* Nasution & Supard., *M. lokok* Geri & Ng, *M. lolodensis* Cheesman,

M. rubra Wall. ex Kurz, *M. sanguinea* Hook. f., *M. schizocarpa* N.W. Simmonds, *M. shankarii* Subba Rao & Kumari, *M. siamensis* Häkkinen & Rich. H. Wallace, *M. sikkimensis* Kurz, *M. thomsonii* (King ex Baker) A.M. Cowan & Cowan, *M. tomentosa* Warb. ex K. Schum., *M. tonkinensis* R.V. Valmayor, L.D. Danh & Häkkinen, *M. velutina* H. Wendl. & Drude, *M. yamiensis* C.L. Yeh & J.H. Chen, *M. yunnanensis* Häkkinen & H. Wang, and *M. zaifui* Häkkinen & H. Wang.

M. lutea R.V. Valmayor, L.D. Danh & Häkkinen, *M. maclayi* F. Muell. ex Mikl.-Maclay, *M. monticola* M. Hotta ex Argent, *M. muluensis* M. Hotta, *M. paracoccinea* A.Z. Liu & D.Z. Li, *M. peekelii* Lauterb., *M. sakaiana* Meekiong, Ipor & Tawan, *M. salaccensis* Zoll. ex Backer, *M. splendida* A. Chev., *M. textilis* Née, *M. troglodytarum* L., *M. tuberculata* M. Hotta, *M. violascens* Ridl., *M. viridis* R.V. Valmayor, L.D. Danh & Häkkinen, and *M. voonii* Häkkinen.

Genus *Ensete* Horan (x=9; 2n = 18)

The plants are gigantic monocarpic herbs. Lateral (adventitious) buds develop only on damage. Bracts and flowers are integral with each other and with axis. Abscission layer is lacking. Flowers of proximal cymes are predominantly bisexual, the 5 fused tepals divided nearly to the base. Fruit is variable in shape, distally expanded, often shouldered and usually asymmetrical, rarely ovoid or spherical. The seed is irregular with homogeneous endosperm and usually >10 mm in diameter. Main uses are for fibre, vegetables and as ornamental.

Six species are found, 3 in Central Africa from the Cameroons to Ethiopia and Transvaal and 3 in South East Asia from North East India and Burma through China to the Philippines, New Guinea and Java (Kubitzki *et al.*, 1998). The important species are *Ensete ventricosum* (Welw.) Cheesman and *Ensete gilleti* (De Willd.) Cheesman.

Wild plantain

(***Ensete superba*** (Roxb.) Cheesman; Indian bread, rock banana)

The plants are erect shrubs with unbranched globose leaf sheaths formed into a pseudostem of 50-100 cm diameter. Leaves are spirally arranged, of 3 x 0.8 m size, oblong and entire with channelled midrib having many lateral nerves parallel from the midrib. Spadix is 50-100 cm long having 3-5 spathes at the base with several ovate, obtuse and brown bracts of 20 x 14 cm size. Flowers are many on each bract and are unisexual. Female flowers are towards the base with male flowers above. The flower has sepals and petals united into a 3.5 cm long and 5-lobed sheath (tepal), third petal forming a membranous sheath, 5 perfect stamens, 2.5 cm long, linear oblong anthers, free filaments and 3-celled inferior ovary having several ovules in each cell, simple style and globose stigma. Fruit is oblong having few, subglobose and black seeds. Ripe seeds are ground and eaten to treat dysentery and are important ingredient in local medicine in South India.

Musa species

Colla was the first to recognize *M. balbisiana* and *M. acuminata* as wild species distinct from any other species (Cheesman, 1948a,b); *M. balbisiana* typified by Rumphius's species *"Pisang batu"* and different from the previously described species by Linnaeus which were edible and *M. acuminata* typified by Rumphius's species *M. simiarum*. However, Colla's type of *M. acuminata* was one of the naturally occurring edible forms since it had no seeds. A number of species of uncertain identity recognized by their native names from Indochina are *M. seminifera,* a wild form with seeds, which also included another banana Pisang Utan, described as a larger kind of wild banana, now identified with *M. textilis*. Pisang batu is identified with *M. balbisiana*. *M. corniculata* has been described based on *Pisang tando* of Rumphius, being quite distinct because of fewer very long and big fruits. It is an AAB horn plantain and therefore covered by Linnaean name *M. paradisiaca*. Ernest Cheesman noticed that the Linnaeus model of *M. paradisiaca* was a type of plantain. *M. nana,* a native of Cochin-China where it was called *Chuoi duii,* was thought to be the same as *M. cavendishii* described by Lambert in 1837. However, Baker (1893) described it as a form of *M. cavendishii* with a taller stem and fertile flowers. Cheesman (1948) pointed out that *M. rosacea* was an edible seedless banana closely related to one of the two wild species of bananas and suggested that this could be a hybrid between the two wild species of banana and thus covered under the name *M. paradisiaca*. Jacob recognized *M. paradisiaca, M. sapidisiaca* and *M. balbisiana,* although he had previously included *M. paradisiaca* and *M. sapientum* in one group and *M. balbisiana* in the other.

Musa acuminata Colla.

Wild plants are diploid ($2n$=22) and bear fruits containing numerous seeds making them inedible. Cultivated plants are triploid ($2n$=33) and bear seedless edible fruits. The cultivated clones ($2n$=22, 33) are brown, depressed, 5-6 mm in diameter and irregularly angled. Such plants have been called *M. acuminata* 'Dwarf Cavendish' (*M. cavendishii* Lambert ex Paxton; *M. chinensis* Sweet; *M. nana* Loureiro). Pseudostems are cylindrical and green with brown or black blotches. Leaf sheath (4.8 m long) and petiole are pruinose. Petiole is 80 cm, margin is erect or spreading and basally with scarious wings, leaf blade is adaxially green and pruinose, abaxially yellow green and pruinose or not, oblong, 1.9-2.3 m × 50-70 cm, base is cordate and asymmetric, midvein is adaxially green and abaxially white yellow. Inflorescence is sub-horizontal or vertically reflexed with usually downy or hairy peduncle. Pedicels are short. Bracts are bright red to dark violet outside and light red to yellow inside, sometimes yellow at extreme apex, convolute, ovate and apex is usually acute. Male bud is slightly waxy and ovoid. Male flowers are 20 per bract in 2 rows, cream, yellow or orange with no pink flush. Compound tepal is white or cream, lemon yellow at apex, 3.5-4 cm, apex of outer lobes with a hook-like hairy appendage. Free tepal is not more than half as long as compound tepal, apex is emarginated and shortly apiculate. Infructescence is 1.2 m long having 70 × 4 cm, white setose peduncle. Two rows of ovules are present in each loculus. The fruit bunch is asymmetric. The fruit is sub-cylindrical and not waxy. Berries are incurved, green to yellow green, 5-angled when young, cylindric at maturity, 9 cm, white setose having curved base, attenuate into a stalk and apex contracted into a 6-10 mm rostrum. It is found in Assam (India) and in Burma. The cultivar Nendran resembles it most closely.

M. acuminata is highly variable and the number of subspecies accepted by different authorities vary from 6 to 9. The following are the most commonly accepted subspecies (Ploetz *et al*., 2007):

1. *M. acuminata* subsp. *burmannica* Simmonds syn. *M. acuminata* subsp. *burmannicoides* De Langhe
2. *M. acuminata* subsp. *errans* Argent syn. *M. errans* Teodoro, *M. troglodyatarum* L. var. *errans*, *M. errans* Teodoro var. *botoan*
3. *M. acuminata* subsp. *malaccensis* (Ridley) Simmonds syn. *M. malaccensis* Ridley
4. *M. acuminata* subsp. *microcarpa* (Beccari) Simmonds syn. *M. microcarpa* Beccari
5. *M. acuminata* subsp. *siamea* Simmonds
6. *M. acuminata* subsp. *truncata* (Ridley) Kiew
7. *M. acuminata* subsp. *zebrina* (Van Houtte) R.E. Nasution

***Musa balbisiana* Colla.** (2 n = 22)

There is no natural edible parthenocarpic diploid or triploid form of *M. balbisiana* (Simmonds, 1995). This species is widely distributed in tropical and subtropical Asia, including China, India, Indonesia, Malaysia, Myanmar, Nepal, Papua New Guinea, the Philippines, Sri Lanka, Thailand and Vietnam (Ge *et al.,* 2005). No subspecies of *M. balbisiana* have been described although there is substantial molecular and morphological differentiation within the species (Ude *et al.,* 2002a; Ge *et al.,* 2005). *M. balbisiana* is resistant to the major pests and diseases of banana and is able to thrive in dry and cold environments. It is also called leafy banana and is more suited to drier areas.

It produces many suckers. The stems are robust and the adaxial channel is closed. Pseudostems are 6 m long, clumped, yellow green and often with large black markings. Petiole is 60-75 cm having margin open, 2 cm wide and often closed when young. Leaf blade is adaxially green and slightly pruinose or not, ovate oblong, 2.9 m × 90 cm and with auriculate and asymmetric base. Petiole canal margins are incurved. Inflorescence is pendulous, sub-horizontal to oblique, 2.5 m long and the peduncle and rachis are glabrous. The bracts are long and ribbed. Bracts of bisexual and male flowers are adaxially purple red, abaxially brownish purple to yellow green and pruinose, imbricate, ovate to lanceolate, persistent with obtuse apex, reflexed after flowering. Bracts of female flowers are deciduous and fall soon after the flower withers. Male bud is waxy and broadly ovate. Male flowers are up to 20 per bract, in 2 rows, cream with a strong pink pigmentation. Compound tepal is 4 to 5 cm long and about 1.2 cm wide, adaxially pale purple, abaxially pale purple white with emarginated and shortly mucronate apiculate apex, striate with yellow to orange teeth. Pedicels are long. The fruit bunch is very compact. Infructescence is pendulous, with 8 clusters ("hands") each of 15 or 16 berries in 2 rows. Four rows of ovules are in each loculus. Berries are waxy, almost straight, gray green, obovoid, 13 × 4 cm, distinctly angled at maturity, base narrowed into a 2.5 cm stalk, apex contracted or not into a short angled 2 cm column tapering towards the apex. The fruits are seeded. Seeds are numerous, brown, oblate, 5-10 mm in diameter and minutely warty.

Most of the cultivated sweet dessert bananas, cooking bananas and plantains now grown throughout the tropics belong to this section. The triploid cultivars evolved from two wild diploid species *M. acuminata* and *M. balbisiana.* The wild species can reproduce both sexually and asexually (by suckers from a corm). These are used as fruit and vegetable and for fibre.

The main characters used to separate the *Musa* species are basic chromosome number, pseudostem height, sheath hairiness, petiole margin and base, peduncle hairiness, bunch posture, basal flower sex, bunch density, pedicel length, fruit skin hairiness, seed shape and the male bract characteristics such as their deciduous/ persistent behaviour, polished/dull surface, rolling, colour and free tepal length. Based on a study sponsored by International Network for the Improvement of Banana and Plantain (INIBAP; Bioversity International Banana and Plantain Section), Daniells *et al.* (2001) listed 29 species (Table 14.2).

Table 14.2. International classification of genus *Musa* (Daniells *et al.*, 2001).

A. Wild species		
Section	**Species**	**Subspecies**
Eumusa (2n=22)	*acuminata* Colla	*banksii* (F.Muell.) Simmonds; *burmannica* Simmonds; *burmannicoides* De Langhe & Devreux; *malacensis* Simmonds; *macrocarpa* Simmonds; *truncata* (Ridl.) Shepherd; *siamea* Simmonds; *zebrina* R.E. Nesution; and *errans* Allen
	balbisiana Colla; *schizocarpa* Simmonds; *basjoo* Siebold; *itinerans* Cheesman; *flaviflora* Simmonds; *sikkimensis* Kurz; *cheesmani* Simmonds; *nagensium* Prain; *halabanensis;* and *ochracea* Shepherd	
Rhodochlamys (2n=22)	*laterita; ornata* Roxb.; *sanguinea;* and *velutina*	
Callimusa (2n=20)	*coccinea* Andr.; *violascens; gracilis; bomeensis; beccarii; and salaccensis*	
Australimusa (2n=20)	*maclayi* F.Muell.; *peekelii; jackeyi; lolodensis; textilis* Nees; and *bukensis*	
Igentimusa	*ingens* Simmonds; *boman;* and *lasiocarpa*	

B. **Cultivated varieties**		
Section	**Groups**	**Subgroups**
Eumusa	AA (*acuminata*)	Sucrier; Pisang Jari Buaya; Pisang Lilin; Inarnibal; Lakatan and Unknown
	AAA	Gros Michel; Cavendish; Red; Ambon; Ibota; Mutika/Lujugira; Orotava and Rio
	AAAA	
	AB (*acuminata* x *balbisiana*)	Ney Poovan and Kamaramasenge
	AAB	Iholena; Laknau; Mysore; Silk; Maia Maoli/Popoulu; Pisang Nangka; Pisang Raja; Plantain; Nendra Padaththi; Pisang Kelat and Nadan
	ABB	Bluggoe; Pisang Awak; Monthan; Kalapua; Klue Teparod; Saba; Pelipita; Ney Mannan and Peyan
	AAAB	
	AABB	Laknau der
	ABBB	
	AS (*acuminata* x *schizocarpa*)	
Australimusa		Fe'i
Eumusa x Australimusa	AT	
	AAT	
	ABBT	

GRIN taxonomy (2007) recognizes only 15 species. In an enumeration of all the valid *Musa* species, Häkkinen and Väre (2008) have recognized 73 species. Taking into consideration the enumerations of Cheesman (1947-1950), Simmonds (1952a,b) and Häkkinnen and Väre (2008), 81 species are now recognized in the genus *Musa*, but these have not been keyed. Thus, a comprehensive revision of the genus is needed.

The validity and usefulness of sections in *Musa* has been questioned by some authors who examined sectional relationship in *Musa* using molecular tools (Wong *et al.,* 2002). AFLP and chloroplast analysis provided evidence for the merger of sections *Rhodochlamys* and *Eumusa* (Wong *et al.*, 2002). This view has been already supported with morphological data and cross hybridization experiments (Simmonds, 1954a,b,c), RFLP of the nuclear genome (Jarret *et al.*, 1992) and AFLP data (Ude *et al.*, 2002). Wong *et al.* (2002) also suggested that section *Callimusa* and section *Australiamusa* should be combined into a single section. Chloroplast DNA (Nwakanma *et al.,* 2003) and AFLP data (Ude *et al.*, 2002) also showed a close affinity between the two sections.

Origin, evolution and distribution of banana and plantain

The primary centre of origin of banana is thought to be Malesia (a biogeographical region including the Malay Peninsula, Indonesia, Philippines, Borneo and Papua New Guinea) and India as a secondary centre (Simmonds and Shepherd, 1955). The centre of diversity of the species is thought to be either Malaysia (Simmonds, 1962) or Indonesia (Nasution, 1991, Horry *et al.*, 1997).

Majority of cultivated bananas arose from the species of *Eumusa* section, which is the largest in the genus with the most widespread geographic distribution throughout South East Asia from India to the Pacific Islands. Out of the 11 species of the section, most of the present day edible bananas are a mix of wild and cultivated species and hybrids associated with two wild and seedy species, *M. acuminata* Colla (A genome) and *M. balbisiana* Colla (B genome), both with 2n=22 (Horry *et al.*, 1997). In addition, there are bananas of S genome derived from hybridizations with *M. schizocarpa* (Shepherd and Ferreira, 1982; Carreel *et al.*, 1994) and a Philippine clone (Butuhan) resulting from an ancient hybridization between *M. balbisiana* and *M. textilis* (T genome). Several landraces containing the two genomes of *M. acuminata* and species from the *Australimusa* section (T genome) and two landraces containing the three genomes, A, B and T have been found in Papua New Guinea (Carreel, 1994).

The wild seedy diploid *M. acuminata* has fruits inedible by human beings but eaten by birds, bats and monkeys. The evolution from wild to edible bananas involved seed suppression and parthenocarpy development. Edible diploid cultivar subgroups (AA cultivars) derived from hybridizations between different *M. acuminata* subspecies in islands of South East Asia and western Melanesia. Clones of the diploids cultivated in wetter parts of South East Asia (Valmayor *et al*., 2002) produced parthenocarpic fruits, which were seedless so long as the flowers are not pollinated. The structural heterozygosity of these hybrid AA cultivars, caused by chromosomal rearrangements between parental subspecies of *M. acuminata* (Shepherd, 1999), contributed to gametic sterility (Dessauw, 1988). This sterility, aided by human selection and vegetative propagation for pulp enhancement, led to parthenocarpic fruits and improved edibility.

Since the A genome diploid is a variable species with several different subspecies (Simmonds and Weatherup, 1990a,b), the different edible diploids may have originated independently and more than once. This has been confirmed through flavonoid studies (Horry and Jay, 1988). Apart from being seedless the edible diploids remain within the morphological range of their wild parent and therefore should be treated as the same species as the wild parent (Trehane *et al*., 1995; Robinson, 1996).

Natural reproductive barriers developed within the most widespread parental subspecies of *M. acuminata* as a result of chromosomal rearrangements through spontaneous or recombination events. This gave rise to structural heterozygosity, subspecies divergence and genetic diversity in these hybrid AA cultivars.

A wide range of triploid AAA genotypes arose from the edible diploids, perhaps following crosses with wild *M. acuminata* subspecies, possibly through the process of chromosome restitution at meiosis. The edible diploids produced unreduced female gametes. When fertilized by a normal haploid male gamete, these gave rise to triploid edible bananas leading to the development of cultivars that mostly comprise the sweet bananas (Daniells *et al.,* 2001). Cheesman (1947) considered that the wild *M. acuminata* gave rise to the cultivated species of *M. paradisiaca* (AA, AAA) which contains all table cultivars except a few cooking ones. These triploids may have originated independently many times, possibly with contributions from different subspecies of *M. acuminata*. Nine subspecies have been recognized by Horry *et al.* (1997). This is supported by molecular data on differences in DNA of diploid and triploid accessions of bananas. Chloroplast DNA of *Musa* spp. is transmitted maternally, while mitochondrial DNA is transmitted paternally. The use of this feature in phylogenetic studies has suggested that the origin of the edible banana cultivars is linked particularly to two subspecies of *M. acuminata*, namely *M. acuminata* subsp. *banksii* and *M. acuminata* subsp. *errans* (Horry *et al.*, 1997). Variation in anthocy-anin pigments among the edible diploids suggests that three different subspecies, viz. ssp. *malaccensis*, ssp. *banksii* and ssp. *zebrina,* could have been involved (Horry and Jay, 1990). The triploids too should belong to the same species as the wild and cultivated A diploids since increase in the number of chromosomes by autopoly-ploidy will cause very little change in the observable appearance of the plant although there may be increased vigour in different parts of the plant. In most parts of South East Asia, these triploids, which are more vigorous and have larger fruits, have replaced the original AA diploids. Different edible diploids and triploids of *M. acuminata* spread in cultivation and some reached India. Now these dominate the world's bananas. However, in Papua New Guinea, AA diploids remain agriculturally significant and a wide range of diversity is still found in cultivation.

Edible diploids of *M. balbisiana* underwent a parallel evolution in drier parts of Asia (India, Myanmar, Thailand, Philippines). These were similarly taken into cultivation with the selection of natural diploid, triploid and tetraploid hybrids. It gave rise to the cultivated *M. balbisiana* (BB, BBB) or the leafy banana. The BBB bananas would also be of the same species as that of both wild and cultivated *M. balbisiana*. However, no natural edible parthenocarpic diploid or triploids of *M. balbisiana* has been identified (Simmonds, 1966; Simmonds and Weatherup, 1990b; Jarret, 1990; Simmonds, 1995) although hybrids of A and B genome show the character (Heslop and Schwarzacher, 2007).

Two cultivated bananas, Cardaba and Saba, from the Philippines were treated as BBB types by Vakili (1967) and Valmayor *et al.* (1981). But isozyme studies suggested that Cardaba could be an ABB (Jarret and Litz, 1986ab) while based on his scoring technique Simmonds and Weatherup (1990b) keep both Saba and Cardaba in ABB.

Crosses of the diploid and triploid types of *M. acuminata* with *M. balbisiana* led to the formation of heterogenomic triploid hybrids. Such hybrids can be referred to as *Musa* x *paradisiaca.* The triploids may have arisen in two ways: when an unreduced female gamete of A genome diploid is fertilized by a haploid male gamete from B genome diploid or when an unreduced female gamete of interspecific diploid hybrid is fertilized by haploid male gamete from A genome diploid (Pickersgill, 1994). This gave rise to AAB triploids. The ABB triploids may be produced when an unreduced female gamete of interspecific diploid hybrid is fertilized by haploid male gamete from B genome diploid banana. There was some geographical overlap when the diploid and triploid *M. acuminata* cultivars were taken by humans to areas where *M. balbisiana* is native (India, Myanmar, Thailand, Philippines). As a result the Indian subcontinent became a major centre for hybridization (Daniells *et al.,* 2001). Natural hybridization resulted in the formation of homogenomic and heterogenomic diploids, triploids and tetraploids. The genomes of the two species contributed different traits, *M. acuminata* largely contributing parthenocarpy and sterility (Simmonds and Shepherd, 1955) and *M. balbisiana* contributing hardiness, drought tolerance, disease resistance and starchiness (Pillay *et al*., 2002). Thus combining the characters of tolerance to dry environment and resistance to diseases in diploid BB and of good edibility of fruit in diploid AA, the process of hybridization gave rise to a wide range of edible types (AB, AAB and ABB), some of which would have survived and have been multiplied under domestication. This would have extended their geographical ranges out from the wetter tropics into the seasonally drier zones. Consequently, a diverse selection of cultivars of *Musa*, belonging to different genome groups is thought to have arisen in South East Asia. At present, many clones of cultivated bananas are in existence. Of these, AA, AAA, AAB and ABB are the most numerous. Bananas are now cultivated throughout the tropics and in selected areas in the subtropics. Most of the cultivars of the edible bananas, derived from collections of spontaneous mutants in wild plants, were then brought into cultivation and multiplied by vegetative methods. The hybridization events and mutations have occurred many hundreds of times over (Heslop-Harrison and Schwarzacher, 2007) leading to further speciation or improvement.

Triploid bananas may also produce unreduced female gametes and when fertilized by a haploid male gamete give rise to tetraploids. ABBB, AAAB and AABB tetraploid hybrids are presumed to occur in South East Asia (Richardson *et al.*, 1965). Since the interspecific hybrids contain two different genomes they will be different from the autopolyploids. According to the morphological species concept and without knowledge of their origin, they would be regarded as another species differing from those derived entirely from any of the two wild species.

Dispersal of edible bananas outside Asia may have been brought about through movement of human populations (Simmonds, 1962). This resulted in the development of distinct subgroups of cultivars in different geographic locations. Secondary diversification within the major subgroups of cultivated bananas is thought to have been the result of somatic mutations rather than sexual reproduction. The mutants having traits of economic interest may have been selected by farmers and multiplied by vegetative propagation to produce morphotypes.

Movement eastwards resulted in the development of a distinct group of AAB bananas which are cultivated throughout the Pacific Islands, the secondary centre of diversity. These are known as the Maia Maoli/Popoulu group and the progenitors of these bananas are thought to have been carried eastwards by proto-Polynesians from an area in or near the Philippines more than 4000 years ago (De Langhe, 1996, De Langhe and De Maret, 1999). The suggested existence of bananas in South America during pre-Columbian times is an evidence for Early America-Polynesian contact (Langdon, 1993).

A very distinct type of cooking banana (plantain AAB) is found growing in the other secondary centre of diversity in wet tropical zones of West and Central Africa. Plantains are rare in much of Asia, with the exception of India, and their origin in Africa is shrouded in mystery. It is thought that they have been cultivated in this region for more than 3000 years, but the identity of the people responsible for such cultivation is unknown. It is possible that the same proto-Polynesians who carried the banana east to the Pacific islands also carried it west to Africa (De Langhe, 1996). Bananas introduced in the East African Highlands, the area of secondary diversity, between the 5th and 10th centuries giving rise to a wide range of unique cultivars is the work of East Bantu speaking people. As dry suckers can survive storage for several months, long sea voyages would not have been a problem. Such a hypothesis fits with the finding that plantains must have reached Africa more than 3000 years ago. Evidence for the early cultivation of *Musa* in West Africa has been substantiated following the discovery of *Musa* phytoliths dated 840-350 BC (Mbida *et al.*, 2000). Molecular studies by Carreel (1994) revealed two types of A genomes in the East African Highland banana cultivars. One genome appears to have come from *M. acuminata* ssp. *zebrina* (Indonesia) and the other from *M. acuminata* ssp. *banksii* (Papua New Guinea) indicating their origin from Indonesia.

Molecular analysis of a large number of plantain landraces using techniques such as random amplified polymorphic DNA (RAPD), restriction fragment length polymorphisms (RFLP) and sequence tagged microsatellite (STMS) markers indicates that most plantains have a very high level of genetic identity to one another (Carreel *et al.,* 1994; Crouch *et al.,* 1999; Howell *et al.*, 1994). This supports the suggestion that somatic mutations are responsible for the diversity of morphotypes of plantains now found in West Africa.

In the section *Australimusa*, the group of parthenocarpic edible types are collectively known as Fe'i cultivars but can be distinguished from other cultivated bananas by their erect fruit bunches and red sap. Fe'i bananas were originally distributed from the Moluccas to Hawaii and Tahiti. These provided source of food, fibre and a dark red dye extracted from the pseudostems. Simmonds (1959) suggests *M. maclayi* to be their most likely ancestor, while Cheesman (1950) notes their similarity to *M. lolodensis*. Evidence from an RFLP-based study by Jarret *et al.* (1992) indicated that *M. lolodensis* was the closest wild relative of the Fe'i bananas. Studies on diversity within the *Australimusa* section, however, have shown that, while the Fe'i cultivars seem to be closest to the species *M. maclayi*, *M. peekelii* and *M. lolodensis,* diversity amongst these cultivars is as great as that within the section as a whole. Thus the possibility of an interspecific origin for the Fe'i bananas cannot be excluded (Carreel, 1994).

Morphology of banana plant

The cultivated banana plant is a perennial monocotyledon and therefore classed as an arborescent herb. The wild species *Musa ingens* may grow up to 15 m and have a circumference of 2.5 m (INIBAP, 2000). Dwarf Cavendish reaches about 1.8 m in height. The above ground trunk is called a pseudostem and consists of concentric layers of leaf sheaths rolled into a cylinder 20–50 cm in diameter. The height of the pseudostem (distance between the soil surface and the petioles of the highest leaves) is used to divide plantain cultivars into subgroups, 'giant', 'medium', and 'small'. *Musa* clones with short internodes are called dwarf' cultivars.

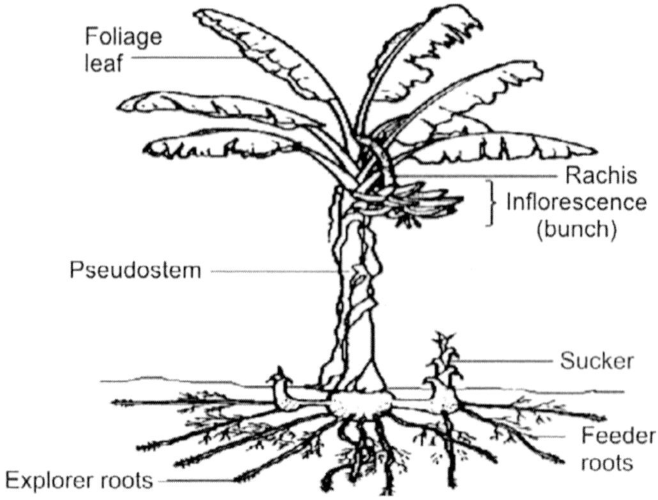

Fig. 14.1. Parts of banana plant (Soure: Swennen and Ortiz, 1997).

The pseudostems of Highland and sweet bananas are predominantly green to dark green with black blotches while those of plantains are yellowish green with brown blotches. The true stem is a large underground corm (also called a butt) and the meristem of the apical bud initially gives rise to the leaves before it elongates up through the pseudostem and emerges some 10–15 months after planting as a large terminal inflorescence. Each pseudostem produces only one inflorescence. The pseudostem dies back after flowering but axillary buds of the corm are able to elongate into rhizomes (underground stems) from which suckers (or offsets) are produced forming a clump called a stool or mat. The root system is adventitious spreading out laterally as far as 5.5 m and forming a dense mat mainly in the top 15 cm soil. Once the bunch ripens and is removed, the mother stem dies and the remaining suckers develop into mature plants (Fig. 14.1).

The rate and time of suckering varies in cultivars. Sword leaf suckers develop on the corm of a current bearing plant. The growth of the suckers is held back by correlative inhibition from the parent on which the suckers depend for nutrition and normal leaves are unable to develop until after flower initiation. The leaves that do develop prior to flowering of the parent are very narrow and hence are referred to as sword leaves. Plants derived from sword leaf suckers can progress to inflorescence emergence stage as soon as 6 months after development of the first normal leaf, under optimal environmental conditions (Espino *et al.*, 1992). Water suckers often form on the corm of an already harvested plant and develop normal leaves early. Plants derived from water suckers are not nourished by a parent plant and therefore mature early and show early nutritional deficiency and as a result produce small, uneconomical fruit bunches.

The leaves of *Musa* plants emerge, tightly rolled, from the centre of the pseudostem in an anticlockwise spiral manner. The leaf sheaths taper on both sides to form the petiole. Among the plantains, there are many forms of leaves, some with pink, red or dark brown leaf sheaths, a few also have coloured midribs or splotches on leaves or fruits. The leaf is more or less vertical when it emerges becoming horizontal and eventually drooping. Most banana plants produce 30–40 leaves in a lifetime but as older leaves are pushed outwards they eventually die leaving 5–15 fully functional leaves on a mature plant. A minimum of 8-10 functional leaves are required to allow proper maturation of a fruit bunch. The size of emerging leaves increases until just before flowering and then decreases until the emergence of the last leaf (flag leaf) immediately before the emergence of the inflorescence. The blade (lamina) can grow to 4 m long and 100 cm wide. Each blade has a pronounced midrib and well marked, pinnately arranged parallel veins. The leaf margins tear along the veins in windy conditions giving the blades a tattered appearance. The shoot meristem transforms into an inflorescence (compound spike) at about the time when the eleventh-last leaf is produced and emerges upwards through the centre of the pseudostem before bending down under the weight of the developing spike. All banana cultivars have same type of inflorescence (or bunch). A complete banana inflorescence consists of 5-10 hands each having 65-155 fingers of moderate size (100-300 g) with many neutral flowers (which do not develop into fruits and fall off during bunch maturation) and a persistent male terminal bud (Fig. 14.2).

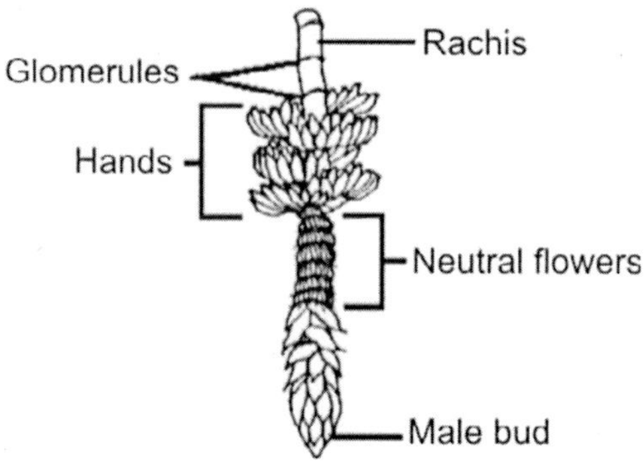

Fig. 14.2. Banana inflorescence or bunch (Soure: Swennen and Ortiz, 1997).

The Horn plantain is subdivided further into three types (Tezenas du Montcel *et al.*, 1983): French Horn, False Horn and Horn (Fig. 14.3). Maia Maoli and Populu (Pacific plantains) are divided into clones and morphotypes.

a). *French plantain:* The inflorescence is complete at maturity. Hands are 6-12 and consist of numerous (60-170) rather small (10-300 g) fingers followed by the bunch axis covered with persistent neutral flowers. The terminal male bud is large and persistent.

b). *False Horn plantain:* The inflorescence is incomplete. Hands are 5-12 and consist of large (230-400 g) fingers (25-80) followed by a few neutral flowers. At maturity, no male bud is present.

c). *French Horn plantain:* The inflorescence is incomplete resembling that of False Horn plantain with 7-8 hands, 30-85 fingers each of 200-300 g and no male bud, but it has many neutral flowers.

d). *Horn plantain:* The inflorescence is incomplete. There are few (1-5) hands, consisting of a few (1-50) large (250-610 g) fingers. Neutral flowers and male bud are not present. A tail or protuberance terminates the bunch axis. It resembles False Horn plantain, but has larger fingers and no neutral flowers (Swennen and Ortiz (1997).

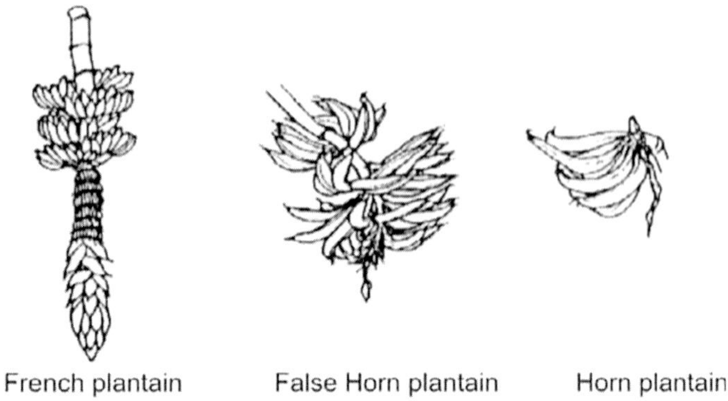

Fig. 14.3. Types of Horn plantain (Soure: Swennen and Ortiz, 1997).

The immature inflorescence is encased inside purple bracts giving the appearance of a large bud (often called bell). Inside the bracts are 5-15 double whorls of floral parts comprising female flowers at the proximal end, male flowers at the distal end and neuter or hermaphrodite flowers sometimes present in between (Fig.14.4). Each node is covered by a purple bract. These bracts open in sequence (1 per day) from base to tip, becoming reflexed before being shed. As the hands of fruits start to develop from the female flowers, the male flowers are usually shed leaving the peduncle bare except for the very tip consisting of the bell containing the last-formed of the male bracts and flowers. In some cultivars, this male part is shed quickly, and this may be a useful distinguishing characteristic.

The tepals are white, tubular and toothed. The flowers secrete nectar at the tip of the ovary and this then collects at the base of the tepals. They are negatively geotropic and turn upwards as they develop. Male and female flowers are morphologically indistinguishable until the inflorescence is about 12 cm long. At this point the ovary in the male flower fails to develop any further (Fig. 14.5). Flowers have a 3-lobed stigma and style and an inferior ovary fused from 3 loculi. Each loculus of a female flower contains two rows of ovules embedded in a strip of mucilage. There are 5 stamens in male flowers. These are reduced to staminodes in female flowers. Pollen, if produced, is sticky.

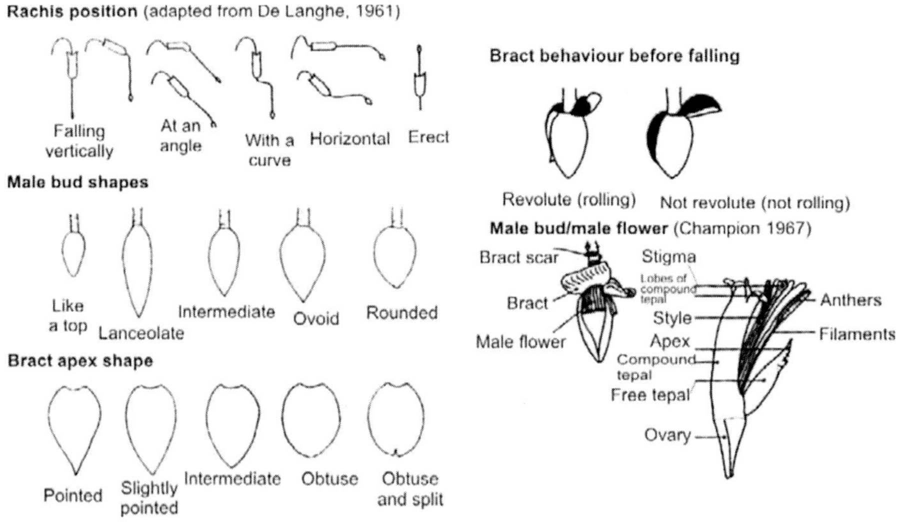

Fig. 14.4. Rachis position, male bud, flower and bract of banana (Source: IPGRI- INIBAP, CIRAD, 1996).

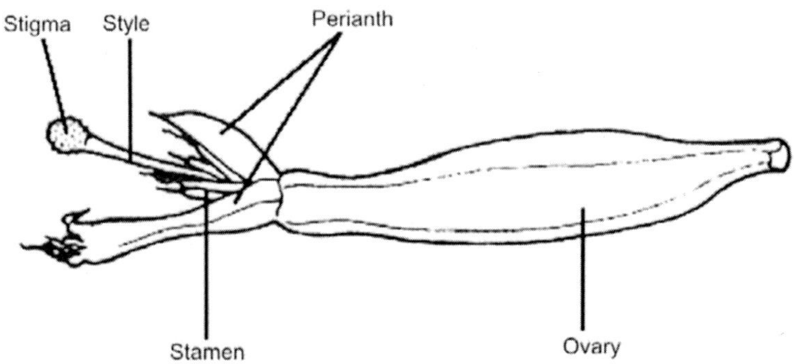

Fig. 14.5. Banana flower (Soure: Swennen and Ortiz, 1997).

Each fruit is a berry and is known as a finger. Each cluster of fruits at a node is known as a hand and the entire collection of hands is known as a bunch. The number of hands varies with species and cultivar. The outer protective layer of each fruit, known as the skin or peel (Fig. 14.6), is a fusion of the hypanthium (floral receptacle) and outer layer (exocarp) of the pericarp (fruit wall derived from the ovary wall). This peel is easily removed from the fleshy pulp that originates mainly from the endocarp (innermost layer of the pericarp). During the development of the fruit from the ovary, the tepals, style and staminodes abscise leaving a characteristic calloused scar at the tip of the fruit. Colour, size, texture and flavour of common cultivated *Musa* fruits vary with cultivar. Orinoco or Horse having a coarse looking fruit about 15 cm long by 5 cm in diameter is primarily used in cooking. Edible *Musa* cultivars have fleshy, seedless fruits while wild bananas may have little flesh and be filled with black 3–16 mm wide seeds. Dessert bananas have distinguishing sweet flavour and are usually consumed raw when ripe. There are different types of banana including Manzanon, baby, red and Cavendish. Manzanons are smaller bananas that are usually dark in colour, often black. The baby bananas are the smallest and are usually sold in large bunches. Red bananas contain a high amount of beta carotene, and as the name states, they have a red peel and a light red pulp inside. Plantain and cooking/beer banana are easily distinguished from dessert banana by their method of consumption. Plantain and cooking/beer banana require some form of processing. Cooking bananas referred to as plantains are consumed when cooked. However, there are two types of cooking bananas. The first type are cooked when the fruits are green and provide a starchy staple nutritionally similar to the potato (Simmonds, 1966). Bananas of this type can be allowed to ripen and then eaten as dessert bananas. Therefore, these cannot be called true plantains. The second type of cooking bananas are unpalatable when raw and even when ripe and therefore, require cooking before being consumed. These are the true plantains (Swennen and Vuylsteke, 1987). The pulp of beer bananas is bitter and astringent. These can neither be eaten raw and nor cooked, but can be used to make juice and alcohol. The seeds have linear embryo, large amounts of endosperm and a thick and hard testa.

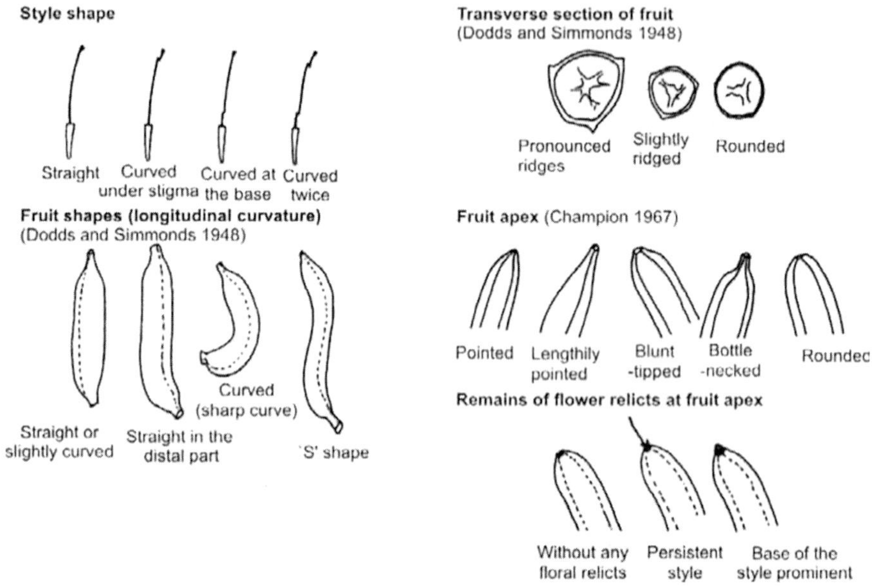

Fig. 14.6. Parts of banana fruit (Source: IPGRI- INIBAP, CIRAD, 1996).

Nomenclature and classification of cultivated banana

Prior to the system proposed by Simmonds and Shepherd in 1955, binomial system developed by Carl Linneaus was used for the nomenclature and taxonomy of cultivated bananas. The earliest description of dessert banana *M. sapientum* and 'silk' banana *M. paradisiaca* was provided by Linnaeus in 1753. Other monospecific nomenclature such as *M. sapientum* ssp. *paradisiaca* by Baker (1893), *M. paradisiaca* ssp. *sapientum* by Schumann and *M. sapidisiaca* by Jacob (1952) were not accepted by taxonomists.

Simmonds and Shepherd (1955) suggested that genome nomenclature was more appropriate for classifying edible bananas according to the relative contribution of the species, designated by the letter A for *acuminata* and B for *balbisiana*. This system basically assigns a score for selected morphological features but also requires chromosome counts in order to assign plants to a genome group (Pillay *et al.*, 2004).

The method proposed by Simmonds and Shepherd (1955) and Stover and Simmonds (1987) for classifying edible banana cultivars uses the relative contribution of their ancestral wild species in the hybrids and the scores based on their morphological characters along with the ploidy (chromosome number).

Simmonds and Shepherd (1955) selected 15 morphological characters in which the two wild species distinctly differ as given in Table 14.3 and Fig. 14.7. On the basis of these diagnostic characters scoring is done to arrive at taxonomic scores for use in the proposed method of classifying edible bananas. For each character in which a cultivar agreed completely with wild *acuminata*, a score of 1 is given, and for each character in which the cultivar agreed with *balbisiana*, a score of 2, 3 or 4 is given according to its intensity.

Table 14.3. Characters used in the taxonomic scoring of banana cultivars (Simmonds and Shepherd, 1955; Stover and Simmonds, 1987).

Character	***M. acuminata***	***M. balbisiana***
Pseudostem colour	 More or less heavily marked with brown or black blotches	 Blotches slight or absent
Petiolar canal	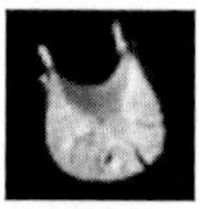 Open, margin erect or spreading, with scarious wings below, not clasping pseudostem	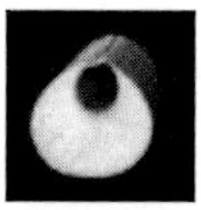 Closed, margin inclosed, not winged below, clasping pseudostem
Peduncle	 Usually downy or hairy	 Glabrous
Pedicels	 Short	 Long
Ovules	 Two regular rows in each loculus	 Four irregular rows in each loculus

Bract shoulder	 Usually high (ratio < 0.28)	 Usually low (ratio >0)
Bract curling	 Bracts reflex and roll back after opening	 Bracts lift but do not reflex
Bract shape	 Lanceolate or narrowly ovate, tapering sharply from the shoulder	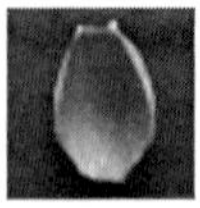 Broadly ovate, not taper sharply
Bract apex	 Acute	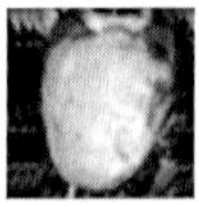 Obtuse
Bract colour	 Red, dull purple or yellow outside; pink, dull purple or yellow inside	 Distinctive brownish purple outside; bright crimson inside
Colour fading	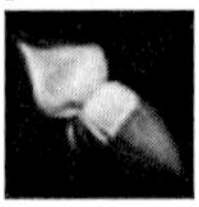 Inside bract colour fades to yellow towards the base	 Inside bract colour usually continuous to base
Bract scars	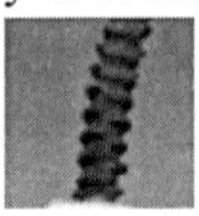 Prominent	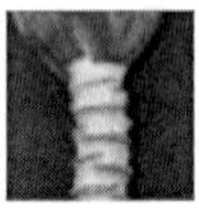 Scarcely prominent
Free tepal of male flower	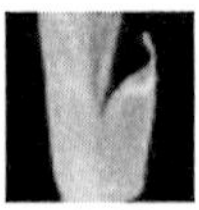 Variably corrugated below tip	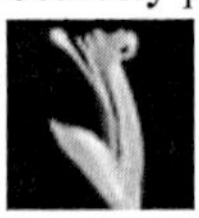 Rarely corrugated
Male flower colour	 Creamy white	 Variably flushed with pink
Stigma colour	 Orange or rich yellow	 Cream, pale yellow or pale pink

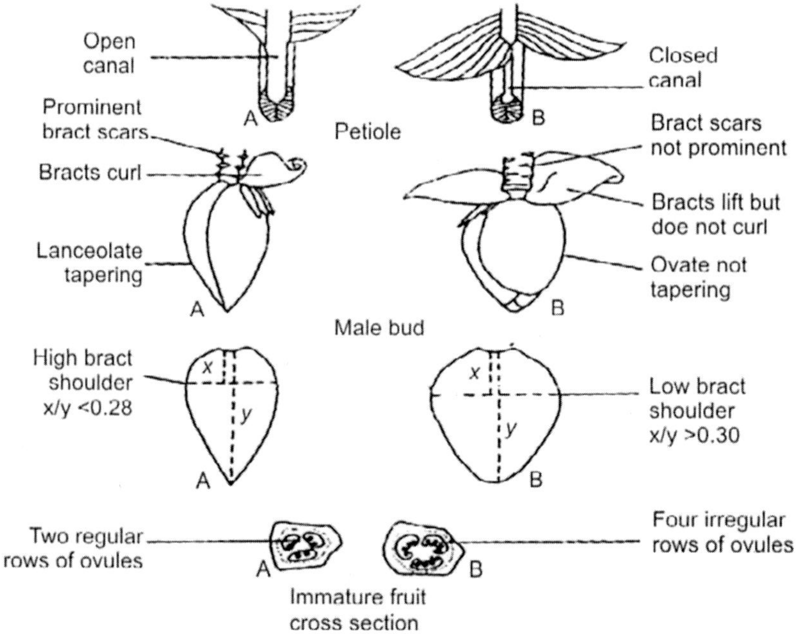

Fig. 14.7. Morphological characters of *M. acuminata* and *M. balbisiana* (Source: Photo by A. Kepler; Simmonds and Shepherd, 1955; Stover and Simmonds, 1987).

The scoring technique based on these 15 plant characters allows for a total score ranging from 15 (for pure *M. acuminata*) to 75 (for pure *M. balbisiana*). Scores for the interspecific hybrids fall between this range based on the relative contribution of the two species plus the level of ploidy. Thus the possible total scores range from a minimum of 15 to a maximum of 75, the expected scores being 15 for AA and AAA, 35 for AAB, 45 for AB, 55 for ABB and 75 for BB. The ploidy is determined by quantitative chromosomal count. Simmonds and Shepherd (1955) and Stover and Simmonds (1987) used the groups and scores shown in Table 14.4 to classify a range of edible bananas. The system eliminates almost all the difficulties and inconsistencies of the previously adopted taxonomy based on *Musa paradisiaca* and *Musa sapientum*.

Table 14.4. Simmonds and Shepherd (1955) and Stover and Simmonds (1987) classification of edible bananas

Genomic group	Score
AA diploid	15-23
AAA triploid	15-23
AAB triploid	24-46
AB diploid	49
ABB triploid	59-63
ABBB tetraploid	67

Silayoi and Chomchalow (1987) revised the method of classification of edible banana (Table 14.5) removing the deficiencies in the original classification given by Simmonds and Shepherd (1955) and Stover and Simmonds (1987).

Table 14.5. Classification of edible bananas based Silayoi and Chomchalow (1987)

Genomic Group	Score
AA/AAA	15-25
AAB	26-46
ABB	59-63
ABBB	67-69
BB/BBB	70-75

A genome nomenclature was further revised by Singh and Uma (1996). They modified score card including the score ranges for AB and ABBB encompassing more clones (Table 14.6).

Table 14.6. Modified score card for assigning tentative genomic groups (Singh and Uma, 1996).

Genomic Group	Score
AA/AAA	15-25
AAB	26-46
AB	46-49
ABB	59-63
ABBB	67-69
BB/BBB	70-75

The recognized taxonomy groups of edible bananas are listed in Table 14.7.

Table 14.7. Taxonomic groups of edible banana.

No.	Taxonomic group	Edible bananas
1	AA Group: Diploid *Musa acuminata*, both wild banana plants and cultivars	i. Chingan banana ii. Lacatan banana iii. Lady Finger banana (Sugar banana) iv. Pisang jari buaya (Crocodile fingers banana) v. Señorita banana (Monkey, Arnibal banana, Cuarenta dias,Cariñosa, Pisang Empat, Puluh Hari, Pisang Lampung) vi. Sinwobogi banana
2	**AAA Group:** Triploid *Musa acuminata*, both wild banana plants and cultivars	• Cavendish subgroup i. Dwarf Cavendish ii. Giant Cavendish (Williams) iii. Grand Naine (Chinquita) iv. Masak Hujau

		v. Robusta vi. Red Dacca vii. Dwarf Red viii. Gros Michel • AAA-EA Subgroup East African Highland banana
3	AAAA Group: Tetraploid *Musa acuminata*, both wild bananas and cultivars	i. Bodles Altafort banana ii. Golden Beauty banana
4	AAAB Group: Tetraploid cultivars of *Musa x paradisiaca*	i. Atan banana ii. Goldfinger banana
5	AAB Group: The Iholena and Maoli-Popo'ulu (Pacific plantains)	• Iholene subgroup of cooking bananas domesticated in the Pacific region • Maoli-Popo'ulu Subgroup of cooking bananas domesticated in the Pacific region i. Maqueño banana ii. Popoulu banana • Mysore subgroup- cooking and dessert bananas • Mysore banana • Pisang Raja subgroup Pisang Raja banana • Plantain subgroup i. French plantain ii. Green French plantain iii. Horn plantain & Rhino Horn plantain iv. Nendran banana v. Pink French banana vi. Tiger banana • Pome subgroup i. Pome banana ii. Prata-anã banana (Dwarf Brazilian banana, Dwarf prata) • Silk subgroup Latundan banana (Silk banana, Apple banana) • Others i. Pisang Seribu banana ii. plu banana
6	AABB Group: Tetraploid cultivars of *Musa x paradisiaca*	i. Kalamagol banana ii. Pisang Awak (Ducasse banana)
7	AB Group: Diploid cultivars	Ney Poovan banana
8	ABB Group: Triploid cultivars	Blue Java banana (Ice Cream banana, Ney Mannan, Ash plantain, Pata hina, Dukuru, Vata) • Bluggoe Subgroup i. Bluggoe banana ii. Silver Bluggoe banana

		iii. Pelipita banana (Pelipia pilipia) • Saba Subgroup i. Saba banana (Cardaba Dippig) ii. Cardaba banana iii. Benedetta banana
9	ABBB Group: Tetraploid cultivars of *Musa x paradisiaca*	Tiparot banana
10	BB Group: Diploid *Musa balbisiana*, wild bananas	Bhimkol, Elavazhai
11	BBB Group: Triploid *Musa balbisiana*, wild bananas and cultivars	Kluai Thepanom, Lep Chang Kut, Pisang Kepok Kuning

Cultivars

The total number of cultivars of bananas and plantains has been estimated to be from around 300 to more than 1000. Names are highly confusing even within a country. Many common names do not refer to a single cultivar or clone; e.g. Lady's Finger or Lady Finger has been used as the name for members of different genome groups including AA and AAB. Many other names are synonyms of cultivars grown in the same or different countries. Attempts have been made to create lists of synonyms. Valmayor *et al.* (2000) listed equivalent local names for 68 cultivars, across 5 South East Asian countries (the Philippines, Malaysia, Indonesia, Thailand and Vietnam), together with their internationally used names. They considered other 81 cultivars to be unique to one country. Ploetz *et al.* (2007) listed cultivar names and synonyms including those grown in India, Africa and South America, but with an emphasis on those grown in Pacific islands. For the widely grown cultivar Dwarf Cavendish, they gave 58 synonyms from 29 countries or different geographical areas. Uma and Sathiamoorthy (2002) have reported names and synonyms of banana and plantains of India. The cultivar Poovan is believed to have 27 synonyms in India, including Rasthali, Sugandam and Ladiyachampa. Singh and Uma (1996a,b) have given a list of synonyms and mutants of cultivated clones of banana and plantain in India (Table 14.8).

Table 14.8. Cultivated clones of banana and plantain in India and their synonyms (Singh and Uma, 1996).

Ploidy level	Group	Subgroup	Synonyms	Mutants
2x	AA	Anai Komban	Anai Komban Hatidat Kanai Bansi	Erachi vazha (S)
		Chingan	Chinga bale Pacha Chingan	Maniyilla Chingan (S)
		Kadali, Matti, Namarai, Paka, Pisang Lilin, Sanna Chenkadali, Siguzani, Surya Kadali	Deva Kadali	

3x	AAA	Amrit Sagar (NE)	Honda (NE)	
		Chakkara keli	Rajavazhai (S), Rajabale (S), Thella Chakkarkeli (SE), Thaen Kadali (S)	
		Cavendish	Pachavazhai (S), Morris (S), Mauritius (S), Basrai (W), Jahaji (NE), Kabuli (NE), Vamankeli (S)	Padarse (W), Ambemohr (W), Shrimanti (W), Shendumi (W), Ardhapuri (W)
		Giant Cavendish, Gros Michel, Karim Kadali, Manoranjitham, Nakitemb, Namikanika, William hybrid, Zelic	Borjahaji (NE), Lacatan (NE, S), Pachottan (S), Kari Vazhai (S)	Gandevi (W)
		Robusta	Pedda Pachi Arati (S), Harichal (W), Manjahaji	
		Red Banana	Chen Kadali (S), Chevvazhai (S), Chandrabale (S), Lalkel (W), Agniswar (NE), Therek Marang (NE), Tulsi Manohar (NE), Anupan (NE), Nichila Kol (NE)	Venkadali (S), Green red, Pacha Kappa
		Wather	Kommu Arati (S), Nagabale (SW), Mohan bansi (E)	
4x	AAAA	Bodles Altafort		
2x	AB	Safed Velchi	Ney Poovan, Elakkibale (S), Elarasi (S), Njali Poovan (S), Nyali Poovan (S), Pacharasi (S), Puttabale (S), Safed Velchi (W)	
		Kunnan	Adukkan (S), Adukka Kunnan (S), Aanan (S), Poomkadali (S), Chitti Bale (S)	
		Nattu Poovan	Jirige Bale (S)	
3x	AAB	Poovan (Mysore)	Alpan (E), Champa (NE), Chini Champa (NE), Karpura Chakkarakeli (S), Kait Sein (NE), Palayankodan (S), Poovazhai (S), Cheenabale (S)	Motta Poovan, Ayiranka Poovan
		Rasthasli	Amrithpani (S), Malbhog (E), Mortman (E), Kulpait (NE), Salsikola (NE), Sabri (NE), Rasbale (S), Poovan (S)	Ayiranka Rasthali
		Nadan (Pachanadan)	Kali (S), Thaenkaali (S), Ladan (S), Gali Bali (S), Saladati (W)	Pacha arati (S), Mannan (S)

		Virupakshi (Pome)	Malavazhai (S)	Krishna Vazhai (S)
			Sirumalai (S)	Ney Vazhai (S) (red stem)
		Nendran (Plantain)	French Plantain, Rajeli (W), Bhorot (NE)	Eleri (S) (green French plantain), Anil Vazhai (wine plantain), Karu Nendran (S) (black French plantain), Nana Nendran, Kali ethan, Vali ethan, Manjeri Nendran, Nedu Nendran or Padali Mirian, Chengali Kodan, Attu Nendran
		Myndoli	Giant Plantain	
		Moongil	Horn Plantain, Zanzibar	
		Nendran Padathi	Chara Padathi (S), Radja Sirre	
		Pisang Kelat		
		Pisang Raja		
		Rajapuri (S)	Wazha (S), Kullan (S), Jawari Bale (S)	
		Thiruvanandapuram		Pisang Seribu
3x	ABB	Bluggoe	Bluggoe, Cuba, Kothia (E), Muthia (E), Chakia (E), Sakkai (S), Gauria (NE), Karibontha (S), Bangrier (N)	Coated Chakia (SE)
		Monthan	Kachakel (NE), Monthan (S), Madhuranga bale (S), Bontha (S), Yenagu Bontha (S), Nukala Bontha (S), Ponnan (S)	Sambrani Monthan (S), Boodida Bontha (S)
		Botheesa	Pacha Bontha, Batheesa	Boodida Bontha, Bontha
		Ney Mannan (S)	Ney Vannan, Vayal Vazhai	
		Peyan (S)	Pey Monthan (S), Pey Ladan, Boothi Bale (S), Bhurkel (N), Pitha guri (NE)	Vennettu Mannan (ice cream) Mayil Vazhai (S)
		Pisang Awak	Karpuravalli (S), Kanthali (E), Bharat Moni (NE), Chinali (E), Jammulapalem Collection (S), Pey Kunnan (S), Boodida Bokkisa (S), Kostha Bontha (S), Jhurmani	
		Manohar	Manohar	
		Sail Kola	Shalil Kola (NE), Manuva kola (NE)	
2x	BB	Attiakol	Till Ati (NE), Methi Athi (NE), Chepa Ati (NE), Elavazhai (S), Kallar (S)	

		Bhimkol	Mou Tupe (NE)
3x	AAA	Bodles Altafort	
4x	ABBB	Klue Teparod Hybrid	
3x		Sawai	Bhat Manoher
		Bhat Manohar	

*E= East, W= West, NE= North-East, and S= South India

Therefore, it is necessary that the comprehensive morpho-taxonomic and genetic characterization of bananas in cultivation is achieved to arrive at an internationally accepted name for each cultivar, considering synonymy and homonymy, and a common system of characterization, nomenclature and classification for these cultivars is adopted. ProMusa through Bioversity International has created an online checklist of banana cultivar names attributed to one of 15 informal groups based on ploidy and the surmised genomic contributions of wild species based on the available literature. The website has nearly 7000 entries (www. promusa.org/Banana+cultivar+ checklist).

Ortiz (2008) has clustered these cultivars into 58 types (Table 14.9).

Table 14.9. Banana cultivar types.

Genome	Type	Cultivars
AA	Banana[a]	Kluai Khai (Thailand), Lakatan (Philippines), Pisang Ambong pulih (Indonesia) Pisang lilin, Pisang Mas (Malaysia), Rose
AAA	Export banana[b]	Cavendish, Grand Nain, Poyo, Robusta, Valery, Williams, Gros Michel
AAA	Cooking/beer[c]	Musakula, Nakabululu, Nakitembe, Nfuuka
	Dessert[d]	Green-Red, Red, Yangambi Km. 5
AAB	Dessert[e]	Pome/Silk, Apple, Lady's Finger, Mysore, Poovan, Nendran
AAB	Cooking[f]	Maia Maoli, Maqueft, Popoulou
AAB	Plantain[g]	French (Dominico Harton, Hembra), French Horn, False Horn (Falso Cuerno, Hartbn, Macho), True Horn
ABB	Cooking[h]	Bluggoe (Chacaco or Chato), Cardaba, Fougamou (Pisang awak), Pelilipita, Saba, Monthan
Primary tetraploid bred-hybrids		
[AAAxAA)	Dessert	FHIA-02, FHIA-23
[AABxAA]	Dessert	FHIA-01, FHIA-18
[AABxAA]	Cooking	BITA-2 (or TMBx 5295-1)
IAABxAA]	Plantain	FHIA-21, HIA-22, TMPx series at IITA (548-9 or PITA 2, 7152-2 or PITA-14)
[ABBxBB]	Cooking	BITA-2 (or TMBx 1378)

Secondary triploid bred-hybrid	
(AABxAA]xAA)	PITA-1 6 (or TM3x 15108-6)
Complex pedigree	
Cooking	FHIA-03, FHIA-25

[a]Diploid cultivars with sweet, thin-skinned fruits from a small bunch grown mostly in East Asia.
[b]Triploid dessert cultivars for international trade and most widespread worldwide. Cavendish cultivars replaced Gros Michel in the 1960s because of *Fusarium* wilt.
[c]East African highland bananas grown for cooking or beer.
[d]Minor non-export dessert bananas grown locally in backyards by farmers around the world.
[e]Preferred local dessert bananas in Brazil, India, Hawaii and eastern Australia.
[f]Minor cooking bananas (seldom eaten as dessert) from the Pacific islands.
[g]Important staple food crop in West and Central Africa and some locations in Latin America, the Caribbean and south India; only eaten after cooking unripe or ripe fruits.
[h]Most important cooking bananas of Asia, also grown for cooking in Africa, Latin America and the Caribbean or for beer only in East Africa.
[h]All primary, secondary and complex pedigree hybrids being grown by developing world farmers, particularly when affected by Sigatoka or *Fusarium* wilt.

Fruit characteristics of some major cultivars belonging to different subgroups under the genomic groups (AA, AAA, AB, AAB, ABB, BB and BBB) are given in Table 14.10.

Table 14.10. Fruit characteristics of some major banana cultivars.

Group	Subgroup	Characteristics
AA	**Sucrier** cvs: Pisang Mas, Kluai Khai, Amas, Sucrier; Lady's Finger	Small fruit (8-12 cm long), thin golden skin, light orange firm flesh, very sweet, 5-9 hands per bunch, 12-18 fingers per hand.
	Lakatan cvs: Pisang Barangan, Pisang Herangan, Senortia	Medium to large straight fruit (12-18 cm), golden yellow, flesh light orange, firm, dry, sweet and aromatic, 6-12 hands per bunch, 12-20 fingers per hand.
AAA	**Gros Michel** cvs.: Pisang Ambon, Kluai, Hom Thong	Medium to large fruit, thick skin, creamy white flesh, fine textured, sweet and aromatic, 8-12 hands/bunch
	Cavendish cvs.: Dwarf Cavendish, Basrai, Governor, Giant Cavendish, Grand Naine, Williams	Medium to large fruit, yellow skin, white to creamy flesh, melting, sweet, aromatic, 14-20 hands per bunch.
	East African highland banana cvs.: Musakula, Nakabululu, Nakitembe, Nfuuka	The East African Highland bananas are extensively pigmented black or brown with glossy pseudostems and robust dirty green leaves deeply split along the veins. These are cooking and beer cultivars different from the *M. acuminata* triploids found along the East African coast, which are mainly dessert types.
	Red subgroup cvs.: Red Banana, Red Dacca, Green Red	Fruit is dull scarlet red, medium long, thick and sour.

AB	**Ney Poovan** cvs.: Ney Poovan, Lady's Finger	Sweet, subacid fruit with white flesh.
AAB	**Silk** cvs.: Apple, Pisang Rasthali, Pisang Raya Serek	Small to medium yellow fruit (10-15 cm) yellow orange skin, white flesh, soft slightly subacid, 5-9 hands per bunch, 12-16 fingers per hand skin frequently has blemishes
	Pisang Raja cv.: Pisang Raja	Large fruit (14-20 cm), thick skin cooking banana creamy orange flesh, coarse texture, 6-9 hands per bunch, and 14-16 fingers per hand.
	Plantain cv.. Nendran	Yellow skin, creamy orange firm flesh, 2 hands per bunch
	Pome **cv.:** Virupkshi	Fruits are distinctly beaked or bottle-nosed and have subacid or apple-like taste.
	Maoli-Popoulu cvs.: Manini, Pacific Plantain	This subgroup is recognized by its sausage shaped fruit with blunt ends.
	Mysore cv.: Mysore	Widely spread dessert clone is vigorous and resists Panama and Sigatoka leaf spots.
ABB	**Bluggoe** cvs.: Bluggoe, Dwarf Bluggoe	Medium to large cooking banana, thick coarse skin turns brownish red when ripe, creamy orange flesh, starchy, 7 hands per bunch.
	Monthan cv.: Monthan	Its characterstícts fruits bear large bulbous tips, resembling Bluggoe but large.
	Ney Mannan cvs.: Ney Mannan, Blue Lubin, Blue Java	The fruit is named for its flavor and texture, sweet and smooth.
	Pisang Awak cvs.: Ducasse, Kluai Namwa Khom	It is vigorous and tolerates adverse conditions especially drought but susceptible to race 1 of panama disesease.
BBB	**Saba** cvs.: Benedetta, Cardaba, Saba	Stout, angular, medium to large cooking banana (10-15 cm), thick yellow skin, creamy white flesh, fine textured, 8-16 hands per bunch, 12-20 fingers per hand.

Important cultivars and clones of banana in India

A. Table purpose

i) Red coloured fruits

Red Banana or Lal Kel (AAA) syn. Chen Kadali, Sevazhai, Anupani, Rathambala, Red banana, Red Spanish, Red Cuban, Colorado: It may have originated in India. It is most relished and choice cultivar of Tamil Nadu, Kerala, Karnataka, Andhra Pradesh and to some extent in western and central India. It grows up to 1300 m altitude above msl. Its name is Red Banana because the pseudostem, leaf margin, petiole, midrib and fingers all have marked purple red or reddish pigmentation. The plant is tall, robust and free suckering. It is 3.6-4.5 m in height. It thrives in coastal areas and requires heavy irrigation and manuring. The plant takes 18 months from planting to harvest. The bunch is compact, heavy and weighs about 18-20 kg and may contain over 100 fruits. The fingers are large, spindle shaped, stout and straight having short pedicel and blunt tip. The fruit skin is thick and leathery, dull scarlet red and peels easily. The peel colour turns orange yellow when the fruit is fully ripe. The pulp is saffron coloured, moist, juicy and sweet having pleasant flavour but is slightly starchy and does not match in quality with other bananas. It is highly susceptible to leaf spot diseases, bunchy top, *Fusarium* wilt and nematodes.

Green Red: The plant of the mutant is variegated green and red, becomes 8.5 m tall with the pseudostem 45 cm thick at the base. The bunch bears 4 to 7 hands. The fruits are thick and 12.5-17.5 cm long. The purplish red peel changes to orange yellow and the flesh is firm, cream coloured and of good quality.

Sanna Chenkadalai (AA): It resembles Red Banana as the pseudostem, petiole and midrib are red coloured. It is a hardy cultivar. It is tolerant to leaf spot diseases. The cultivar performs well even under shade in coconut groves. Crop duration is 12 months. Bunch is medium sized. The fruit is small, slender having a pronounced tip and red peel. The pulp is light orange yellow.

ii) Green coloured fruits

Cavendish Banana (AAA): It is very hardy and can thrive in dry climates away from the sea coast. It can also stand strong winds. Humid climate is not a prerequisite for its cultivation but it requires irrigation. It is resistant to Panama disease but is susceptible to leaf spot (*Cercospora*). It is male as well female sterile and thus it is not possible to develop its hybrids with other cultivars. Parthenocarpy is present. The cultivars under this group are:

Dwarf Cavendish (AAA) syn. Basrai, Basrai Dwarf, Pacha Vazhai, Hirvi, Mauritius, Vamankeli, Kabuli, Jaahaji, Bhusaval, Chittidar: The cultivars developed by mutation from tall members of the Cavendish subgroup (Constantine and Rossel, 2001) and are easily recognized because the male bracts and flowers do not shed. Being high yielding and able to withstand strong winds, Dwarf Cavendish group cultivars contribute 57% of total production. These prefer moist coastal climate and are widely cultivated especially in the Canary Islands, East and South Africa and are mostly grown in Maharashtra, Andhra Pradesh and Tamil Nadu. They perform well in light soils with high inputs and are suitable for dry areas where irrigation facility is available. These are resistant to Panama wilt but are highly susceptible to Sigatoka leaf spot and bunchy top. The plants are dwarf (1.5-2 m in height), less prone to wind damage and suitable for high density planting, and are sterile. The bunch is large weighing about 30 kg with 6-7 hands and having about 130-160 fingers. The bunch is somewhat irregular and loose (less compact). The fingers are large, somewhat curved, dull yellow or green yellow, thin skinned and ripen late and drop after ripening. The peel retains the greenish colour to some extent even when the fruits are ripe. The flesh is soft, sweet, and highly aromatic and has practically no starch. The keeping quality of the fruit is poor and must be handled and shipped with care. Fruit is used for both table purpose and processing.

Several superior Cavendish clones have been identified. Gandevi Selection known as Hanuman or Padase is gaining popularity despite longer crop duration. It produces bunches weighing 5560 kg and performs better in light soils with higher inputs.

Giant Cavendish (AAA) (Mons Mari, Williams, Williams Hybrid, or Grand Naine): It is of uncertain origin. It closely resembles the Gros Michel and has replaced the Dwarf Cavendish in Colombia, Australia, Martinique, in many Hawaiian plantations and to some extent in Ecuador. It is the commercial banana of Taiwan. The plant reaches 2.7- 4.9 m height. The pseudostem is splashed with dark brown. The bunch is long and cylindrical and the fruits are larger than those of the Dwarf Cavendish and not as delicate. The bunch has 7-14 hands and weighs 20-60 kg (22 kg average). Male bracts and flowers are shed leaving a space between the fruits and the terminal bud.

Grand Naine (AAA): It is a selection from Giant Cavendish, identified to be the major export cultivar. It has potential to bear a 40 kg bunch. This cultivar has replaced the famous Gros Michel which succumbed to *Fusarium* wilt. Plant characters resemble Cavendish in most of the parameters except for its robust stature, well spaced hands with straight fingers of bigger size. Each bunch has 10 to 12 hands each with 175 to 225 fruits. The bunch is heavy weighing 2530 kg and requires propping. The fruits develop attractive yellowish green colour at maturity and are delicious to eat and have good keeping quality. The pulp to peel ratio is high making it highly suitable for processing.

Robusta (AAA): It is also called Morris. It is a semi-dwarf mutant of the tall Lacatan. It is very similar to Lacatan and has largely replaced it in Jamaica and the Windward Islands and the Gros Michel in Central America because its plants are shorter, thick stemmed and less subject to wind damage. The plant is medium sized having dark purple stem with greenish tinge. It is also grown commercially in Brazil, eastern Australia, Samoa and Fiji. The cultivar is resistant to Panama disease but is highly susceptible to Sigatoka and susceptible to leaf spot, corm weevil, rhizome rot and mosaic diseases. The crop duration is 12-14 months. The bunch is pendulous having 7-9 hands each with 12-15 fingers. The bunch, on an average, weighs 25-30 kg and has 100 fingers. The fruits are green to dull yellow and large having medium thick skin. Fruits turn bright yellow upon ripening. Ripe fruits drop off easily. The fruit pulp is sweet, juicy having agreeable flavour. The fruits have better keeping quality than those of Dwarf Cavendish but are not suitable for long distance transport.

Valery (AAA): It is a triploid Cavendish clone, closely resembling Robusta and is believed to be the same but is grown as a successor to Robusta. It is more widely cultivated than Lacatan for export. Compared to other cooking banana clones, it has low rating because on cooking its flesh hardens giving a waxy texture. Jamaica has developed a number of tetraploid clones with superior disease resistance. Some are equal in dessert quality to Lacatan and Valery.

Chakkerakeli (AAA): The plant is slender, medium in size with open and conspicuously red petiole borders. Crop duration is 13 months. The bunch weighing 10 kg has 8 hands of 12 fingers each. The fruit is of medium size, cylindrical with somewhat 5 cornered non-prominent ridges, long and tough pedicel and thin skin that peels off easily. The pulp is yellowish, juicy, tasty, exceedingly sweet but of poor keeping quality.

Virupakshi (AAB): This high quality cultivar can be grown rainfed as monocrop or mixed with coffee plantation. It can be grown in perennial system but this aggravates Banana Bunchy Top Virus (BBTV). The plant is tall (4.5 to 5.0 m). Crop duration is 15-18 months. It is a poor yielder. The bunch is small (8-12 kg with 80-90 fruits) having 7-8 hands of 10-12 fruits each. The fruit is small to medium, prominently ridged having thick, leathery and greenish yellow skin that turns black when overripe. It peels easily. The fruits are strongly attached to pedicel even on ripening. The pulp is white or pale yellow, dry and sweet and develops delightful characteristic flavour when cultivated at high altitudes. Keeping quality is very good.

iii) Yellow coloured fruits

Matti (AA): It is grown largely in southern districts of Tamil Nadu especially maintained in backyards. The plants are less hardy, of medium size and slender growing to a height of 2-2.5 m. Its yellowish green pseudostem has unevenly spread brown blotches. Leaves are pale. Inflorescence emerges 12-13 months after planting and is horizontal to the main axis. Peduncle is very short and fruits appear right from the axils of the leaves. Although slender, the plant has the potential to put forth as heavy bunch as 25 kg. The bunch has 8-15 hands and each hand has 14-20 fruits. Male axis is inclined at an angle of 45° and has 5-8 persistent male flowers just below the bunch. Male flowers are white in colour. Fruit is small, long, thin and slender with a conspicuous beak. Pulp is juicy, very sweet and cream coloured with characteristic aroma. Being male and female fertile, the cultivar is useful in breeding. At ripe stage, its bunches do not have berry shatter.

Kadali (AA): The cultivar is known by names such as Ambalakadali, Nivedya Kadali, etc. The bunch weight is 8-10 kg. It is a small fruited cultivar and is mainly grown for offerings in the temple.

Namarai (AA): It is a good male parent for breeding. It is not a hardy cultivar and grows in pulney hills of Tamil Nadu. Crop duration is 12 months. The fruits are small and have good taste. Plants are susceptible to Sigatoka disease and nematodes.

Ney Poovan (AB) syn. Elakki Bale, Ney Kadali, Hoobale, Vadakkan Kadali, Deva Bale, Putta Sugantha, Chini Champa: It used to be a delicate backyard plant of choice, but now occupies large area in Karnataka. The cultivar is an unique diploid assuming large scale commercial monoclonal cultivation. The plant is slender and medium tall having about 12-13 months crop duration. The bunch orientation is horizontal weighing 1820 kg with small fruits packed closely and having a windblown appearance. The fruits have good keeping quality. The pulp is ivory coloured, firm, sweet having good aroma with conspicuous ovules. The cultivar is highly susceptible to Banana Bract Mosaic Virus (BBMV) and *Fusarium* wilt.

Ney Mannan (AB) syn. Vayal Vazhai, Ney Vannan, Naattu Vazhai: The plant is robust and of medium height. Crop duration is 12 months. The bunch is large (18 kg), compact having up to 10 hands. The fruits are small to medium, plump at base, tapering at apex and irregularly 5 sided with a thick beak. The peel is thick, tough and dark green turning orange yellow when ripe. It peels easily. The pulp is firm, white and not very sweet.

Poovan (AAB Mysore) syn. Champa, Lal Velchi, Chini Champa, Karpoor Chakrakeli: It requires comparatively warmer climate. It is considered to be an important table cultivar in India and is grown commercially in southern and northeastern States close to the coast and commands large area. The plants are tall and slender, vigorous, very hardy and drought tolerant. Midrib of the petiole is marked with pink colouration. The cropping is abundant and year round. Crop duration is 11-14 months. It bears a large compact bunch weighing about 25 kg having 225 fingers. The fruits are small to medium in size, cylindrical and plump, thin-skinned, attractive and of bright yellow colour having thin skin that peels easily. The flesh is firm and sour-sweet of subacid taste and good flavour. The fingers do not drop after ripening. The fruits are resistant to cracking and have fairly high keeping quality. It is resistant to Panama wilt and Sigatoka and fairly resistant to bunchy top. It is highly susceptible to BBMV and Banana Streak Virus (BSV). In Trinidad, it is cultivated as shade for cacao.

Rasthali (Silk AAB) syn. Mortman, Amritpani, Muthali, Rasbale, Soneri, Malbhog, Sonkel: It is similar to Poovan in many respects but is of bit superior quality. It thrives well in high rainfall districts. It is rated as one of the most preferred cultivar in West Bengal. The plant is tall (4-4.5 m) and has distinct brownish specks/blotches on the bright yellowish green stem with reddish petiole and leaf sheath margin. Few male flowers persist after the female flowers phase out. The crop duration is 14-15 months. The bunch weighs about 20 kg having 5-7 hands and 130 fingers. The fingers are plump and small to medium in size like that of Poovan. The fingers are cylindrical to spindle shaped having weak pedicel, shining and ivory-like yellow and thin to medium thick skin that peels easily. The fruits ripen slowly and do not hang well after ripening. The pulp is fairly firm, sweet acidic with pleasant flavour. Keeping quality of the fruit is good. Susceptibility to Panama wilt, formation of hard lump in pulp and finger drop are limiting factors. The fruits are prone to cracking due to sun scorch.

Ayrinka Rasthali (AAB) syn. Poovilla Konnai, Ayrinka Poovan: It is a bud variant of Rasthali. It varies from Rasthali only because there are no male flowers and the whole axis is full with fruits. Crop duration is 15 months. The bunch weighs 25 kg and has 500 fruits. The fruits on first 5-6 hands are similar to those of Rasthali and differ only in size.

Sirumalai (AAB): It is considered to be an ecotype of Virupakshi. It is more profuse in flowering and the fruit pulp is juicier and sweeter but not as dry. The attachment of fruit to the pedicel is not as strong as in Virupakshi. Crop duration is 14 months.

Safed Velchi (AAB): It is considered to be a superior cultivar. The plants are tall and slender. The fruit is very small. The fruit skin is papery thin and milky yellow in colour. The pulp is firm, milky white, rather dry and sweet and has agreeable flavour but is slightly starchy. The keeping quality of the fruit is good.

Thella Chakkerakeli (AAA): It is also popular as Bharath Moni. It is grown commercially in Andhra Pradesh, but is a choice backyard cultivar in Tamil Nadu and Assam. The plants are delicate growing to a height of 2.0-2.3 m completing their crop cycle in 12 months. The fruits have excellent orange pulp with unique taste. Fruit skin is green when mature and turns golden yellow upon ripening. The cultivar is susceptible to wilt and Sigatoka leaf spot diseases and to parasitic nematodes like

Radopholus similis and *Pratylenchus coffeae.* Due to these biotic factors and abiotic stresses the overall yield level is considerably low.

Lacatan (AAA): It is a dessert cultivar. The fruits develop an attractive golden yellow colour and a very aromatic and excellent flavour when ripe. The fruit is 10-20 cm in length. The peel can be removed easily. On peeling, some sticking rags reveal a light orange to orange pulp.

Njalipoovan (AB): It is a popular shade loving cultivar and is suitable for intercropping in coconut both under rainfed and irrigated conditions. It is less susceptible to most of the pests and diseases and is adapted to ratooning. It is more valuable than Palayan Kodan. The fruits are delicious having very sweet and soft pulp and thin peel. But the fruits fall off the bunch and have poor keeping quality.

Kunnan (AB): It is very commonly grown in Kerala. The dual purpose cultivar has a duration of about 16 months. The bunch weighing 5-8 kg has 7-9 hands. The fruits have good keeping quality and are used as dessert and for making powder.

Pachanadan (AAB): It is popular in Tamil Nadu. The cultivar is well suited as an intercrop in coconut/arecanut. It is tolerant to leaf spot and Banana Bunchy Top Virus (BBTV) but is susceptible to wilt disease. It can be used for gap filling Nendran as the fillers become ready for harvest along with the main plantation. Crop duration is about 15 months. The bunch weighs 12-15 kg after 11-12 months. The fruits can be used both when green and ripe.

Karpuravalli (ABB) syn. Kanthali, Jammulapalem Collection, Pisang Awak, Chinali, Pey Kunnan, Kosta Bontha and Jhurmani Kanthali: It is commercially cultivatied in central and southern districts of Tamil Nadu and Kerala. It is a very sweet dessert cultivar and does well in marginal soils even under alkaline conditions. It is fairly tolerant to corm weevil. The plant is stout, vigorous and about 3.0 m tall with large leaves and light pink streaked pseudostem. It can also be grown for leaf production. Crop duration is 12-14 months. The bunch has 100 to 120 fruits on 8-9 compact hands each having 13-14 fingers. The fruit is of medium size, persistent on pedicel even after ripening. The skin is medium thick, yellow with ashy coating. The pulp is sweet, juicy and firm having pleasant flavour.

B. Dual purpose

Nendran (AAB) syn. French Plantain: This cultivar is believed to have originated in southern India from where it spread to Africa. It is the most prized cooking cultivar in Kerala, fetching premium price during festive occasions. The cultivar is grown in the lower Palani Hills of Kodaikanal in Tamil Nadu. It is grown as monocrop or mixed in coffee plantation but is not suitable for ratooning. The cultivar is good for processing. Products made from this cultivar have high value.

The plants are tall (4.5-5.0 m) and slender with distinct pigmentation on younger leaves and pink shade on pseudostem. Male axis is not naked but is covered with persistent male bracts and flowers. Crop duration is 11-12 months. Bunch is not compact and weighs 10-15 kg having 4-6 hands and 3050 fingers with 3 prominent ridges and a distinct nipple. Fruits are large, long and have a distinct neck with thick and leathery green skin turning buff yellow on ripening. It is difficult to peel. The fruit remains starchy even after ripening. The pulp is firm, coloured and medium sweet having fairly conspicuous core and mild flavour. The fruits have good keeping quality and are edible both when ripe and raw or used as vegetable at mature unripe stage.

The cultivar is highly susceptible to BBTV and BBMV and leaf diseases like Black Sigatoka. It is also susceptible to Neer Vazhai, a malady of unknown etiology where fingers remain poorly filled and only of pencil thickness.

The strain Rajeli is somewhat dwarf having 2.7-3.6 m tall plants. It is comparatively sterile. The bunch is small and loose. The fruit is 22.5-25.0 cm long, angular, curved and tapering towards the apex. The fruit skin is thin. The pulp is very hard, starchy and sweet. A number of mutants, perhaps bud mutants, such as Zanzibar, Otta Moongil, Moongil, Kali Ethan, Valietnan, Manjeri, Chengalikodan, Nedu Nendran, Chenganacheri Nendran, Attu Nendran, Myndoli and Padali Murian are known.

Hill banana (AAB) syn. Virupakshi: The cultivar prefers cool conditions and performs the best at 600-900 m altitudes. It is very popular in the hills of Tamil Nadu. Plants are usually perennial. The fruits drop after ripening. The bunch is small, of 10-12 kg having 80-100 fingers. The fruit is of medium size, angular and dusty yellow in colour and of good quality. The fruit skin is thick. The pulp is white, slimy and moist with buttery consistency. It is not so juicy but is rather dry and sweet and slightly sour in taste. It has dwarf cultivar Rajapuri (1.8-2.1 m height) and tall cultivars Sirumalai and Virupakshi (3.3 m height).

Sakkai (ABB) syn. Chakia, Gauria, Muthia: It is commercially cultivated under low input conditions owing to its tolerance to drought, salinity and nematodes. It is grown in Bihar, Tamil Nadu (Madurai, Tirunelveli and Kanyakumari districts) and Kerala. The plant is medium tall having sturdy pseudostem growing to a height of 2.75 m with sparsely spread blotches. The plant takes 12-14 months to come to harvest. Inflorescence has pendulous female axis with 5-8 hands each having 12-14 fruits. Bunch weighs about 15-18 kg. Fruits are short, stout, without knob and with a small inconspicuous beak without any cap of uniformly green colour. Thus it is grouped under Bluggoe. Fruit skin is 0.3 - 0.4 mm thick and peels off easily. Green Sakkai is an ash coated mutant similar to Sakkai in all aspects except for the ash coating of fruits.

C. Cooking bananas

Monthan (ABB) syn. Kanchkela, Ponthan, Bontha, Bainsa, Bankel, and Khasadia: It is an important exclusive culinary banana widely cultivated for processing and for its therapeutic value. It is a cooking type but can also be eaten fresh. This is the only banana that can be grown in northwest India. Bud sports also exist. The plants are tall and stout, hardy and grow well under low moisture regimes. It is highly tolerant to drought, salinity and high winds and fairly tolerant to nematodes and leaf spot and rhizome rot diseases. The cultivar is suitable for growing as intercrop in coconut garden and for leaf production. The crop duration is 12-14 months. The bunch is small, of about 15-25 kg having 100 fingers. The fruit is angular and shoe-shaped, slightly curved, almost straight on one side, broad at base and tapering towards the apex with prominent knob-like beak and long pedicel. It is irregularly five sided having prominent ridges. The fruit skin is very thick, tough and dark green turning straw yellow and is difficult to peel. The pulp is moist, soft, spongy, slightly sweet, subacid with a hard core in the centre. When properly ripe, it becomes soft and fleshy. It is susceptible to '*Fusarium* wilt race 4'.

Batheesa (ABB): The bunch is broad at the base and then tapers below giving a uniform and symmetrical shape. This is because the opening of the flowers is in succession from the base to the apex and thus while the basal fingers are long and ripe, the fingers at the apex are still unripe and some of the flowers may still be opening. Therefore, unevenly ripened bunches are usually harvested.

Bontha (ABB): The bunch has 5-6 hands. The fruit is short, slightly curved with prominent ridges and blunt apex and has thick and green rind and whitish pulp. The male bud is also used for culinary purpose.

Saba (ABB): It is an introduction from Philippines. Sometimes it is also known as Cardaba (the name more correctly applied to a very similar cultivar also classified within Saba subgroup). It is a promising culinary cultivar suitable for saline sodic soils (pH 8.5-8.75). It is primarily a cooking banana though it can also be eaten raw. The plant is sturdy and somewhat cold tolerant. The pseudostem is very large and robust that can reach height of 6.1-9.1 m. The fruits become ready for harvesting 150 to 180 days after flowering, later than in other banana cultivars. The fruits are 8 to 13 cm long and 2.5 to 5.5 cm in diameter and distinctively squarish and angular depending on ripeness. The pulp is white and sweet when ripe but is very starchy making it ideal for cooking. The bunch weighs 26 to 38 kg having 16 hands, each with 12 to 20 fingers. The cultivar has good resistance against Sigatoka leaf spot.

Promising cultivars

Bluggoe (ABB): It is a cooking banana especially resistant to Panama disease and Sigatoka. It bears a few distinctly separated hands of large, almost straight and starchy fruits that are of great importance in Burma, Thailand, South India, East Africa, the Philippines, Samoa and Grenada.

Pisang Masak Hijau (Bungulan): This triploid Cavendish clone of the Philippines, Indonesia and Malaya is erroneously called Lacatan in Jamaica where it replaces Gros Michel because of its immunity to Panama disease, though it is subject to Sigatoka. The plant is tall and slender and prone to wind injury. Its fruits ripen unevenly in winter, bruise easily and tend to spoil in storage. The fruits are commonly used as cooking bananas in Jamaican households. Simmonds declared that this cultivar is not the true Lacatan of the Philippines and suggested that Pisang Masak Hijau may have been the primary source of all the members of the Cavendish group.

Silk, Silk Fig or Apple (Manzana in Spanish): It is the most popular dessert banana and is widely distributed around the tropics and subtropics but is never grown on a large scale. The plant is 3-3.6 m tall, medium in vigour, very resistant to Sigatoka but is prone to Panama disease. There are only 6 to 12 hands in the bunch, each with 16 to 18 fruits. The plump fruits are 10-15 cm long, slightly curved, astringent when unripe but pleasantly subacid when fully ripe and apple-scented. If left on the bunch until fully developed, the thin skin splits lengthwise and breaks at the stem end causing the fruit to fall, but it remains firm and keeps well in the home.

IC 2 (AAAA) (Golden Beauty): The cultivar (bred at the Imperial College of Tropical Agriculture, Trinidad by crossing Gros Michel with wild *M. acuminata*) is resistant to Panama disease and is very resistant to Sigatoka. The cultivar has small fruits borne on short bunches. They ship and ripen well. This cultivar is grown for export in Honduras and has been planted in Hawaii, Samoa and Fiji.

Lady's Finger (AAB): The plant is of normal size. The bunch has 7-10 hands and weighs 10-30 kg (13 kg average). The fruit is thin-skinned, about 2.5 cm in diameter and 10 cm in length. Its flavour is superior to the common bananas.

Blue Java (ABB) (Ice Cream banana, Hawaiian banana, Ney Mannan, Krie or Cenizo): It is a relative of Bluggoe. The plant grows to 3-4.5 m height. The leaf midrib is light pink, the flower stalk may be very long, but the bunch has only 7 to 9 hands. The fruit is 17.5-22.8 cm long, up to 6.25 cm thick, 4 to 5-angled, bluish with a silvery bloom when young and pale yellow when ripe. The flesh is white, sweetish and is eaten raw or cooked.

Orinoco (ABB) (Horse, Hog, Burro): The plants are medium tall, sturdy and hardy. The fruit bunches consist of only a few hands of very thick, 3- angled fruits about 15 cm in length. The flesh is firm and has salmon tint. The raw fruit is edible but when fully ripe it is much better when cooked, fried and baked as plantains.

Promising selections and hybrids

Udhayam (ABB): A single plant selection from Kenthali (Pisang Awak (AAB) subgroup). Bunch weight is 45-50 kg (average 37 kg; 40% higher than Karpuravalli). It is a hardy cultivar suitable for growing in wind prone areas. The cultivar is resistant to bunchy top and salinity but is highly susceptible to *Fusarium* wilt. The plant is tall and robust. Crop duration is 13 months. It produces high yield from ratoons also. It exhibits field tolerance to Sigatoka leaf spot and nematodes. The bunch is cylindrical having well spaced hands and hence less liable to damage during long distance transportation. Fruits have 31°B TSS with harmonious blend of acidity making it suitable for processing into figs, juice, wine, etc. The cultivar is considered suitable for Tamil Nadu, Andhra Pradesh, Kerala, Bihar, West Bengal and Tripura.

BRS-1 (Agniswar x Pisang Lilin): It is a pome type triploid (AAB) hybrid and having a short cropping cycle with resistance to leaf spot, *Fusarium* wilt and nematode (*Radopholus similis*). The plant is medium statured with 14-16 kg bunch having elongated fruits that turn attractive golden yellow on ripening. Fruits are rich in sugar and have slight acidity that vanishes upon full ripening. It has fast ratoonability, completing 4 crop cycles in 3 years.

BRS-2 (Vannan x Pisang Lilin): It is Poovan type cultivar and belongs to Mysore subgroup. Plants are medium-statured growing up to 2-2.5 m in height. Its crop cycle is short with bunch coming to harvest in 11-12 months. Bunch weight is 15-20 kg with short, stout, dark green fruits as of Poovan that are arranged very compactly. Fruits are slightly acidic with pleasant sweet sour aroma. It is tolerant to leaf spot and nematodes.

CO-1 (Laden (AAB) x Clone Sarvar (BB) --F_1 x Kadali): It is a pome hybrid with AAB genome developed by 3-way sequential crosses. The cultivar is suitable for growing in the plains and hills up to 1200 m altitude. Crop duration is 14 months. Fruit yield is 22 t/ha. It retains the typical apple flavour of Virupakshi even when grown in the plains and has small bunch. Virupakshi develops aroma only when grown at higher altitudes.

H-1 (Agniswar x Pisang Lilin; AAB): It is short duration cultivar having resistance to leaf spot, *Fusarium* wilt and burrowing nematodes and has early ratooning ability.

H-2 (Vanan x Pisang Lilin): It is a short duration cultivar, tolerant to leaf spot and nematodes having average bunch weight of 15-20 kg.

FHIA-01 (SH-3142 x Dwarf Prata; AAAB): It is also known as Gold Finger. The cultivar is heavy yielder, tolerant to sodic and saline soils and resistant to Sigatoka, *Fusarium* wilt and nematode. Bearing commences in 14-15 months. The bunch weighs 20-25 kg. The fruit pulp has sub acidic apple-like flavour and good keeping quality. This high yielding hybrid replaces Pachanadan and Bluggoe.

FHIA-02 (William x SH-3393; AAAA): It is from Honduras. It is highly resistant to Sigatoka but is susceptible to *Fusarium* wilt.

FHIA-3 (SH-3386 x SH-3320; AABB): It is from Honduras. It is drought tolerant hybrid, dwarf and resistant to Sigatoka disease.

FHIA-17 (Highgate x SH-3362): It is from Honduras. It has good quality attributes and is resistant to black Sigatoka.

FHIA-21 (AVP-67 x SH-3142): It is from Honduras. It has good plantain quality, resistance to black Sigatoka and produces larger bunches.

BITA-1 (Bluggoe x Calcutta 4): It is from Nigeria. It is tetraploid and resistant to black Sigatoka and *Fusarium* wilt.

BITA-2 (Pisang Awak x *Musa bulbisiana*): It is from Nigeria. It is tetraploid and resistant to black Sigatoka and *Fusarium* wilt.

Table 14.11. Relative susceptibility of some banana cultivars to diseases (Broadley *et al.*, 2004).

Cultivar	Yellow Sigatoka	Black Sigatoka	Panama Disease Race 1	Panama Disease Subtropical Race 4
Williams and other Cavendish	Susceptible	Susceptible	Resistant	Susceptible
Ladyfinger	Susceptible	Susceptible	Susceptible	Susceptible
Ducasse	Resistant	Resistant	Susceptible	Susceptible
Pacific Plantain	Moderately susceptible	Moderately susceptible	Susceptible	Susceptible
Gold Finger	Moderately resistant	Moderately resistant	Resistant	Resistant
Red Decca group	Moderately susceptible	Moderately susceptible	Susceptible	Susceptible
Bonanza	Moderately resistant	Resistant	Resistant	Resistant

Notable cultivars

Rose (AA), Pisang Lillin (AA), Gros Michel (AAA), Dwarf Cavendish (AAA), Robusta (AAA), IC2 (AAA), Bodles Altafort (AAA), Ney Poovan (AB), Poovan (AAB), Silk (AAB), Nendran (AAB), Monthan (ABB), Klue Teparod (ABBB), Atan (AAAB), and Gold Finger (AAAB). The cultivars Highgate (AAA), Gros Michel (AAA), Poovan (AAB), Motta Poovan (AAB), Ayiranka Rasthali, Rasthali, Novaria and Grand Naine are mutants.

The cultivar Calcutta is resistant to black Sigatoka, Pisang Lillin to Panama wilt, SH3142 to *Fusarium*, SH699 to moko disease, Pisang Jari and Buaya (PJB) to burrowing nematode and Tangat and Anaikomban to nematodes.

⑧ ⑧ ⑧

Chapter 15

POALES

It has a large group of 16-17 families. The plants are mostly herbaceous with siliceous epidermis. Mycorrhiza is usually absent. Leaves are grassy, minute, chaffy and without nectaries. Styles are separate or connate but strongly branched. The order includes several basal groups which have showy insect pollinated flowers. Many of its members have small, reduced and typically wind pollinated flowers.

Family Bromeliaceae (pineapple or bromeliad family)

This is almost exclusively native to the Americas, occurring from Virginia in the USA to Patagonia in South America. *Pitcairnia feliciana* is native to Africa. *Racinaea insularis* is found in Galapagos Islands and *Greigia berteroi* and *Ochagavia elegans* in Juan Fernandez Islands in the Pacific. *Tillandsia usneoides* is supposed to be one of the world's widest-ranging plants. Bromeliads occur in a variety of different habitats, characteristically in Neotropical forests, but are also common in arid areas and at altitudes up to 4500 m in the Andes mountain range. The family is divided into three subfamilies, Pitcarnioideae, Tillandsioideae and Bromelioideae. Pineapple belongs to subfamily Bromelioideae. It contains 56 genera and 2600 species. According to Luther and Sieff (1998) this is the largest family having 56 genera and 2794 species whose natural distribution is restricted to the New World. Pineapple of the genus *Ananas* is the most important economic plant in the Bromeliaceae. The other edible species are *Bromelia antiacantha* Bertoloni, *B. balansae* Mel, *B. chrysantha* Jacquin, *B. karatas* L., *B. hemisphaerica* Lamarck, *B. nidus-puellae* (E. Morren) L.B. Smith and L.B. Smith, *B. pinguin* L. and *B. trianae* Mez.

The plants are acaulescent, epiphytic or eminently xerophytic and shrub-like. Most bromeliads are herbaceous epiphytes, but a few have elongated stems or are rosette trees. Their epidermal cells are usually associated with solitary silica bodies. They vary in size from few centimeters in some epiphytic species of *Tillandsia* to 3 m in *Puya raimondii*. The roots in epiphytic species anchor the plant. The most specialized epiphytic genus (*Tillandsia*) lacks roots (except in young seedlings) and leaf base tanks and absorb water from the atmosphere by means of multicellular peltate hairs.

The leaves are stiff, usually evergreen with spiny margins and spirally arranged forming a rosette. The basal leaves are long, slender, trough-like sheathing at base.

There is seamless transition between the sheath and the blade, but often show characteristic differences in colour. In the terrestrial species, the leaves have unexpanded leaf bases and leaf hairs that serve only to reduce transpiration. In some tank forming species (*Ananas*), the overlapping leaf bases act as reservoirs for water and humus, which are utilized by adventitious roots growing between the leaf bases. The majority of genera have larger leaf base tanks and absorption from the tanks is mainly carried out by specialized hairs (trichomes) composed of a foot, a stalk of living cells, and a shield of dead cells. These hairs are often positioned at the bottom of a pit and expand when wetted so that water is drawn into the dead cells of the hair and then osmotically through the living cells of the stalk of the trichome into the leaf. The scales collapse when dry, closing the pit forming a lid and permitting gas exchange through the stomata (almost entirely confined to the underside of the leaves) but reducing water loss from the surface of the plant. The plants can thus survive in extremely arid habitats, but not in very humid habitats such as rain forests. The tanks may hold up to 5 litres of water.

The inflorescence is terminal and indeterminate, produced out of the centre of the tank in tank forming species and may be a spike, raceme or panicle, often with brightly coloured, conspicuous bracts, rarely with solitary flowers (*Tillandsia*). Many bromeliads die after flowering. The flowers are bisexual or rarely functionally unisexual (*Hectia*), usually actinomorphic, although slightly zygomorphic in some genera (*Pitcairnia*). The flowers have perianth differentiated into a calyx and corolla, borne in the axil of often brightly coloured bracts. These are in two series– outer one calyx-like and the inner one corolla-like having free or united segments. The segments are 6, mostly attached to the base of the petals and often adnate to them. The flowers are 3-merous, with a greenish calyx and a showy petaloid corolla. The 6 free stamens are often attached to the base of the perianth or more or less fused. Pollen grains are monosulcate or disulcate or with 2 to several pores. The ovary is superior to inferior with axile placentation and are 3-celled consisting of 3 fused carpels with many ovules. Nectaries are usually in septa of ovary. The stigmas are 3-lobed, usually spirally twisted and borne on a slender style. The perianth is accessory when the ovary is inferior. The fruit is a berry or capsule. The seeds contain a small embryo and copious mealy and starchy endosperm. In several genera, the seeds have wings, are plumose or have tailed appendages. In most genera, the showy inflorescences and the nectaries on the septa of the ovaries are adaptations to facilitate pollination by humming birds and bats or insects (Heywood *et al*., 2007).

Genus *Ananas* Mill. (n=25, 2n=50, 3n=75)

Type: *Bromelia ananas* Linnaeus (1753)

Plants do not produce stolons. The leaves are rosulate; scape evident. Inflorescence is densely strobiliform, usually crowned with a tuft of sterile foliaceous bracts, often producing slips at the base. Flowers are sessile having free sepals and petals, each typically bearing 2 slender funnel form scales, including stamens. Pollen is ellipsoid with 2 pores. Ovaries coalesce with each other and with the bracts to form a fleshy syncarp and epigynous tube having short apical placentas and caudate ovules. It is native to Uruguay, South America.

Classification of genus *Ananas*

The views on pineapple taxonomy have varied considerably from the time it was first discovered. The first botanical description of cultivated pineapple was by Charles Plumier at the end of 17th century when he created the genus *Bromelia* for the plants called *karatas*, in honour of the Swedish physician Olaf Bromel and also described *Ananas* as *Ananas aculeatus fructu ovato, carne albida*. However, Miller (1768) maintained the name *Ananas*. Linnaeus in his *Species Plantarum* (1753) designated the pineapple as *Bromelia ananas* and *Bromelia comosa*. To simplify the classification, Mez (1892) recognized, in the *Flora Brasiliensis*, only one species *Ananas sativus* with 5 botanical varieties. In 1919, Hassler divided the genus *Ananas* into 2 sections, *Euananas* and *Pseudananas*. In 1930, Harms raised *Pseudananas* to the status of genus.

From 1934, pineapple taxonomy was dominated by the views of L. B. Smith and F. Camargo who divided the genus *Ananas* renaming the species without describing new variations (Coppen d'Eeckenbrugge and Leal, 2003). The classification of the genus by Smith and Downs (1979) into 9 species (*Pseudanans sagenarius* (Arruda da Camara) Camargo, *Ananas ananassoides* (Baker) L.B. Smith, *Ananas nanus* L.B. Smith, Ananas *lucidus* Miller, *Ananas parguazensis* Camargo & L.B. Smith, *Ananas comosus* (L.) Merill, *Ananas monstrosus, Ananas bracteatus* (Lindley) Schultes f., and *Ananas fritzmuelleri* Camargo) was disputed being based on probability and because of inconsistency with the available data on reproductive behaviour and morphological, biochemical and molecular diversity (Leal *et al*., 1998).

In the present classification, all pineapples are regrouped into the genus *Ananas* with 2 species, characterized by the unique feature of the inflorescence, which is fused into a syncarp. The 7 *Ananas* species proposed by Smith and Downs (1979) were downgraded to the level of 5 botanical varieties of *A. comosus* (Coppens d'Eeckenbrugge and Leal, 2003). The 5 botanical varieties are *A. comosus* var. *bracteatus, A. comosus* var. *parguazensis, A. comosus* var. *comosus, A. comosus* var. *ananassoides* and *A. comosus* var. *erectifolius*. These produce edible fruits having good aroma and TSS/acid blend and are also source of biotic and abiotic resistance.

Key to the species and botanical varieties of *Ananas*

la. Apical coma inconspicuous or lacking, plant propagating by elongate stolons .... *Ananas macrodontes*

lb. Foliaceous coma usually crowning the syncarp. Plant propagating by the crown and shoots from the stem or peduncle (slips).... *Ananas comosus*

2a. Flower bracts conspicuous, imbricate and covering the ovary .... *Ananas comosus* var. *bracteatus*

2b. Flower bracts relatively inconspicuous, soon exposing the ovary apices

3a. Spiny leaves. Leaf spines, both antrorse and retrorse, blades narrowed towards base .... *Ananas comosus* var. *parguazensis*

3b. Spiny or smooth leaves. Leaf spines all antrorse, blades not narrowed at base

4a. Dense rosette, wide blades, scape wide, fruit medium to large .... *Ananas comosus* var. *comosus*

4b. Sparse rosette, blades usually narrow, scape thin and long, usually erect, fruit small to medium

5a. Blades recurved or erect, spiny. Fruit small to medium .... *Ananas comosus* var. *ananassoides*

5b. Blades erect, usually narrow and unarmed with the exception of the apical thorn. Abundant production of shoots .....*Ananas comosus* var. *erectifolius*

Ananas macrodontes Morren; yourja (2n = 4x = 100)

The common name 'yourja' means fibre, fishing net bromeliad, fierce fence bromeliad and strong spine pineapple. The species has natural distribution from southern Brazil to Paraguay and northeastern Argentina. The plants are propagated by elongated basal stolons, very rarely by axillary shoots, up to 2 m high. The leaves are densely rosulate. The inflorescence is simple, globose to ovoid, 8-20 cm long and 6-9 cm wide having 100-200 flowers. The flowers are self compatible. The succulent fruit (syncarp) is without leafy crown and is up to 20 cm long in diameter and does not grow appreciably after anthesis.

Pineapple
(*Ananas comosus* (L.) Merril)

The pineapple originated in South America. It was domesticated by the Tupi-Guarani Indians from *A. comosus* var. *ananassoides* and carried it with them in their northward migrations to the Antilles, northern Andes and Central America (Bertoni, 1919).

It seems that *A. comosus* var. *comosus* and *A. comosus* var. *erectifolius* were developed from *A. comosus* var. *ananassoides* and/or *A. comosus* var. *paraguazensis*. Selection of *A. comosus* var. *comosus* appears to be based on characters such as larger size and better quality (low acidity and seediness) of fruit and higher number of fruitlets. For *A. comosus* var. *erectifolius,* the selection appears to be based on long, fibrous and smooth leaves for fibre production. Other traits were necessarily modified during the course of domestication and further selection. The excellence of the selections obtained by the Amerindians, their knowledge of the crop and wide pre-Columbian distribution of the pineapple, all indicate an ancient domestication, dating back several thousand years (Coppens d'Eeckenbrugge and Leal, 2003). The ancestor of pineapple may probably be *A. microstachys*, the wild Brazilian pineapple. Pineapple is grown mostly in Hawaii, South Africa, East Indies and Queensland. It got introduced in India in 1548 and is mostly grown in Kerala, Assam and Orissa.

The plant is hardy, perennial and evergreen and is adapted to both humid and drylands but prefers a rather mild climate, from coastal regions to the hills in Assam up to 900 m altitudes. Fairly large amount of heat is required for widening of its leaves but too much of sunshine is harmful. A cool winter improves the quality of the fruit but frost conditions cause damage.

The stem is short, stout and hidden by a rosette of stiff leaves. The leaves are long, pointed, upright, spiny or serrated. The upper surface is waxy. The stomates on the lower surface are surrounded by hairs that reduce transpiration. Water accumulates in the leaves close to the stem from where the roots absorb it (epiphytic). The flowering stalk is the extension of the main stem. It bears a head of flowers each in the axil of a fleshy bract. The perianth is thick. Stamens are 6. One pistil is with a single style and 3 cells in the ovary having many ovules. The fruit is a syncarpium, the multiple of accessory fruits that are berries or drupelets. Non-stimulated parthenocarpy is found and thus pollination is not required and the fruit is seedless. Some commercial cultivars are self sterile. Viable seeds are rare. The main stem continues to grow. The perianth, bract and stalk all become accessory parts of the fruit. The plant dies after fruiting and then the suckers emerge. The roots grow from the axil of the leaves and consist of two sets – (i) lower roots enter the ground, and (ii) the upper roots clasp the stem. As a result the plants are poorly fixed in the ground.

The plants are propagated by suckers emerging from the subterranean part of the stem, crown of the plant, slips arising just below the fruit from the fruiting stalk, and stumps or shoots arising from the main plantings after fruit harvest. The fruiting is earlier when suckers are used as planting material and the fruits are larger when planting is done using slips. Crowns are used in the types that produce small suckers. Larger number of plants can be raised if stumps are used as planting material. The plantings may last for 3 to 12 years.

Horticultural groups of pineapple

1. Cayenne: This is the most important group. The fruits are large and are of good quality for canning. The flesh is light yellow. The plants are very vigorous and high yielding. The leaves are entire, generally smooth with few spines only at the tip. The fruits are cylindrical slightly tapering at tip, each weighing 2-2.5 kg and usually having flat or shallow eyes, orange rind colour, medium core with pale to yellow, tender, juicy sweet and mild acid flesh low in fibre. Owing to these characters, it is rated very good for canning and fresh fruit trade and thus has fair export potential. The group is susceptible to mealy bug, wilt and nematodes. Smooth Cayenne is the most important cultivar from this group (Fig. 15.1). The other important cultivar is Giant Kew. Cultivars in this group are usually resistant to fruit collapse and bacterial heart rot diseases but are susceptible to black heart disorder. Vegetative propagation is normally by shoots and slips, which are quite limited in production.

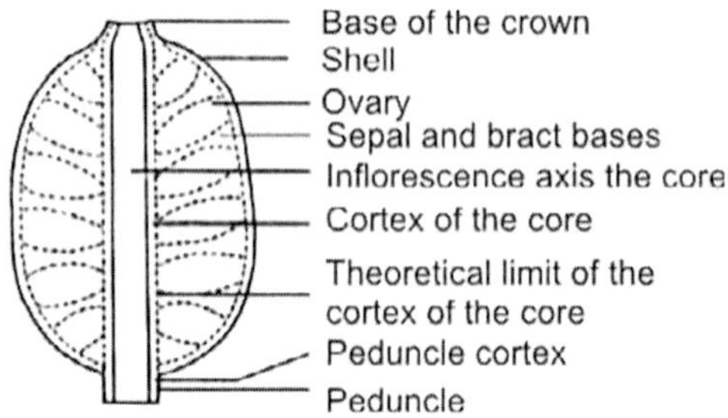

Fig. 15.1. Morphology of Smooth Cayenne pineapple (Source: Coppens d'Eeckenbrugge and Leal, 2003).

2. Queen: The cultivars of this group are widely distributed and are quite extensively cultivated only for fresh fruits because of their high sugar content. In Peninsular Malaysia, it is known as Nanas Moris, derived from the common international name Mauritius. In Sarawak, it is called Sarikei and also known as Phuket, Rough McGregor, Ripley Queen, Alexandra and Victoria in other parts of the world. It is also called Common Rough in Australia. Seventy per cent of the fresh pineapple fruits produced in Malaysia is from Nanas Moris. It is also the leading cultivar in South Africa, Queensland and the Philippines and an important cultivar group in India for fresh fruit market.

The Queen group generally has smaller plants and fruits and the leaves are shorter than in the Cayenne group.The dwarf plant has short and very spiny, dark purplish green compact leaves having prominently serrated margin. It is more cold and disease resistant than Smooth Cayenne. The plant sometimes produces robust slips in some variants and produces an average of 2 suckers or more which is sufficient for ratooning or replanting.

The fruit is very small, conical tapering at tip, spiny, golden yellow in colour with deep set eyes which require a thick cut to completely remove the peel and is less fibrous than Smooth Cayenne and has a small, tender core. It is juicy and sweet. The flesh is less acidic compared to that of Cayenne. When ripe the fruits emit pleasant aroma and flavour. The fruits are harvested when eyes turn yellow. The fruit ripening is uniform. Average weight of fruit varies from 600 to 800 g. It possesses all the good organoleptic qualities. Juice is bright yellow in colour having 10 to 14°Brix TSS depending upon stage of maturity and season, 4 to 4.5 pH and 80-90% water content. The fruit is sold fresh and keeps well. It is considered the best for table purpose, good for export but less suitable for canning. Queen cultivars are robust and show higher tolerance to stress, pests and diseases than Smooth Cayenne. However they are susceptible to black heart disorder. The important cultivars are Queen and Ripley. The Z-Queen or James Queen is reported to be a mutant of 'Natal Queen' and is a natural tetraploid.

3. Spanish: The Spanish group of pineapple is not widely cultivated. However, it is well adapted to the coastal peat and is the main canning cultivar in Malaysia. It is an important group grown in tropical America. The plant is moderate in vigour, generally smaller than those of the other groups, and produces two to three suckers,. Crowns are medium, occasionally with multiple proliferations. Leaves are lightly purple tinged, usually with smooth spineless margins except for the leaf tip where a few spines may be found. Slips are sometimes prolific. It also produces suckers readily for ratooning or replanting. Spanish cultivars are susceptible to fruit collapse and bacterial heart rot diseases. These are resistant to mealy bug and wilt, but susceptible to gummosis caused by the larvae of *Batrachedra* moth.

The important cultivars are Mauritius and Charlothe Rothschild. The Red Spanish or Espanola Roja is the major cultivar in the Caribbean region. Singapore Spanish or Singapore Canning and Nanas Merah are the principal canning cultivars in west Malaysia because of their adaptability to peat soil. The flesh has a bright yellow colour. From Singapore Spanish pineapples improved cultivars for canning such as Masmerah and Gandul have been selected. Masmerah is a spineless type with large fruit. Others in this group, not popularly cultivated, include Selangor Green,

Nangka and Betik. Two other cultivars which are suitable for fresh fruit market are Hybrid 36 and Josapine. The plants are moderate in vigour and bear typically square shouldered (cylindrical) fruits of 1-2 kg. The eyes are broad, fairly flat and deep and thus results in lower flesh recovery. The flesh is quite fibrous with attractive deep, golden yellow colour. Sugar (10-12°Brix) and acid (0.3-0.5%) are usually low but very much higher in Hybrid 36 and Josapine which are suitable for fresh fruit market.

A Cayenne-Spanish hybrid Nanas Jabor is susceptible to fruit marbling and cork spot. But Cabezona, a natural triploid having large plants and fruits weighing 4.5-6.5 kg is an exception. It is grown primarily in the Tabasco State of Mexico and in a small area of Puerto Rico, where local consumers prefer larger fruits. The Puerto Rico clone PR 1-6 is suspected to be a hybrid between Red Spanish and Smooth Cayenne as these were the only clones grown in adjacent fields. The fruit has light yellow flesh with adequate sugar having good shipping qualities and good slip production. It is resistant to gummosis and fairly tolerant to mealy bug and wilt.

4. Abacaxi: This group is grown mostly in Latin America and in the Caribbean region. Py *et al.* (1987) called this group as 'Pernambuco'. The fruit is not considered suitable for canning or as fresh fruit, but the juicy flesh having sweet flavour is favoured in the local markets. Perole, Pernambuco, Eleuthera and Abacaxi are the principal clones in Brazil along the eastern Espirito Santo in the south through Bahia and Pernambuco to Paraibo.

5. Maipure: This group is cultivated in Central and South America as fresh fruit for local markets. Being almost unused gene pool of adapted forms, these clones may be of interest to breeders.

Leal and Soule (1977) enumerated the characteristics of the 5 pineapple groups (Table 15.1).

Table 15.1. Characteristics of pineapple groups (Leal and Soule, 1977)

Characteristics	Group				
	Spanish	Queen	Abacaxi	Cayenne	Maipure
Leaves	Spiny	Spiny	Spiny	Smooth	Smooth
Fruit weight (kg)	0.9-1.8	0.5-1.1	1.4	2.3	0.8-2.5
Fruit shape	Globose	Conical	Conical	Cylindrical	Cylindrical
Eyes	Large, deep eyes	Deep eyes		Flat eyes	
Colour of fruit skin	Orange, Red	Yellow	Yellow	Orange	Yellow to orange red
Colour of flesh	Pale yellow to white	Deep yellow	Pale yellow to white	Pale yellow to yellow	White to deep yellow
Core	Large	Small	Small	Medium	Small-medium
Taste of flesh	Spicy acid, fibrous	Sweeter, less acid, low fibre	Sweet, tender, juicy	Sweet, mildly acid, low fibre, juicy	Sweeter than Cayenne, fibrous tender, very juicy
Canning use	Fair	Fair	Fair	Very good	Fair

Local market	Good	Good	Good	Good	Good
Export market	Very good	Good	Fair to poor	Fair	Fair to poor
Disease problems	Susceptible to gummosis, resistant to mealy bug wilt	More resistant than Cayenne	Resistant	Susceptible to mealy bug, wilt	Unknown
Clones	Red Spanish, Singapore Spanish, Green, Selangor, Castilla, PRI-67, Cabezona	Queen, MacGergor, Natal, Ripley, Alexandria	Abacaxi, Abakka, Sugar Loaf, Papelon, Venezolara, Amarella,	Smooth Cayenne, Cayene, Lisse Smooth, Guatemalan, Typhone, St Michael, Esmeralda	Maipure, Perolera, Lebrija, Monte Lirio, Abacaxi, Randon

Pernambuco (Eleuthera) and Mordilona

The cultivation of these cultivars is restricted to countries like Brazil, Ecuador, Colombia, Venezuela and Peru. Pernambuco is semi-vigorous with long spiny leaves and has erect growth habit. The fruits are small, slender and are borne on long peduncles. The flesh is white, tender and juicy with low acid and mild flavour. Slips are prominent and numerous, occasionally to the extent of hiding the fruit. Perola is the best known in this group and the most important commercial cultivar in Brazil. It is very susceptible to fusariosis disease which is devastating in Brazil.

Mordilona is typified by the piping leaf margin where a part of the lower epidermis folds over the edge of the leaf to give a completely spineless leaf form. Perolera and Manzana are the best known cultivars in this group. These are grown mainly in the northeastern Andes of Colombia and Venezuela. The irregular, cylindrical fruit is large (1.5 to 3 kg) with attractive yellow to orange peel borne on a long peduncle. The flesh is cream to yellow, firm and sweet. Numerous crownlets protrude from the base of the crown and the upper eyes and slips are numerous. Perolera has high vitamin C content, is resistant to fusariosis disease and is commonly used as a parent in breeding programmes.

Cultivars

There is no standard basis for cultivar classification in pineapple. Colour and shape of fruit, flat or sharpness of eyes and spine and leaf characters have often been used for classification. The important cultivars are:

Giant Kew: Giant Kew is a mutant of Kew and thus most of the characters are same except that the fruit size is bigger. The cultivar Kew found in Tamil Nadu having smaller fruit resembles Giant Kew.

Plants are vigorous. It is a shy suckering cultivar giving 0-2 suckers per plant. The number of slips per plant varies from 2 to 3. Therefore, propagation is done from the crowns in Hawaii. The leaves are long, entire and trough-shaped and their upper surface is dark green. The central 2-3 leaves are superficially brownish red with ash gray lower surface.

It is a late cultivar. The fruit is very large, weighing 3 to 4 kg and as high as 10 kg. The fruit shape is oblong and slightly tapering towards the crown. The eyes are broad and shallow making it suitable for canning. The fruit is dark blackish green when unripe and becomes orange yellow when ripe. The flesh is light yellow becoming whitish near the core end and seed cavity. It is most juicy, sweet and fibreless cultivar with pleasant aroma and is thus good for canning. The core is large and its extraction results in too large a hole in canned slices. It is commercially very important in India.

Queen (McGregor, Natal, Ripley Queen, Alexandra): it is a heavy suckering cultivar. The plants are smaller than those of Giant Kew. The leaves are spiny and shorter having brownish red colour and prominently serrated with closely arranged spines.

The cultivar is the earliest to ripen in India having uniform fruit ripening. The fruit is small weighing 0.5 to 2 kg. The fruit shape is cylindrical. The eyes are prominent, irregular and deep set. The scales cover almost one-third of the pip and end in a sharp point. Fruit skin is yellow. The flesh is deep yellow, firm, transparent and somewhat stringy. It is highly flavoured, fibreless, juicy, sweet and low acid making it an outstanding table cultivar but less suitable for canning. It is good for export. The cultivar is more resistant to pests and diseases than Smooth Cayenne.

Mauritius: The fruits are medium in size and medium sweet. The two strains are:

i). Yellow skinned: The fruits are oblong and slightly tapering from the middle towards the apex. The fruits are green in colour when unripe and deep yellow when fully ripe. The flesh is light yellow and fibrous. The crown is large and spiny.

ii). Red skinned: The fruits are broader (round) at the base and taper abruptly towards the crown. The fruits are red when fully ripe. The flesh is reddish coppery yellow and sweeter than those of the yellow skinned strain. It is a mid season cultivar.

Jaldhup: It belongs to the Queen group. It is found in Assam. Its fruits are smaller than even those of cultivar Queen. The fruits have somewhat alcoholic flavour and well blended sugar/acid ratio.

Lakhat: It is found in Assam. Its fruits are sour.

Simhachalam: It is found in Vishakhapatnam (Orissa, India).

PR-1-67 (Red Spanish x Cayenne): It is from Puerto Rico. This hybrid shows high plant vigour and is resistant to wilt disease.

H-7 (Valera Monendi x Kew): This hybrid produces large fruits each weighing 3.0-3.5 kg.

Abacaxi: The cultivar is grown for local market in Brazil. The plants are erect. Leaves are spiny at margin and tip. Fruit is yellow, conical in shape, broader at base and narrow at apex or crown and weighs about 1.5 kg having very small core. The flesh is pale yellow to whitish, paler at core, tender, sweet and juicy having good flavour and low fibre. It is rated fair to poor for canning and export but is relatively good for local market.

Maipure (Perolera, Lebrija, Monte Lirio, Abacaxi, Rondon): The leaves are smooth. The fruit weighs 0.8-2.5 kg and is cylindrical ovoid to cylindrical in shape having yellow to dark orange rind with reddish tinge and small to medium core size. The flesh is whitish to deep yellow, fibrous, tender and juicy. The fruits are sweeter than those of Cayenne. It is rated fair to poor for canning and export but good for local market.

Cabezona: It is a tropical type extensively grown in Puerto Rico mainly for fresh fruit.

Red Spanish: The cultivar has proved most dependable despite the spiny plant. It is popular in the West Indies, Venezuela and Mexico. It constitutes 85% of all commercial planting in Puerto Rico and 75% of the production for fresh fruit market. It is only fair for canning. The fruit is more or less round, orange red externally with deep eyes with weight ranging from 1.36 to 2.7 kg. The flesh is pale yellow, fibrous, aromatic and flavourful with a large core. The fruit is hard when mature, breaks off easily and cleanly at the base while harvesting and stands handling and transport well. It is highly resistant to fruit rot but is subject to gummosis.

Smooth Cayenne (Cayenne, Cayenne Lisse, Kew, Maipuri, Sarawak, Esmerada, Clarie, Typhoon, Saint Michel, Champaka, 73-050 (MD-1), 73-114 (MD-2)): The cultivar was selected and cultivated by Indians in Venezuela and introduced from French Guyana (Cayenne) in 1820. More than 70% of the pineapple grown both for canning and fresh fruit in the world is from this cultivar. The production cycle for Smooth Cayenne is longer than most of the other cultivars. The plants have smooth leaves that are nearly free from spines except for the needle at the leaf tip. The fruit size is 1.8 to 4.5 kg having cylindrical form, shallow eyes, orange rind, yellow and juicy flesh with 13-19% TSS, low fibre and rich mildly acid flavour. The cultivar is good for fresh fruit. It is preferred for canning as along with excellent flavour it has sufficient fibre for firm slices and cubes. Thus, the cultivar has great importance worldwide even though it is subject to problems of mealy bug and wilt disease and does not ship well.

In most areas, Smooth Cayenne constitutes a mixture of clones as a result of new introductions, mutations and lack of roguing. Local selections are mostly named after their areas of origin. In Malaysia, the local clones of this group are Sarawak (Peninsular Malaysia), Samarahan, Nanas Durian and Nanas Paun (Sarawak) and Babagon (Sabah). Sarawak is vigorous growing and bears large (about 2.5 kg), egg-shaped fruit held on a short and strong peduncle. The fruitlets or eyes are broad and flat. The flesh is pale yellow, very juicy with fairly high acid (0.5-0.9%) and sugar (12-16°Brix). Leaves are generally smooth with occasional spines at the tips. The Sarawak clone did not respond readily to flower induction in Malaysia, especially when grown on peat soil as it encourages robust vegetative growth. Hence, the cultivation of the Cayenne type of pineapple is limited to mineral soil areas such as Titi (Negeri Sembilan), Setiu (Terengganu) (Penampang/Babagon) Sabah and some parts of Sarawak. There are several clones of Smooth Cayenne in Hawaii which have been selected for resistance to mealy bug and wilt. It is the leading cultivar in Taiwan. A dual purpose cultivar is Queensland Cayenne.

Champaka: It is a selection of Smooth Cayenne originated in India and widely grown in Hawaii.

Hilo: It is a variant of Smooth Cayenne selected in Hawaii. The plant is more compact, the fruit is smaller, more cylindrical and produces no slips but numerous suckers. It may be the same as the Cayenne Lisse strain grown in Martinique and on the Ivory Coast, the fruit of which weighs from 1-1.5 kg and has a very small crown.

St. Michael: It is another strain of Smooth Cayenne and is the famous product of the Azores. The fruit weighs 2.25-2.75 kg, has a very small crown and small core. The fruit is sweet with low acidity and sometimes insipid when fully ripe.

Singapore Spanish (Singapore Canning, Ruby, Red Pine, Nanas, Merah, Nangka, Gandul, Masmerah, Anthocyanless Mutant, Selangor Green): The leaves are spiny to nearly spineless and smooth. Fruits are small, 0.9-1.8 kg, cylindrical with reddish orange skin, pale yellow flesh having aromatic flavour, 10-12% TSS, low acid juice and fibrous core when ripe and hence good for fresh fruit and fairly good for canning and very good for export. It is resistant to gummosis and wilt.

Espanola Roja (Red Spanish, Black Spanish, Key Largo, Havannath, Cowboy, Bull Head, Cumanesa, Native, Abaka, Sugar Loaf, Papelon, Venezolara and Amarella): The leaves are spiny. Fruit is 1.2-2.0 kg, barrel shaped with yellow skin, pale yellow flesh having 12% TSS, low acid and aromatic juice. It is good for fresh fruit, fairly good for canning and very good for export. The cultivar is vigorous and tolerant to high temperature, drought, internal browning, butt rot, wilt, nematodes and *Phytophthora*.

Bumanguesa of Venezuela and Colombia: It is probably a mutation of Perolera. The fruit is red or purple externally, cylindrical with square ends, shallow eyes, deep yellow flesh, very slender core but has slips around the crown and too many basal slips to suit modern commercial requirements.

Kona Sugarloaf: the fruit is 2.5-3 kg in weight and cylindrical in shape having white flesh with no woodiness in the centre and high sugar content but no acid. It has unusually sweet fruit.

Charlotte Rothschild: It is second to Giant Kew in size in India. The fruit tapers toward the crown and is orange yellow when ripe, aromatic and very juicy. The crop comes early. Baron Rothschild, a Cayenne strain, grown in Guinea, has a smaller fruit of 0.8-2 kg in weight and is marketed fresh.

Santa Marta of Colombia: The fruit is subject to cracking of the core in hot, dry weather. The old common Criolla is still grown in Peru because it can be sold fresh and is not easily damaged in shipment.

Perolera (Tachirense, Capachera, Motilona, and Lebrija): It is a Smooth Cayenne type ranking second to Red Spanish in importance in Venezuela. It has long been grown in Colombia. The plant is entirely smooth with no spine at the leaf tip. The fruit is yellow, large of 3-4 kg and cylindrical. Monte Lirio of Mexico and Central America also has smooth leaves with no terminal spine. The fruit is rounded, white fleshed with good aroma and flavour.

Other variants of Smooth Cayenne include the Esmeralda grown for local markets in Mexico and Florida. Typhone of Taiwan, Cayenne Guadeloupe of Guadeloupe are more disease resistant than Smooth Cayenne and Smooth

Guatemalan and Palin grown in Guatemala and also Piamba da Marquita of Colombia. Efforts to propose grouping of all smooth-leaved pineapple types under the collective name Maipure have been done. In Amazonas, Venezuela, this name is given to a large plant having smooth leaves stained with red. The fruit has 170 to 190 eyes.

Hybrid 36: It is a hybrid from a cross between Gandul (Spanish) and the Smooth Cayenne. It is a very robust cultivar and produces medium sized fruits (1.5-2 kg) with large crowns. It has high sugar content (14ºBrix) and acid (0.6-0.8%) but its flesh colour is rather pale. It is quite tolerant to black heart disorder but is susceptible to marbling diseases.

Josapine: It is a new cultivar in the Spanish group with very bright prospects as a table fruit. It is a hybrid between Johor (Spanish) and Sarawak (Smooth Cayenne). It fruits very early and is cultivated on an annual cycle in Malaysia. The plant is vigorous and produces 2-3 suckers. Leaves are lightly purple-tinged, usually with spineless margins except for the leaf tip. Crowns are medium, occasionally with multiple proliferations. Fruit weighs between 1.1 and 1.3 kg and is cylindrical with dark purple peel that changes to attractive orange red on ripening. The flesh colour is deep golden yellow with strong aroma and sugar content of 17ºBrix on peat soil to 22ºBrix on mineral soil. Josapine fruits have good storage life and are resistant to black heart disorder or internal browning caused under low temperatures. This allows shipping of Josapine fruits in refrigerated containers.

Maspine: Replanting of Gandul pineapple on peat soil resulted in sudden decrease in yield and rapid decline in the canning sector of the Malaysian pineapple industry. Therefore, this new vigorous and high yielding cultivar having quality fruits and medium size crown was developed. This is a complex hybrid from five types of pineapple seldom has stem, aerial and ground shoots. This cultivar of Manzanah group inherits the vigour of Queen, high sugar content of Cayenne, golden yellow aril and fruit shape of Singapore Spanish, disease resistance from Pernambuco and non-spiny leaves from Perolera. Flowering in this cultivar can be induced in 37 days by hormone treatment.

Maspine is respectively 40% and 70% more productive than Gandul and Josepine giving 56 tonnes fruits/ha. Morethan 80% produce develops red heart. Its fruits have excellent canning quality due to large size (1.8 kg), cylindrical shape, thin skin and high recovery rate of more than 20% compared to that in Gandul (6-18%). The core diameter of 30 mm and lower makes it more acceptable to the canners. It is reported to be resistant to bacterial heart rot (BHR) and thus has high potential for planting on mineral soils.

The attractive golden yellow colour of the flesh is retained even after processing. The round shapes of flesh pieces does not easily break if canned with suitable pH. Its fresh and ripe fruit contains low acid (0.58%) and high sugar (14-17%). The TSS increases to 16-18ºB after processing which helps to reduce sugar input during processing for canning. Maspine fruits can also be used for production of fresh juice that can be canned or bottled as clarified carbonated or non-carbonated juice. The balanced high sugar and low acid makes the fresh fruit taste better without 'biting effect' and thus makes it suitable as dessert. Besides, dried and semi-dried products can also be made. Since the leaves are without spines, the plants can be easily handled in the field, especially while harvesting and can be used as feed for farm animals.

Singapore Red (Red Jamaica, Singapore Spanish, Singapore Queen, Singapore Common): It is second to Mauritius in popularity. The leaves are usually all green but sometimes have a reddish stripe near the margins. These are rarely spiny except at the tips. The fruits are cylindrical, reddish with deep eyes and are small, 1.6-2.25 kg in weight having slender core, golden yellow, fibrous and insipid raw flesh but is valued for canning. The plant is disease and pest resistant.

The related **Green Selangor** (also called Selangor Green, Green Spanish, and Selassie) of Malaysia has all green leaves prickly only at the tips. The flesh is golden yellow often with white dots. This cultivar is grown for canning.

Pineapple Panare: It is named after the Indian tribe that has grown it for a long time. It is commercially grown to a small extent in Bolivia and Venezuela. The plant is of medium size having long spiny leaves. The fruit is bottle-shaped, small, 0.45-0.70 kg with small crown, ovate with deep eyes, externally orange with deep yellow, slightly fragrant flesh with little fibre and small core.

MacGregor: It is a variant of Nasal Queen selected in South Africa and is also grown in Queensland. The tree is spreading and more vigorous having broad leaves and less freely produced large suckers. The fruit is cylindrical, medium to large having firm flesh and flavour resembling that of Queen.

James Queen: It is a mutant of Nasal Queen that originated in South Africa. It has larger fruit with square shoulders.

Ripley or Ripley Queen: It is grown in Queensland and has a dwarf, compact plant with crimson tinge on leaves. It takes 22 weeks from flowering to fruit maturity and is an irregular bearer. The fruit weighs 1.36-2.7 kg and is externally pale copper having pale yellow, non-fibrous, very sweet and rich flesh. In Florida this cultivar tends to produce suckers without fruiting.

Kallara Local: It is a little known cultivar in India. Its minor strains in Thailand are Pattawia, Calcutta, Sri Racha, Intorachit and Chantabun.

Mauritius (European Pine, Malacca Queen, Red Ceylon and Red Malacca): It is one of the two leading cultivars in Malaya and is also important in India and Ceylon. The leaves are dark green with broad red central stripe and red spines on the margins. The fruit is small, 1.36-2.25 kg in size, externally yellow and having a thin core and very sweet flesh. It is sold fresh and is utilized for making juice.

Natal Queen of South Africa: It is grown in El Salvador. It produces many suckers. The leaves are spiny. The fruit weighs 0.75-0.9 kg having golden yellow flesh, crisp texture and delicate mild flavour. It is well adapted for fresh consumption. The fruit keeps well after ripening.

Pernambuco (Eleuthera): This cultivar is from Hawaii. Leaves are without spines. The fruits are 1-2 kg in weight, cylindrical in shape having pale yellow to white, sweet and melting flesh with high sugar and acid content, excellent for eating fresh. It is poorly adapted for shipping but is well adapted to canning and processing.

⑧ ⑧ ⑧

[EUDICOTS]

Flowers are cyclic, parts arranged in whorls with the members of individual whorls alternating, stamen filaments are rather narrow, bearing well differentiated basifixed anthers. Pollen is tricolpate. Differentiated outer and inner perianth members (calyx and corolla) are present. Nodes are trilacunar, stomata, anomocytic, ethereal oils are absent. Most members have plastids of sieve elements with starch grains (S-type).

Chapter 16

RANUNCULALES

The plants are herbs, sometimes lianas or erect sub-shrubs or shrubs. Vascular bundles are usually amphivasal and the xylem is straight, not V-shaped in cross section. Vessels are mostly with simple perforations; lateral pitting is mostly alternate. Fibres are commonly with simple pits. Woody forms are with broad medullary rays. Nodes are trilacunar or more often multilacunar. Leaves are alternate or rarely opposite, compound or simple and mostly exstipulate. Stomata are anomocytic or paracytic. Flowers are solitary or in cymose inflorescences, bisexual or sometimes unisexual and actinomorphic or zygomorphic. Perianth is double or simple and rarely completely wanting. Stamens are usually numerous, spirally arranged and centripetal; anthers are basifixed, extrorse or introrse, usually tetrasporangiate, opening longitudinally. Tapetum is usually secretory. Microsporogenesis is simultaneous or successive. Pollen grains are 2-celled or rarely 3-celled, tectate-columellate; tectum is spinulose and punctate/perforate or rarely reticulate or striate. Gynoecium is mostly apocarpous. Ovary is superior with one to many ovules, mostly anatropous, bitegmic or sometimes unitegmic, crassinucellate or rarely tenuinucellate. Female gametophyte is commonly of *Polygonum*-type. Fruits are of various types. Seeds are with small to large embryo and with copious or scanty endosperm, sometimes without endosperm. Endosperm is nuclear. Chromosomes are of either *Ranunculus*-type (long chromosomes generally winding or curved several times and with irregularly distributed heterochromatic regions) or of *Thalictrum*-type (small chromosomes generally simply curved and with well marked heterochromatic chromocentres). It contains 7 families and about 3490 species.

Family Berberidaceae (barberry, sacred bamboo and May apple)

It is a small family of shrubs and herbs most of which have ornamental value. The family contains 12-16 genera and 650-700 species (Heywood *et al.*, 2007). The herbaceous species are native to north temperate regions in both Old and New World with several species pairs disjunct between the Far East and North America. *Berberis* (including *Mahonia*) extends to Tierra del Fuego in South America.

The plants are woody shrubs (*Berberis* and *Nandina*) or herbs with rhizomes or tubers. Stems are with vascular bundles sometimes ±scattered, usually with alkaloids, the wood is usually coloured yellow by berberine (an isoquinoline alkaloid). The leaves are normally alternate and spiral (almost opposite in *Podophyllum*), basal in some herbaceous species, simple to pinnately or alternately compound (peltate in

Podophyllum and *Diphylleia*) and usually without stipules. *Nandina* and some species of *Berberis*, including the *Mahonia* group, have evergreen persistent leaves. In *Berberis,* the leaves of long shoots are often transformed into spines while the short shoots bear simple leaves. The flowers are bisexual, actinomorphic and borne in panicles (*Nandina*) with reduction through racemes to solitary flowers on leafless basal peduncles (*Jeffersonia*). The perianth consists of several whorls of usually 6 or 4 variously differentiated segments, the innermost (petals) being usually distinct from the outer and inner sepals in being petaloid and bearing nectaries or else being reduced to small nectariferous sacs or scales. However, *Achlys* has no perianth and consequently no nectaries. *Podophyllum, Diphylleia*, and *Nandina* have perianth segments without nectaries. There are 6 stamens opposite the innermost perianth segments, except in *Epimedium* (with 4) and *Podophyllum* (with up to 18). The anthers open by lengthwise slits in *Nandina* and *Podophyllum* and by valves hinged at the top in others. Pollen grains are tricolpate. The ovary is superior with a single carpel and 1 locule with several or many ovules on the suture or 1 at the base. The style is short or rarely the stigma is sessile. The fruit is succulent in *Nandina, Berberis, Mahonia* and *Podophyllum* but forms a 2-valved capsule in *Epimedium* and *Vancouveria* and a papery bladder that is wind dispersed in *Leontice. Caulophyllum* is remarkable in that the enlarging berry-like seeds burst through the wall of the ovary and develop in a completely exposed state. *Gymnospermium* also has exposed seeds.

Genus *Berberis* L. (agarita, barberry) (n = 7, 14)

The plants are shrubs with short spiny shoots. Spines are solitary, trifid, manifold and foliaceous or absent. Leaves are simple, pinnate, evergreen or deciduous with entire, toothed or spiny margin. Inflorescence is a raceme, umbel or solitary flowers emerging from short shoots. Flowers are calyculate with yellow perianth, 3-12 sepals, 6 basally nectariferous staminodia and 6 stamens. Fruit is a berry with 1-15 seeds. It has more than 500 species in North America, South America, Asia, Europe and North Africa (Kubitzki *et al*., 2007).

Indian barberry
(***Berberis aristata*** DC. ***Rasaut***)

It is a shrub found mainly in the Himalayas and in the Nilgiris. The small dried berries are edible. The other related species yielding edible fruits are *B. asiatica* Roxb., *B. lycium* Royle and *B. vulgaris* L.

⑧ ⑧ ⑧

Chapter 17

PROTEALES

The plants are trees or more often shrubs or often lignotuberous sub-shrubs, sometimes geoflorous, very rarely almost herbaceous, glabrous or more often provided with characteristic uniseriate and 3-celled trichomes, mostly more or less xeromorphic. Lateral roots have limited growth forming clusters and are proteoid and rarely mycorrhizal. Vessels are nearly always with simple perforations, but some are with simple and scalariform plates with few bars, usually with small bordered pits. Rays are nearly or quite homogeneous. Axial parenchyma is scanty paratracheal, most commonly as narrow bands; occasionally most of the bands are independent of the vessels (apotracheal). Sieve element plastids are commonly of S-type. Nodes are mostly trilacunar with three traces, very rarely pentalacunar.

Leaves are evergreen, small to very large, alternate or sometimes opposite or verticillate, simple and entire to variously divided, less often compound, mostly very coriaceous, leathery or fleshy or modified into spines, petiolate to sessile, often aromatic and exstipulate. The leaves are without a persistent basal meristem. Stomata are paracytic or rarely laterocytic.

Flowers are solitary or paired (seldom several) in the axils of bracts (which are sometimes absent), arranged in racemes, umbels or cone-like inflorescences, often in involucrate heads, or the primary inflorescences often reduced to a pair of flowers arranged into secondary racemes, bisexual or rarely unisexual (monoecious or more often dioecious), actinomorphic or zygomorphic, mainly 4-merous, protandrous, pollinated by various animals including small marsupials. Perianth is with distinct calyx and corolla (sometimes being 'glands' or 'scales', perhaps representing petals, internal to and alternating with the conspicuous tepals), or sepaline (the conspicuous perianth component seemingly representing the calyx, though 'petaloid'). Sepals are 4, valvate, usually petaloid, free or more or less connate below into a calyx tube and is sometimes cleft on one side or three sepals connate and one free. Intrastaminal annular or horseshoe-shaped nectary disc is represented by (2)-4 free or variously connate nonvasculated alternisepalous scales or glands, sometimes considered vestigial petals. Stamens are 4, rarely 3-4 (*Grevillea, Petrophile*), antesepalous, usually with broad filaments adnate to sepals in varying lengths (*Conospermum, Synaphea*) or rarely free from the calyx (*Bellendena*). All filaments are equal or markedly unequal. Anthers are tetrasporangiate or rarely bisporangiate, erect, basifixed, usually introrse, rarely latrorse opening longitudinally, appendaged (connective often distally prolonged) or unappendaged. Staminodes, when present, are in the same series as the fertile stamens. Tapetum is secretory. Microsporogenesis is simultaneous. Pollen grains are 2-celled, (2)3(-8)-porate or sometimes 3-colpoidate, more or less triangular in polar view, pores are broadly operculate, three pores arranged at four points in the tetrad. Gynoecium is conduplicate and often stipitate, carpel is sealed to a varying degree (in Grevilleoideae mostly open up to the summit of ovary), sometimes 2 carpels, slightly deflected abaxially as in *Didymeles*; stylodium is elongated, thickened distally with terminal or lateral dry stigma, often modified into a "pollen-presenter". Ovary is superior and sessile to stipitate. Ovules are one or two or less often several to more or less numerous, from anatropous to orthotropous, but mostly orthotropous, bitegmic, crassinucellate. Placentation is mostly marginal or apical. Female gametophyte is of *Polygonum*-type.

Fruits are tardily dehiscent or indehiscent follicles, achenes or drupes, often 1-seeded. Seeds have endotestal tegmen, sometimes with specialized exotesta, small to large, commonly winged in follicles with internally fibrillar endotestal cells and fibrous tegmen, thick-walled and crystalliferous exotestal cells, straight, oily, achlorophyllous embryo with 2 or very rarely 3-9 cotyledons. Endosperm is nuclear. Endosperm haustoria are chalazal. Endosperm is wanting and contain cyanogenic glycosides proanthocyanidins, (delphinidin or cyanidin and delphinidin), flavonols (kaempferol, quercetin a myricetin), arbutin, sometimes saponins. It contains three families that are similar in having mostly one ovule per ovary. The Nelumbonaceae and Platanaceae are similar in having apical placentation. The Platanaceae and Proteaceae have similarities in wood anatomy.

Family Nelumbonaceae (water lotus family)

It is a small family with single genus *Nelumbo* Adanson and two species (Heywood *et al*., 2007). *Nelumbo lutea* grows in eastern and central North America while *N. nucifera* is native to tropical and subtropical East Asia and Australia. These are naturalized and widely cultivated.

The plants are perennial aquatic herbs. The rhizomes are creeping and fleshy, becoming tuberous and have adventitious roots. Well developed air chambers (aerenchyma) are found in the vegetative parts of the plant. The leaves are alternate, arising from the rhizomes in groups of three, 2 of which are scale leaves and one is emergent or floating peltate leaf with dichotomous main veins extending to the margin. The flowers are solitary, bisexual, actinomorphic, large and showy, borne above the water surface on long peduncles. The perianth consists of 2 to several outermost sepals merging into the 20-30 spirally arranged petals that are yellow, pink or red. The stamens are 200-400, spirally arranged with long filaments and the connective with a long appendage. The ovary is apocarpous with numerous free carpels immersed in a turbinate, spongy receptacle, 1 locule with basipetal placentation and a single ovule. The fruit consists of indehiscent nutlets lying loosely in the accrescent receptacle that disintegrates to release them. The seeds are large.

Genus *Nelumbo* Adanson

It is a genus of aquatic plants with large showy flowers resembling the water lily but is not closely related to it.

Lotus
(***Nelumbo nucifera*** Gaertn.)

It is native of southern and eastern Asia from Iran through South East Asia to tropical Australia. It has been cultivated for thousands of years in China and tropical parts of Asia. It is an aquatic rhizomatous herb having large round leaves up to 1 m in diameter. Its flowers are large and attractive and may be red, pink or white in colour. The one-seeded fruit (nut) is a characteristic flat-topped compound fruit. Canned rhizomes of lotus provide about 15 kcal/100 g and contain 6% starch, 2% protein, minerals and vitamins. The seeds contain 60% starch, 15% protein and 2% fat and are also rich in vitamin C.

American lotus
(***Nelumbo lutea*** Willd. syn. ***Nelumbium luteum*** Willd., ***N. pentapetala*** (Walter) Fernald; yellow lotus, water chinquapin, and volée)

It is native to north America distributed in the southeastern USA, Mexico, Honduras and the Carabbean. It was apparently distributed northwards in the United States by Native Americans who carried the plant with them as a food source.

American lotus is an emergent aquatic plant. It grows in lakes and swamps as well as in areas subject to flooding. The roots are anchored in the mud but the leaves and flowers emerge above the water surface. The petioles of the leaves may be as long as 2 m terminating into a round leaf blade of 33–43 cm diameter. Mature plants are from 0.8 to 1.5 m in height. Flowering begins in late spring and may continue into the summer. The flower may be white to pale yellow and is 18–28 cm in diameter and has 22-25 petals. The plant having a large tuber is called macoupin in Miami-Illinois (USA) and is used as a food source. The seed is also edible and is known as alligator corn.

Family Proteaceae (Protea family)

The plants are trees and shrubs, mostly characterized by flowers with a single whorl of 4 tepals. Stamens are 4, opposite the tepals with filaments partly or wholly fused to them, rarely free. It contains about 80 genera and 1700 species (Heywood *et al.*, 2007).

The plants are perennial sub-shrubs, shrubs or trees growing to 40 m height. Clusters of short, lateral roots (proteoid roots) are often produced and are not mycorhizae forming. Hairs are simple or forked, 3-celled with short basal cells and elongated terminal cells, often thick-walled. The leaves are highly variable but are mostly leathery with pinnate venation. They are compound, deeply dissected or lobed up to fourth order dissection, lobed are toothed or simple and entire. The degree to which leaf shape varies between different developmental stages is a striking feature of some species, especially of many rain forest taxa. The inflorescence varies spectacularly but can be interpreted as variation on 2 basic "structural plans"; simple or branching racemes of flower pairs in the subfamily Grevilleoideae and racemose, simple or compound inflorescences in the other subfamilies. These are modified in some taxa by reduction, elaboration, compaction and thickening to yield cone-like, head-like leafy and 1-flowered inflorescences. The flowers are usually completely bisexual but sometimes unisexual (plants dioecious or monoecious), usually either radially or bilaterally symmetrical, with a perianth of 4 (rarely 3 or 5) free or variously united tepals. The stamens are 4 (rarely 3 or 5), opposite the tepals with their filaments partly or wholly fused to them or rarely free, usually all fertile but sometimes 1 or more sterile, usually with 2-locular anthers, but occasionally the lateral anthers are 1-locular. One to 4 hypogynous nectary glands are usually present, free or fused into a crescentic or annular nectary. The ovary is superior, sessile or stipitate with a single carpel (rarely 2, free) containing 1 to many ovules inserted on marginal placentae. The style is usually distinct, often with its apex as a pollen presenter. The fruits are dehiscent or indehiscent, dry or succulent containing 1 to many, sometimes winged, seeds.

Genus *Macadamia* F. Muell.

The trees have whorled, entire or dentate leaves. Inflorescence is terminal or lateral raceme of flower pairs or a panicle of such racemes. Flower pair is subtended by a scale-like bract, actinomorphic or slightly zygomorphic perianth. Staminal filaments are basally adnate to tepals or free only towards the tips (Kubitzki *et al.*, 2007).

There are two important nut bearing species, *Macadamia integrifolia* Maiden and Betche (the smooth shell macadamia) found in rain forests along the coast of central and southern Queensland and *M. tetraphylla* L.A.S. Johnson (rough shell macadamia), native of northern coastal part of New South Wales and southeastern Queensland (Australia).

Macadamia nut
(*Macadamia integrifolia* Maiden et Betche) (2n=28)

The macadamia nut originated in rain forests of southeastern Queensland and northeastern New South Wales (Australia). It is an evergreen tree growing up to 18 m or more in height with a spread of about 15 m. The bark is rough, brown and dark red when cut. Leaves are long, linear lanceolate, often spiny when juvenile, usually entire when adult, 10-13 cm long and 2.5-7.5 cm wide in whorls of 4. Young leaves of smooth shell macadmia are light green and are reddish in rough shell trees. The flowers are small and perfect, have no petals but four petaloid sepals and stamens with superior ovary having 20 ovules. The racemose and pendant spike borne on 2, 3 or more year's old wood has 100-300 flowers. Smooth shell macadamia has creamish flowers whereas the rough shell macadamia produces pinkish flowers. Honeybees are the usual pollinating insects but wind pollination may also occur. Most cultivars are partially or completely self incompatible. Cross pollination greatly increases fruit set. Fruit is a follicle opening along a single suture and enclosing a seed. The kernel (seed) is the creamy embryo with two cotyledons having high oil content and a very hard seed coat. It is enclosed in a green pericarp (husk), 1.5-2.5 cm in diameter (IBPGR, 1986; Verheij and Coronel, 1991).

Cultivars

The smooth shell macadamia cultivars of Hawaii are Waimanalo, Keauhou, Kau, Keaau, Kakea, Ikaika, Mackai and Mauka whereas those of Australia are

Hinde, Own Choice, Rickard and Tinana Schimke. The rough shell macadamia cultivars of Australia are Burdick, Cate, Elimbah, Sewell and Beaumont (hybrid). The hybrids from South Africa are Nelmak 1 and Nelmak 2. The cultivars vary in tree vigour, branch angle, fruit size, shell thickness, etc.

Kakea: The cultivar is less hardy under hot dry conditions. The tree has moderately spreading branches with foliage clustered towards the terminals. The cultivar is early and produces small nuts. The trees start flowering early and continue for long duration. The nuts are medium sized and round with somewhat thick and brown shell having few irregular spots and white and round kernels.

Keauhou: It is a very old Hawaiian cultivar. The tree is large having well developed and spreading branches. The leaves are dark green. Its flowers emerge almost 2 weeks earlier than in most of the other cultivars. The nuts are medium to large in size with brown shell having buff coloured spots.

Keaau: The cultivar has tall and upright trees having rounded crown and medium-sized branches suitable for high density plantation. It gives high yield of excellent quality nuts. The nuts tend to mature and fall early. The nuts have rounded and medium to thin shell and white and round kernels.

Kau: The cultivar is similar to Keauhou but is hardier and produces 2-3 upright branches per node. The productivity and nut characters are also similar but the quality is better. The young trees require thinning to develop good frame.

Mauka: The cultivar is from Hawaii and is suitable for higher elevations. It resembles Kau in tree characteristics. The nut quality is good but has some kernel discolouration.

Genus *Gevuina* Molina (2n = 26)

The trees have imparipinnate to tripinnate adult leaves and often 3-lobed terminal leaflets with serrate margins. The lateral inflorescence is a raceme of flower pairs. Flower pair is subtended by a scale-like bract. Flowers are shortly pedicellate or sessile on common peduncle having zygomorphic perianth, 2 hypogynous glands, anterior and free. Carpel orientation is antero-posterior, 2 ovules are orthotropous, style is strongly curved, pollen presenter is swollen and strongly oblique and the stigma is lateral. Fruit is drupaceous and seed is not winged. It has one species, *G. avellana* Molina found in rain forests and disturbed sites in Chile and Argentina (Kubitzki *et al.*, 2007).

Avellano
(***Gevuina avellana*** Molina; Chilean nut; Chilean hazel)

It is native of Chile. It is an evergreen tree growing more than 15 m in height. Leaves are pinnate with oval leaflets having toothed margin. Inflorescence is racemose bearing snow to ivory white flowers appearing from February to May in the late Chilean summer and early autumn. Fruit is a drupe, coral red, bearing one globular seed with smooth and tough shell (Menninger, 1977; Rosengarten, 1984).

⑧ ⑧ ⑧

Annona

Balanagar

Arka Sahan

African Pride

Mammoth

Atemoya

Avocado (Griesbach, 2005 & CHES, Chethali)

Hass

Fuerte

Zutano

Pinkerton

CHES A-1

Coconut (CPCRI, Kasaragod, Kerala)

Chowghat Orange Dwarf

Kalpa Mitra

Kalpa Sankara (CGDxWCT)

VPM 3

Date Palm (Dr. C.M. Muralidharan, Date palm Research Station, Mundra)

Medjool

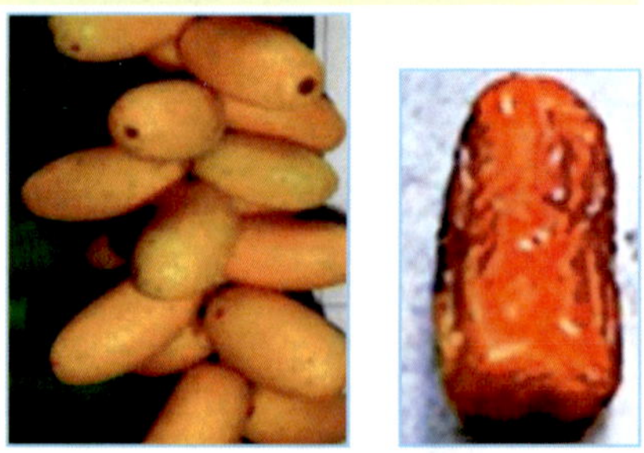

Halawy

Barhee

Zahidi

Khuneizi

Banana

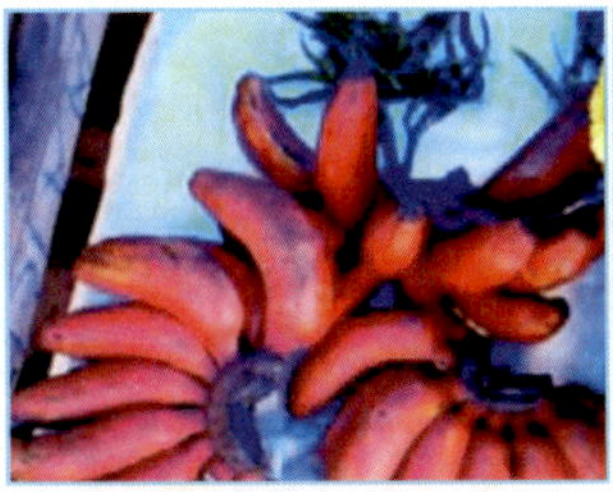

Fe'i

Bluggoe

Grand Naine

Poovan

Robusta

Red Banana

Rasthali

Nendran

Pineapple (TFnet, 2008)

Kew

Mauritius

Queen

Smooth Cayenne

Macadamia

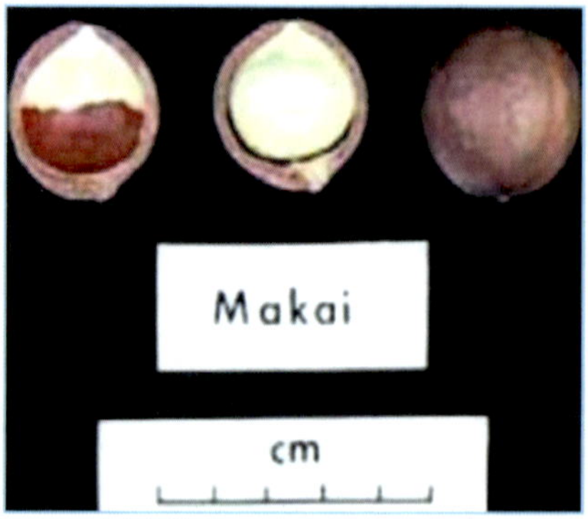

White currant (White Dutch)

Red currant

Strawberry (Camarosa)

Grape

Thompson Seedless

Ruby Seedless

Sonaka

[CORE EUDICOTS]

Flower is polyandrous, pentacyclic with alternating parts. Gynoecium is connate, calyx and corolla are free, pollen is tricolporate and placentation is usually axile. Trihydroxyl flavonoids are present.

Chapter 18

DILLENIALES

The plants are mostly trees (sometimes buttresses or tortuous to small rosette trees) and shrubs, rarely woody lianas, sub-shrubs or semi-herbaceous. Woody rhizome and raphides are common in the wood. Vessel elements are angular to circular, from medium to extremely long, usually very long with scalariform perforations that have 5-130 bars (mostly 15-40) or scalariform and simple perforations and lateral pitting from scalariform to opposite. Fibres are with distinctly bordered pits. Rays are heterogeneous. Axial parenchyma is apotracheal diffused and aggregate diffused, often paratracheal diffused to incomplete vasicentric. Sieve element plastids are of S-type. Nodes are trilacunar, pentalacunar, multilacunar or sometimes unilacunar with one trace per gap.

Leaves are usually alternate, very rarely opposite, entire or serrate to dentate, rarely pinnatifid or trilobed, pinnately veined, often with prominent parallel lateral veins, seldom much reduced and needle-like or scale-like (species of *Pachynema* with stems and branches flattened into phylloclades). Stipules are usually wanting, but rarely petioles with stipule-like, often wholly or partly caducous wings. Walls of epidermal cells are mostly silicified (as in Magnoliaceae and Calycanthaceae). Stomata are of various types, but mostly anomocytic.

Flowers are small to medium-sized, rarely large, in various cymose or racemose inflorescences or sometimes solitary, bisexual or rarely unisexual (monoecious or dioecious), actinomorphic or sometimes zygomorphic (but only with reference to the androecium) with spirocyclic perianth. Receptacle is flat or conical between the carpels. Sepals are mostly 5, rarely more (up to 15) or less (3), strongly imbricate and persistent. Petals are 5 or rarely fewer, imbricate, often crumpled in bud and deciduous. Stamens are usually numerous (from 50 to 500 in *Tetracera* to 900 in *Dillenia ovalifolia*), rarely 10 or fewer. Filaments are usually filiform, rarely broad and flattened, variously united into fascicle at the base; the members of each fascicle are in centrifugal sequence or the whole androecium developing centrifugally. The androecium of *Schumacheria* is unique in its placement at one side of the gynoecium with the large number of stamens united basally by their filaments into an oblique cylindric column. Anthers are tetrasporangiate, often more or less embedded in the connective tissue, from short to very elongate, sometimes with more or less prolonged connective, opening by longitudinal slits or apical pores. Microsporogenesis is simultaneous. Pollen grains are 2-celled, 3-colpate (*Acroterma, Dillenia, Hibbertia* and *Pachynema*), 4-colpate or 3-colporate, tectate-columellate, with an incomplete tectum, finely lunctate to coarsely reticulate. Gynoecium is usually of 1-20 carpels. Carpels are free, less often partly connate at the base, rarely fused to above the middle (*Curatella*) or even to the apex (*Neowormia*), more or less conduplicate and sometimes not fully sealed. Stylodia are usually slender and elongated with an apical, often capitate and minute stigma. Ovules are one to many in each carpel, anatropous to amphitropous or campylotropous, bitegmic and crassinucellate with zigzag or exostomal micropyle. Female gametophyte is of *Polygonum*-type (Takhtajan, 2009). Fruits are apocarpous or syncarpous, mostly dry and dehiscent, sometimes indehiscent (*Dillenia*). Seeds are mostly with a well developed crested or laciniate funicular aril (very large in *Dillenia sarmentosa* and *Tetracera* spp.), less often antivestigial or even wanting. Seed coat is formed by both integuments and with sclerotic endotesta and tracheidal exotegmen (endotestal-exotegmal). Embryo is usually minute, straight and more or less differentiated. Endosperm is copious, oily and proteinaceous, sometimes truminate. Tissues are tanniniferous, containing a great diversity of flavonoids, but mostly without alkaloids and always without benzylisoquinoline alkaloids (Takhtajan, 2009).

Family Dilleniaceae (Dillenia family)

It is a large family of mainly tropical trees and shrubs. It contains about 11-12 genera and 335 species (Heywood *et al.*, 2007). The trees, shrubs, lianas and perennial herbs are medium-sized. The leaves are alternate, simple, persistent or caducous, without stipules having serrate or dentate lamina often with prominent lateral veins. The inflorescences are axillary or terminal, cymose, paniculate or fasciculate. The flowers are actinomorphic, bisexual or unisexual (plants monoecious or functionally dioecious in neotropical species of *Tetracera*), sometimes large and conspicuous. The sepals are 3-(5)-20, imbricate and persistent. The petals are 3-5, imbricate, deciduous and often crumpled in the bud. The stamens are numerous, developing centrifugally, the anthers often with a prolonged and well developed connective. The ovary is superior of 1-5 or more carpels, free or variously connate, sometimes compound with marginal placentation and 1-5 locules. The styles are separate and divergent. The fruits are follicular, ventrally or dorsally dehiscent or indehiscent and dry (nuts) or fleshy (berries). The seeds are one to many per carpel with copious oily endosperm, sometimes starchy and often arillate.

Genus *Dillenia* L. (n = 13, 16, 24, 27)

The plants are trees, rarely shrubs, mostly evergreen, rarely deciduous. Leaves are with or without amplexicaul petiolar wings. Inflorescences are 1-10(-30)-flowered, a cincinnus, thyrsoid with cincinnate partial inflorescences, panicle (often depauperate) or monad, terminal or rarely axillary. Flowers are infrequently borne on cataphyll bearing short shoots. Sepals are (4)5(-18), unequal to ±equal, petals are (0,4)5(-7), androecium has (60-)100-700(-900) members, sometimes partly staminodial, fertile stamens often distinctly heterantherous (the inner group of stamens bearing anthers overtly longer than those of the outer group). Anther dehiscence is frequently via 2 apical or subapical pores, less frequently via 2 longitudinal slits. Staminodes, when present, are typically external to the fertile androecium, rarely internal. Gynoecium is typically hemi-syncarpous having (4)5-1

5(-20) carpels forming one whorl on a conical, centrally protruding part of the receptacle, 5-80 ovules per carpel borne in 2(4) vertical rows on submarginal placentae. Fruit is an aggregate of basally coherent follicle or it is indehiscent and completely enclosed by the fleshy, accrescent calyx. Seeds are with a white or red fleshy aril or the aril is vestigial in some species with indehiscent fruits. The family contains about 65 species from Madagascar and Seychelles to Fiji, 45 species from Malesia and 1 from Australia (Kubitzki *et al.*, 2007).

The *Dillenia* species are endemic to India and South East Asia. *D. indica* L. (chalta) and *D. pentagyna* Roxb. (karmal) are native of India. *D. pentagyna* Roxb. (karmal) is found throughout India and produces smaller fruits than those of chalta and are eaten raw or cooked. *D. scabrella* Roxb. is found in northeastern India. It bears small globose berries and attractive foliage and flowers. *Dillenia megalantha* Merr. (katmon bayani) is endemic in the Philippines and gives fruits that have acid taste. *D. reifferscheidia* Villar (Katmon-kalabau) is also endemic in the Philippines and its edible fruit has flavour of an acid tasting apple and makes excellent jam. *D. serrata* Thunb. (dengilo) is endemic to Indonesia and its acidic fruits are used fresh or pickled as a substitute for lemon (Anon., 1952; Verheij and Coronel, 1991).

Elephant apple

(***Dillenia indica*** L. syn. ***D. speciosa*** Thunb.; ***chalta***)

Elephant apple is native to southeastern Asia, from India, Bangladesh and Sri Lanka, in the east to southwestern China (Yunnan) and Vietnam through Thailand to Malaysia and Indonesia. The plant is an evergreen large shrub or small to medium-sized tree growing 15 m tall. The leaves are 15–36 cm long with a conspicuously corrugated surface with impressed veins resembling those of loquat. The flowers are large, 15–20 cm in diameter with 5 white petals and numerous yellow stamens. It has enormously fleshy calyx that is edible. Its characteristic round fruits are large, greenish yellow and have many seeds. The fruit is a 5–12 cm in diameter, aggregate of 15 carpels, each carpel containing 5 seeds embedded in an edible but fibrous pulp. The fruit pulp is bitter-sour and used in Indian cuisine in curries, jam (ouu khatta) and jellies. It is often mixed with coconut and spices to make chutneys and is extensively used in fish preparations in Assam.

⑧ ⑧ ⑧

Chapter 19

SAXIFRAGALES

It is the basal member of the Rosidae. The plants are woody shrubs or perennial and annual herbs. Vessels are mostly with scalariform or more often simple perforations. Sieve element plastids are of S- or P-types. Nodes are trilacunar, multilacunar or unilacunar. Leaves are alternate, opposite or verticillate, simple or compound or exstipulate. Stomata are of various types.

The flowers are solitary, bisexual, actinomorphic or less often zygomorphic, usually with double perianth, sometimes apetalous. Perianth forms a more or less well developed floral tube, free or more or less adnate to the base of the ovary. Sepals are mostly 5, less often less (3- 4) or more (up to 10), free or more or less connate, imbricate or valvate. Stamens are few to numerous, mostly as many or twice that of the sepals having basifixed or less often slightly dorsifixed, introrse or latrorse, tetrasporangiate anthers opening longitudinally. Tapetum is secretory. Microsporogenesis is simultaneous. Pollen grains are 2 or 3-celled, mostly 3-colporate to pentaporate Nectary disc is mostly present. Gynoecium is of free or more or less united carpels, stylodia is free, stigma is decurrent to capitate and ovary is superior, semi-inferior or inferior with 1 to numerous ovules per carpel or per locule. Ovules are usually anatropous, bitegmic or rarely unitegmic and crassinucellate. Female gametophyte is of *Polygonum* or *Allium*-type or rarely *Peperomia*-type. Endosperm is cellular or less often helobial or nuclear. Fruits are multifollicles (Penthoraceae, majority of Crassulaceae), capsular, baccate (Grossulariaceae), drupaceous (Gunneraceae) or nut-like (Aphanopetalaceae). Seeds are small or minute, exotestal (*Astilbe* and *Rodgersia* in Saxifragaceae) or rarely exotestal endotegmic. Embryo is small or large, mostly straight and endosperm is usually copious. Flavones, flavonoids, proanthocyanidins alkaloids are present. It includes 15-16 families.

Family Grossulariaceae (Currants, gooseberries)

Plants of northern temperate and Andean region, reaching high latitude and altitudes comprising the single genus *Ribes* and 200 species. The plants are shrubs, sometimes prostrate or scrambling with alternate leaves and usually with multicellular glandular hairs. The leaves are usually evergreen, sometimes deciduous, simple, often toothed, usually petiolate, often palmately lobed. Stipules are attached to petiole, usually winged or fimbriate. The inflorescence is a raceme with the flowers typically borne on a short lateral shoot. The flowers are actinomorphic, bisexual or unisexual (plants dioecious) with a pronounced tubular to rotate hypanthium. The sepals are usually (4-)5, free, sometimes strongly reflexed at anthesis. The petals are as many as the sepals and usually shorter, free, sometimes minute and obovate. The stamens are 4-5, free, usually as many as the sepals with short filaments attached to top of hypanthial tube. The ovary is inferior, of 2 joined carpels, with 1 locule. The fruit is a berry, often covered with dense glandular hairs.

Genus *Ribes* L. (gooseberries and currants) (x = 8; 2n = 16)

Seven subgenera are recognized: subg. *Ribes*, including the hermaphroditic sect. *Ribes* (red currants), sect. *Heritiera* (skunk currants) and the dioecious alpine currants (sect. *Berisia*); subg. *Coreosma* (black currants); subg. *C. alobotrya* (ornamental currants), the paraphyletic sect. *Calobotrya* (including sect. *Cerophyllum*); subg. *Symphocalyx* (golden currants); subg. *Grossularioides* (spiny currants); subg. *Grossularia* (gooseberries); and subg. *Parilla* (South American currants) (Kubitzki *et al.*, 2007). More than 150 species of currants and gooseberries grow in the colder regions of northern hemisphere and in the Andes of South America.

The deciduous shrubs growing to 1.5-1.8 m height are usually unarmed but sometimes have bristly branches with mostly 3-parted stipular spines and about 1 cm long bristles. The leaves are glabrous or pubescent, cordate to broad cuneate, 24 cm wide, 3-5 lobed with crenulate dentate and obtuse lobes, palmately veined and of firm texture. Flowers are in racemes, rarely clustered, hermaphrodite or unisexual and then dioecious. The greenish flowers (1-2) have pubescent and often glandular villose but never spiny ovary with pedicels joined below, often with 2 minute bractlets from shallowly saucer shaped or rotate to tubular disk-like top, often thickened with rings. Sepals are usually pubescent, about as long as the short campanulate receptacle and stamens shorter than sepals. The fruit is an epigynous berry, globose to ovoid, disarticulating from the pedicel, red, white, yellow, black or green, often with bloom, glabrous, glandular or glandular hairy.

European gooseberry (*Ribes grossularia* L. syn. *R. uva-crispa*) and American gooseberry (*R. hirtellum* Michx.)

Gooseberries are derived mostly from two species; *Ribes grossularia* (European gooseberry), native to the Caucasus Mountains and North Africa and *R. hirtellum* (American gooseberry), native to northeastern and northcentral USA and adjacent parts of Canada. The so called European cultivars are pure species, but virtually all American cultivars have European genes also.

Gooseberries are deciduous shrubs growing up to 1 m tall and 2 m in width. The leaves are alternate, single, deeply lobed and glossy dark green (European types) or pale to gray green and sometimes finely pubescent (American types). The stems are thin becoming woody with a large thorn at each axil. American gooseberry stems are densely bristly with one or more additional thorns at each axil. The inconspicuous flowers having green with pink flushed petals open in early spring. They are borne laterally on one year old wood and on short spurs of older wood. The flowers are self fertile and pollinated by wind and insects, including bees. Each flower bud opens to unfold one to four flowers, depending on cultivar. The fruit, borne singly or in pairs at the axils, is a berry having many minute seeds at the centre. A gooseberry may be green, white (gray green), yellow or shades of red from pink to purple to almost black. Fruits of the European gooseberry may be very large, like a small plum, but are usually 2.5 cm long and less in width. American gooseberry fruits are smaller (about 1 cm), perfectly round, all becoming pink to wine red at maturity. Skin colour becomes most intense in full sunlight. Berries generally drop when overripe. The fruit has its own typical flavour and the best dessert cultivars are as luscious as the best apple, strawberry or grape.

Cultivars of red gooseberry

Abundance: It originated in North Dakota, USA from *R. missouriensis* x Oregon Champion. The bush is hardy, strong and very productive. The fruit is medium in size, purplish in colour and round in shape and borne on long stems. The fruit skin is thick and tough that helps in long storage and transportation.

Clark: It originated in Burlington, Canada as chance seedling or natural hybrid of European and American species. The bush is hardy, moderate in vigour and medium in productivity. The fruits are mid-late in ripening, easy to pick, very large, initially greenish yellow and turning red at maturity having thick and quite tough skin and of good quality.

Jahns Prairie: It is a disease resistant high quality dessert gooseberry developed at Corvallis, Oregon. The plants are upright with some drooping branches, spineless or having few spines of less than 4 mm. These are resistant to powdery mildew, leaf spot, aphids and sawflies. The cultivar has high productivity. The fruits are large, globose in shape, red in colour with slight pink tinge. Fruits ripen from middle to end of July.

Rokula: It originated in Germany from a cross between Mauk's Early Red and mildew resistant *R. uva-crispa*. The bush is medium in vigour, slightly drooping, medium in production and resistant to powdery mildew and leaf spots. The fruits ripen very early in the season and are red, round, large, with outstanding flavour and quality but crack in rain.

Cultivars of green gooseberry

Pembina Pride: It originated in Manitoba, Canada. The bush is very winter hardy like Thoreson and is productive. The fruits are green in colour at maturity and medium in size having fair quality and thick and tough skin.

Mucurines: It is a green cultivar selected from *R. uva-crispa*. The bush is vigorous, upright. Suckers emerge freely from the base. On the basis of fruit size, regular productivity and yield traits, the cultivar is considered suitable for commercial production and for home gardens. The berries are easy to pick, large, green, broad elliptic in form with good flavour and resist cracking and hang well on the bush.

Malling Greenfinch: The cultivar was developed at East Malling Research Station, England from a double cross, Careless x (Whinham's Industry x Resistenta).

The plants are compact with upright growth, spineless, resistant to powdery mildew and moderately resistant to leaf spot and very productive. It is good for fresh consumption and for growing in home garden. The fruit is medium in size, green in colour and attractive. The flesh is somewhat soft having good flavour and has moderate canning and freezing quality.

Malling Invicta: It originated from a double cross, Keepsake x (Whinham's Industry x Resistenta). The plants are vigorous, spreading with many spines and resistant to powdery mildew. The fruit is large, irregular in shape, light green in colour having somewhat bristly skin, good flavour and is suitable for processing.

Cultivars of white gooseberry

Keepsake or Berry's Early Kent: It is an excellent white gooseberry. The plants are usually spreading and very tender to frost damage. It is very productive and regular cropper. The fruit ripens early in the season and is good for fresh consumption. Berries are usually white in colour tinged with green.

Whitesmith: The cultivar is very prolific and consistently regular bearer. The fruit ripens early. The berries are quite large in size, oval in shape and pale green tinged with light yellow having good taste and flavour.

Careless: It is a widely cultivated white gooseberry. The cultivar is very heavy copper and the fruits ripen in mid season. The ripe greenish white fruits are suitable for fresh consumption. These are extensively used for jam making and canning.

Cultivars of yellow gooseberry

Pilot: It is a highly splendid cultivar but is not grown extensively because it is not a heavy cropper. The cultivar does well where Leveller fails. It is a dessert gooseberry, produces berries that are usually oblong oval having attractive yellow colour and good flavour.

Golda: The cultivar was developed in Netherlands from cross between Whitesmith and May Duke. The plant is a bush of medium size. It is high yielding but is susceptible to powdery mildew. The fruits are yellow in colour, large and ripen in mid-late season.

The following gooseberry cultivars were developed at East Malling Research Station, East Malling, England :-

Greenfinch (Careless x (Whinham's Industry x Resistenta); Selection B994/27).

Pax (Whinham's Industry x a derivative of Captivator x Lancashire Lad); Selection 1815/123).

Invicta (Keepsake x (Whinham's Industry x Resistenta)); Selection B995/2).

Currants
(*Ribes* spp.)

The principal cultivated species are *Ribes sativum* Syme (red or white), *R. rubrum* L. (red) and *R. nigrum* L. (black). Red, pink and white currants belong to three European species (*Ribes rubrum, R. petraeum, R. sativum*). Black currants are related to European (*R. nigrum*) and Asian (*R. ussuriense*) species. The related species are *R. grossularia, R. aureum* (buffalo currant) and *R. nigrum x hirtellum* (jostaberry) besides the gooseberries.

All forms of currants are fast growing, deciduous, low to medium sized, prickly or thornless shrubs. The leaves are alternate, simple, petiolate, lobed and serrate. Black currant leaves are pale green while those of the red currant are deep blue green. The flowers are borne toward the bases of one year old stems and on spurs on older stems in early spring with new growth. Each flower bud opens to unfold number of flowers (up to 20), joined together on a delicate, drooping 12-15 cm stem called a raceme (strig). Individual flowers (green in the case of red currants and blush pink in black currants) are not showy, but joined together on the strig they give the bush a lacy texture. Flower is unisexual or hermaphrodite. The petals are (4-5), inserted in the calyx throat, often small and scale-like, usually shorter than calyx. It has 4 or 5 stamens, inferior and unilocular ovary and 2 distinct or connate styles. The berries of red, white and pink currants are translucent, juicy and contain 3-12 minute bony seeds.

Cultivars

Important cultivars of red currants are Red Lake, Minnesota 71, Stephens No. 9, Wilder, Perfection, Rondom, Rote Spatlese, Jonkheervan Tets, Laxton's No.1 and Stanza. The cultivars of white currants are White Imperial, White Dutch, White Grape and White Versailles. The cultivars of black currants are Boskoop Giant, Laxton's Giant, Tesema, Ben Lomond, Ben More, Ben Nevis, Blackdown, Black-smith, Amos Black, Bladwin, Ben Saek and Ben Tirran. Certain Canadian cultivars (Consort, Crusader and Coronet) are *R. nigrum x ussuriense* hybrids.

Ogden: The cultivar originated in Ottawa, Canada. The bush is vigorous, medium in size, very productive and bears clusters that are small to medium in size. The fruits are black in colour, small to medium in size having quite tender/soft skin and ripen irregularly in mid season. The flesh is sub-acid of fair quality.

Fleming: The cultivar originated in North Dakota, USA from *R. americanum*. It is regarded to be one of the better fruiting types. The fruits are black in colour. The cultivar was adjudged better in quality and production than most other cultivars.

Tor Cross: It originated at Bristol, England from a cross between Baldwin and Rogue. The bush is medium in vigour and high yielding. The fruit is black in colour, ripens early in season, resembles Mandip Cross and has more resistance to splitting and dropping.

Albatross: It originated in Netherlands from the cross, Red Lake x Fay's Pride. The plant is moderate in growth, produces moderate to high yields and flowers early. It is a white currant with excellent flavour. The fruits ripen early in the season, are easy to harvest and medium in size having attractive pale yellow colour, sweet taste and excellent flavour.

Detvan: It originated at Bojnice, Slovakia from a cross between Joukheer van Tets and Heinemann's Rote Spatlese. The bush is tall growing and vigorous and adapts to warmer places and produces high yield regularly. The fruits are produced on long shoots. These are large, attractive and ripen early.

Red Start (Red lake x (*Ribes koehneanum* x Red Lake)): The plants are erect with vigorous growth, resist high winds and are high yielders. The fruits are borne on long shoots and are red in colour having acidic flavour and are good for processing.

Malling Red Start: The cultivar was developed at East Malling Research Station, England from a cross between Red Lake and B 156/34 [(*R. sativum* x *R. multiforum*) x Red Lake]. The plants are erect with vigorous growth, resist high winds and are high yielders. The fruits are borne on long shoots and are red in colour having acidic flavour and are good for processing.

Random: The cultivar was selected from *R. multiflorum* in Netherlands. The cultivar is somewhat susceptible to leaf spot and powdery mildew. The plants are vigorous and have upright growth. It is a mid season and very productive cultivar. The fruits are bright red and medium in size and are easy to harvest.

The following red currant cultivars were developed at East Malling Research Station, England:-

Redstart (Red Lake x (*Ribes koehneanum* x Red Lake); Selection B608/3).

Redpoll (Red Lake x *(Ribes longeracemosum* x *R. multiflorum*); Selection 1503/11).

Redwing (Red Lake x *(Ribes longeracemosum* x *R. multiflorum*); Selection 1503/35)

Jet (*Ribes bracteosum* x *R. nigrum*) x Brodtorp B674/108.

Wellington XXX Boskoop Giant x Baldwin).

Farleigh (BC_2 *Ribes bracteosum* x BC_3 from gooseberry); Selection 1661/150).

Foxendown (Ben Lomond x (BC_3 from gooseberry x BC_2 *R. glutinosum*); Selection 1840/121).

⑧ ⑧ ⑧

ROSIDS

The Rosids are members of a large monophyletic group of flowering plants having about 70,000 species, more than a quarter of all angiosperms. The clade is divided into 16-20 orders. These in turn comprise 140 families. The plants have leaves with stipules.

Chapter 20

VITALES

The order probably originated from some Rosanae ancestor. The plants are small trees, erect shrubs and herbs or more often woody lianas. Roots are sometimes adventitious. Cambium is storied. Vessel elements are usually rather large with simple perforations with scalariform or sometimes opposite to alternate lateral pitting. Fibres are with simple or sometimes bordered pits and septate. Rays are heterogeneous. Axial parenchyma is mainly paratracheal. Sieve element plastids are of Pcs-type and contain several polygonal protein crystalloids similar to the plastids of *Gunnera*. Nodes are 3 to 7-lacunar.

Leaves are alternate or very rarely opposite, simple or compound, of diverse shapes and structures, stipulate or exstipulate, often bearing specialized, multicellular, stalked and deciduous "pearl glands" and sometimes also peltate scales. Stomata are of diverse kinds.

Inflorescences are leaf-opposed or terminal, rarely axillary, cymose or racemose, sometimes with 1-2 tendril-like branches. Bract and bracteoles are small, sometimes nectar secreting subtending each branch. Flowers are rather small, bisexual or polygamo-monoecious or dioecious, actinomorphic and (3)4-5(6-7)-merous. Calyx is mostly weakly developed, lobed, dentate or truncate, often much reduced. Petals are 4-5 (rarely 3 or 6-7), valvate, free or basally connate or sometimes coherent distally and calyptra-like (*Vitis*), rarely persistent. Stamens are 5-4 (3-7), opposite the petals having filaments free or connate into a tube. Anthers are dorsifixed, tetrasporangiate or rarely disporangiate, introrse, opening longitudinally. Tapetum is secretory. Microsporogenesis is simultaneous. Pollen grains are 2 or 3-celled, 3-colporate with reticulate ornamentation. Nectary disc is usually well developed, annular or cupular or sometimes of 5 free glands, usually more or less adnate to the ovary. Gynoecium is of 2-6(-8) united carpels with stylodia connate into a style with capitate, seldom (*Tetrastigma*) quadrifid, rarely sessile stigma, superior ovary, but sometimes partly sunken in the nectary disc, completely or incompletely divided into locules with one or two ovules per locule. Ovules are erect, axile or basal, anatropous, apotropous with ventral, bitegmic and crassinucellate raphe. Female gametophyte is of *Polygonum*-type. Endosperm is nuclear. Haustoria of the female gametophyte are present or absent. Fruits are berries (sometimes rather dry). Seeds are endotestal (with lignified, several-layered endotesta and persistent thin tracheidal tegmen). Embryo is small to minute, straight, surrounded by copious, horny, generally ruminate and oily endosperm with two main folds, one from each side of the raphe. Alkaloids (ellagic acid, myricetin) are rarely present or absent. It contains only family Vitaceae.

Family Vitaceae (formerly Ampelidaceae) x = 19, 20; 2n = 38, 40

The plants are mostly tropical, subtropical and warm temperate in distribution. These are deciduous, rarely evergreen woody shrubs, usually vines climbing by tendrils. Some species are erect shrubs or trees. The stem nodes are swollen often with raphide sacs. The stem is dentate having brown pith, interrupted at the nodes by diaphragms. The leaves are not distinctive, usually lobed, simple or variously compound, rarely palmately compound, alternate and sometimes the lower leaves are opposite. The inflorescence arises opposite the leaf. These are modified tendrils. The flowers are small, many, borne in panicle or cyme, greenish and conspicuous, hypogynous, variously clustered, regular, bisexual or polygamous. These are 5-merous. Calyx is entire or 3-7 toothed, usually 4-5 in number. The petals are 4-5, free or united, valvate, falling off as cap. The stamens are prevailingly 4 or 5, opposite the petals. The ovary is superior, 2 or more celled with 1 or 2 ovules in each cell. The style is simple or missing. Placentation is axile. The fruit is pulpy, fleshy, 2 to 4-seeded or seedless berry. Seed is usually pyriform with a contracted beak-like base having 2 grooves on the ventral side. It has a cord-like raphe on the adaxial surface, extending from the hilum to the seed apex and onto the convex abaxial side, where it joins a round linear, depressed to somewhat elevated "chalazal knot" and is also with a deep groove varying in shape and length flanking both sides of the raphe. The seed has cartilaginous endosperm and small embryo. About 60 species occur in the Northern Hemisphere, chiefly in the temperate region. Based on the classification of Planchon (1887), the family comprises following 10 genera :-

1. *Vitis* (Tournef) L.
    - Section 1: *Euvitis* Planch.
    - Section 2: *Muscadinia* Planch.
2. *Ampelocissus* Planch.
3. *Pterisanthes* Blume
4. *Clematicissus* Planch.
5. *Tetrastigma* (Miq.) Planch.
6. *Landukia* Planch.
7. *Parthenocissus* Planch.
8. *Ampelopsis* Mich.
9. *Rhoicissus* Planch.
10. *Cissus* L.
    - Section 1: *Eucissus* Planch.
    - Section 2: *Cayratia* Juss.
    - Section 3: *Cissus* Planch.

Subsequently, Galet (1988) revised the classification enlarging the family to include 14 living genera.

Genus *Vitis* L. (x=19, 20; 2n=38, 40)

It contains about 60 species, mostly distributed in temperate regions of the northern hemisphere (Kubitzki *et al*., 2007). About 25 species are found in India. The plants are deciduous woody climbers, temperate and subtropical, polygamodioecious, usually with shreddy bark on old stems. The vines have tendrils, which are modified stems. The nodes are thick. The internodes have pith. A diaphragm may be present at the node or may be absent as in bamboo. The genus, based on morphological, anatomical and karyological characters, can be divided into two subgenera or sections; *Euvitis* (the true grapes) and *Muscadinia* (Table 20.1 and Fig. 20.1). Lenticels are absent or inconspicuous in subg. *Vitis* and prominent in subg. *Muscadinia*. Pith is brown and interrupted by diaphragms within the nodes in subg. *Vitis* and continuous through the nodes in subg. *Muscadinia*. Tendrils are leaf-opposed and 2-3-furcate in subg. *Vitis* and simple in subg. *Muscadinia*, usually on two consecutive nodes or less commonly on three or more consecutive nodes without adhesive disks.

Table 20.1. Characters of subgenera *Euvitis* and *Muscadinia*

Characters	***Vitis* or *Euvitis***	***Muscadinia* (bunch grape)**
Bark	Shreds off	Chips like in trees
Lenticels	Absent	Present, numerous
Tendrils	Forked	Simple
Seeds	Ovoid, pear shaped, smooth chalaza	Oblong, Oval, wrinkled chalaza
Pith	Discontinuous, diaphragm at nodes	Continuous, no diaphragm at nodes
Phellogen	Deep seated	Sub-epidermal
Phloem fibers	Tangential	Radial
Specific gravity of wood	<1	>1
Number of berries/cluster	50-500	3-15
Berry shatter	With pedicel	Without pedicel
Chromosome number	2n=38	2n=40
Number of species	59	3

As growth commences, the leaves emerge first and are followed by flowers. Leaves are simple, often lobed, dentate to serrate and palmately veined having caducous stipules. The fruit buds are borne laterally and are mixed. The inflorescence is a compact panicle, borne laterally at the node on current season's growth, opposite 2-3 to many consecutive nodes, sometimes with a tendril at the apex of the peduncle. The flowers may be male, female or hermaphrodite. *Vitis rotundifolia* is dioecious. The inflorescence is a cyme borne at the node opposite the leaf. Flowers are small, 5-merous morphologically, bisexual and unisexual but functionally unisexual having minute calyx (reduced to a narrow ring with 5 teeth) to entire, petals (3-)5(-9), apically connate separating at the base forming a calyptra at anthesis, usually 5 stamens, erect in male and bisexual flowers and reflexed or occasionally absent in female flowers, disk of 5 glands alternating with stamens. Gynoecium is rudimentary in male flowers. In female flowers, style is with conical, short, small and capitate stigma. The plants are generally self pollinated but some are self incompatible and require cross pollination. Stimulated, not vegetative, parthenocarpy is found. Fruit is 2-loculed, pulpy, globose, purple to black, rarely whitish or greenish, 1-4-seeded and often glaucous. The ovary has 2 ovules in each locule but generally only one or two seeds develop. Seeds are obovoid to pyriform and caruncle with the adaxial surface having two longitudinal grooves on either side of the raphe and the abaxial surface with a round to elliptic chalazal knot, extending to 1/3 of the seed length from the base. Endosperm is M-shaped.

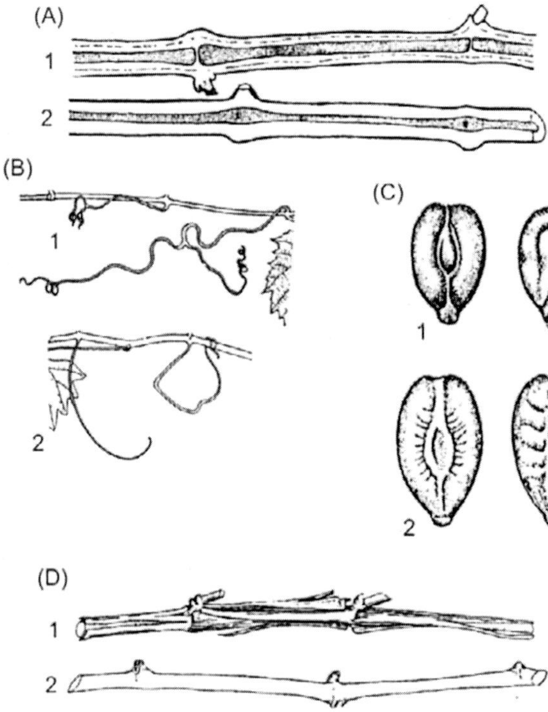

Fig. 20.1. Properties of subgenera *Vitis* and *Muscadinia*: A. internal cane morphology, B.tendrils, C. front and back of seed, and D. bark shredding (Source: Jackson, 2014).

Classification of genus *Vitis*

The first classification of *Vitis* by Planchon (1887) placed the American and Asiatic species in separate series. Some of the later French amateur breeders concentrated their interest on a relatively small number of species that were considered useful germplasm to combat *Phylloxera*, the predominant problem of French viticulture at the end of 19th century. Consequently, their view of the genus *Vitis* remained somewhat restricted resulting in little attention to the species having less practical importance. By contrast, Bailey (1934) produced an extensive classification of the North American *Vitis* species. Weaver (1976) also classified the species based on their geographical distribution. Galet (1988) has listed 59 species under genus *Vitis* of which 56 belong to the subgen. *Euvitis* or section *Vitis* distributed in 11 series (Table 20.2).

Table 20.2. Classification and geographical distribution of species of genus *Vitis* (Galet, 1988)

Subgenus *Euvitis* or section *Vitis*		
Series	**Species and synonym**	**Origin**
I. Candicanae	*V. candicans* Englemann (Mustang grape), *V. champinii* Planchon (Calcoire grape), *V. doaniana* Munson (Panha-ndle grape), *V. longii* Prince (solonis and novo-mexicana) (bush grape), *V. simpsonii* Munson (currant grape), *syn. V. smalliana* Bailey (fig leaf grape), *V. coriacea* syn. *V. shuttleworthii* House. (Calloosa grape)	North America (East)
II. Labruscae	*V. labrusca* Linnaeus (fox grape), *V. coignetiae* Pulliat.	North America (East), Asia
III. Caribaeae	*V. caribaea* syn. *V. tiliaefolia, V. blancoii* Munson, *V. lanata* Roxburgh	North America (South), North America (East)
IV. Arizonae	*V. arizonica* Englemann (canyon grape), *V. californica* Bentham (Pacific grape, California wild grape), *V. girdiana* Munson. (valley grape), *V. treleasei* Munson. (Gulch grape)	North America (West)
V. Cinereae	*V. cinerea* Engelmann (Grayback grape), *V. berlandieri* Planchon (Spanish grape), *V. baileyana* Munson (Possum grape), *V. bourgeana* Planch.	North America (East) North America (South)
VI. Aestivalae	*V. aestivalis* Michaux. (summer grape), *V. linecumii* Buckley (Post-oak grape), *V. bicolor* syn. *V. argentifolia* Munson (silver leaf grape), *V. gigas* Fennell. (Florida blue grape), *V. rufotomentosa* Small. (Redshank grape), *V. bourquina* Munson	North America (East)
VII. Cordifoliae	*V. cordifolia* Lamarck. (winter grape), *V. rubra syn. V. palmata* Vahl. (cat grape)	North America (East)
	V. monticola Buckley (sweet mountain grape), *V. ilex* Bailey (Manatee grape), *V. helleri* Small (round leaf grape)	North America (East)
VIII. Flexuosae	*V. flexuosa* Thunberg, *V. thunbergii* S. and Z., *V. betulifolia* Diels and Gilg., *V. reticulata* Pampanini, *V. amurensis* Ruprecht, *V. piasekii* Maxim., *V. embergeri* Golet, *V. pentagona* Diels and Gilg., *V. chunganensis, V. chungii, V. piloso-nerva* Metiacalf., *V. balsansaeana, V. hancockii* Hance, *V. hexamera* Gagnep., *V. pedicellata* Lawson, *V. retordii* Rom. Caill ex Planch., *V. seguinii* H. Lev., *V. silvestrii* Pamp., *V. tsoii* Merr., *V. bryoniifolia* Bunge	Asia
IX. Spinosae	*V. armata* Diels and Gilg., *V. davidii* Romanet du Coillaud, *V. romaneti* Romanet ex Foex	Asia
X. Ripariae	*V. riparia* Michaux, *syn. V. vulpina* Linn. (frost grape), *V. rupestris* Scheele. (sand grape)	North America (East)
XI. Viniferae	*V. vinifera* Linnaeus (wine grape, European grape)	West Asia and Middle East

Subgenus *Muscadinia*	
M. rotundifolia Michaux (muscadine grape)	distributed from Delaware to Missouri, and south to Texas
M. munsoniana Simpson (little Muscadine grape)	distributed in central and southern Florida
M. popenoei Fennel (Mexican Muscadine grape)	found in New Mexico

The genus is often divided into two major groups; the American and the Eurasian (Table 20.3). The dominant species of the two groups differ in useful agronomic traits, which makes them attractive breeding partners (Keller, 2010).

Eurasian group: Approximately 40 species are known in this group, most of which are confined to eastern Asia. Chinese species are particularly diverse, growing in the dry southwest, the northern and southern foothills of the Himalayas, the very cold North East, and the hot and humid South East. Some of these are resistant to fungal diseases and may tolerate high humidity. Most of these species are little known and there may be several others that have not yet been described. Most of the Eurasian species are not resistant to the North American grapevine diseases. Yet one of them dominates the grape and wine industry throughout the world.

Table 20.3. Broad viticultural traits of American and Eurasian *Vitis* species.

Trait	**Eurasian species**	**American species**
Fruitfulness	Good	Poor or highly variable
Fruit quality	Good	Poor
Usefulness	Highly diverse products	Niche products
Propagation capacity	Good	Variable
Lime tolerance	Good	Highly variable
Tolerance to *Phylloxera*	Poor	Good or variable
Resistance to diseases	Poor	Good or variable

American group: This group is reported to contain between 8 and 34 species by different taxonomists. Several of these are economically important as wine or juice grapes. These have varying resistance to the North American grapevine diseases and pests and are thus used as rootstocks or as partners in breeding programmes. The species of the group generally have thinner shoots with longer internodes and less prominent nodes than the Eurasian species. They have small buds and the leaves with very shallow sinuses and often a glossy surface. The species native to North America are strictly dioecious and most of them grow near a permanent source of water such as river, stream or spring.

Key to the classification of *Vitis*

A. Skin adhering tightly.. *V. vinifera*

AA. Skin not adhering tightly

B. Bunch is small (3-15 berries) and rounded, berries falling off when ripe .... *V. rotundifolia*

BB. Bunch large (more than 15 berries) and oval, berries do not fall.

C. Berries 1.25 cm or more in diameter, purple black or reddish brown or greenish yellow in colour and have a foxy taste.. *V. labrusca*

CC. berries smaller than 1.25 cm in diameter... *V. aestivalis, V. vulpina*

Fig. 20.2a. American Vitis species (1. *V. coriacea,* 2. *V. lincecurnii,* 3. *V. monticola,* 4. *V. rupestris,* 5. *V. aestivalis,* 6. *V. arizonica,* 7. *V. munsoniana*, 8. *V. candicans*) (Source: Galet, 1979).

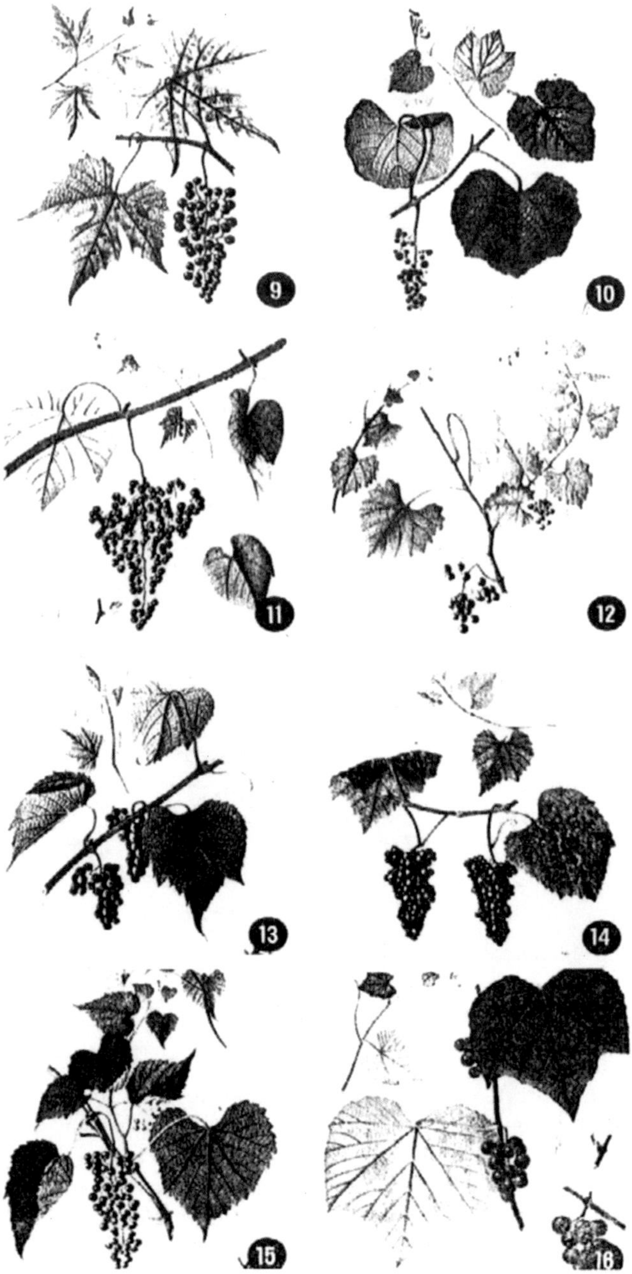

Fig. 20.2b. American Vitis species (9. *V. rubra,* 10. *V. californica,* 11. *V. cinerea,* 12. *V. rotundifolia,* 13. *V. riparia,* 14. *V. berlandieri,* 15. *V. cordifolia,* 16. *V. labrusca*) (Source: Galet, 1979).

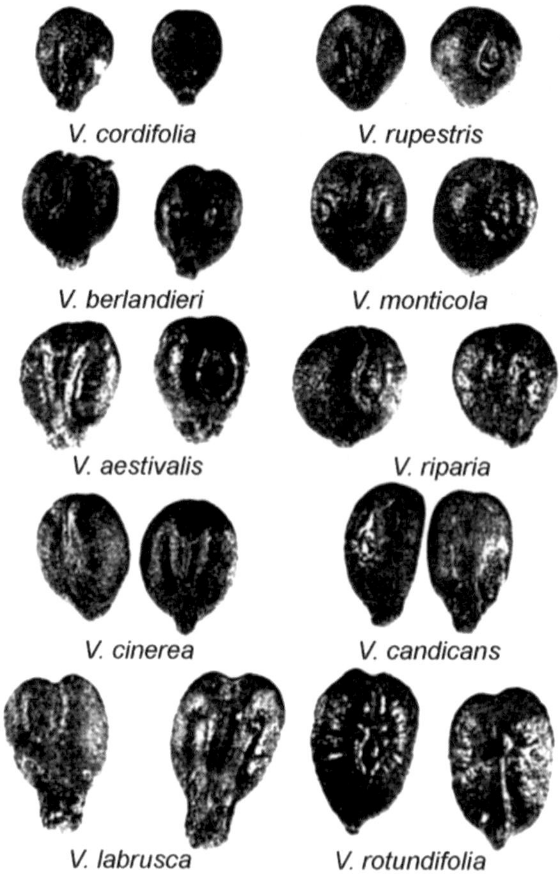

Fig. 20.3. Seeds of American *Vitis* species (Source: Galet, 1979).

European or Old World grape (*Vitis vinifera* L.)

This is native to western Asia and Europe between 30 and 50°N, but temporarily confined to the humid to arid volcanic forested mountain ranges of the southern Caucasus between the black Sea and the Caspian Sea and to the Mediterranean region. This is the most well known species of the Eurasian group because it gave rise to most of the cultivars grown today. Because the vines are hermaphroditic or rarely bear physiologically female flowers, these are often grouped into *V. vinifera* ssp. *sativa*. However, according to many taxonomists, *V. vinifera sativa* is merely the domesticated form of *V. vinifera* ssp. *sylvestris* as the differences between the two forms are the result of the domestication process arising through human rather than natural selection. The species is highly tolerant to lime, even more than *V. berlandieri,* and to drought.

The vines are hardy and deciduous, subtropical and heat and drought tolerant. The vines are not as tall as in the American species. The tendrils are intermittent. The leaves are round cordate, lobed with toothed or coarsely toothed margin. The flowers are perfect and self fertile. The bunch is large and oval. The berries are oval, variable in size having the skin adhering tightly to the flesh at maturity. The flesh is firm but tender having high sugar content. It is susceptible to *Phylloxera*, powdery mildew and downy mildew.

Cultivars

More than 10000 cultivars are known from all over the world. Cultivars are broadly classified into seedless and seeded types. The cultivars have also been classified based on uses such as table grapes, raisin grapes and grapes for canning and for making juice and wines. Cultivars have been selected/developed for these uses. The first cultivar classification was attempted in Rome by Plinius (AD 50) who created 3 groups based on berry colour and yield:

- Anemic group: Cultivars having small, white grapes
- Nomentanic group: Low yielding cultivars having red grapes
- Apianic group: High yielding cultivars of poor quality

During the Middle Ages, European wine grapes were simply divided into 2 groups according to the perceived wine quality:

- *Vinum francicum:* "Frentsch" grapes, low yielding cultivars of high quality (e.g. Traminer)
- *Vinum hunicum:* "Huntsch" grapes, high yielding cultivars of poor quality (e.g. Heunisch)

The Russian scientist Negrul (1946) distinguished 3 main groups (*proles*) of grapevine cultivars (Table 20.4).

Proles pontica: It comprises the oldest cultivars that arose close to the centre of origin of viticulture in Transcaucasia and then spread to the Balkans, the 'Fertile Crescent' and Egypt. Two sub-proles were distinguished: (i) *georgica*, which includes the cultivars Rkatziteli, Saperavi, 0djalechi and Mtsvane; and (ii) *balkanica*, which includes the cultivars Furmint, Clairette, Harslevelu, Vermentino and Zante Currant (Black Corinth). The grapevines that were introduced into the Middle East during 3000-2000 BC were probably *Proles pontica*.

Proles orientalis: Cultivars from the region of the Caspian Sea are so different from *Proles pontica* that Negrul proposed that these arose from a different form of *Vitis sylvestris*, i.e. *V. sylvestris aberrans* as distinct from *V. sylvestris typica*. These cultivars include the grapevines that were used for wine making before the advent of Islam and were attributed to the *Proles orientalis sub-proles caspica*.

Modern cultivars that belong to this group include the Muscats and Cinsaut. The *Proles orientalis sub-proles antasiatica* are mostly table grape cultivars. These genotypes arose by selection from wine grapes belonging to *sub-proles caspica* during the time of Islamic influence in the Mediterranean basin (500-1100 AD). The best known and most widely grown cultivar of the *sub-proles antasiatica* is Sultanina (syn. Thompson Seedless).

Proles occidentalis: The earliest cultivars in western Europe introduced by the Phoenicians and Greeks probably belonged to *Proles pontica* or to *Proles orientalis sub-proles caspica*. These being unsuitable for northern Europe, better cultivars adapted to cool conditions were selected from the native populations. These cultivars comprise the group *Proles occidentalis* that includes most of the well known wine grapes of France and Germany.

Levadoux (1956) classified the main cultivars grown in France according to their morphological and geographical similarities or based on the indication of the origin of the genotypes either from the same population of wild vines or from the same population of the introduced vines. In his classification the family *Noiriens* contains well known cultivars such as the Pinots, Chardonnay, Meunier, the Gamays, Melon, Sauvagnin and Traminer and lesser known cultivars such as Teinturier du Cher. However, by his classification it is difficult to establish the true origin of many cultivars grown in western Europe because the wild progenitors are extinct. Studies on the distribution of flower types in the wild grapes in the Rhine Valley and Pays Basque led Carbonneau (1983) to the conclusion that many wild grapevines were feral (derived from plants that were once cultivated rather than from wild plants in the true sense).

Table 20.4. Classification of cultivars of *V. vinifera* (Negrul, 1938).

Proles orientalis	***Proles pontica***	***Proles occidentalis***
	Regions	
Central Asia, Afghanistan, Iran, Armenia, Azerbaijan	Georgia, Asia minor, Greece, Bulgaria, Hungary, Romania	France, Germany, Spain, Portugal
	Vine properties	
Buds glabrous, shiny	Buds velvety, ash-gray to white	Buds weakly velvety
Lower leaf surfaces glabrous to setaceous pubescent	Lower leaf surface with mixed pubescence (webbed and setaceous)	Lower leaf surfaces with webbed pubescence
Leaf edges recurved toward the tip	Leaf edges variously recurved	Leaf edges recurved toward the base
Grape clusters large, loose, often branching	Grape clusters medium size, compact rarely loose	Grape clusters generally very large, compact
Fruit generally oval, ovoid or elongated, medium to large, pulpy	Fruit typically round, medium to small, juicy	Fruit often round, more rarely oval, small to medium, juicy
Cultivars mostly white with about 30% roses	About equal numbers of white, rose and red varieties	Cultivars commonly white or red
Seeds medium to large with an elongated beak	Seeds small, medium or large (table grapes)	Seeds small with a marked beak
	Fruiting properties	
Many cultivars partially seedless, some seedless	Many cultivars partially seedless, some completely so	Seedless cultivars rare
Cultivars produce few, low yielding fruiting shoots	Cultivars often produce several, highly productive fruiting shoots	Cultivars typically produce several, highly productive fruiting shoots

Cultivars short day plants with long growing periods, nor cold hardy	Cultivars relatively cold hardy	Cultivars long day plants with short growing periods, cold hardy
Most cultivars are table grapes, few possess good wine making properties	Many cultivars are good wine making cultivars, a few are table grapes	Most cultivars possess good wine making properties
Grapes low in acidity (0.3-0.6%), sugar content commonly 18-20%	Grapes acidic (0.6-1.0%) sugar content commonly 18-20%	Grapes acidic (0.6-1%), sugar content commonly 18-20%
Self crossed seedling of certain cultivars possessing simple leaves	Self crossed seedlings of certain cultivars with dwarfed shoots and rounded form	Self crossed seedlings of certain cultivars having mottled coloured leaves

Source: Levadoux (1956)

The study of the botanical description, identification and classification of plants belonging to the genus *Vitis* and of their usefulness for viticulture is termed ampelography (Greek ampelos = vine, graphos = description). The descriptors have traditionally included such visual traits as shape, hairs and pigmentation of shoot tips, shape, lobes, sinuses and serrations in leaf lamina, size and shape of fruit clusters and size, shape and pigmentation of the berries (Galet, 1988; Viala and Vermorel, 1901). DNA fingerprinting has also been used to uncover the historical origins and genetic relationships of the *Vitis* species and for identification of the selections in grape collections.

A. Classification of grape cultivars on the basis of uses (Jacob, 1950)

Table grapes

These grape cultivars are used as food and for decorative purposes. Therefore, the fruits must have good eating qualities, good shipping and storability including resistance to injury by handling besides an attractive appearance. Large berries of uniform size, firm pulp, tough skin and sturdy rachis and strong adherence to cap stems are preferred, especially for transport by truck, train, sea or air. Compact clusters that cannot be bent or loose clusters lacking a full set of berries are discarded. There is a strong preference for seedless grapes.

Raisin grapes

The cultivars that meet the desirable criteria for preparation of raisins (dried or dehydrated grapes) are used for this purpose. The vines should be highly productive and the berries should dry rapidly. Early ripening is important to allow drying of berries under favourable weather. Seedlessness is preferred. The berries should either be large for eating or small for use in bakery trade. Few cultivars can meet all the criteria. The raisins should also meet some standards. The dried raisins must be soft in texture and should not stick together when stored and must have good flavour.

Some of the best and most widely grown grape cultivars for raisins are Thompson Seedless (Sultanina), Black Corinth and Muscat of Alexandria. The latter has seeds that can be removed by machine. Raisins are made from Fiesta grapes also.

Juice grapes

In the manufacture of sweet unfermented juice, the clarifying and preserving procedure should not destroy the natural flavour of the berries. In USA, juice is usually pasteurized after it has been clarified. Natural flavour of the *vinifera* cultivars gets destroyed in the process producing a cooked and undesirable taste. Some American cultivars can stand the processing and pasteurization processes retaining their strong foxy flavour. Therefore, in USA, grape juice is usually produced from Concord grapes or from a blend of Concord and other cultivars. When close filtration is used for sterilization, *vinifera* grapes can be used for juice making.

Wine grapes

The majority of grapes grown over the world are used for wine making. For dry or table wines, grapes of high acidity and moderate sugar are desirable, while those having high sugar content and low acid are suitable for making sweet or dessert wines. Cultivars such as Cabernet Sauvignon, Riesling and Pinot Noir have outstanding bouquet and flavour essential for the production of high quality premium wines. Some cultivars are used to prepare wines of specific quality in some localities.

Thin skinned berries having very soft pulp may require more care during mechanical harvesting, transportation and picking than those with thicker skin and a firmer pulp. Grape cultivars having berries that detach easily from the cap stem are suitable for mechanical harvesting.

The colour of wine is not determined by the colour of juice of grapes, which is always almost clear, but rather by the presence or absence of the grape skin during fermentation. Grapes with coloured juice, e.g. Alicante and Bouschet, are known as teinturier. Red wine is made from red or black grapes, but the red colour is bestowed by a process called maceration, whereby the skin is left in contact with the juice during fermentation. White wine can be made from grapes of any colour as the skin is separated from the juice during fermentation. The cultivars for red wine and white wine are given respectively in Table 20.5 and 20.6.

Table 20.5. Cultivars for red wine.

Cultivar	Origin	Remarks
Aleatico	Italy	A very rare, fragrant, dark skinned cultivar.
Alicante Bouschet	France	A red fleshed, red skinned cultivar.
Alvarelhão	Portugal	Widely planted throughout Portugal.
Barbera	Italy	Produces light, fresh fruity wines with prominent acidity.
Cabernet Franc	France (Bordeaux)	A component of Bordeaux blends and Loire Valley reds.
Cabernet Sauvignon	France (Bordeaux)	A principal component of Bordeaux reds. Grown world wide to produce well structured, full bodied red wines.
Carignane	Spain (Aragon)	An inferior red grape cultivar of Spanish origin.
Carmenère	France	Although a traditional Bordeaux cultivar, it has risen to prominence and acclaim in Chile.
Chambourcin	France	A hybrid cultivar grown successfully by Cassegrain in New South Wales, Australia.

Cinsault	France	A prolific cultivar of southern France.
Concord	America	The most important cultivar grown outside California in the US, belonging to *V. labrusca*.
Corvina	Italy	The predominant cultivar of the Valpolicella region of Italy.
Dolcetto	Italy	Produces soft and fruity wines.
Durif	France	Successfully grown in northern Victoria, Australia.
Flora	California	A hybrid of Gewürztraminer and Semillon.
Gamay	France	Used in the production of Beaujolais.
Graciano	Spain	A rich, perfumed grape with deep colour.
Grenache	Spain	Widely grown producing a range of styles from light rose to full bodied reds.
Lambrusco	Italy	Used to produce a fruity, effervescent Italian wine.
Lemberger	Unknown	Planted in southern Germany and Austria. Produces medium-bodied red wine.
Malbec	France	A successful cultivar in Argentina. Also used in Bordeaux blends.
Merlot	France (Bordeaux)	Produces wines of great softness and richness. Wines are made worldwide. A key component in Bordeaux.
Mondeuse	Italy	Powerfully flavoured, deep coloured cultivar.
Montepulciano	Italy	Widely planted through out Italy.
Mourvèdre	Spain	Widely planted.
Nebbiolo	Italy (Piedmont)	An Italian black grape cultivar.
Petit Verdot	France (Bordeaux)	A minor component in Bordeaux blends.
Pinotage	South Africa	A hybrid cultivar widely grown in South Africa.
Pinot Noir	France (Burgundy)	A light skinned aromatic cultivar, most famous as the cultivar of red Burgundy. Successfully grown throughout the New World.
Rondinella	Italy	Used in the production of Valpolicella.
Ruby Cabernet	America (California)	A hybrid cultivar, Carignane and Cabernet Sauvignon cross.
Rubired	America (California)	A hybrid cultivar, commonly used in blends for its deep colour.
Sangiovese	Italy (Tuscany)	Widely planted throughout Italy. It is the principal cultivar used in Chianti.
Saperavi	Southern Russia	A cool climate cultivar grown in North East Victoria.
Shiraz	France (Rhone)	A flavoursome cultivar, highly renowned in Rhone and Australia.
Tarrango	Australia	A hybrid cultivar: a Touriga and Sultana cross.
Tannat	Spain	A dark skinned, astringent cultivar.
Tempranillo	Spain	An important component of Rioja.
Terret Noir	France	Grown in southern France.
Touriga National	Portugal	Prominent in the Dao region of Portugal for the production of good quality dry red wine.

Trollinger	Germany	Widely planted in Württemberg, Germany. Produces light bodied, fresh, fruity red wines which are often sweet.
Zinfandel	Italy	Substantial plantings in both California as well as Italy, where it is known as Primitivo.

Table 20.6. Cultivars for white wine

Cultivar	Origin	Comment
Alvarinho	Portugal	Widely grown in northern Portugal and Spain.
Chardonnay	France	Widely grown throughout the world.
Chasselas	Unknown	Widely planted around the world. Good quality wines produced in Switzerland.
Chenin Blanc	France (Loire)	Widely planted throughout the world, including the Loire Valley and South Africa.
Clairette	France	An old fashioned cultivar grown throughout France.
Colombard	France	Widely grown in California and Australia.
Crouchen	France	A neutral cultivar.
Doradillo	Spain	A neutral cultivar grown in Australia.
Frontignac	Greece	The Australian synonym for Muscat Blanc À Petits Grains. Produces highly fragrant, delicate white wines.
Furmint	Hungary (Tokaj-Hegyalja)/Austria	Planted throughout Hungary, Austria and Slovenia.
Garganega	Italy	Widely planted throughout Italy. The principal grape used in the production of Soave.
Gewürtztraminer	France (Alsace)	Produces highly fragrant and spicy wines.
Hárslevelü	Hungary (Tokaj-Hegyalja)	Planted throughout Hungary.
Gruner Veltliner	Unknown	The most commonly planted cultivar in Austria.
Kerner	Unknown	A Trollinger x Riesling cross. Produces delicately perfumed, leafy wines that are similar in style to Riesling. Substantial plantings in Germany.
Macabeo	Middle East	Planted throughout Spain and France.
Marsanne	France (Rhone)	Most popular in the Rhone Valley in France. Also grown in California and Australia.
Mauzac	France	An important grape cultivar in southwest France.
Melon	France (Burgundy)	Renowned for the production of Muscadet.
Müller-Thurgau	Germany	A mediocre German Irbid.
Muscadelle	France (Bordeaux)	An aromatic cultivar.

B. Classification of grape cultivars on the basis of colour of skin and origin

1. Colour of the berries

   i. White: Perlette, Thompson Seedless.

   ii. Red: Cardinal, Ruby Red.

   iii. Black: Beauty Seedless, Kali Sahebi.

2. Origin
    i. New World: Concord, Buffalo.
    ii. Old World: Thompson Seedless, Anab-e-Shahi.

C. Classification of grape cultivars on the basis of seediness of the berries

Seedless cultivars

Beauty Seedless (Queen of Vineyard x Black Kismishi): The cultivar was introduced in India from Davis, California (USA). The vine has medium vigour. Fruiting occurs on basal buds and thus the vine responds well to spur pruning. It is a very early ripening cultivar and is a prolific bearer. Its fruits ripen towards the end of May in North India well before the onset of monsoon. The fruit bunch is long, shouldered, compact and medium to large in size having bluish black, spherical and medium sized berries. The fruits have poor keeping quality.

Delight: This cultivar was evolved from a sister seedling of Perlette at Davis, California, USA. It is less vigorous and has performed well in north Indian States of Punjab and Haryana. The cultivar is very early ripening. The berries start ripening by the first week of June. The bunch is medium, compact, conical and attractive having green, small and almost round berries. The fruits have characteristic muscat flavour. It has good eating and shipping quality.

Himrod (Ontario x Thompson Seedless): This table grape cultivar has done well in Punjab, Haryana and Uttar Pradesh. It is a mid season cultivar resistant to diseases and pests. The vines are vigorous and prolific bearer giving heavy yield of excellent quality berries. Bunches are attractive, medium large, shouldered and well filled with yellowish green berries having thick and tough skin.

Perlette (Scolokertek hiralynoje 26 x Sultanina Marble): The cultivar was developed at California, USA. The most striking feature is the translucency of its mature berry and thus the French name 'Perlette' meaning 'little pearl'. It is one of the earliest maturing cultivars that performed well in North India and gave almost double the fruit yield of that obtained from the cultivar Thompson Seedless. The vine is vigorous. The fruit bunch is medium large, conical, shouldered and very compact and thus needs berry thinning. Berries are medium, whitish green and spherical and have good keeping quality. Flesh is soft having wild muscat flavour. The juice is clear having 16-18°B TSS. Average yield is up to 35 t/ha. Keeping quality is good and is used for table purpose but is not suitable for making raisins due to compactness of the clusters. It is highly susceptible to anthracnose.

Manjri Naveen: It is an early ripening, white seedless cultivar with naturally bold, crisp and mildly muscat flavoured berries giving average yield of 25 t/ha.

Pusa Seedless: It is a clonal selection from Thompson Seedless. It has performed well in North India. It resembles Thompson Seedless except that the berries are smaller and slightly more elongated. It is a medium yielder ripening uniformly during 2nd to 3rd week of June at Delhi. The berries have high TSS, good keeping quality and are suitable for both table purpose and raisin making.

Thompson Seedless (Oval Kishmish, Sultana, Sultania): It originated in Asia Minor and was first grown by William Thompson. The cultivar has wide adaptability. Vine is medium in vigour and responds well to long cane pruning. It is essentially a raisin grape and is also used for making white sweet wine or as table grape. The bunch is large, long and conical to cylindrical, shouldered and compact. The seedless berries are weakly attached to the bunch. The berries are oval, medium-sized, yellowish green to golden yellow when fully ripe having medium thin skin and very high sugar content. The juice is straw coloured, sweet with a TSS of 20-22°B. It is considered to be an early to mid season cultivar. It ripens in the middle of June in North India and during February-April in Maharashtra, Andhra Pradesh, Tamil Nadu and Karnataka. Berries have good shipping quality and multiple uses (table, raisin and wine). The cultivar produces average yield of 20-25 t/ha.

Seedless Sultana: It is very similar to Thompson Seedless except that the berries are round.

2A Clone of Thompson Seedless: It is late maturing white cultivar suitable for fresh eating and for making raisins. The cultivar is highly responsive to hormonal treatments to increase size of berry and clusters. Average fruit yield is 25 t/ha and 4-5 t/ha raisins.

Tas-e-Ganesh: This is a mutant similar to Thompson Seedless in all respects except that the size of berry and cluster are larger. It responds more than Thompson Seedless to girdling to improve fruit quality.

Sonaka: This is a clone of Thompson Seedless and has similar characters. The berry elongation is better and the berry skin is thin but the berries crack and rot if it rains at harvest time.

Manik Chaman: This is a clone of Thompson Seedless. It is similar to Sonaka and is well known for drought and salt tolerance.

Kishmish Charni: The cultivar was introduced from Uzbekistan. It is consistent in productivity. Berries are black and are good for table purpose.

Sharad Seedless: It is a mutant of Kishmish Charni (Black Seedless). The berries are black to purple in colour with medium-sized. This is an early cultivar maturing from December to February.

Black Corinth (Zante Currant): This cultivar probably originated in Greece. Clusters are small to medium, winged and uniformly cylindrical. The berries are very small, spherical to oblate, reddish black, mostly seedless, very juicy, neutral in flavour with very thin and tender skin. The berries ripen early and dry easily into very small raisins of soft texture and pleasing tart taste. It is well suited to the central and southern parts of the San Joaquin Valley.

Fiesta: It is a medium sized white seedless grape that matures 12 to 14 days earlier than Thompson Seedless. The berries are oval but rounder than Thompson Seedless. Skin is tender and the flavour is good. Clusters are medium to large and usually not compact.

Flame Seedless: The cultivar originated in USA. It is an early ripening cultivar. The red seedless berries are very crisp and muscat flavoured. During ripening, the berries tend to crack because of morning humid weather or if it rains. It gives average yield of 25 t/ha.

Crimson Seedless: Seedless berries are coloured and bold having excellent keeping quality.

Centennial Seedless: The cultivar was introduced from USA and Australia. It is an early ripening cultivar. Bunches are attractive. The seedless berries are bold and white having mild muscat flavour.

Fantasy Seedless: The cultivar was introduced from USA. Vines are vigorous. The seedless berries are bluish black, crisp and bold and conical in shape having neutral flavour. It gives average yield of 24 t/ha.

Canadice: The cultivar is more hardy than most seedless grapes, although trunk injury has been observed at some sites. The bunches are medium sized and compact and are thus prone to fruit rot in wet season. The berries are small, red and similar to Delaware in flavour and appearance.

Concord Seedless: Productivity of the cultivar is erratic. In warm years, the cultivar produces fully developed seeds. The clusters and berries are much smaller than those of Concord. The flavour and texture is similar. The fruit matures earlier, has high flavour and makes excellent pies and preserves.

Einset Seedless: The cultivar is winter hardy. The clusters are medium sized and bear bright red, ovoid berries that have unique strawberry-like flavour and good storage potential. Occasionally, seed remnant is noticed. The clusters respond well to gibberellic acid or cane girdling to improve cluster compactness and berry size. The skin is slightly tough and adheres to the tender flesh. The cultivar is susceptible to fungal diseases.

Jupiter: It is an early mid season cultivar. The clusters are medium sized having large, oval, firm and seedless blue berries. It has an excellent mild muscat flavour.

Interlaken Seedless (Ontario x Thompson Seedless): It is an early ripening seedless cultivar having a strong flavour. The clusters are medium sized and compact with small (1.5 g), white berries that ripen very early.

Lakemont (Ontario x Thompson Seedless): The cultivar has mild flavour and more compact clusters of small to medium size (1.7 g) berries than in Himrod. Cluster thinning prevents over-cropping. Bunch rot is often a problem.

Marquis: Vines are moderately hardy, medium in vigour and productive. Clusters are very large, medium compact and attractive with large, round, yellow green berries (3.5-5.0 g). Texture is melting. The flavour is mild fruity when first ripen and develops stronger Labrusca flavour 2 weeks later. Ripe fruits hold well on the vine. Well timed cluster thinning and girdling can increase berry size and improve cluster compactness.

Mars: Vines are vigorous and may bear precociously. The clusters are medium sized, cylindrical and well filled. The berries are blue seedless having mildly labrusca flavour similar to Campbell's Early. The berries are slipskin (tough skin that separates readily from the pulpy flesh).

Neptune: The clusters are large and very showy, but productivity is moderate. It is a yellow green seedless cultivar of moderate vigour. The flavour is mild and fruity and the texture is firm with relatively thick skin.

Reliance: It is among the most cold hardy seedless cultivars. The clusters are large having round, red and medium sized berries. The skin is tender and flesh is melting having a sweet labrusca flavour. The berry may be poor in colour in some years and may crack in wet seasons.

Remaily Seedless: The vines are only moderately hardy but are more winter hardy. The clusters are large and very attractive in appearance but are subject to bronzing when exposed to sunlight. The berries are oval seedless with firm texture having neutral and mildly fruity flavour. The cultivar is suitable for planting in backyards.

Saturn: The vines are precocious and moderately hardy and require cluster thinning. The clusters are medium large and conical bearing large, crisp and bright red berries with adherent skins and mild flavour. The seed remnants sometimes become noticeable. The berries have good storage potential and can be processed into an acceptable blending wine.

Suffolk Red: The clusters are medium large and loose but can be made more compact by use of gibberellic acid and cane girdling. The berries are red and mild flavoured.

Vanessa: It is a red seedless dessert grape of excellent quality. The vine is moderately vigorous and the hardiest among the seedless grapes.When grafted on Taleki 5C show poor fruit set and produce very small berries.The bunches are medium sized and well filled. The berries are medium in size having mildly fruity flavour and firm texture. The seed remnants are sometimes seen and are usually large and soft. Storage potential is good.

Venus: It is a vigorous and productive blue black seedless grape. The medium large clusters ripen early producing large berries of fair quality with labrusca flavour. Berry size is 2.9 g. The seed remnants are hard and noticeable. Fruit rot may be a problem at harvest.

Seeded cultivars

Anab-e-Shahi: The cultivar, perhaps a bud sport, was selected by Shanker Pillay in 1930 from the home gardens of Nawab of Hyderabad and was named Anab-e-Shahi (meaning royal grape). It gained importance in the Indian States of Andhra Pradesh, Maharashtra and Karnataka. The cultivar is late maturing and has uniform ripening. Vine is vigorous and gives very high yield (35 t/ ha) on bower system of training. It has shown exceptional success around Hyderabad where high yield of over 25 t/ha has been obtained. In North India, the vigour of its vines gets reduced and the fruit yield also reduces. The very large bunches are attractive. The berries are medium to large, elongated, seeded, yellowish white and have good shipping and keeping quality. Juice is clear and sweet with 18 to 20°B TSS. The eating quality is average. It is used for table purpose. In humid regions and in case of early monsoon during fruit ripening, the berries become watery and insipid. It is highly susceptible to downy mildew.

Dilkush: It is a mutant of Anab-e-Shahi having white coloured seeded berries that are sweet in taste and have few seeds.

Bangalore Blue: It is possibly a cross between *V. vinifera* and *V. labrusca* as indicated by the thick separable skin character of *labrusca* berry. Its cultivation is mainly confined in India to the area around Bangalore where the vines bear fruits twice a year by following staggered pruning. Its berries do not ripen in the north Indian subtropics. The vines are hardy, resistant to diseases and medium in vigour and productivity. The bunch is small and compact. The berries are more or less round, small to medium in size and dark blackish purple in colour with thick skin covered with a very heavy bloom. Berry ripening is uniform and is the earliest in the season. The quality is poor but the berries can keep well. Juice is clear and pleasantly flavoured having 16-18°B TSS. The berries are used for table purpose as well as for preparation of juice and wine.

Bhokri: It was introduced in 1838 under the name Bokhari and is one of the oldest cultivars in cultivation in India. It is a commercial cultivar of Tamil Nadu and Maharashtra. The vine is very vigorous and high yielding. The bunch is large, compact and is usually shouldered. The berries are of medium size, greenish and oval with soft pulp. The fruit quality is medium. Ripening is late and uniform. Berries crack on occurrence of rainfall and their keeping quality is poor.

Black Champa: The cultivar is a selection from the genotypes introduced at IIHR, Bengaluru, India. The vines are vigorous having medium productivity. Bunch is small, well filled having small to medium size berries that are purple and of excellent quality. It is suitable for table purpose and for making juice and red dessert wines. The berries crack and rot during rains.

Cardinal: It is very early ripening red table grape cultivar that has done well in the arid irrigated regions of North India. The vine is medium in vigour. Clusters are attractive, medium to large, loose and conical having large, bright red and spherical berries. The colour of berries changes from green to reddish black as ripening proceeds. The cultivar has great promise.

Cheema Sahebi (Selection-7): This cultivar was selected from the open pollinated seedlings of Pandhari Sahebi and designated 'Selection 7' by Dr. G. S. Cheema. It is mainly grown in Maharashtra. The vine is vigorous and very heavy yielder. It is a late ripening cultivar having uniform ripening. Bunch is long, conical and shouldered with medium sized oval berries. The quality is better than Bhokri and Anab-e-Shahi but is poor in North India. Shipping quality is poor due to weak pedicellar attachment.

Gold: It has done well in the arid irrigated tracts of Punjab and Haryana. The vine is medium in vigour. It is an early to mid season cultivar bearing large, oval and golden berries having a mild muscat flavour. The berries ripen by the first week of June in Haryana. The bunch is loose and medium in size. This table purpose cultivar has good eating and keeping quality.

Early Muscat: The cultivar is medium cropper bearing small and irregular bunches ripening in the first week of June. Berries are bold, roundish and amber coloured each with 3 to 5 seeds and contain 73% highly scented juice having 18°B TSS and 0.60% acidity.

Banqui Abyad: The cultivar is early and medium cropper bearing large sized bunches and greenish, bold, roundish, very thin skinned berries each having 2 to 4 seeds and contain 66% juice, 19 to 20°B TSS and 0.72% acidity. It ripens in the first week of June.

Gulabi (Kranchi, Paneer Drakshi, Muscat, Black Prince): The cultivar resembles Muscat Hamburg of Australia. It is mostly grown in Tamil Nadu. The vine is medium in vigour and productivity. Bunch is small and loose with deep purple, small and spherical berries. It has thick skinned berries and thus has good keeping quality. The ripening is early and fairly uniform. It has muscat flavour.

Kali Sahebi: This cultivar is believed to have been introduced under the name 'Habshi' in Pune and Nasik area of India. It is grown in Maharashtra and Andhra Pradesh. The vine is vigorous but is shy bearing giving moderate yield. The bunch ripens irregularly. It ripens about 15 days later than Bhokri. It is next to Pandhari Sahebi in fruit quality. Bunch is very attractive, well filled and of medium size. The berries are large, black and elongated having thin skin and sweet pulp. It has good keeping quality.

Muscat of Alexandria: It originated in Egypt and is a very old cultivar. It is essentially a raisin grape but can also be used for wine making. The bunch is of medium size. The berries are large, oval, seeded and light green and have strong musk flavour. It is a mid season or late cultivar.

Flame Tokay: The cultivar is from Algeria. It is an important table cultivar. The bunch is large. The berries are clustered, oval, large, dark red, firm and seeded.

Concord: The cultivar is suitable for somewhat colder climate. The berries are large, blackish and round with a heavy bloom and are used for making juice.

Fakdi: The cultivar is grown around Pune and Nasik. The vines are very vigorous but are poor yielding. The berries are of good quality but have poor shipping quality.

Pandhari Sahebi: This partly self unfruitful and shy bearing cultivar has white berries. The fruit quality is very good. It has good shipping quality.

Pacha Drakshi (Green Grape): The fruit quality is poor. The cultivar has given high yield at Madurai in Tamil Nadu.

Kandhari: Fruit bearing is doubtful in this cultivar. The fruit bunches are quite large. The berries are oval, seeded, translucent, purplish red and of bigger than average size. The fruit quality is good.

Chandigarh: It is similar to Kandhari and Hur.

Foster's Seedling (Bharat Early): The fruit bearing is high. The berries are small and green. The fruit quality is high with high sugar content.

R. L. S.: The cultivar is from Saharanpur (India) and has fairly high bearing.

Red Globe: The cultivar was introduced from USA. It has bold red berries with firm pulp and thick skin. It has excellent keeping quality. It has given average yield of 25 t/ha.

Italia: The Italian cultivar has seeded, bold berries having pleasant muscat flavour.

Cabernet Sauvingnon: The cultivar was introduced from France. Bunches are small and cylindrical having small, round and purple berries suitable for making red table wine.

Chenin Blanc: The cultivar was introduced from France. It has winged bunches of moderate size. Berries are seeded, medium sized and round. It is suitable for making white wine.

Sauvingnon Blanc: The cultivar was introduced from France. It has compact and often winged bunches of medium size. Berries are seeded, small and white suitable for making white table wine.

Shiraz: The cultivar was introduced from France. It is a late maturing cultivar. Bunches are medium-sized and cylindrical. Berries are of medium size, round and suitable for rose wine or blending to provide colour.

Zinfandel: The cultivar was introduced from France. It has moderately compact bunches of medium size. Berries are small, dark purple and suitable for making rose wine.

Malbec: The cultivar was introduced from France. Bunches are medium in size. Berries are small to medium and spherical, suitable for making red wine.

Ugni Blanc: The cultivar was introduced from France. It has compact, medium-sized and winged clusters. Its berries are used with those of other cultivars for blending to improve aroma of white wine.

Grenache: The cultivar was introduced from France. The cultivar has clusters of variable size and shape. It is a late maturing red wine cultivar mostly used for blending.

Pinot Noir and **Merlot:** These cultivars are suitable for making red wine.

Chardonnay: It is a popular cultivar for making white wine but has not done well in India.

New cultivars

Arkavati (Black Champa x Thompson Seedless): Bunch has medium size. The berry is yellowish green, sweet (22-25°B TSS) and seedless with thin skin and is suitable for table use and for making raisins and good quality dry and white table and dessert wine.

Arka Chitra (Angur Kalan x Anab-e-Shahi): It is tolerant to powdery mildew. The vine is moderately vigorous having good yield potential (34 kg). All the buds are fruitful and thus the vine is suitable for training on head system. It gives two crops in a year. Bunch is well filled and medium to large (310 g) in size. The berry is very attractive, golden yellow with pink blush, slightly elongated, large (3.18 g), sweet (20-21°B TSS) and 0.4-0.6 per cent acidity. It is suitable for table purpose.

Arka Hans (Bangalore Blue x Anab-e-Shahi): It is resistant to anthracnose. The bunch is medium in size having seeded, yellowish green and sweet (18-21°B TSS) berries having pleasant foxy flavour. The berries are suitable for making quality table wine with suitable acid amelioration.

Arka Kanchan (Anab-e-Shahi x Queen of Vineyards): Bunch is large. The berries are seeded, golden yellow, ellipsoidal to ovoid and sweet (17-20°B TSS) having muscat flavour. The berries are suitable for table use and for making dry white table and dessert wines.

Arka Krishna (Black Champa x Thompson Seedless): The vine is vigorous and productive. It is suitable for head system of training and gives two crops in a year. Bunch is of medium size, well filled, weighing 255 g on an average. The berry is dark red, seedless and sweet (20-21°B TSS) having 0.6-0.7 acidity. The berries are suitable for juice making.

Arka Majestic (Angur Kalan x Black Champa): The vine is moderately vigorous, productive (34 kg/vine) and tolerant to anthracnose. All the buds are fruitful and thus the vine is suitable for training on head system. It gives two crops in a year. Bunch is well filled and medium to large (370 g). The berry is roundish and bold, of 7.7 g, deep tan colour and sweet (18-20°B TSS) having 0.4-0.6% acidity. It is suitable for table purpose.

Arka Neellamani (Black Champa x Thompson Seedless): It is moderately vigorous, productive (25 kg/vine) and tolerant to anthracnose. The vine is suitable for training on head system. The bunch is well filled and weighs 360 g on an average having sweet (20-22°B TSS) and black seedless berries. Berry weight is 3.2 g having crispy pulp. It is good for table purpose and for making red dessert wine.

Arka Shyam (Bangalore Blue x Black Champa): The vine is resistant to anthracnose. The bunch is medium in size. The berries are seeded, bluish black, spherical to obovoid and sweet (20-25°B TSS) having mild foxy flavour. These are good for table use and for making dry table dessert wines and juice.

Arka Soma (Anab-e-Shahi x Queen of Vineyards): The vine is vigorous having heavy yield potential (36 kg/vine) and gives two crops in a year. The bunch is well filled of medium size (410 g) and cylindrical. The berry is greenish yellow, round to ovoid, large (3.8 g), sweet (20-21°B TSS) having 0.5% acidity and muscat flavour. The berries are suitable for making good white dessert wine.

Arka Trishna (Bangalore Blue x Convent Large Black): The cultivar is an improvement over Bangalore Blue. It is a male sterile hybrid and is resistant to anthracnose and tolerant to downy mildew. The vine is vigorous having high yield potential. The vine is suitable for training on head system. The bunch is of medium size and well filled. The berries are very sweet (20-23°B TSS) having 0.3-0.4% acidity with deep tan colour. The berries are suitable for juice and red dessert wine.

Arka Shweta or Shweta Seedless (Anab-e-Shahi x Thompson Seedless): The vine is moderately vigorous having yield potential of about 28 kg. The bunch is cylindrical, well filled, of medium size weighing 260 g and responds to GA_3 for thinning and enlargement of berries. The berry is greenish yellow, seedless and sweet (18-19°B TSS) having 0.5-0.6% acidity and suitable for table purpose.

Pusa Navrang (Madeleine Angevine x Rubired): Vines are moderately vigorous, resistant to anthracnose. It is an early maturing cultivar and prolific bearer on basal buds. The bunch is loose and of medium size. The berry is seeded and sweet (19°B TSS) having tenturier peel and pulp both rich in anthocyanin pigment. The berries are suitable for making coloured juice and port wine. Juice of this cultivar retains attractive red colour for 12 months.

Pusa Urvashi (Hur x Beauty Seedless): Vines are moderately vigorous and prolific bearer. It is an early maturing (1st week of June) and productive cultivar and bears on basal buds. The bunch is loose, of medium size and well filled. The seedless berry is greenish yellow, spherical and transparent having 20-22°B TSS. It is suitable for table purpose and raisin making.

Madhu Angoor: It is a clonal selection made at Pune probably from Carolina Black Rose. Vines are tolerant to downy mildew. Bunches are medium large. Berries are seeded, deep red and bold having mild muscat flavour. It is suitable for table purpose.

Punjab Purple (Catawba x Beauty Seedless): The cultivar has been developed at Pune. It is early maturing and high yielding cultivar with medium vigour. Bunch is loose, medium in size having seeded and purple berries having 17^0B TSS and 0.45-0.55% acidity. It is suitable for making red wine and is tolerant to rain damage, anthracnose and powdery mildew.

Regina: The vine has medium vigour and is resistant to anthracnose and downy mildew. The cultivar is seeded and medium yielder bearing small to medium size and loose bunches having purple to black and spherical berries of medium size. The pulp TSS is 21°B and acidity is 0.79 to 0.81%.

Grape cultivars of American origin

Fox grape
(*Vitis labrusca* L.)

It is native to eastern USA from Georgia to southeastern Canada with Indiana as its western limit. The vines are vigorous climbers and are winter hardy and deciduous. The tendrils are continuous. The leaves are large, thick, cordate to rounded, entire or 3-lobed. The lower surface of the leaves is densely pubescent. The flowers are perfect or dioecious, polygamous and sometimes self sterile. The berries are medium to large (1.25 cm in diameter) and are of several colours. The skin is thick and separates readily from the pulp. The flavour is foxy. The bunch is large (more than 15 berries). It is resistant to pests and diseases and can be used as rootstock for the European grapes.

Concord: It is a leading commercial cultivar in North America, outside of California. It is adapted to a wide range of soils and climatic conditions. The vine has vigorous growth and yet is relatively winter hardy. It has perfect flowers being probably a natural hybrid of *V. labrusca* and *V. vinifera.* Thus it has been classified as *Vitis* x *labruscana* Bailey.

The cultivar constitutes about 80% of the *labrusca* production. The berries are attractive, round and blue black borne on medium sized clusters. The berry has tough skin that separates readily from the pulpy flesh. It matures rather late in the season. In cool localities maturity can be a problem. It is quite susceptible to dead arm disease but resistant to cold and powdery mildew. It is the only important cultivar for preparing sweet juice, jelly and preserves. The pronou-nced aromatic "foxy" flavour makes it a good dessert grape. It is also used for wine production.

Catawba: It is a late ripening red cultivar, hence adapted only to carefully chosen sites having long growing season. The vine is vigorous and winter hardy but is considered to be relatively sensitive to fungal diseases.

Delaware: This cultivar does the best on deep, fertile and well drained soils. It produces compact and medium sized clusters of small red berries. The fruit has a distinctive, spicy and aromatic character. Although it is a slip skin cultivar, the berries are delicately tender and may crack under conditions of high relative humidity or rainfall. The fruit ripens 10 to 14 days earlier than Concord. The fruit yields may approach those of Concord. It is relatively sensitive to fungal diseases, particularly the foliage.

Isabella: This is a very old black cultivar. It is the most widely grown American cultivar in other parts of the world, but in North America it has been largely replaced by other cultivars, especially Concord. The vine is only moderately winter hardy and quite late maturing. It is grown commercially in tropical and subtropical regions of Colombia, Brazil and India. It is favoured for growing in home gardens in many parts of the world.

Niagara: It is the leading white cultivar among American grapes. It is an old cultivar, not as winter hardy as Concord. It is used for white wine production and for table use. The berries are large having moderately acid, medium sweet and strong "foxy" flavour. It is moderately affected by diseases.

Summer grape
(***Vitis aestivalis*** Michx.)

It is native to eastern North America from southern Ontario, east to Vermont, west to Oklahoma and south to Florida and Texas. The vine is vigorous growing 10 m or more high on trees. The leaves are 7–20 cm long, suborbicular and usually a little broader than long, variable in shape, unlobed to deeply three- or five-lobed, green above and densely hairy below. The flowers are produced on a 5–15 cm long dense panicle. The fruit is small, 5–14 mm in diameter and dark purple or black in colour. Several cultivars have been selected, including Norton, believed to be the oldest American grape cultivar in commercial production. Interspecific hybrids made with Norton have shown several useful traits for commercial wine production when compared with other North American cultivars. These are low in acidity having neutral, “vinifera-like” flavour profile, good tannin structure, tolerance to cold and drought and excellent resistance to powdery mildew, downy mildew and Pierce’s disease.

Amur grape
(***Vitis amurensis*** Ruprect.)

It is a relic of pre-glacial subtropical vegetation of the Far East, reaching the continental latitude Lake Kizi in Russia (about fifty-first parallel) along the coast of the Sea of Japan to the north, the mouth of the Muli river and the Amur region to the west to the river Zeya (Russia). It grows in the forests of Manchuria, Amur Oblast, Primorsky Krai, North East China, Japan (Honshu) and Korea.

Vine stem is 5–10 cm in diameter and spreading 15–18 m, rarely up to 20–25 m. Tendrils are capable of wrapping around things, entwine the branches of the neighbouring plants or any other support. The bark of old shoots is dark, scaly and with vertical stripes. Young shoots are green, often with a reddish hue, reddish brown in autumn. The leaves vary greatly in shape. They can be solid, three or five-lobed, ovate or rounded, arched at the base. The size ranges from 9 to 25 cm with sharp edges and rounded triangular serrate teeth. The surface of the leaves is glabrous above, densely covered with short bristles. In autumn the leaves turn bright red, yellow, orange or brown. The flowers are small, and a nectar source for bees. They appear in the second week of May in its natural habitat. The Amur grape is usually dioecious, although rarely hermaphrodite vines do occur. The fruits ripen in late September in their natural habitat. Fruits are spherical, 12 mm in diameter with thick skin and black or purple, sometimes dark blue colour. The flesh is juicy, usually very acidic to sweet, sugar content reaching 22-23%. The cluster usually weighs 20-70 g. In exceptional cases, the bunches are up to 25 cm long weighing 250 g.

River bank grape or Frost grape
(*Vitis riparia* Michx.)

It is a native American climbing or trailing vine, widely distributed from Quebec to Texas and Montana to New England. It is long lived and capable of reaching into the upper canopy of the tallest trees. It produces dark fruits that are appealing to both birds and people. It is used for breeding several French-American hybrids as well as rootstocks, e.g. Rupestris St. George.

Mature vines have loose, fissured bark, and may attain good diameter. Leaves are alternate, often with opposite tendrils or inflorescences, coarsely toothed, 5–25 cm long and 5–20 cm broad, sometimes with sparse hairs on the underside of veins. The inflorescence is paniculate, 4–15 cm long and loose. The flowers are small, fragrant, dioecious and white or greenish in colour. The vines bloom in May or June and produce small 6–15 mm blue black seeded berries with a bloom. These are juicy, edible, vinous in flavour, lacking the "foxy" characteristics of *V. labrusca*, but usually quite sour and herbaceous. It may deviate considerably, e.g. white berries, perfect flowers, large clusters, large berries and sweet fruits are among the known variations. These are often considered as evidence of natural hybridization with other *Vitis* species.

The fruit is small in size making it prone to predation by birds. These are highly acidic (often up to 5%) and have intensely pigmented juice, herbaceous aroma for use in wine making. The berries are sometimes used to make flavourful jellies, jams and wine. Its most significant use is as rootstock for *V. vinifera*.

Its foliage is typically resistant to mildew and black rot and the roots are resistant to *Phylloxera*. The berries, however, are often sensitive to mildew and black rot if the vine is exposed to prolonged wet and humid conditions.

The vines are known to withstand as low temperatures as -57°C. Thus it can be used as a donor for cold hardiness and resistance to *Phylloxera*. The French-

American hybrid grapes are notable examples. It has been used extensively to create hardy hybrids to make a commercially viable wine grape that can survive very low temperatures. Commercially important cultivars with significant *V. riparia* ancestry include Baco Noir, Marechal Foch, Triomphe d'Alsace and Frontenac. These are used as rootstock for adaptation to adverse soil conditions.

French-American hybrid grapes

French hybrids have been derived from crosses between *V. vinifera* and a number of wild American species to develop *Phylloxera* resistant cultivars that would produce wines having less fruity and more neutral flavour.

Nearly all American cultivars or hybrids contain *V. labrusca* in their parentage, but the French have used mainly other American species with different fruit and plant characteristics. Thus two groups of hybrids are quite distinct. The shoots of most French hybrids grow more upright than the American hybrids. The leaves usually have deeper sinuses, are more glossy and lack the heavy tomentum common on the underside in American cultivars and *V. labrusca.* The flavour of the fruit is generally more neutral, lacking the fruitiness of the native cultivars.

Red French hybrids

These are listed according to increasing colour intensity and season of ripening, from early to late.

Morechal Foch (Kuhlmann 188-2): It is a very early, small-clustered, small-berried black grape that produces an excellent red table wine. Vines are hardy and medium in vigour and production.

Leon-Millot (Kuhlmann 194-2): The fruit, vine and wine are similar as in cultivar Foch. It is early ripening and has high sugar content.

Cascade (Seibel 13053): It is an early blue grape. Clusters are medium to large and loose. It is very productive and hardy, but the fruit attracts birds. The wine can be very good but may have light colour.

Baco Noir (Baco No. 1): It is an extremely vigorous and disease resistant cultivar that grows well on arbours and is used for red wine. Bud break occurs early in the spring and may be subject to late spring frost damage.

De Chaunac (Seibel 9549): It appears to be one of the best French hybrids for red wine. It is hardy, relatively free from disease and is less susceptible to bird damage.

Chelois (Seibel 10878): It is a vigorous and productive cultivar used for a claret-type wine. Vines are only moderately winter hardy.

Rougeon (Seibel 5898): It is a commercial red wine grape that yields a highly coloured wine used for blending. Vines are hardy but are erratic producers.

Rosette (Seibel 1000): It is an old French hybrid having hardy and moderately productive vines. The fruit lacks intense colour and is used for rose wine.

Chancellor (Seibel 7053): It is widely grown cultivar in France. It is hardy and productive and the wine produced is of very high quality. The fruit is susceptible to downy mildew.

Colobel (Seibel 8357): It is a "teinturier," or a cultivar with highly coloured juice, used for blending with paler wines. Vines are moderately hardy and productive.

White French hybrids

These are listed according to increasing colour and from early to late season of ripening.

Aurore (Seibel 5279): It is hardy, vigorous and productive. The fruit ripens early, has good dessert quality and makes a very good wine.

Vignoles (Ravat 51): It makes a fine Chablis-type white wine. The clusters are compact and the berries tend to crack in wet season. Vines are hardy but have medium vigour and production.

Verdelet (Seibel 9110): It is a yellow dessert and wine cultivar. It tends to overbear and the crop must be thinned. It is subject to winter injury.

Seyval (Seyve- Villard 5-276): It is a high quality, mid season, white grape that produces a fine white wine. It tends to overbear and must be cluster-thinned for proper ripening and to prevent weakening of the vines.

Vidal 256: It is a late, white, hardy and heavy producer. The wine is neutral in flavour and is rated good to very good.

Villard Blanc (Seyve-Villard 12-375): It produces large, loose clusters. The wine is very good and the fruit is dessert type.

Muscadine grape
(***V. rotundifolia*** Michx. syn. ***Muscadinia rotundifolia*** Michaux)

Muscadine grapes are native to and grown commercially in the southeastern quadrant of USA. It is more suitable for warm climates. It requires warm temperate climate. The vines are very vigorous and high climbing. The bark is very smooth and characteristic. The leaves are small, broadly cordate rounded, not lobed, glabrous above and lightly pubescent along the veins on the lower surface. The flowers are usually self incompatible. The sexes are usually separate. The clusters are small and loose having usually 3 to 20 berries, sometimes more especially in the perfect flowered cultivars. Berries are round to short oval, usually large and vary in colour from green to black or purplish or purple yellow. The skin is thick. The berries drop on maturity. For commercial use, the fruit is usually harvested by jarring the vines, the berries being caught on tarpaulin. The odour of the fruit is musky. They have distinctive aromas and flavours and are used to prepare special wines. The fresh fruit is generally sold locally owing to the rapid deterioration in its aroma and flavour under the usual methods of handling. The grape cultivars from this group are used extensively for home planting because these are seldom affected by diseases or pests.

Among many cultivars, the best ones have pistillate flowers only while those of more recent origin have perfect flowers. Some of the more popular ones are:

(a) Cultivars with pistillate flowers

Hunt: The cultivar is the preferred all purpose black sort. Berries and clusters are large maturing early and uniformly. The vines have good vigour and dependable productivity.

Scuppernong: This is the oldest cultivated North American grape cultivar found in North Carolina. Clusters are small and shatter badly owing to uneven maturity. Berries are medium large, bronze in colour and have distinctive flavour. The vines are vigorous with variable productivity.

Thomas: This is another old standard cultivar having red black and medium small berries with very fine and crisp flavour prized for sweet juice. The vines are very vigorous and productive.

Topsail: The cultivar is preferred because of high maturity. The berries are medium large and green to bronze with smooth skin. Vines are vigorous but are somewhat irregular in cropping.

(b) Cultivars with perfect flowers

The perfect flowered cultivars are used primarily as pollinizers for the pistillate cultivars. Their pollen has high germinability and result in good crops of fair quality berries. Otherwise, the cultivar is more susceptible to diseases and pests than the pistillate ones.

Burgaw: It is a selection from Thomas. The berries are medium sized, reddish black and are of fair quality.

Dearing: Vine is fairly vigorous and productive. The berries are medium in size and of better quality than of the other light coloured and perfect flowered cultivars.

Tarheel: Vine is very vigorous and productive. The berries are very small, borne in large loose dusters having a characteristic flavour.

Willard: The berries are of medium size and of greenish bronze colour. The clusters are large and loose.

The other *Vitis* species are *V. vulpina* having low vine height and berries of 1.25 cm diameter and can be used as a rootstock, *V. barbata* found in Bengal, *V. parviflora* found in Kashmir, *V. rumcisperma* found in Sikkim, *V. rugosa* found in Burma and Kumaon, *V. rupestris* (sand grape) useful as a rootstock and *V. riparia* (river bank grape) also useful as rootstock and the tropical species *V. scaralia*. The other tropical species are *V. lanata, V. flexuosa* and *V. labruscana* (*V. vinifera* x *V. labrusca*). Besides these, the pest and disease resistant species *Ampelocissus latifolia* is found wild in Bihar.

⑧ ⑧ ⑧

[FABIDS: EUROSID I]

It contains 8 orders; Celastrales, Cucurbitales, Fabales, Fagales, Malpighiales, Oxalidales, Rosales and Zygophyllales.

Chapter 21

ZYGOPHYLLALES

The plants are small trees, shrubs or sub-shrubs, less often perennial or annual herbs. Stems are often swollen or jointed at the nodes. Trichomes are usually unicellular and simple, more rarely unicellular and 2-armed, sometimes glandular, usually without scattered mucilage cells and without secretory cells. All elements of wood are usually storied, except in *Balanites*. Vessel elements are very small to moderately large, exclusively with simple perforations and with vestured pits. Lateral pitting is alternate and very small and numerous or intermediate between opposite or alternate, rarely intervascular pits are vestured. Fibres are with bordered or simple pits. Rays are usually narrow and short, homogeneous or rarely slightly heterogeneous. Axial parenchyma is predominantly apotracheal, almost entirely paratracheal in *Bulnesia* and *Nitraria*, scanty metatracheal and vasicentric in *Tetraena*. Sieve element plastids are of S-type (some Zygophyllaceae) or less often of Pcs-type. Nodes are trilacunar.

Leaves are opposite or less often alternate, mostly paripinnate, often 2-foliolate, less often simple and entire, very rarely dotted glands (*Pintoa*), usually with well developed and commonly slender stipules (sometimes modified into spines). Stomata are anomocytic or encyclocytic.

Flowers in inflorescences (cymose or seldom racemose) are solitary, usually bisexual, commonly actinomorphic, (4)5(6)-merous. Sepals are free or sometimes basally connate, imbricate or valvate. Petals are usually free, imbricate or contorted, rarely valvate, sometimes wanting. Stamens are in (1)2(3) cycles with filaments often with basal glands. Anthers are small or large, tetrasporangiate, dorsifixed and introrse, opening longitudinally. Tapetum is secretory. Microsporogenesis is simultaneous. Pollen grains are 2-celled or rarely 3-celled, of various types, but mostly 3-colporate. Nectary disc is usually well developed, more or less distinctly intrastaminal, sometimes modified into a gynophore. Gynoecium is of 5 or less often 4, seldom 6 or only 2 united carpels, with a slender (sometimes very short) simple style; stigma capitate or sometimes lobed or cleft. Ovary is superior, multilocular, with one to several pendulous ovules per locule. Ovules are epitropous or rarely apotropous, anatropous to sometimes hemitropous, campylotropous or orthotropous, bitegmic, crassinucellate, mostly with an endothelium, sometimes with a funicular placental obturator. Female gametophyte is of *Polygonum*-type. Endosperm is nuclear.

Fruits are often capsules or scizocarps, rarely drupes or berries. Seeds are typically exotestal endotestal, with endotegmic cells elongated tangentially with straight or slightly curved embryo in hard and oily endosperm, which is sometimes absent. Resinous, lignins/neolignins and harman alkaloids occur. The order contains two families.

Family Zygophyllaceae (Balanitaceae) (creosote bush and lignum-vitae family)

The family contains about 24 genera and 275 species (Heywood *et al.*, 2007), mostly occurring in drier parts of the tropics and warm temperate regions and are absent or poorly represented (*Tribulus* only) in much of the tropical Asia and wetter parts of Africa and South America. Many species occur in desert or sub-desert areas. Some New World genera include evergreen shrubs and trees, which may occur at altitude of 3000 m in the Andes. Some *Balanites* species are large trees of lowland forests in Africa.

The plants are annual or perennial herbs or sub-shrubs to deciduous or evergreen shrubs and trees. The stems are often sympodial and jointed at the nodes having xylem with vessels, tracheids and fibres arranged in horizontally aligned tiers, usually producing steroidal or triterpenoid saponins, sesquiterpenes and alkaloids. In *Balanites,* occasionally large, evergreen tree up to 50 m is seen that has supra-axillary branch spines. The leaves are opposite or alternate or fascicled (especially *Tribulus*) and may be markedly anisophyllous. They are essentially pinnately compound and may have up to 10 pairs of leaflets but are often reduced to 1 pair with or without a single terminal leaflet, occasionally reduced to a single terminal leaflet and appearing simple (*Larrea*) with a pair of leaflets fused at the base. The leaflets are sessile, entire to occasionally pinnatisect (*Larrea*), usually markedly oblique, sometimes very fleshy (especially *Augea*). Stipules are present and sometimes developed into 2 cm long needle-like spines (especially *Fagonia*).

The inflorescence is an axillary or terminal cyme or the flowers are paired or solitary in leaf axils. The flowers are actinomorphic, bisexual or unisexual (dioecious plants, *Neoluederitzia*), 4-merous or more, usually 5-merous, usually up to 1(2) cm across but up to 5 cm in *Morkillia*. The sepals are free or connate at the base. The petals are free or absent in *Seetzenia* and rarely so in *Zygophyllum*. The stamens are twice as many as the petals. The ovary is syncarpous with (4)5 carpels and as many locules or usually with 10 locules with axile placentation and many pendulous ovules per locule as in *Augea* and *Kallstroemia*. The ovary is often deeply lobed or winged or with paired spines on each carpel, attenuate above into a simple style (or 5 styles in *Seetzenia)*, with lobed or capitate stigma. It may be glabrous or pubescent, or conspicuously villous in some genera. The fruit is a capsule or schizocarp or a fleshy drupe in *Balanites*. Seeds are arillate having endosperm.

Genus *Balanites* Delile

The plants are shrubs or small trees, often with axillary simple or forked spines. Leaves are alternate or spirally arranged and bifoliolate having minute caducous stipules. Flowers are yellowish green borne in short axillary cymes, rarely solitary having (4)5 sepals that are silky hairy within and deciduous, (4)5 spreading petals, fleshy 10-grooved disc surrounding the base of ovary, very villous 8-10 stamens without appendages and embedded in disc, which is 4-5-locular with one ovule per locule, short style and simple stigma. Fruit is large, fleshy, 1-seeded and oily with leathery exocarp and woody endocarp. Endosperm is absent. Nine species have been reported to occur throughout Africa except in the northwest, besides in India, Burma and the Middle East (Kubitzki *et al.*, 2007).

Desert date
(***Balanites aegyptiaca*** (L.) Delile syn. ***B. roxburghii*** Planch; soapberry tree; hingota; Jericho balsam)

It is a native of Africa and is semi-evergreen and spiny small shrub or tree growing up to 5-7 m tall. It has gray to dark brown bark with thick ragged scales and long vertical fissures in which new yellow bark is visible. The branchlets are green, smooth, armed with 8 cm long, green, straight and forward-directed supra-axillary spines. The leaves are gray green and 2-foliate. The leaflets are obovate to orbicular rhomboid, usually 2.5 to 5 cm long and 1.3 to 3 cm broad. Flowers are green to yellow green, small, 1.3 cm in diameter, borne in supra-axillary clusters. Flowers are hermaphrodite, pentamerous and actinomorphic, 8-14 mm in diameter and generally greenish yellow. The 5 coriaceous sepals are free and 5 petals are green and usually glabrous with 10 yellow stamens and ovary surrounded by fleshy disc. The fruit is 4 cm long and broadly oblong ellipsoid plum-sized drupe, at first green turning yellow, with large, hard-pointed stone surrounded by yellow, brown and sticky edible flesh. It contains one seed and the embryo has thick cotyledons (FAO, 1988; Duke, 1989; Hocking, 1993; Hall and Walker, 1991).

⑧ ⑧ ⑧

Chapter 22

FABALES

During their evolution, the plants established early with subsequent aneuploid reduction loading to low diploid number (n=7, with n=14). The plants are trees, shrubs, sub-shrubs and perennial and annual herbs including lianas, aquatics and xerophytes, mostly bearing root nodules containing nitrogen fixing bacteria. Secretory cells are common. Vessels are with simple perforations. Lateral pitting is alternate. Vessels are with or without vestured pits. Fibres are mostly with small, simple pits, sometimes septate. Rays are homogeneous or heterogeneous. Axial parenchyma is commonly abundant, mostly paratracheal. Sieve element plastids are mostly of P-type and less often of S-type. Nodes are trilacunar or less often pentalacunar. Leaves are alternate or rarely opposite, pinnate to palmately compound. Flower is often papilionaceous having wing, standard and keel, mostly one pistil and 10 stamens. Fruit is a pod. The seed has a large green embryo. The plants generally produce proanthocyanins and sometimes cyanogenic, often producing alkaloids, especially of the pyridine, quinolizidine and indole groups. Flavonols are mostly present and ellagic acid is absent. The legumes differ from Rosalean taxa by possessing vestured pits in the secondary xylem. It contains 4 families and about 18860 species.

Family Fabaceae (Leguminosae)

It contains about 732 genera and 19000-19700 species (Heywood *et al*., 2007). The plants are cosmopolitan but only those of Mimosoideae are predominantly tropical and warm temperate and those of Papilionoideae have diversity in the temperate regions.

The plants often have root nodules containing nitrogen fixing symbiotic *Rhizobium* that enrich the nutrient poor soils, sometimes with secretory canals or cavities. These have high nitrogen metabolism with unusual amino acids. Tannins are usually present often with alkaloids, sometimes cyanogenic. Sieve cell plastids have protein crystals and usually also starch grains. The plants are herbs, shrubs and trees, woody (*Wisteria*, some *Entada*) or herbaceous climbers, geophytes and rarely fresh water aquatics (*Neptunia*). The leaves are usually alternate, sometimes simple (*Ulex*), sometimes absent or present only in juveniles, then replaced by leaf-like petioles (some *Acacia*) but usually 3-foliate (*Trifolium, Medicago*), palmate (*Lupinus, Lupinaster*), pinnate (*Vicia, Lathyrus*) or bipinnate (some *Leucaena* and *Acacia*), sometimes terminating in a tendril (*Vicia*). The petioles and leaflets have pulvini, sometimes reacting to touch (*Mimosa pudica*), allowing leaflets to fold up at night. Stipules are present, sometimes as spines (some *Acacia*), large and leafy (*Pisum*) or otherwise modified, but usually small and green.

The inflorescence is terminal or axillary raceme, head, spike or single flowers. The flowers are bilaterally or radially symmetrical (Mimosoideae), hermaphrodite or unisexual (plants monoecious, some Mimosoideae). The sepals are 5, joined or partially so in bilaterally symmetrical flowers, sometimes with 2 or 4 lobes by fusion. The petals are 5-4(-1) or absent, variable in size and symmetrical, all free or the lower 2 fused to form a keel (Papilionoideae). Stamens are usually in 2 whorls of 5, 10 fused in a tube (monadelphous) or 9 fused and 1 free (diadelphous) or all free and sometimes 50-100 or more (Acacieae, Ingeae). *Acacia myrtifolia* has up to 500 stamens. A nectary frequently surrounds the superior ovary usually with 1 carpel, but several (free) as in Ingeae. The fruit is usually a 1-locular dry or fleshy, dehiscent or indehiscent pod that is inflated, compressed, winged or not, variously dull or brightly coloured, from 4 mm to 3 m in length having one to many seeds. The seeds usually have a tough coat and vary greatly in size and colour, some having a caruncle but all have little endosperm and 2 large cotyledons in proportion to the seed size.

Subfamily Caesalpinioideae

The plants are mainly tropical and subtropical trees and shrubs (171 genera, 2200-2300 species). Leaves are usually 2 pinnate but sometimes bipinnate. The flowers are usually more or less irregular with the lateral petals (wings) covering the standard in the bud. Stamens are 10 or fewer, free or monadelphous. There are 4 tribes, Cercideae having 12 genera (such as *Bauhinia* with 155 spp., *Phanera* with 125 spp.), Detarieae having 82 genera (such as *Cynometra* with 85 spp.), *Cassieae* having 21 genera (such as *Chamaecrista* with 330 spp. and *Senna* with 300 spp.), and Caesalpinieae having 56 genera (such as *Tachigali* with 65 spp.).

Genus *Tamarindus* L.

The genus is a monotypic taxon having only one species.

Tamarind

(***Tamarindus indica*** L. syn. ***T. occidentalis*** Gaertn., ***T. officinalis*** Hook.) (2n=24)

Tamarind is native of tropical Africa (Martin *et al*., 1987). It grows wild throughout Sudan, Kenya, Ethiopia and Tanzania. Arabs call it *tamar hindi* (Indian date). The fruit was well known to the ancient Egyptians and the Greeks in the 4th century BC. The tree has long been naturalized in India and the islands of Pacific and was introduced into tropical America and the West Indies (Morton, 1987). It is cultivated to some extent in India, Thailand, Mexico and Brazil (Verheij and Coronel, 1991). The tree is handsome, long lived and evergreen and attains 12-30 m height, 12 m spread and has 7 m trunk circumference. Its branches are strong, supple and gracefully drooping having dark gray and fissured bark and resist strong winds. Thus it is an important shade and avenue tree. The leaves are alternate, even pinnate, 8-15 cm in length, each having 10 to 20 pairs of oblong leaflets of 12-32 x 3-11 mm size. The leaflets fold at night. The flowers are inconspicuous, borne in small recemes having 5 petals of which two are reduced to bristles and are yellow with orange or red streaks. The flower buds are distinctly pink due to the outer colour of the 4 sepals that shed when the flower opens. Flowers are entomophilous, protogynous and self incompatible, 2-2.5 cm in diameter, zygomorphic, hypogynous with four sepals and three petals, 3 stamens and superior ovary with 18 ovules. The fruits are flattish and bean like irregularly curved pods usually 5-18 cm in length and 2 to 4 cm in width. The pods are cinnamon brown or grayish brown externally. The unripe pods are green having highly acidic flesh and soft whitish underdeveloped seeds. As they mature, these get filled with somewhat juicy, acidulous and brown or reddish brown pulp. The skin becomes brittle and gets easily cracked and the pulp dehydrates naturally to a sticky paste enclosed by a few coarse strands of fibres extending lengthwise from the stem. The shiny red brown seeds are hard, flat and roughly square, of 1.25 x 0.4 cm size. The pods are indehiscent and remain on the tree for a year if left unpicked. The pods produced on a tree vary greatly in size and shape and contain 1 to 10 seeds (FAO, 1982; Morton, 1987; Verheij and Coronel, 1991).

Cultivars

Cultivars differ mainly in colour and sweetness of the flesh. Tamarind pods vary considerably in size and shape (Shivanandam, 1980; Karale, 1998). The pod may be sickle shaped, long (16 to 22 cm) and straight or short with varying number of seeds. Seeds also exhibit a wide range of variation in shape, size, colour and ornamentation of the seed coat. In America, tamarind pods are of the shorter type. Thailand cultivars have shorter pods and sweet pulp. Great diversity of tamarind types is found in the African savannas with respect to tolerance to drought, wind, poor soils and water logging. The cultivars have been classified on the basis of one or several of these characteristics. Tamarind is highly cross pollinated and therefore seedling plants show great variation from which superior types having exceptionally large, well filled, sweet and red fleshed fruits can be selected.

Bailey (1947) recognized two types of tamarind:

i. **East Indian type** (*T. indica*): The pods are shorter up to six times or more longer than wide and contain 6-12 seeds.

ii. **West Indian type** (*T. occidentalis*): The pods are three times longer than wide and contain 1-4 seeds.

Paulos (1975) recognized a tamarind type known as Valakatchi that bears long and rectangular pods as against the other types that bear short and cylindrical pods.

Thailand cultivars

These are sweet type (Makahm Wahn) cultivars grown in regular orchards. Some named cultivars are Nuen Chong, Nazi Zad and Sichompoo.

Philippines cultivars

The important cultivars are Manila Sweet, Cavite, Batangas, Bulcan and Laguna.

Cultivars having sweet flesh

Sweet cultivars are found mainly in Thailand. The ripe fruits have sweet pulp with low acidity, e.g. Makham Waan, Secthong Breed and Manila. A sweet type, No. 263, has been located at Parbhani in Maharashtra (India). The fruits of such cultivars are mainly used for dessert purpose (Karale, 1998).

Cultivars having sour flesh

The pulp is highly acidic. Their pods as well as pulp are commercially marketed for culinary use. Some of the cultivars are:-

Pratisthan: The pod contains 61% pulp, 12% seed and 27% shell (Anon., 1984).

Urigam and Cumbum: These are high yielding selections popular in Tamil Nadu.

PKM 1: This is a high yielding clonal selection (Azhakiamanavalan and Vadivel, 1997). Fruit bearing is in clusters of 3 to 7. Fruits are characteristically semi-circular having high pulp (39%) rich in tartaric and ascorbic acids. The cultivar exhibits precosity and regular bearing giving heavy yield of good quality pods and is claimed to be suitable for high density planting (400 plants/ha).

DTS 1: This is a clonal selection made at Dharwad. The plants start bearing within 5-6 years after planting. It yields 500 kg pods per tree. Another selection is DTS-28 giving 450 kg pods per tree.

The other selections made at MPKV, Rahuri, India are T-3, T-6, T-9, T-10, T-11, T-12 and T-13. Goma Prateek is a selection made by CIAH, Bikaner.

Cultivars having reddish pulp

The red type has various shades of pink colour. This is sweeter than the type having brown pulp (common type) due to lower free acid content. It is generally harvested when the pods are immature and green. It is preferred for making preserves. A high yielding cultivar having red pulp, named Yogeshwari, has been released by Marathwada Agricultural University, Parbhani, Maharashtra. Another locally known cultivar is "Raktichinch".

Cultivars having brown and yellow pulp

These are the common acidic types. The yellow or brown pulp turns dark brown on storage. The pods are harvested on full maturity.

Genus *Ceratonia* L.

It is a genus consisting of flowering trees belonging to the subfamily Caesalpinioideae and the tribe Caesalpinieae that are endemic to the Mediterranean region.

Carob

(***Ceratonia siliqua*** L.; locust bean; St. John's bread; Algarrobo)

The carob is a slow growing, handsome, evergreen, long lived, sclerophyllous medium sized tree growing up to 10-17 m in height. The leaves are glossy, alternate and pinnate formed by 2 to 5 pairs of round to oval, short-petioled, entire and shining leaflets having deeper green shade on the upper surface. The cream or greenish pentamerous flowers are borne in 5-10 cm long lateral racemes arising from the older branches and even from the trunk. Each raceme bears 30 to 50 flowers of which only 1-5 usually set. Female flower consists of a pistil (6-8.5 mm) on a disk and rudimentary stamens surrounded by 5 hairy sepals. The ovary consists of two carpels and several ovules. Male flowers consist of a nectarial disk having 5 stamens with delicate filaments surrounded by hairy sepals. Hermaphrodite flowers combine both types of flower (Batlle and Tous, 1997). Carob trees are usually dioecious but some hermaphroditic forms also occur. Thus male, female and hermaphrodite flowers are generally borne on different trees. Generally pistillate flowers develop into fruit. The fruit is dark brown, indehiscent, flattened, 10-30 cm long and 2-6 cm wide ribbed pod which is coriaceous outside and fleshy and sweetish inside, containing 4-12 obovate, transverse brown and bony seeds (FAO, 1982; Morton, 1987). Four cultivars named Banya Cabra, Duraio, Matalafera and Rojal are reported (Tous *et al.*, 2009). The pods are about 23 cm long and 3-4 cm wide. The pods are almost straight except of Banya Cabra.

Genus *Cordeauxia* Hemsl. (x= 12, 2n= 28)

The plant is shrub without specialized short shoots. Phyllotaxy is spiral. Leaves are compound, pinnate, paripinnate with adaxially ridged rachides. Venation is neither palmate nor parallel. The leaflets are few per leaf with purple gland dots below, alternate with noticeably not twisted petiolules. Inflorescences of racemose units are terminal. Bracteoles are absent at anthesis. Flowers are hermaphrodite, pentamerous in simple corymbs (few flowered), not distichous. Hypanthium is present. Calyx is polysepalous covering the rest of the flower in bud and is more or less regular, 5 partite and not imbricate. Corolla is present, slightly zygomorphic, polypetalous and without any greatly reduced petals. Petals are spathulate, 5 and imbricate ascending. Clawed petals are present. Androecium is of 10 parts with all members free of one another and without staminodia. Fertile stamens are 10. Anthers are attached well above the base of connective. Dehiscence is introrse. Ovary is stipitate. Ovules are few. Fruit is a two-valved pod, not becoming woody and is short beaked, scarcely falcate and not winged. Seeds are non-endospermic with a straight or slightly oblique radicle. Cotyledons are not flat. Two species occur in tropical Africa.

Yeheb nut

(***Cordeauxia edulis*** Hemsl.; ye-eb; ye-eb nut; hebb; yehib)

The plant is bushy, unarmed, multi-stemmed evergreen shrub, usually 1.6 m in height. Under favourable locations, it may grow up to 2.5 m tall. Leaves are paripinnate with numerous red glands below having 4 pairs of ovate to oblong ovate leaflets. Flowers are bisexual, yellow in colour borne in clusters at the end of the branches. The fruit is a indehiscent pod which contains 1-4 round or ovoid seeds of the size of a macadamia nut or a large filbert (hazel nut) (Wicknes and Storey, 1984; Booth and Wickens, 1988; FAO, 1988).

Two cultivars Moqley and Suley are recognized in Somalia. The latter has fewer and larger leaves and less sweet and smaller fruits (Wickens, 1998).

Genus *Hymenaea* L.

The genus has 14 species, all except one are native to the tropics of the Americas with one additional species (*H. verrucosa*) on the east coast of Africa. Some authors place this African species in a separate monotypic genus, *Trachylobium*. In the neotropics, *Hymenaea* is distributed through the Caribbean islands, and from southern Mexico to Brazil. Linnaeus named the genus in 1753 in *Species Plantarum* for Hymenaios, the Greek god of marriage ceremonies. The name is a reference to the paired leaflets. Most species of *Hymenaea* are large trees and are primarily evergreen. They may grow to a height of 25 m and emerge above the forest canopy. Some species grow both as tall forest trees and as smaller shrubby trees depending on their surrounding habitat. The leaves are pinnately bifoliolate. The flowers grow in a panicle or corymb inflorescence. The pulpy centre of the fruits are edible and contain starch. The leaves may be used to make a tea. The trees produce a dense wood used for timber in making ships and furniture. The thick bark of some species is used by indigenous peoples of the Amazon to make canoes. Seeds contain large amounts (40% of dry weight) of a highly viscous polysaccharide (xyloglucan) which can be used in food, paper, cosmetic and pharmaceutical industry.

West Indian locust
(***Hymenaea courbaril*** L.; jatoba)

It is native of Central and South America and the West Indies. The tree grows up to 30-40 m in height and 2 m in diameter. Bark is usually smooth, grayish, 1-3 cm thick and reddish internally. The leaves are alternate, compound and 2-foliate. The stipules soon fall. The petioles are 12-30 mm long. The leaflets are 2, ovate to lanceolate, 3-12 x 1.5-7 cm in size with acute to obtuse apex, entire margin and small glands and prominent veins on the glabrous, shining and leathery undersurface. Inflorescence is a short terminal panicle with few branches of flowers. The flowers are bisexual with 3-10 mm long pedicels. The sepals are 4 which are concave, oblong and obovate and 12-22 mm long. The stamens are 10 with 3-8 mm long anthers. Ovary is 1-10 locular with 6-10 or more ovules. Fruit is an indehiscent, oblong pod, 8-15 x 3-5 cm in size having dull brown, hard, woody and 5 cm thick pericarp. Seeds are 1-6, light to dark brown, hard, flattened, obovoid to ellipsoid, 1-2 cm long and surrounded by a dry creamy brown or greenish pulp (FAO, 1986; Brücher, 1989).

Subfamily Mimosoideae

The plants are mainly tropical and subtropical trees and shrubs (78 genera and 3200-3300 spp.). The leaves are often bipinnate and the flowers are regular having valvate petals in the bud and 10 or more stamens. There are 4 tribes; Mimoseae having 40 genera (such as *Mimosa* with 500 spp.), Mimozygantheae having one genus (*Mimozyganthus carinatus*), Acacieae having one genus (*Acacia* with 1,450 spp.) and Ingeae having 36 genera (such as *Inga* with 300 spp.). The ice-cream bean (*Inga edulis* Mart.) is grown for succulent arils in Central America and West Indies.

Genus *Prosopis* L.

It contains around 45 species of spiny trees and shrubs distributed in subtropical and tropical regions of the Americas, Africa and West and South Asia. They often thrive in arid soil and are resistant to drought developing extremely deep root systems. Their wood is usually hard, dense and durable. The fruits are pods and may contain large amounts of sugar. The generic name means "burdock" in Latin and originated in the Greek language.

Khejri
(*Prosopis cineraria* (L.) Druce syn. *P. spicigera* L.)

Khejri is an evergreen, much branched, medium large and thorny tree attaining height of 4-9 m with a spreading crown. It has a tap root often going to a depth of 20 m or more and is thus able to withstand the most severe droughts. It is a very slow growing tree. Bark is thick, gray and rough in texture having deep furrows. Leaves are alternate, 2.5 to 8.0 cm long and bipinnate usually with two pairs of pinnae and 7 to 14 pairs of leaflets. The small, yellowish white, fragrant and bisexual pentamerous flowers appear from March to May on the spikes emerging from the leaf axils. The cup shaped and faintly toothed calyx is of 5 x 1.5 mm size. The corolla is yellow and 3 mm long. The recurved 20 stamens have 3 mm long filaments. Ovary is sessile with numerous ovules. The pods are either straight or coiled into a cylindrical, glabrous, about 20 cm long spiral borne on long to small stalks in clusters of up to 12. The pods contain several seeds embedded in the sweet, dry and yellow pulp. The amount of pulp (mesocarp) in a pod constitutes half of its weight. Seeds are 10-15, compressed, ovate, dull brown, smooth, hard and immersed in the sweetish mealy pulp (Anon., 1969, 1990; Hocking, 1993; Arya *et al.*, 1995).

Cultivars

There are two distinct ecotypes of khejri, one having less spiny drooping twigs and comparatively acute angle of branching giving the tree a compact look, and the other having non-drooping branches with slightly wide angle of branching, comparatively open crown and having prominent spines. From 10 promising selections made from the natural variability in western Rajasthan one cultivar named Thar Shobha having sweet, tender and long pods has been identified and released.

Genus *Parkia* Robert Brown

About 31 species were known in 1995 to which 4 more have been added. The type species for the genus is *Parkia biglobosa*. Parkias are found throughout the tropics; 4 in Africa, about 10 in Asia and about 20 in the neotropics.

Tree bean

(***Parkia roxburghii*** G. Don syn. ***P. javanica*** (Lam.) Merrill.)

It is native of northeastern India and grows wild in forests of Manipur, Assam and Burma. It is cultivated in Manipur. A related edible species is *P. biglandulosa* Wight and Arn., which is native of Malaysia. The tree bean requires hot humid climatic conditions for good growth and fruiting. Well drained rich soils are considered suitable (Barooah and Meitei, 1977).

The tree is 9-12 m tall having spreading branches and pubescent shoots. The bark is light gray to brown with white patches. The branchlets have raised lenticels. The leaves have bipinnate main rachis, which is puberulous or glabrescent. The length of the rachis is 30-60 cm with a gland below the lower pair of pinnae and a few between the upper pinnae. The pinnae are in 8-30 pairs, opposite and the secondary rachis is 7-15 cm long. The 40-80 pairs of leaflets are sessile, linear oblong and slightly curved towards the acute tip having unequally truncate base with lower half subhastate, dark green above and puberulous on the margin. The flowers are in dense turbinate or clavate long peduncled heads of 3.75-5.63 x 1.88-3.0 cm size. The peduncles are 25-40 cm long. The head is sterile towards the bottom. The bracts are up to 0.75 cm long, spathulate and silky pubescent outside. The calyx is tubular, 0.63-0.75 cm long, 5-cleft and tomentose. Corolla is pale yellow, tubular, upper portion free and segments extruded above the subvalvate calyx. The 10 stamens are exerted. The filaments are connate below and adnate to the corolla tube. The anthers are narrow without glands. The ovary has many ovules, style is filiform and the stigma is capitate. The smooth and dark brown pods are 25-50 x 3.75 cm in size (Barooah and Meitei, 1977).

African locust bean

(***Parkia biglobosa*** (Jacq.) Benth.; West African locust bean; nere)

It is a native of West Africa and is found growing wild in Savanna forests. The related edible species native of tropical Africa are *P. clappertona* Keay, *P. filicoidea* Welw. ex Oliv. and *P. bicolor* A. Chev. *P. speciosa* Hort. ex Hassk (Pete) is distributed in Malaysia and Indonesia.

The tree is deciduous and grows to a height of 10-20 m with large umbrella shaped crown. Leaves are dark green, pinnate, the smallest division measuring about 1-1.5 cm x 5 mm. Leaf stalks are grayish brown and velvety. Flower head is a ball of red or orange flowers about 5 cm in diameter hanging on a long stalk up to 30 cm in length. Inflorescence is biglobose capitulum with distal part having fertile flowers and the smaller proximal part having staminodal nectariferous flowers. Hermaphrodite flowers are orange or red in colour having 10-13 mm long calyx, 10-14 mm long corolla, very short lobes, 1-3 mm long filaments exerted about 4 mm beyond the calyx mouth. Nectar secreting flowers have 6-7 mm long calyx. Staminodal flowers have about 5.5-7 mm long calyx, filaments exerted 2-3 mm beyond the calyx mouth with only a rudimentary gynoecium occurring among them on the same capitula. Pollination is carried out by bats. Fruits are long pods, 45 x 2 cm in size, slightly curved, hanging in clusters from the flower stalks. The pods contain up to 30 seeds embedded in a yellow pericarp. The pods split open when mature. Seeds are red brown to black, flattened and embedded in a yellow floury pulp (FAO, 1988; Hall *et al*., 1997).

Genus *Pithecellobium* Mart.

It is a genus of flowering plants. The generic name is derived from the Greek words meaning "ape" or "monkey" and "earring" referring to the coiled shape of the fruit pods. The plants are generally known as black beads.

Manila tamarind

(***Pithecellobium dulce*** (Roxb.) Benth; Madras thorn; guayamochil; sweet inga)

It is a native of Central America and Mexico. It has been naturalized throughout the tropics. It was introduced in Indonesia by the Portuguese and in the Philippines by the Spaniards. It is also common in India, Malaysia and Thailand (Verheij and Coronel, 1991; Hocking, 1993). Manila tamarind is mainly grown as a hardy roadside tree or hedge plant. It is grown for its fruits in South India. The related species, which are grown for fruit are *P. bubalinum* (Jack) Benth. (in Malaysia) and *P. jiringa* (Jack) Prain (in Myanmar to western Malaysia).

It is a medium armed shrub or tree growing up to 10 m in height with glabrescent rough branchlets armed with straight, paired, stipular and 4-10 mm long spines. The leaves are abruptly bipinnate with 1-2.5 cm long rachis and single pair of pinnae, each 2-2.5 x 1-2 cm in size. The rachis of the pinna is up to 7.5 mm long and has small, terminal stipular spines, two leaflets per pinna which are opposite, sessile, ovate, 1.5-3.5 x 1-2 cm in size and glabrous. Inflorescences are borne in terminal panicles, up to 10 cm long having 1-2 cm long peduncles and bearing globular heads with 15-20 sessile whitish flowers. Calyx and corolla are tubular. Filaments are white. The fruit is a flattened pod, linear oblong but curled up, 1 cm wide, fleshy, coriaceous and reddish brown. The seeds are flattened, obovate, 9x7x2 mm in size and blackish with a thick spongy and rather dry aril (Verheij and Coronel, 1991; Hocking, 1993).

The cultivar **PKM (MT) 1** is a selection from open pollinated seedlings of Soolakkarai. The trees have a compact drooping canopy amenable for high density planting. Fruit bearing is in clusters. The pods are spirally twisted with clear constrictions. The pods are pale yellow having black seeds, white aril and 18^0B TSS suitable for making candy. The fruit yield is 79 kg/tree.

Subfamily Papilionoideae (Papilionaceae)

The plants are temperate, tropical and subtropical, mostly herbs but some are trees and shrubs (c 478 genera and 13,600-14,060 spp.). Leaves are usually pinnate but sometimes simple. The flowers are irregular with the lateral petals enclosed by the standard in the bud. Stamens are 10, usually diadelphous but sometimes monadelphous or free. More than 20% of all species belong to the two genera *Astragalus* and *Acacia*.

There are 28 recognized tribes; Swartzieae having 17 genera (such as *Swartzia* with 180 spp.), Sophoreae having 45 genera (such as *Ormosia* with 130 spp.),

Dipterygeane having 3 genera (such as *Dipteryx* with 12 spp.), Brongniartieae having 10 genera (such as *Brongniartia* with 63 spp.), Euchresteae having 1 genus (*Euchresta* with 4 spp.), Thermopsideae having 6 genera (such as *Thermopsis* with 23 spp.), Podalyrieae having 8 genera (such as *Amphithalea* with 42 spp.), Crotalarieae having 11 genera (such as *Crotalaria* with 690 spp., *Aspalathus* with 278 spp.), Genisteae having 25 genera (such as *Lupinus* with 225 spp.), Amorpheae having 8 genera (such as *Dalea* with 165 spp.), Dalbergieae having 49 genera (such as *Dalbergia* with 250 spp., *Adesmia* with 240 spp.), Aeschynomene with 180 spp.), Hypocalypteae having one genus (*Hypocalyptus* with 3 spp.), Mirbelieae having 25 genera (such as *Daviesia* with 135 spp.), Bossiaeeae having 6 genera (such as *Bossiaea* with 60 spp.), Indigofereae having 7 genera (such as *Indigofera* with 700 spp.), Millettieae having 45 genera (such as *Tephrosia* with 350 spp.), Abreae having 1 genus (*Abrus* with 17 spp.), Phaseoleae having 89 genera (such as *Rhynchosia* with 230 spp.), Desmodieae having 30 genera (such as *Desmodium* with 275 spp.), Psoraleeae having 9 genera (such as *Otholobiurm* with 61 spp.), Sesbanieae having one genus (*Sesbania* with 60 spp.), Loteae having 22 genera (such as *Lotus* with 125 spp.), Robinieae having l genus (*Coursetia* with 35 spp.), Galegeae having 24 genera (such as *Astragalus* with 2.400 spp., *Oxytropis* with 350 spp.), Hedysareae having 12 genera (such as *Hedysarum* with 160 spp.), Cicereae having one genus (*Cicer* with 43 spp.), Trifolieae having 6 genera (such as *Trifolium* with 250 spp.) and Fabeae having 5 genera (such as *Vicia* with 160 spp.).

Genus *Inocarpus* J. R. Forst. & G. Forst

The genus has three species distributed in Malesia including Malay Peninsula, the Malay Archipelago, New Guinea and Bismarck Archipelago.

Tahiti chestnut
(***Inocarpus edulis*** Forst. syn. ***I. fagiferus*** Fosb.; otaheite chestnut; Polynesian chestnut)

It is a native of Malaysia and Pacific Islands (Martin *et al*., 1987). The plant is 25 m tall tree with deeply furrowed, fluted or buttressed trunk. The leaves are simple, entire, large, oblong lanceolate short petioled and leathery. Flowers are white, cream or yellow and fragrant and are borne on simple or branched spikes. The calyx is tubular, campanulate, membranous and 2-5 toothed. The petals are 4 to 6, usually 5 with stamens twice the number of petals having small uniform anthers and subsessile or short stalked ovary with 2 ovules, very short style and oblique stigma. Fruit is oblique obovate, flattened, 2-valved, sub-drupaceous, leathery, indehiscent and one seeded (Duke, 1989).

⑧ ⑧ ⑧

Chapter 23

ROSALES

The plants are herbs, shrubs and trees. Leaves are alternate, rarely opposite, mostly simple (except Rosaceae) or compound with toothed margins. Stipules are present, rarely absent. The leaves are not insectivorous. The plants are rarely dioecious. The floral parts are cyclic but the androecium is not always so. The sepals are valvate and hypanthium is persisting. Flower is bisexual and actinomorphic. Petals are free. The gynoecium is mostly unipistillate and each pistil is usually syncarpous. Perianth is usually differentiated into calyx and corolla but the corolla is sometimes missing. Stamens are mostly epigynous or perigynous. Carpels are free, usually 1 or 4 or more with one ovule and dry stigma. Ovules are anatropous. Embryo is usually straight. The ovary is usually inferior or surrounded by a hypanthium. Seeds are devoid of endosperm. Dihydroflavonols are present. The order contains 9 families.

Family Rosaceae

The family contains about 85-100 genera and 2000 sexual in addition to many obligate or facultative apomictic microspecies (1300-1500) (Heywood *et al.*, 2007). Judd *et al.* (1999) described Rosaceae to include herbs, shrubs or trees, which are sometimes rhizomatous, climbing or thorny. The plants are deciduous, evergreen, often with thorns. The stems are herbaceous or woody. Cyanogenic glycosides and sugar alcohol sorbitol is present. Plant hairs are simple or stellate and can be present with prickles. Leaves are of various types but are usually alternate, simple to palmately or pinnately compound and stipulate and the lamina is commonly with glandular tipped teeth. The flowers are often large and showy, in many colours, single or in clusters, mostly perfect and regular or infrequently unisexual, perigynous or epigynous. The hypanthium or receptacle assumes various forms; e.g. in rose it encloses the numerous pistils while in the drupaceous flowers the ovary is superior and is surrounded but not attached to the hypanthium. It ranges from flat to cup-shaped or cylindrical and either free or adnate to the carpels, often enlarging into fruit. Sepals are usually pentamerous, sometimes alternating with epicalyx lobes. The calyx and corolla are 5-parted. Petals are usually pentamerous, coloured, scented, and polypetalous. Stamens are usually numerous, (2 to 3 times of the number of petals, frequently 15 or more, sometimes 10 or fewer), arranged in one or many whorls and rarely connate. Filaments are distinct or basally fused to the nectar disk. The anthers are small and 2-celled. Pollen grains are tricolpate. Carpels are one to many, and are distinct or connate, sometimes adnate to the hypanthium. The ovary varies from superior to inferior depending on the genus. Ovules are 1-2 or several on axile placentae. The styles are present in the same number as carpels. Thalamus may be fleshy conical or dome shaped. The fruit can be a follicle, achene, pome, drupe and aggregate or accessory with drupelets or achenes, rarely a capsule. Endosperm is usually absent in the seed. The occurrence of numerous stamens and the absence of endosperm have been the key structural apomorphies for systematic classification.

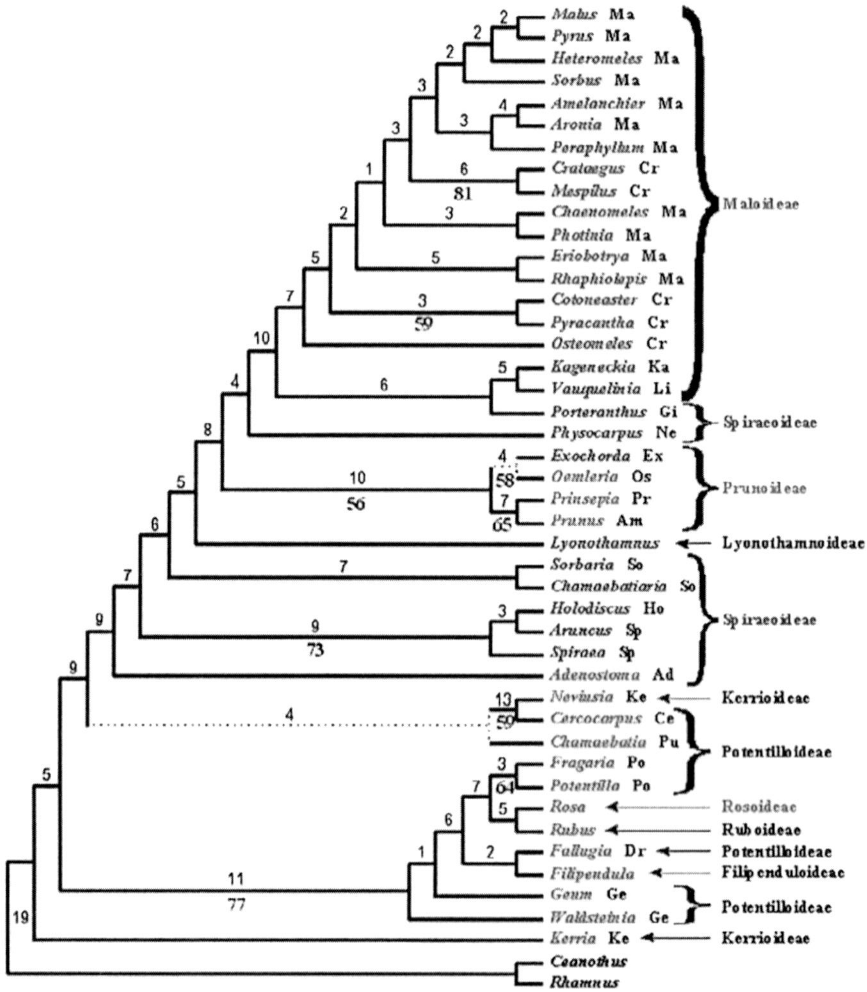

Fig. 23.1. Classification of Rosaceae. (Source: Hummer and Janick , 2009).

The variation in gynoecium among species has been used for classification of the family to subfamilies (Takhtajan, 1997). Many apocarpous pistils mature into achenes in Rosoideae. A single monocarpellate pistil matures into a drupe in Amygdaloideae. The gynoecium consists of two or more apocarpous pistils that mature into follicles in Spiraecoideae. The ovary is compound and inferior and an epigynous zone may occur in Maloideae. The composition of genera within subfamilies has been confusing. Genetic analysis has been performed to examine phylogenies for the family, individual subfamilies, tribes and the larger genera. Potter *et al.* (2007) have recognized 3 subfamilies: Rosoideae, including *Filipendula, Rubus, Rosa* and 3 tribes; Dryadoideae, comprising 4 actinorhizal genera; and Spiraeoideae, comprising *Lyonothamnus* and 7 tribes based on studies by using nucleotide sequence data from six nuclear (*18S, gbssi1, gbssi2, ITS, pgip* and *ppo*) and four chloroplast (*matK, ndhF, rbcL* and *trnL-trnF*) regions, separately and in various combinations, with parsimony and likelihood-based Bayesian approaches. They included, all genera previously assigned to Amygdaloideae and Maloideae, in Spiraeoideae and recognized 3 supertribes, one in Rosoideae and two in Spiraeoideae.

Dickinson *et al.* (2002) have produced a parsimonious tree derived from the cladistic analysis of 125 combined morphological and molecular characters from members of Rosaceae (Fig. 23.1). The accepted genera for the family have been listed by ICBN. It is a large family of 95 to more than 100 genera and 2830-3100 species.

Most of the important fruit plants belong to the tribes Pomeae, Pruneae, Rubeae and Potentilleae. L. H. Bailey gave considerable attention to temperate fruits. U. P. Hedrick published a book entitled *"Cyclopedia of Hardy Fruits"* and a number of monographs on these fruits. Some economically important fruits belonging to subfamilies and genera are given in Table 23.1.

Table 23.1. Some economically important subfamilies, genera and species of Rosaceae (Hummer and Janick, 2009).

Subfamily	Genus	Species	Common name	Uses
Amygdaloideae	*Prunus*	*armeniaca*	Apricot	Fresh and processed fruit
		avium	Sweet cherry	Fresh and processed fruit
		cerasus	Tart (sour) cherry	Fresh and processed fruit
		domestica	European plum	Fresh and processed fruit
		dulcis	Almond	Fresh and processed nut
		mume	Japanese apricot or mume	Ornamental
		persica	Peach, nectarine	Fresh and processed fruit
		serotina	Black cherry	Timber species
Maloideae	*Amelanchier*	*alnifolia*	Saskatoon, service berry; shad bush	Landscape ornamental
	Aronia	*melanocarpa*	Black chokeberry	Processed fruit for juice, nutraceutical
	Chaenomales	*japonica*	Japanese quince	Landscape ornam-ental, processed fruit

	Cotoneaster	*spp.*	Cotoneaster	Landscape ornamental
	Crataegus	*spp.*	Hawthorn, Thorn apple	Landscape ornamental, craft uses for wood
	Cydonia	*oblonga*	European quince	Fresh and processed fruit, dwarfing rootstock for pear and loquat
	Eriobotrya	*japonica*	Loquat	Fresh and processed fruit
	Malus	*×domestica (M. pumila)*	Apple	
		spp.	Crabapples	Landscape ornamental
	Pyrus	*calleryana*	Callery pear	Landscape ornamental
		communis	European pear	Fresh and processed fruit
		serotina	Japanese pear (nashi)	Fresh fruit
		ussurienses	Chinese pear	Fresh fruit
	Mespilus	*germanica*	Medlar	Fresh fruit (bletted)
	Photinia	*spp.*	Photinia	Landscape ornamental
	Pyracantha	*spp.*	Firethorn	Landscape ornamental
	Sorbus	*spp.*	Mountain ash, rowan	Landscape ornamental
Rosoideae	*Fragaria*	*×ananassa*	Strawberry	Fresh and processed fruit
	Geum	*spp.*	Avens	Herbaceous perennial
	Kerria	*japonica*	Kerria	Landscape ornamental
	Potentilla	*spp.*	Cinquefoil	Landscape ornamental
	Rosa	*spp.*	Rose	Cut flowers, landscape ornamental, perfume oil, medicinal
	Rubus	*spp.* and hybrids	Blackberry, rasp-berry, hybrid berry	Fresh and processed fruit
Spiraeoideae	*Spiraea*	*prunifolia*	Bridal wreath	Landscape ornamental
	Exochorda	*racemosa*	Exochorda	Landscape ornamental
	Physocarpus	*opulitolius*	Ninebark	Landscape ornamental

Subfamily Rosoideae

The rose, member of this subfamily, has provided the name for the family Rosaceae. It includes small fruits including strawberry (*Fragaria)* and the brambles, blackberry, raspberry and various hybrid berries (*Rubus*). The related genera are *Duchesnea* and *Potentilla* having basic chromosome number of n=7.

Genus *Fragaria* Linn. (x=7; 2n=14, 28, 42, 56)

The plants are acaulescent, more or less hairy perennial herbs with basal leaves and long runners emerging from the axils. The runners produce roots and form new plants. The petioles are long and channeled above with large, mostly scarious and brown and persistent stipules adnate at their bases. The leaves are 3-foliate or sometimes unequally imparipinnate (i.e. with pair of much smaller lateral leaflets below the nodal leaflets, sharply dentate but entire at the more or less wedge-shaped base, the lateral ones oblique, the inner half usually smaller). Scape is mostly about as long as the petioles and cymosely branched. The slender pedicels are erect when in flower and curved when in fruit. Flowers are polygamous, rarely hermaphrodite, the male flowers larger and showier and all 5-parted. The central flowers open first, often 6 to 8-parted and larger than the lateral ones. Calyx lobes form a flat hypanthium, augmented by as many shorter and mostly narrower outer calyx lobes or branchlets. Stamens are about 20 or less or abortive with filaments mostly shorter than the receptacle, oblong anthers and roundish or conical receptacle bearing numerous pistils with lateral styles. At maturity the receptacle becomes enlarged and juicy forming an aggregate fruit, popularly known as strawberry (Fig. 23.2).

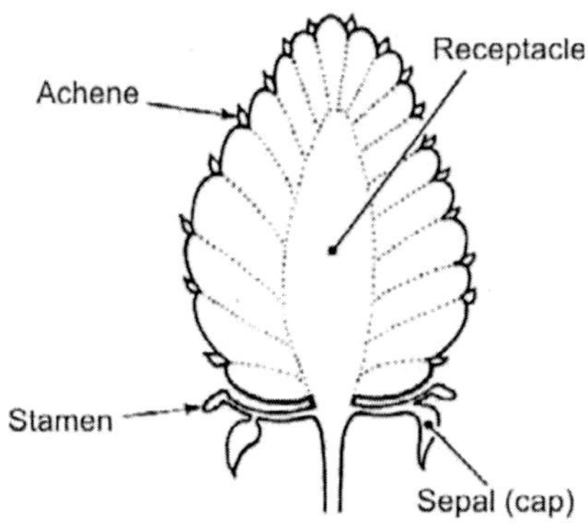

Fig. 23.2. Typical aggregate fruit of strawberry (*Fragaria* x *ananassa* Duchesne) (Source: Strand, 1994)

The species of the genus *Fragaria* fall into 4 ploidy groups; diploids (2n=14), tetraploids (2n=28), hexaploids (2n=42) and octaploids (2n=56).

Diploid species (2n = 14)

F. vesca L. is the most extensively distributed species. It occurs naturally in North America, northern Asia and Europe.

F. viridis Duch. is native to grassy meadows and forest edges in Europe and western Asia.

F. nilgerrensis Schlect. is native to South East Asia.

F. daltoniana. J. Gay is found in a small area of the Himalayan Sikkim at elevations from 3000 to 4500 m.

F. nubicola Lindl. ex Lacaita is native to the temperate Himalayas at elevations from 1500 to 4000 m.

F. iinumae Makino is found in the alpine mountains of central and northern Japan (particularly Hokaido) and is similar in appearance to *F. daltoniana*.

F. yezoensis Hara. is native to the colder northern areas of Japan along with *F. iinumae*.

F. nipponica Makino is found in the mountains of Japan. It closely resembles *F. yezoensis* but has pedicels with ascending rather than spreading hairs.

F. mandschurica Staudt is native to Manchuria. It is similar to the autotetraploid *F. orientalis* and may be its progenitor species.

Tetraploid species (2n = 28)

F. orientalis Losinsk is found in western Siberia, Mongolia, Manchuria and Korea in forests and on open slopes.

F. moupinensis (Franch) Card is native of southwestern China.

Hexaploid species (2n = 42)

F. moschata Duch. is found in northern and central Europe extending eastward into Russia. It is found in shaded (sheltered) places under trees, shrubs and tall grass.

Octaploid species (2n = 56)

F. chiloensis (L.) Duch. is found along the Pacific coast from Alaska through central California, along the beaches of Chile and inland to the Andes mountains.

F. virginiana Duch. is found in meadows throughout central and eastern North America.

F. viriginiana has undergone considerable genetic differentiation and many taxa have been recognized within it.

F. iturupensis Staudt. is found on Iturup Island of the Kuril Islands, northeast of Japan. It has obviate subglaucous leaves similar to the colour of *F. iinumae*.

F. x *ananassa* Duchesne appeared in Europe as an accidental hybrid of *F. chiloensis* and *F. virginiana.*

The common cultivated strawberry, *F.* x *ananassa* Duchesne, is a hybrid of *F. chiloensis* and *F. virginiana.* It originally appeared in Europe between 1714 and 1759 when pistillate plants of *F. chiloensis* were brought by Frezier from Chile and planted near *F. virginiana* from the Atlantic seaboard area of USA. It is characterized by its large fruit size, high yields and strong vigour.

Strawberry cultivars

Tioga: It was evolved in California from a complex cross involving a number of cultivars. It tolerates salinity. It is an early maturing cultivar, tolerant to viruses. The fruit is long conical to wedge shaped, very large, weighs 12-15 g having thick, tough, shiny and red skin. The flesh is medium red, firm with pleasant flavour, 7-10ºB soluble solids and medium acidity. It is a heavy yielding cultivar. The fruits ship well. It is good for dessert and processing.

Torrey: It originated from a cross between Larsen and California Selection and tested as a sibling of Fresno. The plants are vigorous, have short rest period and are tolerant to virus and salinity. It produces numerous runners. The leaflets are deeply incised, the lobes are irregular and the leaf blade is wrinkled. The fruits are large, uniform and wedge shaped having darker skin than that of Fresno and loose calyx cap. The flesh is very firm and of excellent dessert value and good processing quality.

Senga Sengma: It originated in Germany from a cross**,** Markee x Sieger. The plant is erect, high cropper and starts runner production in late August. The fruit is large having red, bright glossy and attractive skin. The fruits remain till later picking. The flesh is medium firm having loose calyx cap and usually remains on the plant.

Gorella: It originated in Holland from a cross between Juspa and US Selection. The plants are erect having thick and tough leaves, sometimes 4-5 foliate and very firm trusses. The fruits are large, conical, having bright red and attractive skin, firm flesh with good flavour. The fruits ripen early.

Catskill: The cultivar originated in New York from a cross between Marshall and Howard. It can grow under varied soil conditions. The plants are vigorous, produce runners freely and are productive. The fruits are large, long conical and somewhat irregular having bright red, shiny and attractive skin. The flesh is light red, fairly firm having very good eating quality. The fruits have good shipping quality and are suitable for freezing.

Selva: The cultivar evolved from a complex cross. The plants are large and semi-erect. It is a day neutral cultivar having capacity to produce off season fruits. The fruits are large and medium to long conical in shape. In some fruits the apex may be wedged or flat. The fruit skin is dark red glossy and attractive. The flesh is bright red in colour, firmer than that of Tioga, Tufts and Pajaro having somewhat hollow core.

Chandler: It evolved from a cross, Douglas x Califontia Selection. The cultivar is self fertile, excellent runner producer and suitable for summer and winter plantation. The fruits are large, long conical having flat or wedged apex and glossy red skin and of exceptionally high dessert quality with outstanding colour and flavour. The flesh is light red and firm having excellent flavour. The fruits ripen early and are used both as dessert and for processing.

Pusa Early Dwarf: The cultivar is suitable for subtropical region. Fruits are attractive red having soft pulp and 7-9ºB TSS

Pajaro: The cultivar is very successful for growing during summer. Plants are tolerant to virus. Fruits are quite susceptible to damage caused by rain. Fruits are large and flesh is very firm having firm and red skin and good dessert and processing quality.

Camarosa: Plant growth of this cultivar is similar to Chandler but the colour on the underside of leaf is distinctly lighter. Individual leaflets are larger, somewhat longer and narrower. Leaves (including petioles) are similar in length to those of Chandler but are much broader. It produces fruits early that have good storage properties.

Winter Down: It is a highly productive cultivar. Fruits are medium to large in size and are moderately resistant to *Botrytis* and anthracnose.

The following strawberry cultivars were developed at East Malling Research Station, England:-

Pandora (Von Humboldt x Redstar) x Merton Down; Selection JILA 33)

Pegasus (Redgauntlet x Gorella; Selection ES608)

Marshmello (Honeoye x Hapil; Selection EM224)

Calypso (Rapella x Selva; Selection EMR28)

Tango (Rapella x Selva; Selection EMR25)

Laura (Complex pedigree EM147 x EM86; Selection EM396)

Eros (Elsanta x Allstar; Selection EM220)

Florence (Complex pedigree EM20 x LA657; Selection EM372)

Sophie (Hapil x Streamliner) x Kent; Selection EM341)

Bolero (Complex parentage includes Redgauntlet, Wiltguard, Gorella, Cardinal and Selva; Selection EMR63)

Perfection (Complex x Rainer; Selection LA9340)

Rosie (Honeoye x ITA 80-52-1 (complex); Selection EM575)

Alice (Complex pedigree EM474 x EM478; Selection EM726)

Flamenco (Evita x EMR077; Selection EMR154)

Mae (Rosie x Marmolada; Selection EM884)

Judibell (Complex pedigree EM533 x EM580; Selection EM965)

Malling Pearl (Complex pedigree EMR153 x EM707; Selection EMR286)

Malling Opal (Complex pedigree EMR153 x EM707; sib of Malling Pearl; Selection; Selection EMR287)

Delia (Honeoye x ITA80-52-1 (Italian seedling); Selection EM835)

Amelia (Complex pedigree includes Pandora, Onebor, Kent and Providence; Selection EM1103)

Cassandra (Rosie x EM0791; Selection EM1064)

Sallybright (Complex pedigree includes Alice, Selva and Eros.; Selection EM1296)

Irresistible (Complex pedigree includes Alice, Selva and Eros; Selection EM1294)

Viktoriana (Eros x EM0783; Selection EM1125)

Elegance (Complex pedigree includes Honeoye, Alice, Selva and Eros; Selection EM1276)

Lucy (Complex pedigree includes Honeoye, Selva and Rapella; Selection EM0931)

Sasha (Star x Rosie; Selection EM1159)

Cupid (Complex pedigree includes Marmolada, Kent, Providence and Linn; Selection EM1395)

Fenella (Lucy x EM0972; Selection EM1308)

Finesse (Rosie x Marmolada) x Everest; Selection EMR346)

Sweetheart (Rosie x Marmolada; Selection EM1148)

Vibrant (Complex pedigree includes Marmolada and Rosie; Selection EM1119)

Sunberry (*Rubus* hybrid berry; *Rubus ursinus* x soft tetraploid mutant of Malling Jewel (4x) self No. 2143/9.

Genus *Rosa* L.

Genus *Rosa* is found throughout the colder and temperate regions of Northern hemisphere form the Arctic to the subtropics with more than 100 species. Modern cultivars are mostly interspecific hybrids derived from only 10 species; *R. canina*, *R. chinensis*, *R. foetida*, *R. gallica*, *R. gigantea*, *R. moschata*, *R. multiflora*, *R. phoenicea, R. rugosa* and *R. wichuriana.* The multiflora rose *(R. multiflora*) is considered a noxious weed.

Rose
(***Rosa indica*** L.)

The rose, admired since antiquity for its beauty and fragrance is used for cut flowers, perfume oil (attar), culinary rose water and Vitamin C-rich hips (fruits) and as a landscape plant.

Genus *Rubus* L. (2n = 14 and multiples, recorded up to 2n = 98)

The plants are shrubs having determinate flowering shoots developing on indeterminate woody stems of one or more years age, usually climbing, straggling or creeping, rarely erect. Only few species are herbaceous and perennial. Twigs and other parts are nearly always have prickles. Leaves are pinnately, palmatey or pedately compound or simple. When simple, these are usually lobed. Stipules, on the base of the petiole or at the junction of twig and petiole are free, persistent or fugacious, rarely absent. The plants are dioecious. Inflorescences are terminal, determinate, elaborately branched or little unbranched and in axillary bundles, rarely strongly reduced. The flowers are (sub)solitary, usually 5-merous, mostly bisexual and rarely unisexual. Hypanthium is saucer to cup-shaped. Epicalyx is absent. Sepals are imbricate, often unequal and exposed margins are often lobed.

The colour of petals may be white, cream, pink, purplish or red and in few species partly or entirely absent. Stamens are many, rarely few. Disk is absent. Pistils are many, rarely few, free borne on a mostly elevated torus; stylodia is (sub) terminal, stigmas are capitate or bifid, ovules are 2, inserted almost at same height but situated one above the other usually only the lower one developing, descendent and epitropous. Fruits are drupes having black, red, yellow, orange or white exocarp, juicy or fleshy mesocarp and hard endocarp, drupelets cohering and falling as a collective fruit without or together with the dry torus, rarely separating individually. Seed is within the testa and endosperm is scarce.

There are three large subgenera; *Rubus, Malachobatus* (Focke) Focke and *Idaeobatus* (Focke) Focke. Several monotypic to species-poor subgenera have also been recognized, e.g. *Anoplobatus* Focke, *Charnaebatus* Focke, *Chamae-morus* Focke, *Cylactis* (Raf.) Focke and *Dalibarda* (L.) Focke.

Apart from several thousands of 'micro-species' in subg. *Rubus*, there are possibly about 250 species having almost cosmopolitan distribution in temperate region. Several species have been introduced to places outside their natural habitat, some of which are completely naturalized and some became noxious weeds. Originally found in natural open habitats, these also occur in forest and in many anthropogenic types of vegetation like hedges, shrubberies, etc.

Table 23.2. Cultivated *Rubus* species and hybrids

Subgenus	Ancestors of cultivated species and hybrids	Source of new germplasm
Idaeobatus (raspberries)	*R. idaeus* subsp. *vulgatus* Arrhen	*R. biflorus* Buch.-Ham.
	R. idaeus subsp. *strigosus* Michx	*R. cockburnianus* Hemsl.
	R. occidentalis L.	*R. crataegifolius* Bunge
	**R. glaucus* Benth.	*R. coreanus* Miq., *R. kuntzeanus* Hemsl., *R. leucodermis* Dougl., *R. parvifolius* Hemsl., *R. phoenicolasius* Max., *R. pileatus* Focke, *R. sachalinensis* Leveille, *R. spectabilis* Pursch., *R. vulgatus buschii* Rosanova
Eubatus (blackberries)		
European *Moriferi***	*R. bartoni* Newton, *R. laciniatus* Willd., *R. nitidioides* Wats., *R. procerus* Muell., *R. rusticanus* var. *inermis* Merc., *R. thyrsiger* Ban. & Focke	
North American *Moriferi*	*R. allegheniensis* Porter, *R. argutus* Link, *R. baileyanus* Britt, *R. frondosus* Bigel, *R. rubrisetus* Rydb., *R. setosus* Bigel., *R. trivalis* L.	
North American *Ursini*	****R. ursinus* Cham. & Schlecht	

Cylactis (Arctic raspberries)	*R. arcticus* L. *R. stellatus* Sm.	*R. acaulis* Michx.
Anoplobatus (flowering raspberries)	-	*R. odoratus* L. *R. parviflorus* Nutt.
Orobatus (hybrid fruits)	-	****R. macrocarpus* Benth.
	***Loganberry (*R. vitifolius* x *R. idaeus*), ***Tayberry (*R. vitifolius* x *R. idaeus*), ***Youngberry (*R. vitifolius* x *R. idaeus*) x *R. baileyanus* Bedford Giant (*R. rusticanus* x *R. idaeus*) selfed, Boysenberry (origin unknown, probably similar to youngberry)	

* *R. glaucus* is probably a natural hybrid of *R. occidentalis* and *R. bogotensis* O. Ktze.
Species of the European *Moriferi* are sometimes denoted as the aggregate species *R. fruitcosus* L. agg.,**R. ursinus, R. macropetalus* and *R. vitifolius* are probably ecospecies of a single large species

Subgenus *Rubus* is taxonomically the most problematic. It comprises a group, variously called *Eubatus*, the *Moriferi* or the '*Rubus fruticosus/caesius* complex', that consists of sexually reproducing, self sterile, diploid species and a larger number of facultatively apomictic diploids of hybrid origin (Table 23.2). The complex is represented in Europe and North America and it has been studied most extensively in Europe where 2000 species have been described. Apomixis seems to be absent or very rare in the other subgenera. The fruits are edible. Blackberries, dewberries and loganberries (selections from species and crosses in subg. *Rubus*), and raspberries (cultivars of *Rubus idaeus* L. and crosses with other species in subg. *Idaeobatus*) are commercially cultivated in many places. Other species are only harvested from the wild (e.g. cloudberry, *Rubus chamaemorus* L. of subg. *Chamaemorus*) or grown on a small and often non-commercial scale (e.g. the wineberry, *Rubus phoenicolasius* Maxim. of subg. *Idaeobatus*) (Kubitzki, 2004).

Brambles
(***Rubus*** spp.) (x=7; 2n=14-84)

Bramble is a collective term for various berry fruits that are prickly shrubs or small bushes. All brambles are species of *Rubus* that includes blackberry (European and American species), raspberries (*R. ideaus*) and various hybrid combinations including upright and trailing types such as eastern dewberry (*R. trivialis*) and blackberry x raspberry crosses such as youngberry, marionberry, loganberry and layberry. Raspberries include red raspberry, black raspberry (*R. occidentalis* and *R. leucodermis*) and purple raspberry (red raspberry × black raspberry). The genus *Rubus* contains about 400 species found growing primarily in the northern hemisphere, but also in Africa, Australia, New Zealand and the Pacific Islands. The common blackberry (*Rubus* spp.) and hybrid berries are native to many parts of the world.

Blackberry

(*Rubus* spp. Focke) (x = 7; 2n = 14-84)

The blackberry is called bramble in the eastern USA and Europe but as cranberry in the western USA. The hybrids (youngberry, marionberry, olallieberry, tayberry, auroraberry, dewberry, layberry, loganberry and boysenberry) have arisen from crosses between *Rubus* species or cultivars. Production areas are Oregon, Texas, California and Washington producing about 80 per cent of the total production in USA (Westwood, 1993).

The blackberry is deciduous or evergreen, erect, climbing or prostrate shrub, occasionally herbaceous, with or without thorns and usually with short lived stems. The leaves are alternate, simple, lobed or 3-foliolate or palmately or pinnately compound with stipules fused. The flowers are perfect, rarely dioecious, white or pink, mostly in terminal or axillary umbellate racemes or panicles. The calyx and corolla are 5-parted, rarely 3-7-parted with persistent 5 calyx lobes. Stamens are numerous. Disk is ring form. Pistils are many, sometimes few, and numerous ovaries situated on a convex or obtusely conical receptacle. Styles are nearly terminal and mature carpels are usually drupelets, sometimes dry. The fruit is drupaceous and single seeded, usually grouped into an aggregate form, separating as a unit from the receptacle or is persistent.

Blackberries can be put into 2 groups based on growth habit; erect and semi-erect cultivars derived largely from *Rubus allegheniensis, R. argutus* and *R. frondosus* and trailing cultivars derived from *R. ursinus.*

Cultivars

Early: Bedford Giant Rg, Himalaya Giant Rg, Merton Early, Merton Thornless, Obsidian and Metolius.

Late: Ashton Cross, John Innes, Oregon Thornless, Smoothstem and Thornfree.

Thornless types: Black Satin, Dirksen, Hull and Thornless Evergreen.

Thorny types: Boysen, Longan, Marion, Darrow, Olallie, Cherokee, Shawnee, Tayberry, Womack and Katata.

New cultivars: Black Diamond, Black Pearl and Nightfall.

Hybrids: Kings Acre Berry, Sunberry Rg, Tayberry, Tummelberry and Veitchberry.

Boysen - (Blackberry x raspberry hybrid)

Logan - (Blackberry x raspberry hybrid)

Raspberry (2n = 14)

Raspberry is fruit of a multitude of *Rubus* species most of which belong to subgenus *Idaeobatus*. It is widely grown in temperate regions of the world. The plants are perennial having woody stems. The raspberries can be differentiated from blackberries by the type of core where the stem attaches to the berry. The raspberries are hollow in the centre whereas the blackberries always have a white core.

Red raspberry: Many of the important commercial red raspberry cultivars are hybrids between *R. idaeus* and *R. strigosus*. Some botanists consider that all the Eurasian and American red raspberries belong to a single circumboreal species *R. idaeus,* the European plants classified either as *R. idaeus* subsp. *idaeus* or *R. idaeus* var. *idaeus* and the native North American red raspberries are classified either as *R. idaeus* subsp. *strigosus* or *R. idaeus* var. *strigosus.* Now new thornless and more strongly upright cultivars that do not require staking have been developed.

Black raspberry (***Rubus occidentalis*** L.)**:** It is occasionally cultivated in USA. The berries are used both as fresh and frozen fruit as well as processed to prepare jams, preserves and other products that have distinctive rich flavour.

Purple raspberries (***Rubus* × *neglectus***)**:** These are found in wild form in places where both the American red and the black raspberries naturally grow (e.g. Vermont). These have also been produced by hybridization of red and black raspberries. Its commercial production is rare.

Blue raspberry (*R. strigosus* x *R. occidentalis*): The purple raspberry hybrid Columbian is a cultivar in Ontario, Canada.

Both the red and the black raspberry have albino-like pale yellow natural or horticultural variants due to presence of recessive genes that impede production of anthocyanin pigments. Such plants produce golden or yellow berries and despite their similar appearance retain the distinctive flavour of their respective parents. These are sometimes grown in home gardens. A number of hybrids such as loganberry, boysenberry and tayberry have been produced by crossing red raspberries with species of other subgenera.

Cultivars

Glen Ample AGM: It is a heavy bearing mid summer cultivar. The plants are vigorous, upright having spine free canes. The fruits are borne on long and upright stems making their picking easy. The berries are large and delicious.

Glen Moy AGM: This is a heavy yielding early summer cultivar. It may also produce a small crop in autumn on new canes. The spine free canes are compact. The berries are medium to large and have good flavour.

Leo AGM: This is a new summer cultivar suitable for sheltered locations. Since the stems are very long harvesting is easy. The berries are large, firm having excellent flavour.

Malling Admiral: It is a mid to late summer cultivar, gives good yield and is suitable for sheltered locations. It has vigorous tall canes. The berries are large ripening to deep red colour and have excellent flavour.

Autumn Bliss AGM: It is a popular autumn cultivar producing high yields from late summer to mid autumn. Its canes are short and sturdy. The berries are large, deep red having firm texture and excellent flavour.

Polka: This is an autumn cultivar ripening fruits 2 weeks earlier than Autumn Bliss bridging the gap between summer and autumn. It produces very high yields of well flavoured large berries.

The following raspberry cultivars were developed at East Malling Research Station, England:-

Malling Enterprise (Preussen x (Pyne's Royal x Lloyd George); Selection 33/132)

Malling Landmark (Preussen x Baumforth A; Selection 34/42)

Malling Promise [Newburgh x (Lloyd George x Pyne's Royal); Selection 51/79]

Malling Notable (Preussen x Lloyd George; Selection 32/163)

Malling [Jewel Preussen x (Pyne's Royal x Lloyd George); Selection 33/54]

Malling Exploit [Newburgh x (Lloyd George x Pyne's Royal); Selection 51/84]

Malling Orion (Complex parentage includes Lloyd George, Preussen, Pyne's Royal, Burnetholm and Baumforth A); Selection 540/3)

Malling Admiral (Complex parentage includes Burnetholm, Preussen, Norfolk Giant and Malling Promise); Selection 870/81)

Malling Delight (Complex parentage includes Burnetholm, Preussen, Lloyd George, Baumforth A, Pyne's Royal and Malling Promise; Selection 1287/39)

Leo (Complex parentage includes M. Landmark, Lloyd George, Pyne's Royal, Norfolk Giant, Burnetholm and Cumberland (*Rubus occidentalis*); Selection 1312/19)

Augusta (Complex parentage includes Burnetholm Preussen, Pyne's Royal, Lloyd George, Newburgh and Joy; Selection 3650/6)

Autumn Cascade (Complex parentage includes Lloyd George, Zeva Herbsternte, *Rubus arcticus, R. idaeus strigosus, R. occidentalis* and *R. odoratus*; Selection 4395/65)

Gaia (Complex parentage includes Burnetholm, Lloyd George, Norfolk Giant, Malling Landmark, Pyne's Royal, Preussen, Reid's Seedling, Latham, Newburgh, Canby and *R. occidentalis*; Selection 3655/48)

Julia (Complex parentage includes Burnetholm, Devon, Lloyd George, Malling Jewel, Malling Landmark, Malling Promise, Norfolk Giant, Preussen, Pyne's Royal, Chief, Newburgh, Viking and *R. occidentalis*; Selection 4301/8)

Autumn Britten (Complex parentage; sib of Autumn Bliss; Selection 3676/6)

Autumn Cygnet (Complex parentage; sib of Autumn Cascade; Selection 4395/75)

Autumn Byrd (Autumn Bliss x EM5326/1 (Complex parentage; BC_3 *R. spectabilis* plus*arcticus, odoratus, idaeus strigosus, occidentalis* and *crataegifolius* ancestors; Selection 5961/24)

Autumn Bliss (Complex parentage includes Lloyd George, *Rubus arcticus, R. occidentalis* and *R. idaeus strigosus* 3676/78)

Joy (Complex parentage includes M. Promise, M. Landmark, Burnetholm, Pyne's Royal, Lloyd George, Norfolk Giant and Cumberland; Selection 2476/123)

Octavia (Complex pedigree Glen Ample x EM5928/114; Selection 6512/50)

Valentina (Complex pedigree EM6225/11 x EM5588/81; Selection 6432/71)

Malling Minerva (Complex parentage includes M. Promise, *R. crataegifolius*, *R. occidentalis*, *R. idaeus strigosus* and SCRI 69/67; Selection 6166/98)

Malling Juno (Complex parentage includes M. Promise, M. Delight, Glen Moy, *R. crataegifolius* and *R. spectabilis*; Selection 6544/80)

Autumn Treasure (Complex parentage includes Glen Moy, Autumn Cascade and *R. spectabilis*; Selection 6597/46)

Subfamily Maloideae (Pomoidae; pome fruits**)**

This subfamily includes important edible temperate fruit species known collectively as pome fruits. The basic haploid chromosome number of all *Maloideae* genera is 17. This group probably originated by spontaneous doubling in a sterile hybrid between primitive Prunoideae (x = 8) and Spiraeoideae (x = 9), resulting in allopolyploids that function as normal sexual diploids. Some species (e.g. apple), however, are polyploids; 3x, 4x, 5x and so forth, most of which are apomictic.

It contains 20 genera of mostly temperate zone fruit trees and shrubs. The plants are deciduous or evergreen trees or shrubs. The leaves are alternate, simple or pinnate and stipulate. The stipules are small and often caducous. Flowers are either solitary or in umbels, achenes, cymes, panicles or corymbs, often mixed. The flowers are regular and perfect. Receptacle is urn-shaped on which flower parts are inserted. The (2-5) carpels are usually 2-ovulated, more or less united and adnate to the cup shaped calyx tube, forming an inferior ovary. The styles are 1-5, free or partly united. The fruit is a fleshy pome. The fleshy part is nonovarian calyx and receptacle tissue and thus at times the fruit may be produced without fertilization.

The most important genera of this group are *Malus* (apple), *Pyrus* (pear), *Cydonia* (quince) and *Eriobotrya* (loquat). The two closely related genera, *Cydonia* and *Chaenomeles* are referred as quinces. Other genera although of minor importance for their fruit but having possible use as rootstock are *Chaenomeles* (Asian flowering quinces, Chinese quince), *Mespilus* (medlar), *Crataegus* (hawthorn), Sorbus (mountain ash) and *Amelanchier* (service berry). The degree of graft compatibility among these and other genera is such that some are being developed as specialized stocks having desirable traits such as dwarfing, tolerance to adverse soil conditions and resistance to diseases or insect pests.

Key to the classification of tribe Pomeae

A. Margins of leaves entire

Flowers 2.5 to 5.0 cm across, solitary, styles basally pubescent; fruit carpels with leathery or papery walls; no nutlets present .... *Cydonia*

AA. Margins of leaves toothed, lobed or dissected

B. Leaves are evergreen, if deciduous pedicels are conspicuously warty. Inflorescence is a panicle.

Flowers are on a fawny downy pedicel, 1.25 to 0.625 cm long.................................. *Eriobotrya*

BB. Leaves are deciduous. Pedicels are never warty. Flowers are solitary, fascicled, racemose or umbellate. Inflorescence is not a raceme. Ovary cells are mostly 5, each 2-ovuled. Carpels have leathery or papery walls. Trees are 18-21 m high. Trunk up to 60 cm in diameter.

C. Styles usually separate; fruit with grit cells forming a ring beneath the epidermis. Leaves are involute in the bud. .... *Pyrus*

Good quality fruits. Susceptible to fire blight. .... French pear

was called *P. communis*. Includes *P. pashia* (kainth) and *P. khasiana* of Kumaon and Himalayan hills

Good quality fruits. Previously erroneously called *P. sinensis*...................................Oriental pear
P. pyrifolia, P. pyrifolia var. *culta, P. bretschneideri*

CC. Style usually connate at the base; fruit without grit cells. The leaves are revolute or plicate in the bud. ....*Malus*

Genus *Cydonia* Mill. (x=17, 2n= 34)

It has one species, *C. oblonga* Mill., probably indigenous in the mountain areas of Caucasus and Kurdistan, but is naturalized and cultivated since long in many places as a fruit tree (Kubitzki, 2004). The plant is small, unarmed, leaf shedding woody shrub or tree having small pubescent buds with few scales. Leaves are alternate, simple, penninerved, entire with large, long persistent stipules on junction of twig and petiole. Flowers are showy, bisexual, borne solitary terminally on leafy shoots. The flower has narrowly campanulate hypanthium with upper free part lined with a nectar, 5 reflexed, imbricate, glandular dentate and persistent sepals, 5 white or pink obovate petals, 15-25 stamens, 5 carpels, dorsally adnate to the hypanthium and laterally and ventrally free from each other. Ovary is inferior, 5-celled with a central cavity, free stylodia, oblique stigmas and many ovules in 2 rows and horizontal, pleurotropous horizon. Fruit is large pome with hypanthial and carpellary flesh (mesocarp) with sclereids and not woody coriaceous core (endocarp). Seeds are several in each cell with firm testa and thin layer of endosperm.

Quince
(*Cydonia oblonga* Mill.) x = 17; 2n = 34

The quince is a native of west Asian region from Iran to Turkestan. It has medium cold requirement and high resistance to heat and thus can be grown at lower elevations than that required for apple and pear. The trees are deciduous, spreading, densely branched and thornless growing 5-6 m in height. The leaves are thick, alternate, elliptical to ovate, 6-10 cm long, stipulate with almost rounded apex and an entire margin, more or less woolly beneath and with glandular hairy stipules. Unlike in most of the deciduous fruits, the fruit buds develop at the terminal ends of new shoots produced in the spring of the current year. The fruit buds are mixed and terminal. The flowers are solitary and pure white or slightly pink. The sepals are leaf-like, usually large and pinkish. The petals are 2-3 cm in size with 20 stamens, one pistil and inferior, 5-celled and many ovuled ovary. Placentation is axile. The fruit is subglobose or oblate with rounded ridges and pubescent on very short stems. The fruit is usually pear shaped, 6-10 cm long, very fragrant with numerous seeds in 2 rows in each of its five locules (Westwood, 1993). The seeds are mucilaginous.

Quince is principally used for processing into preserve. Fruits of most cultivars are too astringent to consume fresh. There are non-astringent types grown in Iran, India, Afghanistan, and Central Asia. Quince is used as a dwarfing rootstock for pear and loquat. Intergeneric hybrids of quince and pear occur.

Cultivars

Bereczki: It is a heavy cropper with large, fine flavoured pear shaped fruits and is sometimes listed as Vranja, which is an almost identical cultivar.

Meech's Prolific: The cultivar has very large flowers and starts to crop at an early age bearing pear shaped and medium sized fruits.

Champion: The cultivar bears large, apple shaped fruits with golden yellow flesh. It gave the highest yield followed by Geant de Vranja and Bourgeault in a trial in France.

Orange: In North America, the cultivar is outstanding for its earliness, quality and colour followed by Champion, Fuller, Meech and Smyrna.

Lusitanica (Portuguese quince): It is a very vigorous and floriferous cultivar but is less hardy.

Maliformis: The fruits of this cultivar are apple shaped.

The other important cultivars are Pineapple, Mammoth and Van Deman (Morley-Bunker, 1986b; Westwood, 1993).

The following rootstock cultivars were developed at East Malling Research Station, England:-

Quince A, B, and C: Rootstocks for pear.

EMH: Selection QR 193-16 from open pollinated C51.

Genus *Chaenomeles* L.

The plants grow in temperate regions and belong to 3 species.

Japanese quince
(***Chaenomeles japonica*** (Thunb.) Lindl. and Spach.)

Japanese quince is grown in the Baltic countries. It is a shrubby plant with attractive red flowers and aromatic hard fruits that resemble loquat in appearance. It is popular as an ornamental landscape plant. Chinese quinces (*C. speciosa* (Sweet) Nak.) is also grown for making jellies and sauces.

Mespilus **L.** (2n = 34)

It is native of Asia Minor. Its true homeland is in the southeastern part of the Balkan Peninsula in Asia Minor on the Caucasus Crimes, northern Iran and possibly in Turkemenia (Baird and Thieret, 1989). It was a popular fruit in central Europe during the Roman period. It is hardier than the quince and is able to naturalize in cold climates.

It is distributed from southeast Europe to Iran and is now widely cultivated. The plants are trees or shrubs with thorns (in the wild) or unarmed (mostly in cultivation) and are leaf shedding. Wood is very tough. Leaf margins are serrate having caducous stipules. Flowers are solitary, large, borne terminally on short and young shoots. There is a whorl of dark green leaves behind each flower. Hypanthium is obconical. Sepals are large and persistent. Petals are white. Stamens are 30-40 on the rim of a disk covering the free part of the hypanthium. Carpels are (4)5, completely connate and adnate to hypanthium, forming an inferior, 5-celled ovary with hairy apex. Stylodia are free to halfway connate. Ovules are 2(3) per cell, only the basal one is fertile. Fruit is brownish having mealy flesh with many sclereids and thick and hard stones with woody wall. Seed (1) has thin but firm testa. The fruit becomes edible when overripe (Kubitzki, 2004). It is a monotypic genus. It has one species, *M. germanica* L. Three botanical varieties are *M. germanica* var. *gigantea* Kirk. syn. *M. germanica* var. *macrocorpa* Hort., *M. germanica* var. *diffusa* Ait. (Dutch medlar) having large fruits; *M. germanica* var. *microcarpa* syn. *M. germanica* var. *stricta* Ait. (Nottingham type) having medium sized fruits, and *M. germanica* var. *abortiva* Kirk. syn. *M. germanica* var. *apyrena* Hort. (Neftier Sans Noyeau) having seedless fruits. Three botanical varieties are *M. germanica* var. *gigantea* Kirk. syn. *M. germanica* var. *macrocarpa* Hort., *M. germanica* var. *diffusa* Ait. (Dutch medlar) having large fruits; *M. germanica* var. *microcarpa* syn. *M. germanica* var. *stricta* Ait. (Nottingham type) having medium-sized fruits, and *M. germanica* var. *abortiva* Kirk. syn. *M. germanica* var. *apyrena* Hort. (Neflier Sans Noyeau) having seedless fruits.

Medlar
(***Mespilus germanica*** L.)

Medlar is a hardy and spreading pretty tree of medium size. Its wild form has thorns but the cultivated one is thornless. The leaves are oval ovate, 5-10 cm long and dark green in colour turning tan bronze and purple during the autumn. The flowers are 3 cm in size and white but later turn pinkish and are borne at the tip of short and young shoots. Flowers are pentamerous having 5 white or slightly pink petals, 30-40 stamens, an inferior 5-carpelled and 5-locular ovary (Morley-Bunker,

1986a; Baird and Thieret, 1989). The fruits look like small brown pears with very long sepals left over from the vanished flower. The fruit is remarkable by the 5 seed vessels visible in the eye (receptacle) of the fruit and by the 5 conspicuous calyx lobes around it. The seeds are stone-like because of hardening of the endocarp (Baird and Thieret, 1989). The fruits of medlar must be consumed only after these have undergone the fermentation process called bletting which softens them and develops a spicy flavour.

Cultivars

Nottingham: The cultivar has upright trees. It bears small, richly flavoured and russet brown fruits.

Dutch, Royal, Monstrous: These cultivars have spreading trees and bear large, russet brown fruits.

Genus *Sorbus*

There are about 80 *Sorbus* species in North America, Europe and Asia. These are widely used as ornamentals or as windbreaks. Most species have bitter fruits, but some are sweet and could be developed as new fruits. Intergeneric hybrids between *Sorbus* with *Amelanchier* and *Pyrus* are also available.

Mountain ash or rowan berries
(*Sorbus aucuparia* L.)

It is found in Himalayas. The pear-shaped small fruits turn reddish and are eaten when overripe. Related species is *S. domestica* (service tree).

Genus *Eriobotrya* Lindl. (2n = 34)

The plants are unarmed and evergreen trees or shrubs. Leaves are simple, penninerved having free stipules, rarely intrapetiolarly connate. Inflorescence is a compound raceme. Hypanthium is obconoid open at top. Sepals are persistent, petals are white, stamens are 15-20(-40) and 2-5 carpels are ventrally and laterally connate in upper part and ventrally free, dorsally adnate to the hypanthium and the exposed hairy apex. Stylodia are usually connate at the hairy base and stigmas are capitate. Flesh is pome yellow, orange or red, mostly of hypanthial origin with or without sclereids and thin membranous endocarp. Large 1-3 seeds have thin but firm testa. Endosperm is absent and cotyledons are thick. About 15-20 species are distributed from the Himalayas throughout the continental South East Asia to Japan and the islands of western Malesia. The plants are montane or occur in tropical lowland forest.

Loquat
(*Eriobotrya japonica* (Thunb.) Lindl.)

The loquat is native to China. It is widely cultivated in China (Kubitzki, 2004). Besides China, its major producer is Spain. It is a large evergreen shrub or small tree with a rounded crown, short trunk and woolly new twigs. The leaves are alternate, simple, 10–25 cm long, dark green, tough and leathery in texture with a serrated margin and densely velvety hairy below with thick yellow brown pubescence. The flowers are 2 cm in diameter, white with 5 petals, produced on stiff panicles of 3-10 flowers. The flowers have a sweet aroma that can be felt from a distance. The fruits growing in clusters are oval, rounded or pear-shaped, 3–5 cm long with a smooth or downy, yellow or orange, sometimes red-blushed skin. The succulent, tangy flesh is white, yellow or orange and sweet to subacid. Each fruit contains from one to ten ovules commonly with 3-5 seeds.

Cultivars

The cultivars can be classified on the following bases:-

1. Origin
   - i. Chinese: Fruit is pyriform, large and deep orange in colour.
   - ii. Japanese: Fruit is rounded, small and yellow in colour.
2. Flesh colour
   - i. Orange: Big Jim, Gold Nugget, Mogi, Mrs. Cooksey, Strawberry, Tanaka and Wolfe.
   - ii. White: Advance, Benlehr, Champagne, Herd's Mammoth, Victory and Visa White.
3. Fruit ripening season
   - i. Early: Golden Yellow, Improved Golden Yellow, Large Round, Pale Yellow and Thames Pride.
   - ii. Mid season: Fire Ball , Improved Pale Yellow, Large Round, Agra Mammoth, and Matchless.
   - iii. Late: California Advance and Tanaka.

Golden Yellow: Plants are typically tall, upright to spreading and compact with roundish oval crown. The leaves are typically large, lanceolate with few sharp teeth, dark green above and densely pubescent below. The fruit is oval to oblong and of medium size. Calyx is persistent and pubescence is thin velvety and golden yellow. The pulp is pale yellow to orange, soft, subacidic in taste and with mild flavour and few black and smooth seeds.

Pale Yellow: The cultivar is grown in India. It is an early ripening cultivar. The tree is fairly tall. Fruit is oblique elliptic to round, light yellow, large having white or cream coloured, thin, smooth, melting flesh with subacid to sweet flavour. Each fruit on an average has 5 large seeds.

Improved Golden Yellow: The tree and fruit characters resemble those of Golden Yellow except that the crown is more open, the fruit is oval to pyriform and more seedy and the pulp is thick.

Large Round: The tree is vigorous and spreading, branches are wide crotched and the crown is compact and uneven. The leaves are dark green on upper surface, pubescent below and more so along the veins and the midrib, lanceolate elliptic in shape and with serrated margin at base and dented at the top. Fruit is of medium size, ovate globose in form and yellow in colour. The flesh is thin, firm and somewhat coarse and creamy whitish near the seed.

Safeda: Tree growth is vigorous and upright with medium to tall stature and rounded top. The leaves are typically elliptic lanceolate having pubescence and serrated margin. It is an early to mid season cultivar. The fruit is large, oblong pyriform with pubescent surface and pale yellow colour. The flesh is creamy white, whitish near the seed, smooth, tender, acidic and juicy with excellent taste melting rapidly and having few to medium number of seeds.

Thames Pride: The plants are tall, fast growing and upright with round or dome-shaped top. The leaves are elliptic lanceolate with dentate margin and dense pubescence at apex. Maturity is early in the season. The fruit is pyriform, medium sized and deep yellow having velvety surface. The pulp is pale orange, somewhat coarse and medium thick having sub-acid taste and mild flavour. The fruits are canned commercially. The seeds are moderate in number.

Tanaka: The tree is dwarf having medium and upright growth and compact and semi-rounded crown. The leaves are elliptic lanceolate. The fruit is small, ovate and orange in colour. The pulp is medium thick, yellow, firm, subacidic in taste and moderately seedy.

Centenaria: The cultivar evolved from a cross between Mizuho and Mogui. The trees are vigorous and produce regularly and consistently. The leaves are oblanceolate, dark green and densely pubescent. The fruit is large, yellow orange and attractive. The flesh is yellow and firm having pleasant subacid taste and 5-6 medium sized seeds.

California Advance: The tree growth is moderate, upright and dwarf having more open and round crown. The leaves are oblanceolate with dentate margin. The fruit is oblong pyriform, medium in size and with pale yellow surface. The pulp is yellow, firm and thick having acidic and pleasant taste.

Bessell Brown: The cultivar is from Australia. The fruits are large having acceptable taste and high flesh/seed ratio.

Enormity: The fruits are large having acceptable taste.

Victory: The cultivar is from Brazil. The fruits have white to cream coloured flesh and are juicy and sweet.

Nectar de Cristal: The cultivar developed by open pollination of Togoshi gives high yield of uniform fruits.

Parmogi: The cultivar is from Japan developed by open pollination of Mogi. It gives high yield and the fruits have pleasant taste.

Mendes da Fonseu: The fruits are large.

Precoce de Itaquer: The cultivar selected from Japanese seedlings is very productive.

82-6-26: The cultivar is from Zhejiang Jiangsu, China. It was selected from Jiefangzhong x Baozhu. The cultivar has cold resistance and has large fruits of good eating quality.

Baiyu: It is from Jiangsu, China. It was selected from Baisha seedlings. It bears large uniform fruits with yellowish white flesh and good taste and keeping quality.

Changhong No. 3: The cultivar is from Fujian, China. It was selected from natural hybrid seedlings of Changhong. The fruits are elongate obovate each weighing 50 g. The fruits ripen in mid April giving high and stable yield.

Dahongpao: It is an old seedling cultivar from Zhejiang, China. The trees have strong growth and vigour giving stable fruit yield.

Duhe: The cultivar was introduced from from Jiangxi, China. It gives high yield. The fruit has single seed and medium eating quality.

Guangrong: The cultivar is from Anhui, China. It was selected from seedling of Dahongpao. The trees have vigorous growth and give stable yield of quite large fruits having good keeping quality.

Huaboa No. 2: The cultivar is from Hubei, China. It was selected from Baisha. It has cold resistance, gives stable yield of fruits of good quality.

Jiefangzhong: The cultivar is from Fujian, China. Dazhong. It is a seedling selection. The fruit weighs 70 g with some fruits as large as 172 g.

Luoyangqing: The cultivar is from Zhejiang, China. It was selected from Dahongpao. It has disease resistance and gives high and stable fruit yield having good keeping quality.

Yuaniiang: The cultivar is from Hunang, China. It is an old seedling selection giving fruits with strong flavour and good eating quality.

Zhaozhong No. 6 (Jiefangzhong x Morlowase): The cultivar is from Fujian, China. The fruits ripen in the beginning of April. These are attractive and of good quality.

Zhaozhong: The cultivar is from Jiangsu, China. It was selected from seedlings of Baisha (white peel). The fruits have yellowish white flesh and are juicy having good eating quality.

Golden Ziad: The cultivar is from Egypt. It was selected from seedlings of Premier. It gives high yield early in the season.

Moamora Golden Yellow: The cultivar is from Egypt. It was selected from seedlings of Premier and gives high yield.

Akko 13: The cultivar is from Israel having Japanese origin. The fruits mature early (March) and are juicy, of agreeable flavour having good keeping quality. It requires cross pollination.

Tsrifin: The cultivar is from Israel. It bears regularly and abundantly giving excellent quality fruits that store well.

Nespola di Ferdinando: The cultivar is from Italy.

Nespola di Francesco: The cultivar is from Italy.

Nespolo di Palarm: The cultivar is from Italy giving fruits having superior flavour.

Mogi: The cultivar is from Kyushu, Japan. It is a chance seedling introduced from China. It is prone to cold damage. The fruits ripen in May. The fruit weighs 50-60 g and is of excellent quality.

Tanaka Shikoku: The cultivar is from Honshu, Japan. The fruits ripen in May. The fruit weighs 60-76 g and has good keeping quality.

Nakasakiwase (Mogi x Hondawase): The cultivar is from Kyushu, Japan. It is prone to cold damage. It is very early ripening cultivar giving excellent quality fruits.

Obusa (Tanaka x Kushioki): The cultivar is from Kyushu, Japan. Fruit weighs 70 g and has good keeping quality. The cultivar is resistant to insect pests and diseases.

Algerie: The cultivar is from Alicante, Spain. It accounts for 95% of the total production.

Golden Nugget: The cultivar is from Andalusia, Spain. It is a clone of Tanaka obtained from California. It accounts for 80% of total production in this region. The fruits have good keeping and shipping quality.

Hatif Cukurgobek: The cultivar is from Turkey. The fruit is sweet, juicy and has pleasant flavour.

Advance: The cultivar is from California, USA. It is a seedling selection and is a good pollinizer.

Champagne: The cultivar is from California, USA. The fruits are juicy, excellent in flavour and have good keeping quality.

Fletcher: The cultivar of unknown parentage is from Florida, USA. The fruits have good keeping quality and flavour.

MacBeth: The cultivar is from California, USA. It is a chance seedling. The flavour of fruit is pleasing having low acidity and small seed.

Oliver: The cultivar is from Florida, USA. It is a Tanaka hybrid.

Wolfe: The cultivar is from Florida, USA. The fruit has pale yellow flesh, excellent flavour and resists bruising.

Genus *Pyrus* L. (x=17; 2n=34, rarely 51, 68, and aneuploid numbers)

The plants are deciduous, rarely evergreen, trees or shrubs having leaf shedding sometimes thorny growing 18-21 m in height. The trunk is up to 60 cm in diameter. The leaves are simple, serrate or crenate, entire, rarely lobed, involute in bud, petiolate and stipulate having caducous stipules. The buds are with imbricate scales. Inflorescence is a simple raceme, corymb shaped with few flowers emerging with or before the leaves. These are white, rarely pink having reflexed or spreading, persistent or caducous sepals, clawed and orbicular to broad oblong, white, rarely pinkish petals, 15-30 stamens, red or purple anthers, 2-5 free styles, closed and constricted at the base by disk and 2 ovules per locule having cartilaginous walls. Hypanthium is urceolate having free upper part with a cushion like outgrowth (disc) covering the top of the carpels, leaving a central hole for the stylodia, ±persistent. Carpels are 2-5, dorsally adnate to hypanthium, often free from each other laterally and ventrally at least in the apical part. The ventral sutures are open, stylodia are free and stigmas are truncate to 2-partite. The fruit is a globose or pyriform and persistent or deciduous pome usually having flesh with grit cells brownish to yellow, sometimes lenticellate, and flesh containing many sclerides, which are sometimes compacted to a woody layer. Core (endocarp) is membranous to cartilaginous. The seeds are black or nearly so having thin testa and a very thin endosperm (Kubitzki, 2004).

Between 10 and 20 species occur in Eurasia, North African woods, thickets and hedges and on sunny slopes. Three *Pyrus* species, *P. communis* L. (European pear), *P. pyrifolia* (Burm. f.) Nakai (Japanese pear or Nashi), and *P. ussuriensis* Maxim (Chinese pear) are economically important. Japanese and Korean cultivars are complex hybrids of *P. pyrifolia* and *P. ussuriensis* Maxim. Pear cider called Perry is usually made from the fruits of the cultivars of *P. nivalis*. Pear is considered a sign of good luck in Asia. The popular ornamental pear, Callery pear, is selection from *P. calleryana*. *P. koehnii* is an evergreen species native to Taiwan.

Distribution of *Pyrus* species (adapted from Westwood, 1982; Wiersema, 1985; Zeven and Zhukovsky, 1975).

A. European

1. *P. communis* L.: Native to Eurasia. Distributed in west to southeast Europe, Turkey.

The synonyms are *P. asiae-mediae* Popov, *P. balansae* Decne., *A boissieriana* Buhse, *P. elata* Rubtzov and *P. medvedevii* Rubtzov distributed in Central Asia, Turkey, northern Iran, former USSR and Caucasus.

The other species distributed in southcentral Asia, Afghanistan, southeast Europe, Greece, Turkey, western, central and southern Europe, southeast England, western France, Spain and Portugal are :

2. *P. korshinskyi* Litv. syn. *P. pyraster* Burgsd
3. *P caucasia* Fed. syn. *P. communis* L. (?)
4. *P. nivalis* Jacq.
5. *P. cordata* Desv

B. Circum-Mediterranean

6. *P. amygdaliformis* Vill. syn. *P. sinaica* Dom-Cours., distributed in Mediterranean Europe and Asia Minor.
7. *P. elaeagrifolia* Pall. syn. *P. kotschyana* Boiss. ex Decne, distributed in southeast Europe, Russia and Turkey.
8. *P. syriaca* Boiss., distributed in Tunisia.
9. *P. longipes* Coss. & Dur. syn. *P. cossonii* Rehd., distributed in Algeria.
10. *P. gharbiana* Trab., distributed in Morocco and western Algeria.
11. *P. mamorensis* Trab., distributed in Morocco.
12. *P. syriaca* Boiss.
13. *P. longipes* Coss and Dur. syn. *P. cossonni* Rehd.

C. Mid-Asian

14. *P. glabra* Boiss., distributed in Iran.
15. *P. salicifolia* Pall., distributed in northwest Iran, northeast Turkey and southern Russia.
16. *P. regelii* Rehd., *P. heterophylla* Regal & Schmath, distributed in southcentral Asia (Afghanistan).
17. *P. pashia* D. Don syn. *P. kumaoni* Decne. *P. variolosa* Wall ex G. Don, *P. wilbelmii C.* Schneid., distributed in Pakistan, India, Nepal.

D. East Asian

18. *P. pyrifolia* (Burm.) Nak. syn. *P. serotina* Rehd., distributed in China, Japan, Korea, Taiwan.
19. *P. pseudopashia* Yu syn. *P. kanseunsis,* distributed in northwest China (Yunnan, Kweichov).
20. *P. ussuriensis* Maxim. syn. *P. lindleyi* Rehd., *P. ovoidea* Rehd., *P. sinensis* Lindley, distributed in Siberia, Manchuria, northern China and Korea.
21. *P. calleryana* Decne, distributed in central and south China, Vietnam.
22. *P. betulifolia* Bunge, distributed in central and northern China, southern Manchuria.
23. *P. fauriei* Schneid., distributed in Korea.
24. *P. hondoensis* Nakai & Kikuchi, distributed in Japan.
25. *P. dimorphophylla* Mak., distributed in Japan.
26. *P. kawakamii* Hayata *syn. P. koehnei* Schneid., distributed in Taiwan, southeast China.

The *Pyrus* species can be divided into 2 groups, fruits with persistent calyx (*P. canmunis, P. nivalis* and *P. ussuriensis*) and fruits with totally or partially abscissing calyx (*P. calleryana, P. pashia, P. pyrifolia* and *P. betulifolia*).

Distribution of interspecific and artificial hybrids in *Pyrus* (Bell *et al.*, 1996)

A. Naturally occurring interspecific hybrids species

P. × *bretschneideri* Rehder (*P. ussuriensis* × *P. betulifolia*) and *P.* × *phaeocarpa* Rehder (*P. betulifolia* × *P. ussuriensis*) in northern China; *P.* × *serrulata* Rehder (*P. pyrifolia* × *P. calleryana*) in central China; *P.* × *complexa* Rubtzov in Caucasus; *P.* × *salvifolia* DC (*P. communis* × *P. nivalis*) in Europe and Crimea; and *P.* × *canescens* Sprach (*P. nivalis* × *P. salicifolia*).

B. Artificial hybrids (probable *Arbotea*)

P. × *lecontei* Rehder (*P. communis* × *P. pyrifolia*); *P.* × *michauxii* Bosc ex Poiret (*P. amygdaliformis* × *P. nivalis*); and *P.* × *uyematsuana* Makino (*P. dimorphophylla* × *P. hondoensis*) in Korea.

European pear
(***Pyrus communis*** L. syn. ***P. domestica*** (L.) Ehrh.; French pear)

These are natives of eastern Europe and southwestern Asia including south Afghanistan, Transcaucasia and Asia Minor. The trees are vigorous having upright branches, sometimes attaining a height of 25 m and a girth of 5 m. The trees are resistant to heat and have medium cold requirement. The trunk is long and slender. The bark is checked in squares, has dots and does not curl along the ends while shedding. The wood is glabrous, light coloured and dotted. The leaves appear on short spurs as well as on the axial growths. The pedicel and sometimes the young growth are pubescent, but all parts become glabrous when mature. The leaves are mostly oblong, ovate, bright green and glossy above, stipulate, deciduous, serrated and glabrous. The serratures are small and much appressed and obtuse. The buds are large pointed. The fruit buds are mixed. Flowers appearing with the leaves are white, 2-4 and borne in umbel-like clusters on slender (5-7.5 cm) pedicels and have persistent or rarely deciduous calyx and 15-20 stamens. The styles are free up to the base. The hypanthium is closed by a cushion-like formation. Pedicels are fleshy. Fruit is pyriform usually tapering towards the stem end. There is no cavity at the stem end. The pulp generally has gritty concretions. There are 2 seeds per carpel which are intimately fused.

Cultivars

More than 5000 cultivars are recorded although some of them are synonyms.

William's Bon Chritein (William's or Bartlett): It originated in England about 1770. It is the most important European pear for fresh markets and for processing. It is widely adapted to different climatic conditions and is early, regular and heavy copper. The fruits are large, pyriform to roundish and yellow with faint blush on the skin and have unique flavour. The flesh is juicy, sweet and of good quality (but is not as good as the best pears). The fruits are good for canning. The cultivar is susceptible to fire blight. At least three red skinned bud sports are also grown.

Max Red Bartlett: It is a bud sport of Bartlett found in Washington. The tree characters are like those of Bartlett but the shoots and young leaves are slightly reddish. The fruit ripens with that of Bartlett and is short globose having dark cranberry red skin that turns bright red purple on ripening. The flesh is fine grained, sweet, juicy, firm, crisp and white.

Beurre Bosc (Kaiser) : The cultivar was raised from seed in Belgium by van Mons in 1807. The trees are large, upright and vigorous but are very susceptible to fire blight. The original clone is mostly covered by tan russet but the new mutant clones are completely russet. The fruits ripen late and are large, very long having tapering neck and dark yellow and russetted skin. The flesh is creamy yellow, soft, sweet and juicy with aromatic flavour and is very good to excellent in quality.

Flemish Beauty: It is an old and popular mid season Belgian cultivar. The tree is vigorous, hardy, spreading and productive. The fruits are large and roundish having smooth, shiny and yellow skin blushed with red. The flesh is white, firm, tender, sweet, juicy and aromatic with slight musky flavour and very good in quality.

Beurre Anjou or Beurre d'Anjou: It is an old French cultivar which may have originated close to Angers. It is not grown on a commercial scale outside North America and Argentina. It is noted for its doliform fruit shape, bronze fruit skin with some russet, fine melting texture and long to medium storage life. There are two red skinned bud sports, Gebhard Red Anjou and Columbia Red Anjou.

Conference: It was developed by the English pomologist Rivers, named for the British National Pear Conference of 1885 and introduced in 1895. This is the major cultivar in the UK and western Europe. It is regular, good bearer and regular cropper. The fruits are long pyriform, of medium size, light green with netted russet. The fruits mature about 1-2 weeks after William's. The flesh is salmon coloured.

Doyenne du Comice: The cultivar is a seedling selection made at Comice Horticole, Angers, France in 1849. The cultivar produces turbinate fruits of exquisite flavour but has poor productivity. It is a major cultivar in western Europe and New Zealand. There is at least one red skinned bud sport. Taylor's Gold is a russeted sport from New Zealand which accounts for over 15% of that country's pear production.

Regal Red Comice: It is a bud mutant of Doyenne du Cornice. The tree characters resemble those of the parent cultivar. The fruits are completely red all over with some purple tinge over greenish yellow ground when ripe. The flesh is usually white, fine, soft and melting having excellent eating quality.

Packham's Triumph: It originated in New South Wales, Australia about 1897 from a seedling of Uvedale St Germaine and William's (Bartlett). It has low chilling requirement and is a major cultivar in the southern hemisphere countries of Australia, South Africa and South America. The flavour of the fruit is similar to that of William's as it contains some of the same volatile fatty acid esters. The fruits ripen about one month after William's and have better keeping quality.

Winter Nelis: It is a late maturing Belgian cultivar. The trees are small. The fruit is small to medium, roundish ovate and narrow near the stalk. The colour of the fruit is not attractive and is russeted with ruddy cheeks. The cultivar is regular bearer and the fruits keep well.

Abbe Fetel (Abate Fetel): It originated in France in 1866 and is a major cultivar in Italy. The fruit is pyriform in shape with yellow skin and lenticel, some russet and has a long neck and usually a red blush.

Blanquilla: It is the major cultivar in Spain but is not grown extensively elsewhere. The fruits mature with those of William's.

Doctor Jules Guyot: It originated as a chance seedling in 1870 in France. It is known as Limonera in Spain. The fruits are similar to that of William's in appearance but ripen about 3 weeks earlier and are very susceptible to core breakdown.

Coscia: It is known as Ercolini in Italy. This is the major early season cultivar in southern Europe

Rocha: It originated about 1850 and is grown commercially only in Portugal. The fruits mature during early to middle of September in Spain, about 2 weeks after William's.

Forelle: The cultivar probably originated in Germany in the early 18th century. Once popular in northern Europe, this is now the major export cultivar in South

Africa. The fruits are speckled with red spots around the lenticels and hence the name Forelle, which means 'trouf' in German.

Kristalli: It is the major cultivar in Greece but is not grown elsewhere.

Passe Crassane: It was once a major winter storage cultivar in France but has high degree of susceptibility to Fire Blight. The fruits mature 50 days after Willliam's.

Clapp's Favorite: It is a very old cultivar selected by Thaddeus Clapp in Massachusetts, USA during early to middle of 18th century. It is grown extensively throughout central and eastern Europe. The tree is large and upright and is very productive having good winter hardiness but has high degree of susceptibility to fire blight. The fruits mature early in the season, about 2 weeks before William's. The fruit is medium large with pale lemon yellow skin mottled with bright red colour and is of very good quality but has poor storage life. The flesh is yellowish, very juicy and sweet and has excellent flavour and soft melting texture with grit cells at the core. The fruits ripen late.

Easter Beurre: It is a very late cultivar and gives regular crops. The fruit has good keeping quality and is large, roundish ovate and gritty with short and stout stalk and yellowish green skin.

Jargonellae: Trees are upright with spreading branches. Fruits are obtuse, pyriform to oblong pyriform, lemon yellow over green base with faded red blush on the skin. It has mid season maturity.

Doynne du Comice: The fruit is of medium size, obtuse, pyriform and yellow with russet patches and of good quality but the bearing is not heavy.

Kashmiri nakh: Trees are medium in vigour. Fruits are small to medium in size, obovate to slightly conical in shape having light to dark green skin which turns light yellow. It has mid season maturity.

Rogue Red: It originated in New Jersey, USA from a cross between Gorham and NJ 1. It is resistant to fire blight. The tree is fairly vigourous with somewhat spreading branches. The fruit is of medium size, acute pyriform having straw yellow skin that turns red when ripe. The flesh is creamy white, almost buttery and of good quality and without astringency.

Cure: It was discovered from wild seedlings in France in 1760. It is named as Vicar of Winkfield in UK, after the curator who imported it. The trees are large, vigorous and productive but are highly susceptible to fire blight.

The following pear cultivars were developed at East Malling Research Station, England:-

Beth (Williams' Bon Chertien x Beurre Superfin; Selection EM18).

Nuvar® Anniversary (Williams x Conference; Selection P15-157).

Nuvar® Celebration (Conference x Packhams Triumph; Selection PB30-6).

Concorde (Comice x Conference Selection; P22B/14).

Nashi

(***Pyrus pyrifolia*** (N. L. Burman) Nakai syn. ***P. serotina*** Rehder; Japanese pear; Oriental pear; sand pear) (2n=2x=34)

The Nashi or Oriental pear is native of northeastern and eastern Asia including China, Japan and Manchuria. Wild groves occur in the Szechuan region and southern China. The cultivated Oriental pear originated as a result of interspecific hybridization, either from *P. pyrifolia* or *P. ussuriensis* Maxim. or *P. communis* L., followed by selection and clonal propagation. *P. pyrifolia* is the principal progenitor of the cultivars in warm areas where winters are mild. On introduction into USA in 1800, the Oriental pear crossed with the cultivars of *P. communis* (European pear) having fruits with aromatic and melting flesh and gave rise to several hybrid cultivars such as Baldwin, Kieffer, Hood and Carnes. Kieffer often occurs in tropical highlands. These were used to develop hybrids resistant to Fire Blight and better quality low chilling pears. These include Florida-Home of Florida and Seleta of Brazil (Verheij and Coronel, 1991). Thus, the gene pool of Oriental pear consists of the cultivars ranging from the common sand pears having hardy plants and inferior quality gritty fruits to the ones producing superior quality juicy and sweet fruits (Nashi) that appeal the consumers in Asia. Nashi is sometimes classified as a botanical variety *P. pyrifolia* var. *culta* (Makino) Nakai. Its cultivars have longer leaves than of the wild species. Developing improved low chilling cultivars can widen the scope of its cultivation in the highlands.

The trees are small, deciduous, erect and upright and grow 7-18 m in height. These are sometimes spiny. The trunk is long and slender. The bark and wood characters are similar to those of the French pear. Young branches are glabrous or more often wooly pubescent. Leaves are dark green, ovate oblong or seldom ovate, very large, 7.5-12.5 cm long and 4-6 cm in width, rounded at base and rarely subcordate or cuneate with long acuminate apex and strongly and sharply setose serrate margins with partially appressed serratures, exstipulate and have 3-4.5 cm long petioles. These are villous or cobwebby beneath when young but become glabrous and glossy when mature. The buds are large-pointed. Inflorescences are borne in terminal umbellate corymbs mainly on spurs. The spurs have mixed buds, the bottom bud having priority to set.

The inflorescence is umbellate racemose glabrous at first and produce 6-9 flowers before or with the unfolding of leaves that are glabrous or sometime tomentose. The white flower is 3-3.5 cm in diameter with 3-5 cm long pedicels having triangular ovate and long acuminate sepals or calyx lobes. The tubular calyx is deciduous. The hypanthium is closed by a cushion-like formation. Pedicels are not fleshy. The petals are ovate and white. The stamens (20) usually have red anthers. The ovary is 5-locular having 5 glabrous and free styles.

Fruit is pyriform to subglobose pome, 150-500 g in weight, 2-3 cm in diameter, usually apple-shaped, slender-stalked and brown or yellow and often reddish brown in colour with pale dots. The fruit surface is rough. The stem cavity is well marked. The flesh is firm, crisp, juicy and gritty without stone cells and with sweet taste and delicate flavour reminiscent of cucumber and rose water. The fruits have good keeping quality. There are 2 seeds per carpel that are blackish in colour (Verheij and Coronel, 1991). It is resistant to Fire Blight.

Cultivars

The high quality, gritfree Nashi cultivars Nijiseiki and Chojuro are chance selections made in Japan at the end of 19th century. The other cultivars are Shinsui, Kosui, Hosui, Shinseiki, Tsu Li and Ya Li.

Hosui: The cultivar (meaning much water) introduced by the National Horticulture Research Station, Tsukuba, Japan in 1972 is a cross of Ri-14 (Kikusui x Yakumo) and Yakumo. The tree is of medium size, spreading, very vigorous, productive and resistant to *Alternaria* black spot. The fruits are large, round having skin as of Chojuro with golden tan russet and mature during mid August to September in Oregon. The flesh is white, firm, very sweet, juicy and crisp having very fine texture and excellent quality. The fruits can be stored for 4 weeks.

Nijisseki: The cultivar (meaning twentieth century) originated as a chance seedling is the most important cultivar in Japan. It is susceptible to black spot disease. The trees are very productive. Fruit skin is greenish yellow and glossy when mature. The flesh is crisp, fine textured and juicy. The fruits have good storage life.

Kosul: The cultivar (meaning good water) is a cross of Kikusui and Wasekozo. This is the most important cultivar in Japan and is a high quality Asian pear. It is resistant to black spot. The tree is vigorous and moderate in production. The fruits mature early and can be stored for 2 months. The fruit is small to medium, light green to golden bronze and covered by tan russet. The flesh is white, tender, very sweet, juicy and crisp and of excellent quality.

Shinselki: The cultivar (meaning new century) is a cross of Nijisseiki and Chojuro is productive, precocious and resistant to black spot. The fruit is medium in size with smooth and yellow skin and matures a bit earlier than Nijisseiki and can be stored for 3 months. The flesh is white, crisp, juicy and bland.

Nitaka: It is a cross of Amanogawa and Imamura Aki and is one of the several cultivars introduced by Kikuchi at the National Tree Fruit Research Station, Japan. The fruits are very large weighing 500 g, attractive and having tan russet with orange under colour or blush. The fruits mature late and have long storage life. The flesh is coarser in texture than those of many other Nashi. Pollen sterility has been observed.

Chojuro: The cultivar originated in 1895 in Kawasaki, Kanagawa Prefecture, Japan as a chance seedling. It has spreading trees of medium size that are highly productive and self fruitful under some conditions but require pollinators for high production. The tree is resistant to Asian pear scab and black spot. The fruit matures in mid season, similar to Nijisseilki, and can be stored up to 5 months. The fruit is of good quality and is moderately large, round oblate with a thick brown russet and green to orange or brown skin. The flesh is white, firm and crisp but coarse due to grit cells and has mildly sweet and distinctive aroma and is sourish at the core.

Huang Hua Li: The cultivar (meaning yellow flower) is a cross of Huang Mi and San Hua and was introduced in 1975 by Zhejiang Agricultural University. It is grown in Zhejiang and Hubei provinces. The cultivar is highly productive and resistant to Asian pear scab. The fruits mature during late August but do not have long storage life. The fruits are medium in size, up to 200 g, and are fully russeted with finely textured flesh of sweet flavour and 12-13°B soluble solids and few grit cells.

Su Li: It is an old Chinese cultivar (meaning crisp-sweet) grown since hundreds of years and is one of the most popular cultivars grown for export as well as domestic use. It is precocious and productive giving fruits that have storage life up to 5 months in traditional cold cellars or caves. The fruits are very sweet and crisp but somewhat coarse textured and of moderately large size, up to 250 g, truncate ovate shape and greenish yellow skin colour on maturity.

Ci Li *(P. bretschneideri):* It is a chance seedling grown extensively in Shandong province, China. Trees as old as 200 years are not uncommon. The fruit is yellowish green, turbinate in shape having poor appearance but of good quality. The fruits mature in September and have short storage life.

Korla Xiang Li: The cultivar originated as a chance seedling of *P. bretschneideri* and is grown in Xinjiang Autonomous Region, China, for both local use and export. Fruit is somewhat small as compared to that of the Japanese cultivars weighing about 120 g. Calyx can be partially persistent unlike in *P. pyrifolia* cultivars. The fruits mature in mid September and can be stored up to 7 months. The fruits are yellow with occasional red blush having high soluble solids, excellent flavour and crisp texture.

Xue Hua Li: It is a very popular cultivar (meaning snowflake) grown in Hebei province, China. The fruits mature in late September and can be stored in cold cellars for 8 months. These are very large, ovate and yellow when ripe.

Ya Li: It is an old cultivar (meaning duck pear) from northeastern China. This has been the most widely planted cultivar in China. The trees are vigorous and cold hardy. It has a low chilling requirement with very early bloom. The fruits mature in mid to late September. These are large, pyriform or ovate pyriform having waxy finish with light green skin turning yellow when harvested but are without russet. The flesh is sweet having slightly aromatic flavour.

Zao Su Li: The cultivar (meaning early crisp) is a cross of Ping Guo Li and Shenbu Li. According to Wei and Gao (2002), this is of *P. ussuriensis* parentage. The cultivar was introduced in 1969 by the Research Institute of Pomology, Chinese Academy of Agricultural Sciences. It is drought tolerant, resistant to pear scab and leaf spot and is a productive and very high quality early bearing cultivar. The fruits mature in mid to late July. These can be stored well at room temperature for 2-3 weeks but soften eventually. The fruits are large, sweet and with no grit and are yellowish green when harvested but turn yellow.

Pear cultivars in India

Besides Bartlett (William's Bon Chretien), Winter Nelis, Doyme du comice, Easter Beurre and Kashmiri Nakh, the other pear cultivars popular in India are:-

Baghugosha (Baggugosha; Citron des Carmes): It is considered the same as Bartlett by some people. It is a French pear. It may have originated as an interspecific hybrid. The trees are upright and vigorous and irregular in bearing. The fruits are small to medium, round conical tapering towards stem end, greenish yellow with russet patches. The flesh is greenish white, firm, juicy and moderately sweet and somewhat gritty. Fruits ripen during August giving average yield of 100 kg/tree. If left on the tree, the fruit tends to become mealy.

Kieffer: This is the only cultivar grown in the hills of South India. It also does well in the submontane regions of North India. The trees are very vigorous, resistant to fire blight, San Jose scale and heat but tender to cold and are thus suitable for warmer regions. It is often self incompatible and thus pollinizers are needed. The fruit is of medium size and poor quality but is good for canning. The basin of the fruit is shallow, skin is thick, smooth and tough. The colour of the fruit is yellow often with pinkish blush on the exposed cheeks and numerous small dots. The flesh is granular and coarse.

Pathar Nakh: Named sand pear (*P. pyrifolia* var. *culta*) in English because of the tiny spots on its skin resembling the sand grains. the cultivar is probably a hybrid. It is a prolific bearer and grows in the plains of North India. The trees are quick growing. The shoots are thick having leaves larger than broader compared to those of the parent species. Fruits are hard, sweet and juicy and apple-like with a deep cavity at both ends. The fruits have good keeping quality and can stand long distance transportation.

Jafri: It is an interspecific hybrid. The fruits are pyriform and have pinkish blush.

Pant Pear 3: It is a clonal selection and a mid season cultivar. The tree is medium-sized giving high fruit yield. The fruit is medium-sized and pyriform and has thin skin. The flesh is soft with 15°B TSS.

Pant Pear 17: It is a clonal selection. It is a late maturing cultivar. The tree is medium-sized giving high fruit yield. The fruit is round to pyriform and has thin skin. The flesh is soft with 14.5°B TSS.

Pant Pear 18: It is a clonal selection. It is an early maturing cultivar. The tree is medium-sized. The fruit is large and round. The flesh is hard and juicy with 13^0B TSS.

Punjab Nector: It is a low chilling cultivar giving fruit yield of 80 kg/tree. The fruit is semi-soft of 136 g weight.

Punjab Gold: The cultivar gives fruit yield of 80 kg/tree. The fruit is semi-soft of 166 g weight and 14.5°B TSS.

Punjab Soft: It is an Asian type of pear giving fruit yield of 86 kg/tree. The fruit is soft, medium-sized and of 128 g weight.

Jargonellae: Trees are upright with spreading branches. Fruits are obtuse pyriform to oblong pyriform in shape, lemon yellow over green base with faded red blush on the skin. It has mid season maturity.

Kainth
(*Pyrus pashia* D. Don.)

It occurs in the region from Afghanistan, India and northern Burma to southwest China and grows wild in Kumaon. It is cultivated on a very limited scale in Indochina and in northern India. The trees are 7.5-9.0 m tall. The leaves are ovate and finely toothed. The young shoots, leaves and inflorescences are wooly. The flowers are borne in dense clusters that are rose tinted and turn white later. The anthers are red. The fruit is brown, globose, small, speckled and not uniform. These are rather insipid and have to be stored for several weeks to make them edible. The flesh of some cultivars is nearly black. It is used as a rootstock. *P. pashia* var. *kumaoni* (Decne.) Stapf does not have the dense wooly pubescence and its leaves are glabrous. *P. khasiana,* similar to *P. pashia*, grows wild and is used as a rootstock.

Ussurian pear
(***Pyrus ussuriensis*** Maxim.)

It is a native of northeast China, eastern part of the former Soviet Union, Korea and Japan. It is also cultivated in northern Indochina, Canada and USA. It is the most cold hardy species. The shoots and leaves are nearly glabrous. The leaves are rounded (orbicular), slender pointed and bristly toothed. The flowers are white in dense hemispherical clusters. The fruits are small, globose, yellowish green, sweet-sour, attractive and aromatic.

Snow pear
(***Pyrus nivalis*** Jacq.)

It grows wild in Europe. It is a hardy species and the young growth is covered with dense snowy pubescence. The fruits are used for making cider.

Siberian pear
(***Pyrus calleryana*** Decne.)

It is resistant to Fire Blight and is used in breeding programme.

Chinese white pear
(***Pyrus x bretschneideri*** Rehd.)

It is a cross between *P. ussuriensis* and *P. betulifolia.* It is a native of northern China. It is also cultivated for its edible fruit.

Genus *Malus* Mill. (x = 17; 2n=34, 51, 68, 85)

Between 30 and 50 species occur in northern temperate region in woods and thickets (Kubitzki, 2004) (Table 23.3). The trees or shrubs are leaf shedding, deciduous, rarely evergreen and/or thorny, rarely with spiny branches and have ovoid buds with several imbricate scales, serrate or lobed and stipulate leaves that are folded or convolute in bud. Leaves are simple, lobed or not having caducous stipules. Inflorescences are few flowered terminal racemes on short shoots. Hypanthium is obconical to campanulate, upper part being persistent. Sepals are persistent or deciduous. Petals are white, pink or red. Stamens are 15-20. Carpels are 3-5, adnate to hypanthium dorsally over their entire length and also the apical part is not exposed, laterally connate, ventrally with open sutures. Ovary is inferior with 3-5 cells and 2-5 stylodia connate in lower part, stigmas slightly broadened to capitate and ovules 2 (4?) per carpel. Pome is globose, green to red or yellow, rarely lenticellate having soft and mealy to rather hard flesh, without sclereids, usually without grit cells and with persistent or deciduous calyx. The core (endocarp) is cartilaginous to bony (even slightly woody). Seeds are with thin but firm, dark coloured testa and a thin layer endosperm.

Table 23.3. *Malus* sections and primary species (Huckins, 1972; Robinson *et al.*, 2001)

Species	Chromosome (2n)	Apomictic	Chemical affinity within group	Fruit dia. (cm)	*Calyx	Carpel No.	Ripe fruit drop
section I. *Malus*- subsection A *Pumilae* series A *Pumilae*							
1. *Malus pumila* Miller Paradise apple	34	No	Yes	>2	P	5	Yes
2. *Malus sylvestris* Miller European crabapple	34	No	Yes	>2	P	5	Yes
3. *Malus* x *domestica* Borkh.	34	No	Yes	>2	P	5	Yes
4. *Malus orientalis* Uglizk. ex Juz.	-	-	-	-	-	-	-
5. *Malus sieversii* (Lodeb.) M. Roemer	-	-	-	>2	P	5	Yes
6. *Malus prunifolia* (Willd.) Borkh.	34	No	Yes	2	P	5	No
7. *Malus asiatica* Nakai	34	No	-	>2	P	5	Yes
8. *Malus spectabilis* (Aiton) Borkh. Asiatic apple	34, 68	No	Yes	2	P	5	No
9. *Malus micromalus* Makino	34	No	Yes	1	D	-	-
section I. *Malus*- subsection A *Pumilae* series B *Baccatae*							
10. *Malus baccata* (L.) Borkh.	34, 68	No	Yes	1	D	4,5	No
11. *Malus mandshurica* (Maxim) V. Komarov	34	No	Yes	1	D	5	No
12. *Malus sikkimenesis* (Wenzig) Koehne ex. C. Schneider	51	Yes	Yes	1	D	4,5	No
13. *Malus hupehensis* (Pampani) Rehder	51	Yes	Yes	1	D	3,4	No
14. *Malus halliana* Koehne Hall crabapple	34	No	Yes	1	D	3,4,5	No
section I. *Malus*- subsection B *Sieboldianae*							
15. *Malus sieboldii* (Regel) Rehder	34-85?	?	Yes	1	D	3,4,5	No
16. *Malus sargentii* Rehder Sargent's crabapple	68	Yes	Yes	1	D	3,4,5	No
section I. *Malus*- subsection C *Kansuenses* series A *Kansuenses*							
17. *Malus toringoides* (Rehder) Hughes Cut leaf crab	51	Yes	Yes	1	D	4,5	No
18. *Malus transitoria* (Batalin) C. Schneider	-	-	No	1	D	5	No
19. *Malus kansuensis* (Batalin) C. Schneider	-	No	Yes	1	D	3,4,5	No
20. *Malus komarovii* (Sarg.) Rehder	-	-	-	1	D	3,4,5	No
21. *Malus fusca* (Raf.) C. Schneider Oregon crabapple	34	No	Yes	1	D	2,3,4	No

section I. Malus- subsection C *Kansuenses*							
series B *Yunnanenses*							
22. *Malus prattii* (Hemsley) C. Schneider Pratt apple	34	No	Yes	1.5	P	5	No
23. *Malus ombrophila* Hand. -Mazz.	-	-	-	>2	P	5	Yes?
24. *Malus yunnanensis* (Franchet) C. Schneider	34	No	Yes	1.5	P	5	No
25. *Malus honanensis* Rehder	-	-	-	1.5	P	4	No
section II Sorbomalus series- *Florentinae*							
26. *Malus florentina* (Zuccagni) C. Schneider	34	No	Yes?	1	P,D	3,4,5	No
section III *Eriolobus*							
27. *Malus trilobata* (Poiret) C. Schneider	-	No	Yes?	2	P	5	-
section IV *Chloromeles*							
28. *Malus ioensis* (Alph. Wood) Britton Prairie crabapple	34	No	Yes	>2	P	5	Yes
29. *Malus angustifolia* (Aiton) Michaux Southern crabapple	34	No	Yes	>2	P	5	Yes
30. *Malus coronaria* (L.) Miller American crab apple, Sweet crabapple	51 (68)	Yes?	Yes	>2	P	5	Yes
section V. *Docyniopsis*							
31. *Malus tschonoskii* (Maxim.) C. Schneider	34	No	Yes?	>2	P	5	Yes
32. *Malus doumeri* (Boiss.) A. Chev.	-	No	Yes?	>2	P	5	Yes
33. *Malus melliana* (Hand. -Mazz.) Rehder	-	-	Yes	>2	P	5	Yes

*calyx: P = Persistent; D =Deciduous

Janick *et al.* (1996) have given a list of *Malus* species hybrids: *M.* × *adstringens* Zabel (*baccata* × *pumila*), *M.* × *arnoldiana* (Rehder) Sarg. (*baccata* × *floribunda*), *M.* × *astracanica* Dum.-Cours. (*pumila* × *prunifolia*), *M.* × *atrosanguinea* (Spaeth) Schneid. (*halliana* × *sieboldii*), *M.* × *dawsonia* Rehder (*fusca* × *pumila*), *M.* × *gloriosa* Lem (*pumila niedzwetskyana* × *scheideckeri*), *M.* × *hartwiggii* Koehne (*halliana* × *baccata*), *M.* × *heterophylla* Spach (*coronaria* × *pumila*), *M.* × *magdeburgensis* Schoch. (*spectabilis* × *pumila*), *M.* × *platycarpa* Rehder (*coronaria* × *domestica*), *M.* × *purpurea* (Barbier) Rehder (*niedzwetzkyana* × *atrosanguinea*), *M.* × *robusta* (Carr.) Rehder (*baccata* × *prunifolia*), *M.* × *scheideckeri* (Spaeth) Zabel (*floribunda* × *prunifolia*), *M.* × *soulardii* (Bailey) Britton (*ioensis* × *pumila*), *M.* × *sublobata* (Dipp.) Rehder (*prunifolia* × *sieboldii*), *M.* × *zumi* (Mats.) Rehder (*mandschurica* × *sieboldii*).

Apple
(*Malus* × *domestica* Borkh. = *M. pumila* Mill.)

Apple is the most important fruit tree among the rosaceous species. A fermented product called cider is often made from special apples, many of which may be hybrids with the native species such as *M. sylvestris*. The small-fruited species of *Malus* referred as crabapples are usually popular for their ornamental spring flowers.

The greatest diversity of wild apples has been traced to the central Asian area of Turkestan (Kazakistan, Kyrgystan, Uzbekistan, Turkemenistan and Tadjikistan). Vavilov (1930) suggested that the wild apples of Turkestan, *M. sieversii* and its close relatives, were the progenitors of *M. domestica* since *M. sieversii* bore fruits similar to those of the cultivated forms. Based on morphological characters, Zohary and Hopf (1994) stated that *M. sylvestris* was undoubtedly the principal, but not the only, source for the domestication of apple. Watkins (1981, 1995a) suggested that *M. sieversii* was the major species contributing to *M. domestica*, with minor contributions from *M. orientalis* and *M. sylvestris*. Studies by Dunemann *et al.* (1994) and Savolainen *et al*. (1995) suggested that *M. sylvestris, M. florentina* or *M. dasyphylla* could be the female parents in the origin of *M. domestica*. Robinson *et al.* (2001) based on combination of molecular and chlororoplast sequence data have suggested that all of the close relatives of *M. domestica* occur in the poorly resolved series *Malus* clade. They found two *mat*K duplications, one in series *Malus* and the other in most *M. domestica* cultivars and one Central Asian *M. sieversii* accession.

The trees are low and round crowned, usually about 15 m in height. The trunk is short and stout. The bark does not have dots and sheds in irregular scales. The wood may be somewhat hairy. The branches are spreading. The tips of the shoots and buds are pubescent. The upper surface of the leaves is rough and the lower pubescent. The leaves are serrated and stipulate. These are mostly clustered, borne on spurs, ovate or elliptic to broad elliptic, 4.5-10 cm long having soft texture. The buds are not so much pointed. The fruit buds are mixed, the top bud having priority to set. The calyx tube is open at the top. The flowers are white to light pink and are borne in fascicles. The styles are united. The fruit is oblate or round having deep cavities at both the ends. Grit cells are absent. The carpels are more distinct. There are 2 seeds per carpel.

Apple groups

Delicious group: Delicious group cultivars have undergone somatic mutations for such traits as tree size and branching habit, fruit set, maturity, colour and shape of fruits. Resultantly, during the 1950's many early colouring strains (Richared, Shotwello and Starking) became available. Of these, Starking and Richared were extensively planted. These strains differ from the parent trees or adjacent trees in fruit colour and tree characteristics or both. Westwood observed that the leaves of Starking (a standard strain) and Starkrimson (a spur strain) were different structurally and chemically. Fruits of Starkrimson (Bisbee strain) were more elongated than Starking and matured 5 days later. There is conflicting evidence as to whether or not fruits of delicious strains have differences other than in colour. Little or no differences in maturity among Delicious strains including Starking, Richared and Starkrimson are seen. The fruits of Vance Delicious coloured and matured earlier than those of Starking. Water core associated with over maturity is more severe in Richared than in Starking.

Aport group: These are called fall apples and are especially grown in north coastal apple sections. The fruits are large, coarse in texture and of medium quality.

Some members of the group are adapted to parts of California, Oregon and Washington. The main cultivars are Alexander, Bietigheimer, Bismard, McMahon and Wolf River.

Baldwin group: These are adapted to the cooler districts of New England and northcentral USA. The apples are highly coloured, well flavoured and have desirable size, long keeping quality and similarities in texture, flavour, form and colour markings. The main cultivars are Arctic, Baldwin, Russet Baldwin, Sutton and Virginia Beauty.

Ben Davis group: The fruits are rather large, bright red, coarse and solid in texture, indifferent in flavour having thick skin, good shipping and keeping quality. The main cultivars are Arkansas Beauty, Beach, Ben Davis, Black Ben Davis and Collins Gano.

Black Gilliflower group: This group is less hardy than the Baldwin group and is very particular to soils. The fruits are of medium size, dark red colour, oblong ribbed shape and of good quality, but have rather dry and coarse texture. The main cultivars are Black Gilliflower and Deacon Jones.

Blue Permain group: The group is valuable only for northern cold conditions. The fruits are somewhat large, dull red having bluish bloom, thick skin, mild flavour, dense texture and fair quality. The main cultivars are Baxter, Bethel, Blue Pearmain, Gideon Sweet, Scarlet Beauty, Stone, Windsor and Red Pearmain.

Chenango group: The cultivars of the group are occasionally grown in California and Oregon, USA. The fruits are medium sized, red striped, oblong, conical and of high quality having peculiar aroma and delicate texture. The main cultivars are Chenango and Stump.

Early Harvest group: The cultivars of the group are adapted to warmer parts and are grown in the interior valleys. These summer apples are of medium size, pale yellow or white colour, of good but not superior quality and having delicate breaking flesh. The main cultivars are Early Harvest, Early Ripe and Parry White.

Fameuse group: A tendency to reproduce true from seed is a striking peculiarity of this group.

Asa group: It is a valuable group for colder parts but is susceptible to fungal problems. The fruits are of medium size, handsome red colour, usually striped, roundish, oblate, thin but tough skinned having pure white tender flesh of high quality. The main cultivars are Canada Baldwin, Detroit Red, Fameuse, Hoover, Louise, McIntosh, St. Lawrence, Shiawassee and Scarlet Pippin.

Jonathan group: This group has variable adaptation and is grown in many areas of USA and resembles Baldwin group. The fruits are medium sized and of handsome red colour having high quality and crisp flesh. The main cultivars are Delicious, Esopus, Jonathan, King David, Mother and Red Canada.

Lady group: It is found in 'Thanks giving' and 'Christmas' markets. The fruits have dessert use. The fruits are very small, roundish oblate, handsome in colour and sprightly in quality having crisp and juicy flesh and good keeping quality. The main cultivars are Highland, Lady and Star Lady.

Lawver group: The cultivars of this group do not withstand extreme cold. The fruits have medium size, very high colour and rather dense flesh of medium coarse texture but inferior flavour. The fruits have excellent keeping quality. The main cultivars are Akin, Lawver and McAfee.

Northern Spy group: The group is fastidious as to soil conditions but can be grown in congenial locations in cooler areas. The fruits are large, striped red, roundish oblate and ribbed having delicate bloom and flesh that is juicy, crisp and of fine grain and high quality and flavour. The main cultivars are Doctor, Melon, Northern Spy, Ontario and Wagener.

Oldenburg group: This is probably the most cosmopolitan group successful in all parts of USA. The fruits are medium to above average in size, variously striped with red and generally ripening in comparatively short season. These are tart culinary apples. The main cultivars are Russian, Gladstone, Milwaukee, Oldenburg, Pewaukee, Smith Cider and Gravenstein.

Ralls group: The group is not adapted to the cooler northern states of USA. Mature trees are medium to small in size and are productive. The fruits are rather dull striped red, of superior quality, texture and good keeping quality. The main cultivars are Doctor Walker, Ingram, Ralls, Salome and Yates.

Rambo group: Adaptation of this group is similar to the Ralls group. The fruits are of medium size, rounded oblate, rather dull striped red and of good quality. The main cultivars are Domine, Rambo, Walbridge and Wells.

Red Astrachan group: These are grown in warmer sections and interior valleys. The fruits are of more than medium size having crisp, tart and good quality. The main cultivars are Red Astrachan and White Austrachan.

Reinette group: Members of this group thrive in many areas of USA. It is a large and poorly defined group. The group is divided into five sections:

(a) Newtown section: The cultivars of this group are grown largely. With few exceptions, the fruits are large in size, of green or yellow ground colour with or without blush and generally of good quality.

(b) Fall Pippin section: The section has cultivars such as Boiken, Crowns, Fall Pippin, Golden Pippin, Maiden Blush. Tolman Sweet, Winter Banana and Winter Pippin.

(c) Rhode Island Greening section: The section has cultivars such as Autumn Swaar, Bottle Greening, Northwestern Greening, R. 1. Greening, Swed and Greening.

(d) Newtown section: The section has cultivars such as Green Newtown, Gloria Mundi, Grimes, Golden Delicious, Huntsman, Peck, Pleasant, White Pippin, White Pearmains and Yellow Newtown.

(e) Swaar section: The section has cultivars such as Mann and Swaar.

Romantic group: The fruits are variable in size, highly coloured and poor to good in quality. Keeping quality is very good. The group has mainly southern apples. The main cultivars are Pennock, Gilpin, Minkler, Nero, Payne, Romanite, Stark and York Imperial.

Rome group: The fruits have long stems and saucer shaped cavities and are medium in size, roundish, handsomely coloured and of indifferent quality. The main cultivars are Ben Hur, Champion, Langford and Rome.

Russet group: The fruits are of small to large size, russet coloured and peculiarly fine grained having dense textured flesh of sprightly flavour and good keeping quality. The main cultivars are English Russet, Golden Russet, Roxbury, Pomme Gris and Sweet Russet.

Tompkins King group: These are early winter apples, large in size, attractively striped with red, variable but symmetrical in form and of superior quality and characteristic dense coarse texture and aromatic yellowish flesh. The main cultivars are Blenheim, Ensee, Hubbardston, Ribston, Tompkins King and Westfield.

Twenty Ounce group: These are large, late fall, broadly splashed red apples, roundish in form and of good quality having a coarse, yellowish and aromatic flesh. The main cultivars are Collamer and Twenty Ounce.

Vandevere group: Locally adapted group but is grown in California, e.g. Vandevere.

Wealthy group: The group is hardy and widely adapted. The bearing is early giving abundant crop. The fruit becomes undersized on old trees. The main cultivars are Peter, Wealthy and several Minnesota seedlings.

Winesap group: The winter apples are of medium to large size, dark red colour having solid and fine grain of good but not high quality. These are adapted to cooler coastal areas. The fruits have good keeping quality. The main cultivars are Arkansas, Arkansas Black, Delaware Late Winter, Kinnaird, Oliver, Paragon, Stayman and Winesap.

Yellow Bellflower group: The fruits are medium to large, characteristically oblong conical with predominantly yellow colour and somewhat remarkably large open core. The flesh is firm, crisp, aromatic and of high quality for culinary purposes. The main cultivars are Barry, Moyer, Artley, Summer Bellflower, Titus Pippin and Yellow Bellflower.

Yellow Transparent group: The early summer apples have medium size and characteristically thick skin and tender flesh.

Cultivar classification based on use

A. General purpose cultivars

Yellow Transparent: The cultivar is well adapted to all parts of Indiana and is one of the very early ripening cultivars. The tree is vigorous and spreading and tends to be biennial bearing if not well thinned early in the season. The tree is very susceptible to fire blight. The fruit is greenish yellow until mature when it becomes yellowish white. The fruit is very desirable for use in apple sauce and for this purpose it is harvested immature. When mature, the fruit softens and quickly becomes unsalable.

Lodi: The cultivar ripens fruits a week after Yellow Transparent. The tree is vigorous, hardy and tends to be regular in production. The fruit is larger than that of

Yellow Transparent. It is green but becomes pale yellow upon maturity. Fruits are ordinarily harvested when still green for use in apple sauce. However, its sauce being too tart, it is considered to be less desirable. Fruit tends to "blow up" or break down internally if harvested mature and not stored immediately.

Pristine: The cultivar bears medium-large yellow fruits with a red blush and slightly tart flavour. The tree has excellent resistance to scab, Fire Blight and powdery mildew. The fruits are good for fresh eating and salads.

William's Pride: The cultivar bears medium to large red fruits having nice flavour and a soft texture. The tree has good disease resistance but does not perform well in high temperatures.

Redfree: The cultivar bears large fruits with 90% good red colour on a smooth, waxy and russet free skin. The flesh is white, crisp, juicy and subacid and retains quality for 2 months in cold storage. The tree is immune to apple scab and cedar rust and moderately resistant to fire blight and mildew. Fruit ripens 3 weeks before Prima and 7 weeks before Delicious.

Gala: The cultivar bears small to medium yellow red fruits having excellent flavour, but is highly susceptible to fire blight and moderately susceptible to the other diseases. It is very popular because of excellent eating quality of fruits.

Honeycrisp: The cultivar bears large yellow fruits having red mottling and excellent sweet flavour, but is susceptible to most of the diseases. The tree is weak growing and prone to biennial bearing. Fruit quality is poor in very hot areas, but in northcentral Indiana it produces fruits of exceptional quality.

Paulared: It is a promising early fall cultivar for Indiana It ripens good quality fruits about a month ahead of Jonathan. The tree is upright, rather willowy in growth, hardy and productive but is very susceptible to fire blight and tends to be biennial in bearing if not properly thinned. The fruit stores well and is uniform and medium sized with a shape similar to McIntosh. It has good red colour over a greenish ground colour.

Prima: It is a scab immune cultivar ripening fruits 3 weeks ahead of Jonathan. The tree is vigorous, spreading, productive and moderately hardy. The fruit is medium to large in size and somewhat blocky in shape, most resembling Jonathan. The fruit has 70-80% good, bright red colour over a greenish yellow under colour when mature. The colour and quality are best on low to medium vigour trees. The fruit has tart flavour and excellent quality and texture resembling Jonathan. It does not store well and should be marketed or used promptly. It is good for home gardens because of scab resistance.

Priscilla: It is a scab immune cultivar ripening fruits with McIntosh and a week ahead of Jonathan. The tree is upright, vigorous and hardy. It is somewhat resistant to fire blight and immune to cedar apple rust. The fruit is medium-sized and with uniform bright red blush over 75-90% of the surface. It has a sweet, aromatic flavour and a juicy and crisp texture. This high quality fruit stores extremely well and is best suited for home gardens.

McIntosh: It is a standard cultivar in the northeastern USA. The tree is very vigorous, hardy, regular bearing but very susceptible to apple scab. The fruit is oblate, medium in size and has glossy, smooth and green skin overlain with bright carmine and with few conspicuous lenticels. The flesh is white with some red tinge, crisp, juicy tender, sweet with pleasant acid blend and mild flavour. Under central and southern Indiana conditions, the fruit matures too early with poor colour and flesh quality. In the northern area, it develops satisfactory colour, quality and texture. The fruit is crisp and juicy with excellent flavour. Some red strains of McIntosh are Rogers McIntosh, Blackmac and Geneva. These strains develop better colour but otherwise are similar to McIntosh. Spur types* of McIntosh are Macspur and Spur McIntosh. These have better bearing characteristics than the standard types. Fruit has tendency to drop before reaching full maturity. Wijeik is a spontaneous mutant of McIntosh which arose in British Columbia (Canada). It is a source of dominant gene for columnar habit.

Spartan: It is a promising cultivar originating in Summerland, British Columbia and has fruit characters similar to McIntosh. Spartan ripens just after McIntosh and before Jonathan. The tree is moderately vigorous and upright spreading. It tends to be biennial bearing unless thinned well. The fruit is firm and has an attractive bright red colour. The flesh is white. Its quality is similar to McIntosh but is crisper when grown in warmer areas. Fruit size is small to medium and uniform. Spartan is better than McIntosh in warmer areas.

Grimes Golden: It is an old, high quality yellow cultivar that ripens with Jonathan. The tree is vigorous, highly productive and biennial bearing if not thinned properly. It comes late into production. The tree is very susceptible to collar rot. The fruit is susceptible to bitter pit, especially when the crop is light and fruit size is large.

Jonathan: It is an old standard cultivar. The tree is vigorous, precocious, hardy and productive but very susceptible to fire blight and powdery mildew. Jonathan develops best fruit colour in cooler nights. The fruit is bright red and medium to small in size. The flesh is firm with a tart flavour and excellent quality. Jonathan is excellent for both cooking and fresh eating. It can be stored until mid winter at 1.66-2.22°C to minimize storage problems.

Jonafree: It closely resembles Jonathan but has some disease resistance. The fruit is 5.6 to 8 cm in diameter, 95% medium red in colour and has a smooth, russet free skin. The flesh is pale yellow, of medium texture and firm, crisp, and juicy. It has good dessert quality which retains the flavour well in storage. Jonafree is immune to apple scab, moderately resistant to Fire Blight and cedar rust and moderately susceptible to mildew. The fruits hang well at maturity and do not develop Jonathan spot as is common with the parent cultivar.

Liberty: It is a MacIntosh type cultivar having small to medium sized green fruit with a red overlay and a tart flavour and coarse texture. The fruit is good for fresh eating, salads and cooking. The tree is very productive and has excellent disease resistance.

---

* Trees have dense leafy appearance because of short internodes, many flower buds on 2 and 3 year old wood and few lateral branches on the main scaffold limb (called spur strains). The trees are smaller than those of standard strains and allegedly produce heavier crops during their early fruiting years.

Cortland: The cultivar has many characteristics of McIntosh. The tree is vigorous and spreading. The fruit is red striped or blushed over a greenish yellow ground colour. The flesh is tart, white and tender. It is excellent for cooking, salads and fresh eating.

Delicious: It is the most popular and widely planted apple cultivar in USA. The tree is vigorous and upright, comes into bearing slowly and tends to be regular in bearing. It is moderately productive but is quite susceptible to frost damage. The fruit is conical in shape with five prominent lobes at the apex. The fruit is striped to solid red, depending upon the strain. The fruit has a sweet, mild flavour and is fair to good in quality. It is used as a salad or dessert apple but is not suitable for other culinary uses. It has over 150 strains and most are superior in colour to the old standard Delicious. There are a number of spur-type strains that are desirable in most commercial orchards because of their growth habit and precocity. However, they require special care in early training. Fruit is borne primarily on spurs which are produced on the main scaffold branches. While pruning, more scaffold limbs are allowed. These branch less than the non-spur types. When well trained, spur-type trees tend to come into production earlier and to be more productive than the non-spur types.

Empire: The cultivar has a vigorous and spreading tree. It is productive but tends to be biennial bearing unless well thinned. It is a McIntosh type apple with a slightly coarser fruit texture. The fruit is firmer, more highly coloured and develops an attractive overall blood colour. The flesh is creamy white and of excellent flavour and quality. The fruit size is medium to large. It stores well.

Red Delicious: It evolved as a chance seedling in North America. It is the most widely grown mid season cultivar all over the world having a number of important strains. The tree is moderately vigorous and semi-spreading. The fruits are large, conical oblong with smooth and shiny skin having prominent red streaks on pale yellow background and very prominent calyx lobes that protrude outwards. The flesh is sweet, juicy, very aromatic, creamy white and fine grained and crisp in texture that later becomes tender.

Golden Delicious: It is a high quality yellow cultivar and is second only to Delicious in popularity. The tree is moderate in vigour, somewhat upright with spreading branches. It is a very good pollinizer for Delicious group. The tree comes into bearing early but becomes biennial unless thinned regularly and kept in adequate vigour. The fruit is medium large, oblong having golden yellow skin with prominent brown lenticels and prominent russet at the stalk end. Under certain conditions, the fruit tends to russet severely. The tender, light yellow and high quality flesh is excellent for both culinary and dessert purposes. It is firm and crisp when mature and later becomes sweet with pleasant acidic blend. Storage is more difficult than for other cultivars because of the moisture loss through the fruit epidermis which does not have a heavy waxy coating. The use of polyethylene liners in storage containers maximizes storage life. When stored without liners, frequent wetting and careful maintenance of high humidity is necessary to minimize shrinkage. Careful maintenance of uniform °C (30-32°F) cold storage temperatures also helps.

Melrose: The cultivar originated at the Ohio Agricultural Experiment Station from a cross between Jonathan and Delicious. It matures fruits just after Golden Delicious and before Stayman or Rome. The fruit is firm, large and deep red over a greenish yellow ground colour. It is of outstanding cooking and dessert quality and stores well. While its fruit is not particularly attractive, the quality, flavour and texture make it worthy of planting in home garden and commercial orchards.

Idared: The cultivar developed in Idaho bears well coloured and attractive red fruits ripening with Golden Delicious. The tree is vigorous and productive, similar in size to Jonathan and, like Jonathan, is very susceptible to fire blight and mildew. The tree is precocious and tends to be regular in bearing. The fruit is white fleshed, tart, firm and of good to excellent quality. The storage quality is good.

Sir Prize: The cultivar has immunity to apple scab and bears fruits ripening with Golden Delicious that are yellow and russet free. The tree is vigorous and upright, tending to be regular in bearing. The fruit has high quality and excellent appearance. The large fruit is very attractive, light greenish yellow, waxy smooth and shaped like Golden Delicious. The fine grained flesh texture is tender, juicy, subacid and rich in flavour and excellent for fresh eating. The fruit is too tender and should be graded or handled very carefully to avoid bruising. It stores extremely well. It is excellent for home gardens. Since it is a triploid, it does not pollinize other cultivars.

Gloster-69: It is a German cultivar evolved from a cross between Weisser Winterglockenapfel and Richard Delicious. The tree is vigorous and upright, regular bearing giving high yield. The preharvest drop is moderate. The fruit is large, short conical having uniform light red colour. The greenish yellow flesh is free of bitter pit and sweet but the acid content is more than in Delicious.

Red Chief: It is a bud mutant of Starkrimson Delicious and is a heavy yielding mid season cultivar. The tree is dwarf and spreading having moderate vigour. The fruit is medium large having the shape like that of Delicious with bright attractive cherry red stripes over pale yellow skin. The flesh is creamy white and of excellent quality.

Rome Beauty: It is one of the old cultivars grown in Indiana. Care has to be taken in selecting the best strain suitable for the location. The tree is spreading, precocious, productive and tends to be regular bearing. It blooms relatively late in the season and thus may escape frost damage. It is susceptible to apple scab, powdery mildew, cedar apple rust and *Botrysphaeria* rot. The fruit is red striped to blushed, large, firm and of fair quality. It is best for culinary uses and stores well. Red strains such as Gallia Beauty and Red Rome are quite similar to the parent cultivar but develop better red colour. The colour of the red strains differs considerably. The Law strain appears to be one of the better strains for colour. The spur-type Rome has not been fully evaluated but appears to have improved growth habit. Several spur-type strains retain the red fruit colour of the corresponding non-spur Red Rome strains. They have better growth habit. The new cultivar, Enterprise, is very similar to Rome and also has disease resistance.

Turley: It is a cultivar having large, well coloured fruits ripening 7 to 10 days ahead of Stayman Winesap. The tree is vigorous, productive and forms strong scaffold branches naturally. Although Turley is similar in many characteristics to Stayman, the fruit does not split as badly. It is good for cooking or baking with fair to good dessert quality. The fruit keeps well in cold storage. Since Turley is a triploid, it does not pollinize other cultivars.

Stayman: The cultivar bears large, dark, dull red, firm and coarse-fleshed fruits. The tree is easily injured by low winter temperatures and blossoms are quite susceptible to frost injury in the spring. It tends to set light crops unless optimum conditions for pollination are provided. It is a high quality dessert and culinary cultivar. The fruit is subject to preharvest cracking especially in seasons of variable moisture supply. Stayman fails to colour satisfactorily. The Tuttle strain of Staymared, originating in Indiana, is considered to be less subject to cracking. Since Stayman is a triploid, it does not pollinize other cultivars. Blaxtayman, Staymared. Scarlet Stayman and other red strains of Stayman develop better red colour and are preferred especially in southern areas of Indiana.

Winesap: It is an old cultivar but is grown in some areas. The fruit is red, small, very firm to hard and of good quality and keeps well in storage.

Enterprise: The cultivar has a large, red, juicy fruit and is good for fresh eating as well as in salads. The tree has excellent scab and powdery mildew resistance and moderate resistance to Fire Blight. The fruit ripens late around mid October. Fruits store well.

Goldrush: Goldrush has large, yellow, tart, juicy fruits but requires a very long growing season. The tree has excellent scab and fire blight resistance. The fruit has excellent quality but can russet badly in some years. It is firm and retains the firmness well in cold storage. The cultivar is very precocious and productive.

Royal Gala: It is a bud mutant of Gala, precocious and having very high productivity. The tree is of medium size and moderate vigour. It is a mid season cultivar. The fruit is of medium size and very attractive form having thin, smooth and golden yellow skin overlain with bright scarlet. The flesh is of light yellow colour, sweet flavour, juicy, firm and has crisp texture and excellent quality. The fruits tolerate bruising and are free of bitter pit.

Red Fuji: It is a bud sport of Fuji and is a hardy cultivar. The fruits are medium in size, round to conical in shape with bright red stripes over a light red base and can be stored very well over long period. The flesh at maturity is of firm and fine texture and aromatic flavour.

Anna: The cultivar originated in Israel from a cross between Hadassiya and Golden Delicious. It requires low chilling. The fruits ripen by June end and are large, shiny, pale yellow overlain by bright red, more so on the cheeks. The flesh is white and subacid to sweet in taste.

B. Special purpose cultivars

The cultivars listed below may not be suitable for commercial planting because of poor production, late bearing, low consumer demand, etc. However, because of special quality characters these might be considered for home gardens.

Northern Spy: It is a firm, prized processing apple. It is very desirable for culinary use. The tree is late in coming into bearing and should be planted only on dwarfing rootstocks.

Mutsu: It is a Golden Delicious type cultivar maturing after Golden Delicious. The fruit is very large and stores well. The flesh is firm and of excellent quality. It is susceptible to blister spot. It is suggested for plantings where a large and high quality Golden type fruit is desired. Because it is a triploid, it does not act as a pollinizer for other cultivars.

Braeburn: It bears a large, red and firm fruit having excellent flavour and is good for fresh eating and stores well. However, the tree is susceptible to most diseases especially to fire blight. The fruit ripens late, around mid October. It is susceptible to frost damage due to early bloom time.

Fuji: The cultivar has an unusual looking fruit, light red and is known for poor colour and russeting, but the flesh is very sweet, crisp and juicy. It ripens late, around mid to late October. The tree is susceptible to most diseases.

Granny Smith: It is a very late and tart cultivar. The fruit is green, large, firm and of excellent quality. The tree is highly productive. It is adaptable to areas having a long growing season.

C. Cider purpose cultivars

Cider apples are a group of apple cultivars grown for their use in cider production. For cider production it is important that the fruits contain higher sugar levels than those of the dessert and culinary types to encourage fermentation and raise the alcohol level. Long Ashton Research Station, UK categorised cider apples into four main types according to the nature of their flavour components.

1. Sweets: This group is low in tannins (<0.2%) and acidity (<0.45%). The cultivars belonging to this group are Ashmeads Kernel, Black Oxford, Burgundy and Court Royal (Sweet Blenheim).

2. Sharps: The cultivars of this group have high acidity (>0.45%) and low tannin (<0.2%). The high acidity adds 'bite' to the cider. The cultivars belonging to this group are Baldwin, Bramley's Seedling, and Crimson King.

3. Bittersweets: The cultivars of this group have low acidity (<0.45%) and high tannin (>0.2%). High level of tannin makes the taste astringent and adds bitterness to the cider. A certain amount of bitterness is expected in the ciders of the West Country Style. The cultivars belonging to this group are Brown Thorn, Bulmer's Norman, Calvile Blanc and Centennial Crab.

4. Bittersharps: The cultivars of this group are high in both acidity (>0.45%) and tannin (>0.2%). The important cultivars are Domaines, Dolgo Crab, Frequin Rouge, Golden Hornet and Mettais.

The cultivars can also be classified on the basis of season of fruit ripening:

- Early: Michael, Anna, Chaubattia Anupam, Tydeman's Early and Worcester.
- Mid season: Royal Delicious , Rich-a-Red, Red Delicious, Red Chief, Well Spur, Gala and Granny Smith.
- Late: Firdous, Lal Ambri, Top Red, Sunhess, Golden Delicious, Red Gold, Ambri and Fuji.

Cultivars developed at East Malling Research Station, England

a. General purpose

Tydeman's Early Worcester (McIntosh x Worcester Permain; Selection 431).

Michaelmas Red (McIntosh Red x Worcester Permain; Selection 432).

Tydeman's Martinmas (McIntosh Red x Worcester Permain; Selection 452).

Tydeman's Late Orange (Laxton's Superb x Cox's Orange Pippin; Selection 454).

Tydeman's October (Cox's Orange Pippin x Ellison's Orange; Selection 455).

Tydeman's Harvest (Devonshire Quarrenden x Worcester Permain; Selection 456).

Meridian (Cox's Orange Pippin x Falstaff; Selection A931-15).

Park Farm Pippin (Falstaff x A409-21; Selection E11-20).

Saturn (PRI 1235 x Starkspur Golden Delicious; Selection SA15-4).

b. Dessert cultivars

Jester Worcester (Pearmain x Starkspur Golden Delicious; Selection A116/28).

Falstaff James (Grieve x Golden Delicious; Selection A120/3).

Greensleeves James (Grieve x Golden Delicious; Selection A120/6).

Jupiter (Cox x Starking Delicious; Selection A133/8).

Kent (Cox x Jonathan; Selection A1379).

Suntan (Cox x Court Pendu Plat; Selection A1585).

Fiesta (Red Pippin) (Cox x Idared; Selection T31/31)

Redsleeves (Exeter Cross x TSR15T3; Selection A232/2)

c. Columnar dessert cultivars

Obelisk (Flamenco) (Cox x Court Pendu Plat) x McIntosh Wijcik; Selection SA54-81).

Telamon (Waltz) (McIntosh Wijcik x Golden Delicious; Selection SA251-18).

Trajan (Polka) (Golden Delicious x McIntosh Wijcik; Selection SA252-107).

Tuscan (Bolero) (McIntosh Wijcik x Greensleeves; Selection SA256-24).

d. Culinary cultivars

Bountiful (Cox open pollinated T20/1).

Charlotte McIntosh (Wijcik x Greensleeves; Selection SA219-25).

e. Ornamental columnar cultivars

Maypole McIntosh (Wijcik x *Malus baskatong;* Selection SA244-20).

Totem (Ottawa 521 x *M. zumi* open pollinated) x Maypole; Selection SA572-2).

f. Rootstock cultivars

M.1 to 16, M.17 to 24, M.25 (Northern Spy x M.2), **M.26** (M.16 x M.9 Malling; Selection 3436), **M27** (M.13 x M.93431). **MM.104** (M.2 x Northern Spy), **MM.106** (Northern Spy x M.1), **MM.109** (M.2 x Northern Spy; Selected at EM, Cross John Innes) and **MM.111** (Northern Spy x Merton 793; Selected at EM, Cross John Innes).

Cultivars developed in India

Lal Ambri (Red Delicious x Ambri): The tree is upright with moderate vigour and is free from incidence of scab.

Sunderi (Ambri x Golden Delicious): The tree is upright with moderate vigour and is free from incidence of scab.

Firdous (Golden Delicious x Rome Beauty x *Malus floribunda*): It is a mid season cultivar, resistant to scab, powdery mildew and *Alternaria.* Fruits are large and have good taste. Fruit yield is 7.2 t/ha.

Shireen (Lord Lambourne x Melba XR-1274078): It is a mid season cultivar, resistant to scab, powdery mildew and *Alternaria*.

Akbar (Ambri x Cox's Orange Pippin): The tree is upright, high yielding and resistant to scab and powdery mildew.

Ambred (Red Delicious x Ambri 157): Trees are tall, spreading and open. Fruits mature in second week of September. Fruit has medium size, conical shape, bright red stripes over barium yellow skin colour. The flesh is aromatic, crisp and juicy and has good keeping quality. Incidence of powdery mildew, sooty blotch and apple scab is low.

Ambstarking (Starking Delicious x Ambri 82): The trees have open canopy and fruits mature in second week of September. Fruit has medium size, round conical shape, red streaks over chrome yellow skin colour. The flesh is crisp and juicy. It is tolerant to scab.

Ambrich (Rich-a-Red x Ambri 15): The trees are semi-dwarf having spreading and drooping canopy. Fruits mature in second week of September. Fruit has medium size and round conical shape. The fruit is crisp and juicy with subacid taste. It is moderately susceptible to powdery mildew, sooty blotch and fly speck and tolerant to scab.

Ambroyal (Starking Delicious x Ambri 84): Trees are semi-dwarf with spreading canopy. Fruits mature in third week of September. Fruit has medium size, conical shape and red streaks on yellow ground colour. The fruit has soft and juicy flesh.

Chaubattia Anupam (Early Shanberry x Red Delicious): Trees are vigorous with upright canopy. It is somewhat early maturing cultivar. Fruits are medium-sized and somewhat conical having bright red streaks with red blush on pale ground colour and have good keeping quality. The flesh is aromatic and crisp.

Chaubattia Princess (Early Shanberry x Red Delicious): Trees are medium in vigour with upright canopy. Fruits are medium-sized and conical having deep red streaks on pale skin and have good keeping quality. The flesh is juicy and crisp.

Chaubattia Swarnima (Benoni x Red Delicious): Fruits mature in first to second week of July. Fruits are red coloured with some stripes over pale coloured skin and have good keeping quality. The flesh is juicy and slightly tart in taste.

Chaubattia Alankar (Fanny x Red Delicious): Fruits mature in second week of July. Fruits are round and have red stripes over yellow skin.

Chaubattia Anurag (Esopus Spitzenberg x Red Delicious): Fruits mature in third week of July to first week of September. Fruits are medium-sized, conical and slightly flattened at base. The skin is yellowish with bright red colour at top. The flesh is juicy and sweet.

Chaubattia Agrim: Originated by mutation of Early Shanberry bud wood with gamma rays. Fruits mature in last week of June and are small, egg-shaped and slightly conical. The skin is yellow with slight red tinge. The flesh is dirty yellowish white and sour to sweet in taste.

KKL 1: It is a selection from Parlin's Beauty. It is suited to the warm winter conditions of Kodaikanal hills in South India. The tree is medium-sized giving fruit yield of 22 t/ha (400 fruits/tree). It is a mid season cultivar. Fruits mature during July-August and are tasty having 13^0B TSS.

Commercial cultivars: Red Delicious, Starking Delicious and Richared.

Coloured strains: Top Red, Vance Delicious and Hardeman.

Spur type cultivars: Red Spur, Red Chief, Starkimson and Oregan Spur.

Low chilling cultivars: Tamar, Vered, Tropical Beauty, Mayaan Michael and Schlomit.

Scab resistant cultivars: Sir price, Prima, Liberty, Redfree and Freedom.

Genus *Amelanchier* Medik. (2n = 34, 68 and aneuploid numbers)

The species of the genus are naturally distributed from 500 to 1000 m above sea level in north temperate zones.

The various *Amelanchier* species are known by the common names such as service berry, sarvis, May cherry, June cherry, Saskatoons, shadlow, shadbush, shadcherry, shadblossom, shadflower, shadwood, sugar pear, wild pear, lancewood, boxwood, Canadian medlar, bilberry and snowy mespilus (Stang, 1990; St. Pierre, 1992).

A. alnifolia Nutt.: The plants are 1-7 m tall shrubs and distributed from Ontario, North West Territories and Yukon in Canada, south to Colorado, USA.

A. asiatica sinica Schneid. (2n=34): The plants are 12 m tall trees and distributed in China, Japan and Korea.

A. amabilis Wieg. (2n=34): The plants are 1- 2 m tall shrubs and distributed from Quebec, Canada to New York, USA.

A. arborea Michx.f. (2n=68): The plants are 20 m tall trees and distributed from New Brunswick, Canada to Minnesota, south to Louisiana and North Florida, USA.

A. bartramiana Tausch (2n=68): The plants are 0.5-2.5 m high shrubs, distributed from Newfoundland to Ontario, Canada, south to North Michigan, USA.

A. canadensis L. Medic (2n=68): The plants are 8 m high shrubs, distributed from Maine to Georgia, USA.

A. fernaldii Wieg.: The plants are 0.5-1 m high shrubs, distributed from Newfoundland to Quebec, Canada.

A. gaspensis Wieg.: The plants are 0.5-1 m high shrubs, distributed in Quebec and Ontario in South Canada to Michigan, USA.

A. grandiflora Rheder: The plants are 1-3 m high shrubs, distributed in Europe and north east North America.

A. humilis Wlieg. (2n=34): The plants are 0.3-8 m high shrubs, distributed from Quebec, Canada to South Dakota, USA.

A. huronensis Wieg.: The plants are 3-7 m high trees, distributed in Great Lakes, North America.

A. interior Niel.: The plants are 10 m high trees, distributed in Wisconsin to South Dakota, USA.

A. laevis Wieg. (2n=68): The plants are 13 m high trees, distributed from Newfoundland, Canada to North Iowa, south to Georgia, USA, Quebec, Canada to South Dakota, USA.

A. obovalis Michx.: The plants are 0.2-1.5 m high shrubs, distributed from New Jersey to Georgia Alabama, USA.

A. ovalis Medicus (2n=68): The plants are 2-4 m high shrubs, widely distributed in Europe.

A. sanguinea Pursh. DC (2n=34): The plants are 1-3 m high shrubs, distributed from Quebec, Canada to North Wisconsin, south to North Carolina, USA.

A. spicata Lam. K.Koch (2n=68): The plants are 8 m high shrubs, distributed in Sweden, also Maine to Georgia, USA.

A. stolonifera. Wieg. (2n=34, 68): The plants are 2-3 m high shrubs, distributed in Newfoundland Canada to Minnesota, south to Virginia, USA.

Saskatoon berry

(***A. alnifolia*** Nutt.; June berry; Service berry) x = 17; 2n=34

It is native of North America. The plant is stoloniferous deciduous shrub or small tree of maximum 5 m height with scaly bark and unarmed branches bearing slender terete branchlets. The leaves are simple, alternate and their stipules soon fall. These are coarsely toothed toward the apex to sub-entire, usually sub-glabrous above and somewhat tomentose beneath. The flowers are white, perfect, regular and entomophilous borne on more or less tomentose racemes of up to 4 cm length. The calyx tube (hypanthium) is bell-shaped and 5-lobed. Five white petals are 1 cm long and spathulate. Stamens (10-20) are short and 2 to 5 styles may be free or united with 5-celled ovary. The ovary is wooly and about 1.5 cm in commercial cultivars. Fruits are borne in clusters of 6-12 and may be blue, purple, cream, red or almost black but commonly dark blue or purple. The diameter of the fruit is 0.6-1 cm at the base or in the middle. The flesh is juicy and contains 5-10 seeds (Stang, 1990; St. Pierre, 1992) having sweet and slightly pungent taste with a very mild taste with a nutty almond flavour and very low acidity.

Cultivars (Hilton, 1982; St. Pierre, 1992)

Moonlake: It is a late blooming and frost resistant cultivar.

Honeywood: The cultivar is precocious and shows resistance to leaf spot.

Regent: The cultivar has high productivity and fruit quality. It is resistant to leaf spot disease.

Cultivars **Smoky**, **Pembina**, **Northline** and **Thiessen** bear large good quality fruits. Cultivars **Parkhill**, **Regent** and **Forestburg** bear large and soft fruits. **Paleface** bears white fruits and **Sturgeon** has large fruit clusters.

Genus *Aronia* Medik. (2n = 34, 68, and one aneuploid)

The plants are unarmed shrubs or small trees. Leaves are simple having small, caducous, leaf shedding stipules. Inflorescence is a simple raceme. Hypanthium is obconical to campanulate, upper part free and saucer to cup-shaped. Sepals are persistent. Petals are white, rarely pink. Stamens are usually 20, sometimes fewer. Carpels are 2-5, ventrally free (partly) from each other, laterally more or less connate, dorsally more than half adnate to hypanthium, top dome-shaped and glabrous or hairy. Cells of the ovary are usually divided with incomplete septa between the ovules. Style is free to highly connate having truncate to capitate stigma(s). Fruit is a small pome, red to black having thin flesh of uniform consistency, almost entirely of hypanthial origin, inner layer with sclereids. Carpel wall is thin and core is bony. Seeds are several per fruit with thick testa and a very thin endosperm layer. Around 20 species occur in northern temperate region from North America, East Asia, Europe (one species), America south to Mexico and Guatemala. Some species are grown as ornamentals. Extensive hybridization occurs between species and apomictic reproduction is established (Kubitzki, 2004).

Black Chokeberry
(*Aronia melanocarpa* (Michx.) Ell.; aronia)

It is native to the eastern part of North America (USA and Canada). It has been cultivated in Europe for over a century for its juice which has high antioxidant properties. Fruit extract has been used as a component of nutrient supplements. Its commercial cultivation has spread to other parts of the world including Denmark and Russia. *Aronia* species are popular garden plants and are sometimes included in the genus *Photinia*. The North American red chokeberry (*Aronia arbutifolia*) is also known as *Photinia pyrifolia* (syn. *P. arbutifolia*) and the Japanese chokeberry as *P. glabra*. Black chokeberry differs from red chokeberry by total absence of hairs.

This is a suckering and thicket forming deciduous shrub of up to 2 m height with bright green smooth leaves that have small black glands along the upper midribs. The beautiful red autumn colours are also characteristic. Small white flowers are borne in clusters, followed by pea size berries (about 1 g each) that are glossy violet black when ripe having deep red flesh and small seeds (Van Wyk, 2005). Three cultivars, Viking, Nero and Aron are grown commercially.

Genus *Crataegus* Tourn. ex L. (hawthorn)

There are about 1000 *Crataegus* species that are used in landscape plantings. A number of these bear edible fruits and a few species such *as C. monogyna* (English hawthorn) are used for timber. *C. pinnatifida*, Chinese hawthorn, is processed for juice in China. *C. aestivalis* (Walter) Torrey and Gray, *C. opaca* Hook and Arn. and *C. rufula* Sarg. (Mayhaw) are native of the southeastern USA and grow wild in wet areas, river bottoms and along the streams from North Carolina to Florida and West Arakansas and Texas (Payne and Krewer, 1990). Mayhaw has use in processing industry (Payne and Krewer, 1990). The related edible species are *C. azarolus* L. (mediterranean medlar or azarole) and *C. pubescens* (Mexican hawthorn).

Mayhaw
(*Crataegus aestivalis* (Walter) Torrey and Gray)

The plant is round topped, deciduous shrub or small tree, 8 to 10 m in height having 2-3.5 cm long thorns. The leaves are oblong obovate, 3 cm long with 0.6-2 cm long petioles, sometimes 3-lobed. Flowers appear in glabrous clusters before or with the emergence of leaves. The flowers are showy white to pale pink and 15-28 mm in diameter. The 5 sepals are united below and petals are white, occasionally pink, stamens are in 1-5 rows of 5 each and the ovary is 1-5 celled, immersed in the tube formed by the union of sepals. The fruits are small, 8-10 mm in diameter, yellow to bright red and fragrant with three nutlets. These are acidic and juicy resembling cranberries in appearance and have a taste of crabapple (Payne and Krewer, 1990).

Cultivars

About a dozen selections have been made based on fruit size, ripening period and yield. Some of the important selections are Lori (uniform ripening) and Super Spur (heavy yielder). Promising mayhaw cultivars tested in South Georgia are T.O. Superberry, Manson's Superberry, Saline, Big Red, Crimson, Big V, Turnage 57, Texas Star and Turnage 88.

Subfamily Amygdaloideae (Prunoideae, Drupaceae or Pruneae)

Lee and Wen (2001) conducted phylogenetic analysis using the ITS sequences of nuclear ribosomal DNA (nrDNA) to construct the evolutionary history and evaluate the historical classifications of the subfam. Amygdaloideae and the genus

Prunus. The analyses suggest two major groups within the Amygdaloideae: (1) *Prunus* s.l. (sensu lato) and *Maddenia,* and (2) *Exochorda, Oemleria,* and *Prinsepia.* The ITS phylogeny supports the treatment including *Exochorda* (formerly in the Spiraeoideae) in the Amygdaloideae. *Maddenia* is found to be nested within *Prunus* s.l. in the parsimony and distance analyses, but basal to *Prunus* s.l. in the maximum likelihood analysis. Within *Prunus,* two major groups are recognizable: (1) the *Amygdalus–Prunus* group, and (2) the *Cerasus–Laurocerasus–Padus* group. The clades in the ITS phylogeny are not congruent with most subgeneric groups in the widely used classification of *Prunus* by Rehder and support a broadly defined *Prunus*.

The plants are deciduous or evergreen. Winter buds having many imbricate scales. The leaves are deciduous, alternate and mostly serrate, rarely stipulate. Flowers are solitary, in a raceme or umbellate clusters. Sepals are 5, white, usually some are pink or red. Stamens are many and the receptacle is cup shaped. Carpel is commonly one but may be up to 5 with elongated style. Ovary is superior, one-celled, 2-ovuled of which one generally aborts. The fruit is usually a one seeded drupe. The seed contains one or more glucosides, which on hydrolysis produce HCN.

Genus *Prunus* L. (2n = 16, 24, 32, 48, 56, 64, and aneuploid numbers)

Rehder (1940) classified *Prunus* into 77 species, Knight (1969), Watkins (1981; 1995b) and Kubitzki (2004) included approximately 200 species under the genus and later a considerably greater number was included (Moore and Ballington, 1990). But only 89 are listed in the Genetic Resource Information System (Anon., 1969; Ghora and Panigrahi, 1984). In India, about 36 *Prunus* species have been reported of which 18 are useful for cultivation. These species occur mostly in the temperate zone and some in the tropical and subtropical regions (Rehder, 1940; Willis, 1985; Yu¨ *et al.*, 1986; Ghora and Panigrahi, 1984, 1995). The species are cosmopolitan (very few indigenous in Africa) occurring in forests and open vegetation, often in montane or even subalpine altitudes (Table. 23.4). The species of major importance that produce delicious fruits are *P. persica, P. armeniaca, P. salicina, P. domestica, P. americana, P. avium, P. cerasus, P. dulcis, P. ceracifera, P. behimi, P. cornuta, P. cerasoides* and *P. mahaleb* besides the interspecific hybrids plumcots, pluots and apriums.

Table 23.4. Origin and distribution of some *Prunus* species (adapted from Das *et al.*, 2011).

	Species	Origin and distribution
Peach	1. *P. kansuensis* Rehd.	Northwestern China
	2. *P. davidiana* (Carr.) Franch.	North China
	3. *P. mira* Koehne	Tibetan plateau & neighbouring areas & India
	4. *P. ferganensis* (Kost. and Rjab.) Kov. and Kost.	Western China
	5. *P. consociiflora* Schneid (wild peach)	China
	6. *P. persica* var. *platycarpa* (flat peach)	China
	7. Nectarines	China. Also believed to have originated in Europe

Plum	1. *P. salicina* Lindl. (Japanese plum)	China
	2. *P. domestica* L. (European plum)	Southern Europe or western Asia
	3. *P. americana* Marsh.(American plum)	North America
	4. *P. insititia* L. (damson plum)	Western Asia or Europe
	5. *P. cerasifera* Ehrh. (cherry plum)	Central Asia as well as Europe
	6. *P. cocomilia* Ten. (Italian plum)	Italy, Greece and Yugoslavia
	7. *P. spinosa* L. (blackthorn sloe)	Europe and Asia
	8. *P. ussuriensis* Kov. and Kost. (Manchurian plum)	Manchuria, along the Ussuri river
	9. *P. alleghaniensis* Porter (allegheny plum or sloe)	Northeastern USA
	10. *P. angustifolia* Marsh. (sand plum)	Southern USA
	11. *P. geniculata* Harper (scrub plum)	Florida
	12. *P. gracilis* Engelm. & Gr. (Oklahoma plum)	Southcentral USA
	13. *P. hortulana* Bailey (hortulan plum)	Central USA
	14. *P. maritima* Marsh. (beach plum)	Northeastern USA coast
	15. *P. lanata* (Sudw.) Mack. & Bush (inch plum)	Central USA
	16. *P. mexicana* S. Wats. (Mexican plum)	Southcentral USA and Mexico
	17. *P. munsoniana* Wight & Hedr. (wild goose plum)	Southcentral USA
	18. *P. nigra* Ait. (Canada plum)	Canada and USA
	19. *P. reverchonii* Sarg. (hog plum)	Southern USA
	20. *P. rivularis* Scheele (creek plum)	Texas
	21. *P. subcordata* Benth. (Pacific plum)	Oregon and California
	22. *P. texana* Dietr. (Texas almond cherry or Texas peach bush or Texas wild plum)	Texas
	23. *P. umbellata* Ell. (flatwood plum)	Southeastern USA
Apricot	1. *P. armeniaca* L. (cultivated and wild apricot)	Asia and Caucasus including north and NE China
	2. *P. brigantina* Vill. (alpine or briancon apricot)	Alps in southeastern France
	3. *P.* x *Dasycarpa* Ehrh. (purple apricot)	Southwest Asia including Russia and adjoining regions
	4. *P. mandshurica* (Maxim.) Koehne (Manchurian apricot)	Northeast of China, Manchuria and Korea
	5. *P. mume* (Sieb) Sieb. & Zucc. (Japanese apricot)	Japan and South China
	6. *P. sibirica* L. (Siberian apricot)	Eastern Siberia, Manchuria, northern China and North Korea
	7. *P. ansu* Maxim.	Eastern China, South Korea and Japan
	8. *P. holosericea* (Batal.) Kost.	Tibetian mountain
Cherry	1. *P. cerasus* L. (sour cherry)	Carpathian basin
	2. *Prunus avium* L. (sweet cherries or mazzard)	Southern Russia, north of the Caucasian mountains to the north of France (temperate regions of Europe, from the northern part of Spain to the southeastern part of Russia)

	3. *P. fruticosa* Pall. (ground cherry)	Western and central Asia, specifically in Russia
	4. *P. tomentosa* Thunberg (Nanking or Hansen bush cherry)	Northwest China
	5. *P. besseyi* Bailey and *P. pumila* L. (sand cherries)	North America
	6. *P. serrulata* Lindl. (wild species)	Asia
Almond	*P. dulcis* (Mill.) D. A. Webb syn. *P. amygdalus* Batsch	Central to southwestern Asia. Almond originated in the more western Asian regions having arid, mountainous terrain, dry and desert climatic conditions. Cultivated types emerged within *Amygdalus communis* L. in Iran, Turkmenistan and Tadjikistan or even extended in the Transcaucasus, central Turkey, Syria, Lebanon and Jordan. Hybridization occurred among *P. fenzliana* Fritsch (found in Caucasian mountains), *P. bucharica* (Korsh.)

The plants are trees or shrubs, rarely with thorns, evergreen or leaf shedding with solid branch pith. These are less hardy than the pome fruits as they tend to flower earlier but that makes them susceptible to spring frost. Fruit buds develop axillary on one year old shoots or spurs in peach and apricot (Fig. 23.3). Leaves are with incised or entire margins, usually with glands in the margin or on the underside of the lamina or on the petiole, stipules on the twigs at the junction with the petioles are free and rarely connate. Inflorescence is basically a raceme, rarely branched, often reduced to a few flowered umbel or to only 1 or 2 flowers. Flowers are normally 5-merous and bisexual having usually partly or entirely caducous hypanthium after flowering, imbricate, usually caducous sepals, white or pink petals, 15 to many stamens, one sessile pistil, terminal stylodium and capitate stigma with solitary carpel. Fruit is a drupe having thin, fleshy or juicy to rather dry and sometimes dehiscent mesocarp (almond) with endocarp forming a bony to woody, smooth or rugose pyrene in wild species. Seed has thin testa. The fruits have much poorer storage life being softer at maturity but have exquisite flavours. Many species and species hybrids were domesticated long ago and are cultivated for fruits such as peach, cherry, plum, apricot and almond and as ornamentals and used in folk medicine and phytotherapy (Kubitzki, 2004). Many are consumed dried, especially plum and apricot. Black cherry, *P. serotina* is an important timber species.

Polyploidy resulting from natural interspecific hybridization in *Prunus* (x = 8) played an important role in the process of evolution of new species or strains. This is the main cause for self sterility and intersterility in this genus. Somatic chromosome numbers vary from diploid to hexaploid: *P. salicina* (2n = 16, 32), *P. simonii* (2n = 16); *P. domestica* (2n = 48), *P. spinosa* (2n = 32, 24, 40, 48), *P. cerasifera* (2n = 16, 17, 24, 32, 48), *P. insititia* (2n = 24, 48), *P.* x *dasycarpa* (2n = 16), *P. americana* (2n = 16), *P. amygdalus*, *P. bucharica*, *P. persica*, *P. davidiana*, *P. mira*, *P. armeniaca* and *P. mandshurica* (2n = 16); *P. mume* (2n = 16 or 24), *P. avium* (2n = 16, 24, 32), *P. cerasus* (2n = 32), *P. besseyi* (2n = 16), *P. fruticosa* (2n = 32), *P. mahaleb* (2n = 16), *P. tomentosa* (2n = 16), *P. padus* (2n = 16) and *P. serotina* (2n = 32).

Key to the classification of *Prunus* (After Hedrick, 1911)

A. Surface of the fruit velvety (surface smooth in peach and nectarine) and stone-pitted or furrowed. .... peach, nectarine and almond

B. Flesh is soft, thick and juicy.

Leaves in the bud are folded.

The flowers are mostly in pairs. .... peach and nectarine

C. Fruit is velvety. Winter shoots have terminal bud. .... peach

CC. Fruit is smooth. .... nectarine

BB. Flesh is hard, thin and dry. Flowers are solitary. ....almond

AA. Surface of the fruit is glabrous or nearly so. .... plum, cherry and apricot

B. Flowers are clustered. Stone is usually smooth. .... plum and cherry

C. Fruit is usually large, sulcate and covered with bloom. Stone is compressed, longer than broad, grooved on the dorsal and winged on the ventral suture. Leaves in the bud are rolled. .... plum

CC. Fruit is usually small, round and bloomless. Stone is turgid, round and usually shorter than broad, ridged on the ventral suture. The leaves in the bud are folded. .... cherry

BB. Flowers are solitary or but two. Surface of the fruit is somewhat fuzzy. Stone is smooth or sometimes pitted. The leaves in the bud are rolled. .... apricot

Fig.23.3. Terminal and subterminal twigs of peach and apricot (Source: Zielinski, 1955).

Three subgenera, namely *Amygdalus* (peaches and almonds), *Prunophora* (plums and apricots) and *Cerasus* (cherries), are universally accepted under the genus *Prunus* (Westwood, 1978; Das *et al.*, 2011). However, the genus has been classified into 5 subgenera, *Prunophora* Focke, *Amygdalus* (L.) Focke, *Cerasus* Pers., *Padus* (Mill.) Focke, and *Laurocerasus* (Tourn. ex Duhamel) Rehd.) (Knight, 1969; Watkins, 1995b, 1981; Kubitzki, 2004). Ingram (1948) added one more subg. *Lithocerasus* (Ingram) (=subg. *Cerasus;* cherries).

Subgenus *Prunophora* Focke (plum and apricot)

The flowers are solitary or in umbel like clusters, appearing before or rarely with the leaves. The pedicel usually remains with the fruit. There is no terminal bud and axillary buds are solitary. The fruits are sulcate (with external longitudinal groove), glabrous (typically hairless), usually with bloom on the epidermis and the pressed stone is usually longer than broad and smooth or nearly so. There are 19 species of plum and 6 of apricot. The type species is *P. domestica* (plum).

Section *Euprunus* (16 spp.; 2x-6x; European and Asian plums; distributed from Europe to China): Typically, there are 1-2-stalked flowers per cluster. The leaves in the bud are convolute. Ovary and fruit are glabrous.

P. spinosa Blackthorn. (Sloe; distributed in West Asia, Europe and North Africa). It is a tetraploid (2n = 32). The plant is densely branched very thorny shrub or small tree growing to about 4 m in height having black shoots, 3.75 cm long and obtuse leaves, hairy only in the beginning. Flowers are solitary with smooth pedicels and emerge before the leaves. Fruit is blue black and waxy with distinctive bloom, globose, 1-1.5 cm and very astringent. It is generally accepted that it is involved along with *P. cerasifera* in the ancestry of *P. domestica.*

P. domestica agg. (*P. spinosa* x *P. cerasifera*; Plums, Bullaces, Damsons and Greengages): Natural hybrids of this parentage occur in the Caucasus. The plants are widely cultivated in temperate zones for fruits.

ssp. *domestica* (European or garden plum; 6x) is widely naturalized in West Asia and Europe. The tree is 10-12 m in height and spines are absent. Flowers are in pairs, greenish white and about 2 cm across. Fruit is 4-7.5 cm, longer than wide, bluish black, purple and red.

ssp. *institia* (Bullace, Damson, St. Julien; 6x; distributed in West Asia and Europe). The exact origin of damson, *P. domestica* subsp. *institia*, is debatable. It is often thought to have arisen in Asia Minor from wild crosses, possibly between the sloe (*P. spinosa*) and cherry plum (*P. cerasifera*). It is considered to be between *P. domestica* and *P. institia* but is also considered to be same as *P. institia*. It is archaically called the "damascene"; an edible drupaceous fruit. Cultivars are found across Europe. The name "damson" is derived from the most common forms which are native to the United Kingdom. Damsons are relatively small plums with a distinctive, somewhat astringent taste and are widely used for culinary purposes, particularly in preserves.

The plant is shrub or tree up to 6 m, often with thorns. It is more winter hardy compared even to *P. domestica*. The trees and fruits are similar to those of *P. domestica*. The young shoots are hairy at first. The leaves are smaller and ovate. Flowers are white, small, about 2.5 cm across and are usually in pairs. Unlike *P. domestica*, the pistil is glabrous. Fruit is 2 cm long, blue black or yellow, round and sweet in Bullace and oval and astringent in Damson (originated near Damascus). It does not hybridize freely.

ssp. *italica* (ssp. *domestica* x ssp. *institia*; Greengage, Reine Claude; distributed in Armenia and introduced into England by the Gage family between 1494 and 1547): Fruit is more or less globose, greenish and has very characteristic sweet taste.

P. cerasifera (Myrobalan, cherry plum; 2x, 3x, 4x, 6x); distributed in West Asia): The plant is shrub or tree of 8-10 m height, often spiny. The trees resemble those of *P. salicina* but have no longitudinal striations on the bark and have single and small buds. The leaves are downy on the veins on the lower surface. Some cultivars have dark purple leaves. Flowers (1-3) emerge from each bud on the previous season's growth. Flowers are solitary, about 2.5 cm across, appearing with or a little before the leaves and are mostly white. Fruit is globose, cherry like, 2-3 cm across and red or yellow and indented near the stalk end having a small furrow-like structure. It is known to be in cultivation to a limited extent for its fruit. It is an important rootstock for other plum speeics and as an ornamental plant.

var. *pissardli* has reddish, purple-tinged leaves and pinkish flowers. It is more common as an ornamental plant.

P. divaricata distributed from Caucasus east to Asia: It is diploid very similar to *P. cerasifera* and is considered to be its synonym. It is the wild form of the species differing virtually only by smaller yellow fruits that are not indented near the stalk end.

P. x *syriaca* (*P. cerasifera* x *P. domestica*; Mirabelle Plum; known to occur in a semi-wild state in Europe): It has subglobose yellow fruits.

P. salicina (Salicine, Japanese plum; 2x, 4x; distributed in China): Tree is about 12 m high. Flowers are white, about 2 cm across, appearing typically in clusters of 3, well before the leaves. Fruit is sweet, more or less globose, 5-7 cm long, depressed at stalk end, varying in colour from greenish to yellow, orange red. It is cultivated in Japan and elsewhere especially USA since 19th century, but the fruit is inferior in quality to most other cultivated plums.

P. simonii (Simon or apricot plum): It comes from China. The plants have peach-like, thin, lanceolate and glandular leaves, large, round, brick red fruits that are 5 cm in diameter and nearly sessile, more like the apricot. Its hybrids with the Japanese plum may be important.

Section *Prunocerasus* (18 spp.; 2x; American plums; distributed in North America): It has 2-5 flowers per cluster. Leaves are mostly conduplicate in bud, rarely convolute. Ovary and fruit are glabrous. Stone is mostly smooth.

P. americana (American red plum; 2x; distributed in North America): Tree is up to 10 m in height. Flowers are white, about 3 cm across. Fruit is virtually round, about 2.5 cm across, usually red, rarely yellowish. Hybrids with *P. salicina* have been made in America to produce new types.

Section *Armeniaca* (6 spp.; 2x, 3x; Apricots, mumes; distributed in China): The plants are thornless shrubs or trees. Flowers appear before the leaves and are usually sessile or subsessile. Leaves are convolute in bud. Ovary and fruit are pubescent.

P. mandshurica (Manchurian apricot; distributed in Korea and Manchuria): The tree is up to 5 m in height with pendulous and somewhat spreading branches. Flowers are pink, solitary, about 3 cm across. Fruit is nearly round, 2.5 cm, yellow. Selections are widely cultivated as ornamentals.

P. armeniaca (Apricot; distributed in West Asia): The tree is up to 10 m in height. Bark is reddish. Flowers are white or pink, mostly solitary, 2.5 cm across. Fruit is round, 4-8 cm, short velvety, yellow with red blush. Stone is smooth but is furrowed along one margin. It is widely cultivated in warmer parts of temperate zones of both the hemispheres.

P. brigantina (Briancon apricot; distributed in south east France): The plant is shrub or tree up to 6 m in height. Flowers are white and appear in clusters of 2-5. Fruit is clear yellow, almost round, about 2.5 cm, quite smooth and glabrous. Inflammable perfumed oil, Huile de Marmotte, is expressed from the seeds.

The other related species are *P. armeniaca* var. *siberica* or *P. siberica (*Russian apricot) having narrower and much darker leaves and small fruits of poor quality that hang in clusters, *P. mume* (Japanese apricot) having small trees with grayish or greenish bark, leaves cuneate at the base, beautiful flowers and small fruits with dry and cling type flesh and pitted stone and *P. dasycarpa* (*Prunus x dasycarpa* Ehrh.) is black or purple apricot and is natural hybrid between *P. cerasifera* and *P. armeniaca.*

Subgenus *Amygdalus* (L.) Focke (Peaches, almonds)

Terminal bud is present with 3 axillary buds, the lateral ones being flower buds and leaves conduplicate in bud. Flowers are sessile or short stalked and are in clusters of 1-2, appearing before leaves. Fruit is tomentose (glabrous in nectarine) with external groove, usually dehiscent and the stone is pitted or smooth. There are 76 primary species. Both peach (*P. persica* (L.) Batsch.) and almond (*P. amygdalus* Batsch.) have 2n=16 and a number of common characteristics including graft and pollen compatibility. The type species is *P. dulcis* (almond).

Section *Euamygdalus* (14 spp.; 2x, 8x; distributed from western Asia to China): Calyx tube is cup-shaped and about as long as its sepal lobes.

P. amygdalus (Almond; distributed in West Asia): Tree is up to 8 m in height. Flowers are subsessile, pale pink, 3-5 cm across and are usually solitary. Fruit is velvety, compressed roundish, up to 6 cm long with smooth stone but with pits. It is widely cultivated in South Europe and California, also as an ornamental for its early spring flowers.

var. *dulcis* (2x; sweet almond of commerce; distributed in Britain): It is planted only as an ornamental plant.

var. *amara* (Bitter almond): It is very bitter in taste, contains potentially lethal amounts of prussic acid.

P. persica (Peach; 2x; distributed in China): The tree is 6-7 m in height. Flowers are solitary, pink and up to 3.5 cm across. Fruit is globose, velvety, 5-7 cm, yellowish and tinged reddish on the exposed side. The stone is furrowed and deeply pitted. It is widely cultivated in temperate zones.

var. *nectarina* (Nectarine): Fruit skin is quite glabrous as in the plum.

Some of the other species are *P. persica* var. *pendula* having pendulous branches, *P. persica* var. *pyramidales* having pyramid shaped crown and upright branches, *P. persica* var. *alboplena* having white double flowers and *P. persica* var. *roseoplena* having red double flowers, besides the Chinese peach (*P. davidiana*) having upright trees with smooth shoots, long, slender and glabrous leaves and solitary flowers. It is used as rootstock for peach for resistance to alkaline soil conditions.

Section *Chamaeamygdalus* (1 spp.; 2x, 3x; distributed from southeastern Europe to eastern Siberia): Calyx tube (hypanthium) is much longer than its sepal lobes.

P. tenella (Dwarf Russian almond; distributed from south east Europe to West Asia and East Siberia): It is a bushy shrub up to almost 2 m in height. Flowers appear in clusters of 1-3 and have a fine rose red colour and are 1-2 cm across. Fruit is like a small almond, velvety, 2.5 cm long and ovoid. It has been used in breeding to develop several ornamental types.

The wild species that possibly had role in the development of the present day cultivated almond types are *P. bucharica* Korschinsky from the steppes of Uzbekistan, Tadjistan, Hindu Kush and Pamir Mountains and Afghanistan having smooth pointed nuts with a hard but relatively thin shell and sweet kernels and are hardy with a moderate to high chilling requirement. *P. communis* (L.) Archang. from the slopes and deep gorges in dry and snowless area of Turkmenistan and the slopes of mountains in Uzbekistan have hard nuts with deep grooves, sweet kernels and soft shells. *P. orientalis* (Mill.), *P. argentea* (Lam.) Rehd., *P. eotschyi* (Boissier and Hohen.) Nab. and *P. korschinskii* Hand-Mazz. including *P. eorschinskii* from the mountains of Iraq, Syria and western Iran extending into Turkey have small, hard-shelled nuts with grooved surfaces. *P. tangutica* Batal. (*P. dehiscens* Koehne) from the Chinese provinces of Kansu and Szechwan, *P. webbii* (Spach.) Vieh. from the European region extending from western Turkey into the Balkan peninsula including Greece, Bulgaria and Yugoslavia and *P. scoparia* Spach. have thin and fleshy mesocarp, thin, smooth and very hard shells, small, dark brown, smooth and bitter kernels. The species *P. spartioides* Spach., *P. arabica* Olivier, *P. glauca* Browicz, grow in xerophytic conditions on the steppes and low desert areas of Iran, Turkistan, Afghanistan, Soviet Armenia Saudi Arabia, Iraq, Syria and Turkey. The species, *P. spinosissima* Franchet, *P. turcomanica* Lincz., are adapted to the extremely xerophytic regions in Iraq, through Iran, Afghanistan, southern Soviet Armenia and southern Tadjikistan.

Subgenus *Lithocerasus* (Ingram) (= subg. *Cerasus*; cherries): Axillary buds are in threes. Flowers appear in early spring in corymbs, long-stalked and not on leafed shoots. Fruit is not grooved and stone is smooth. The type species is *P. pumila* (sand cherry)

Section *Microcerasus* Webb. (14 spp.; 2x; distributed in North Temperate Zone): Flowers are solitary or in short few-flowered (less than 10 (12)) racemes. Leaf axils have 3 buds.

P. tomentosa Thunb. (Downy cherry, Chinese bush cherry; distributed in north and west China, Japan and the Himalaya): It is a sprawling shrub up to about 3 m in height, rarely tree-like. Flowers are white or pink tinged and 1,5-2 cm across. Fruit is almost round. 1 cm across, bright red, edible and may be slightly hairy. It has ornamental value. Himalayan collections are possibly from the cultivated plants.

P. glandulosa Thunb. (Niwazakura white and pink, dwarf flowering almond; distributed in China and Japan): The plants are bushy shrubs of about 1.5 m height. Flowers are white or pinkish. Fruit is round, red, 10-12 mm across. Double flowered plants 'Alba Plena' (white), 'Rosea Plena' (pink) are of great ornamental value.

P. pumila L. (Dwarf American cherry, sand cherry; distributed in North America): The shrub is 1-2.5 m high. Flowers are (almost) white appearing in clusters of 2-4. Fruit is subglobose, purplish to black, 8-12 mm long and too bitter to be really palatable. The species has been hybridized with plum species *P. cerasifera*.

P. besseyi Bailey (Rocky mountain cherry, western sand cherry; distributed in North America): It is similar to *P. pumila* but has slightly larger flowers and edible sweet fruits. Both the species have potential value for rootstock breeding.

P. humilis Bge. is distributed in North China, *P. incana* (Pall.) in southeast Europe and West Asia, *P. jacquemontii* Hook. in northwestern Himalayas, *P. japonica* Thumb. in Central China and East Asia, *P. microcarpa* C. A. Mey in Asia Minor and *P. prostrata* Labill. is distributed in West Asia.

Subgenus *Cerasus* Pers. (2n=16, 32; cherries)

The tree is large. The vegetative buds are solitary. Terminal bud is present and the leaves are conduplicate in buds. The fruit buds are mixed and are borne in clusters laterally on thick and long spurs, some are also borne on last season's shoots. The inflorescence is umbel-like. Flowers are 1-10(12), sometimes in short (up to 5 cm) racemes of less than 10 flowers. The flowers are sessile, white or rose-coloured, usually with pedicel, solitary or fascicled in raceme clusters of 2-5. The calyx tube is cup-shaped or tubular, the style is furrowed and the stigma is emarginate with usually glabrous ovary. The fruit is small virtually without groove or bloom and borne on long fruit stalk. The stone is smooth or furrowed and pitted. Very few cultivars are self fertile and are mostly self unfruitful. Many are cross incompatible. The type species is *P. cerasus* (sour cherry).

Section *Pseudocerasus* Koehne (14 spp.; 2x, 3x, 4x; distributed from central Asia to Japan): It is similar to section Microcerasus but the sepals are upright or spreading and buds are solitary. Flowers appear in few-flowered short bunches. Many ornamental flowering cherries have been derived from the Chinese and Japanese species of this section or from their hybrids.

P. subhirtella Miq. (wild spring or higan cherry; distributed in Japan): The tree is up to 9 m in height. Flowers appear in clusters of 2-5, each about 2 cm across, pale pinkish tending to fade with age. It includes many attractive ornamentals, especially cultivar Autumnalis that flowers from late fall to early spring.

var. *ascendens* (wild mountainous form of the species distributed in West China, Japan and Korea): Tree is up to 20 m in height and leaves are large. It is of interest essentially for its involvement in developing cultivated types.

P. incisa Thunb. (Fuji cherry; distributed in Japan): The bushy shrub is up to 5 m, sometimes growing into a tree up to 10 m in height. It was a female parent with *P. campanulata* of the very fine floriferous hardy hybrid Okame.

P. nipponica Matsum (Japanese alpine cherry; distributed in Japan): The bush or bushy headed tree grows up to 6 m in height. It is an early flowering fine cherry.

P. 'Kursar', raised from seed of *P. nipponica* var. *kurilensis*.

P. campanulata Maxim (bell-flowered cherry; distributed in Formosa and South Japan): The tree is up to 9 m in height, less hardy than other species of this section. It was a pollen parent of Okame.

P. rufa (Himalayan pink flowered type): It is closely related to *P. tricantha* from Sikkim.

P. serrula distributed in China and Tibet: The tree is 10-16 m high, prized for its fine flaky bright brown bark. Flowers are white and in clusters of 1-3.

P. concinna distributed in China: It produces a profusion of white flowers before the leaves appear.

P. conradinae distributed in China: It includes some semidouble-flowered selections.

P. yedoensis Matsum (Yoshino cherry; distributed in Japan): It is a source of several attractive ornamental selections. It is possibly a hybrid, *P. speciosa x P. subhirtella*.

P. sargentii Rehd. (Sargent cherry; distributed in North Japan, Sakhalin or Sachalin, a USSR island north of Japan): The tree is up to 25 m in height. Flowers are rose pink, 3-4 cm across, 2-6 in an umbel. Fruit is almost black, subglobose, 8-10 mm across. It has very attractive flowers and orange to red fall foliage.

P. serrulata Lindl. (native of China, Japan and Korea): It is distinguished as *P. serrulata* var. *spontanea* which is the national tree of Japan. Some 60 Japanese flowering cherries ('Sato Zakura' in Japanese, meaning domestic cherries) are listed under it and some are thought to have their origin from *P. serrulata* but the majority of them were probably derived from *P. speciosa* (*P. lannesiane* var. *albida*), the Oshima cherry. It also includes Sakura. It is regarded as a garden form having scentless double white or pink flowers of the hill cherry. The tree reaches a height of 20 m.

P. speciosa (Oshima cherry; distributed in Japan): It is very closely related to *P. serrulata* and is sometimes included under this species but is not synonymous to it. Flowers are single, white and fragrant.

P. siebodii (Carr.) distributed in Japan: It is generally regarded as a hybrid (*P. speciosa x ?*). Tree reaches a height of 8 m with 2-4 large, often double flowers on each short peduncle.

P. cerasoides D. Don is distributed in Himalayas and *P. kurilensis* (Miyabe) Wils. in Japan.

Section *Lobopetalum* Koehne (4 Chinese spp.; 4x; distributed in China): it is similar to section *Pseudocerasus* but has reflexed sepals. Petals are notched at apex or are 2-lobed.

P. cantabrigiensis Stapf. (Cambridge cherry; distributed in China): The tree has 3-6 pink flowers in each short stalked umbel. Fruit is like a bright red cherry, 1 cm across. It is often confused with *P. pseudocerasus*.

P. pseudocerasus Lindl. is distributed in northern China: It is similar to *P. cantabrigiensis* but has 2-6 flowers in a raceme and the bracts at the base of each pedicel are gland-toothed. A selection intermediate between this and *P. cantabrigiensis* was hybridized with *P. avium* to produce the new rootstock 'Colt' for sweet and sour cherries and 'Cornflower' for ornamental cherries.

P. involucrata Koehne is distributed in central China and *P. dielsisana* in China.

Section *Eucerasus* Koehne (3 spp.; 2x, 3x, 4x, 5x; distributed from Europe to central Asia): It is similar to section *Lobopetalum* but the petals are not notched or lobed. Flowers are usually in sessile umbels with persistent bud scales at the base.

P. avium L. (Mazzard, Gean, wild sweet cherry; 2x; distributed in Europe, southwest Russia and North Africa mountains). The tree is 20-24 m in height. Flowers are pure white, 2.5 cm across with calyx tube (hypanthium) constricted above. Fruit is globose, 9-12 (18) mm across, typically blackish red, sweet or bitter but not sour (acidic). It is ancestor of most of the sweet cherries.

P. cerasus L. (sour cherry; 4x; distributed in southeast Europe): It is not known as a wild plant. It is widely cultivated and often naturalized over Europe and West Asia. It is similar to *P. avium* but is often shrubby and does not exceed 10 m in height, commonly suckering. Calyx tube (hypanthium) is not constricted above. Fruit is bright red, sour (acidic) but not bitter. It is the ancestor of Morello cherries.

P. fruticosa Pall. (ground cherry; distributed from Europe to parts of Siberia): The plants are dwarf, spreading shrubs up to 1 m in height. Flowers are white and 1.5 cm across. Fruit is dark red, round, nearly 1 cm across, of cherry-like taste but is scarcely palatable. It has long been cultivated in Europe.

P. canescens Boiss. (gray leaf cherry; distributed in China): The bushy shrub is up to 2(3) m in height. It is of little ornamental value except as a parent, along with *P. avium* of the hybrid *P. x schmittii*, which has pale pink flowers and polished bark. It is distributed in central and western China.

Section *Mahaleb* Focke (4 spp.; 2x; distributed in Europe, western Asia and North America): It is similar to section Eucerasus, but the scales at base of flower clusters drop before flowers open. Flowers are mostly in racemes of 12 or fewer, less often in umbels. Bracts are deciduous and leaf teeth are rounded.

P. mahaleb L. (St. Lucie cherry, Mahaleb cherry; distributed in central and South Europe and West Asia): The trees are small, up to 10-12 m in height, and have greenish coppery bark during the growing season that peels off in rings and has a smell. Young shoots are hairy. The leaves are roundish ovate, 1.25-6.25 cm long (as long as broad), short, abruptly pointed, shallow toothed and are perfumed and hairy beneath. Petioles are 1.25 cm long. The bracts are small and deciduous and are many flowered in short umbel-like racemes. Flowers are white, 12-18 mm across, fragrant, in 6-10(12)-flowered 3-4 cm long racemes. The pedicels are 1.25 cm long. Fruit is black, ovoid and 8-10 mm long. It is used as rootstock for cherries, although the resulting trees have short life.

P. pennsylvanica L. (pin or wild red cherry; distributed in North America): The plants are shrubs or trees up to 12 m in height with very slender, red, shiny and often pendulous branches. Flowers are white, 12 mm across in 2-5(10) umbels or short racemes. Fruit is round, 6 mm across, red and highly productive.

P. emarginata (Hook.) Walp is distributed in USA and *P. prunifolia* (Greene) Shafer in Canada and USA.

Section *Phyllocerasus* Koehne (1 sp.; China): It is similar to section Mahaleb, but the bracts are persistent with pointed leaf teeth and 1-4 flowered umbels.

P. pilosiuscala Koehne distributed in central and West China): The plants are shrubs or trees up to 12 m in height. Flowers are white and 18-20 mm across. Fruit is ellipsoidal, 8-9 mm long and red.

Section *Phyllomahaleb* Koehne (2 spp.; 4x; distributed in Europe, Asia and North America): It is similar to section *Mahaleb.* but the flowers are borne in (4)5-10 flowered racemes.

P. maximowiczii Rupr. distributed in Japan, Korea and Manchuria): The tree is up to 16 m in height. Flowers are 6-10, dull yellowish white, 1.5 cm across, borne in the racemes. Fruit is round, 5 mm across, red and finally turn black. Foliage often becomes strikingly red in the fall.

P. pleiocerasus Koehne and *P. alabamensis* Mohr. are distributed in USA.

Subgenus *Padus* (Mill.) Focke (11 spp.; 4x; cluster cherries; distributed in Europe, Asia and North America): It is similar to subgenus Cerasus but the flowers are borne in long (6 cm or more) racemes of (10)12 or more flowers. Leaves are deciduous. Fruit is not grooved and the stone is smooth. The type species is *P. padus* (European bird cherry).

P. padus L. (European bird cherry; distributed in Europe, North Asia, Korea and Japan): The tree is 10 m (or more) in height. Flowers are white, 8-13 mm across having 6-9 mm long, fragrant petals in pendulous racemes with leafy peduncle. Fruit is round, black and 6-8 mm across. The calyx is deciduous and astringent in taste.

P. cornuta var. *glabra* Fritsch ex C. K. Schneider (*P. cornuta* (Wall. ex Royle) Steud.; Himalayan bird cherry): It is found wild in the Himalayas and in the Philippines. Its leaves look between those of plum and cherry. These are ovate oblong, 7.5-15.0 cm long, slender pointed, finely toothed and downy on the lower surface. The flowers are white, 0.63-0.83 cm in diameter and are dark brownish purple and are borne in 7.5-15.0 cm long dense cylindrical racemes.

P. nepalensis Hort. & C. Koch (*P. nepalensis* Hort. & C. Koch): It is from Nepal and is similar to *P cornuta*, but its leaves have fewer teeth and the petioles are without glands and hair. The inflorescence is very dense and hairy.

P. serotina Ehrh. (rum cherry, black cherry; distributed in North America): It is a prized timber species used for veneer, furniture and paneling as it has beautiful red colour. The tree is up to 30 m in height, usually about 15 m. The trees are in cultivation. Flowers are white, 8-10 mm across with 2-4 mm long petals. The peduncle of raceme is leafy. The fruit is round, 8-10 mm across and finally turn black and has persisting calyx.

P. buergiriana Miq is distributed in Japan and Korea, *P. grayana* Maxim in Japan, *P. maackii* Rupr. in Manchuria and Korea, *P. ssiori* F. Schmidt in North East Asia and Japan, *P. virens* (Woot & Standl.) in USA and *P. viriginiana* L. is distributed in Canada and USA.

Subgenus *Laurocerasus* (Tourn. ex Duhamel) Rehd. (2 spp.; 8x, 22x; Laurel cherries; distributed from Europe to western Asia): It is similar to subgenus *Padus* but the plants are evergreen (all the other subgenera are deciduous). Peduncles of the racemes are always leafless and short-stalked. Fruit is not grooved and stone is smooth. The type species is *P. laurocerasus* (European laurel cherry).

P. lusitanica (Portugal laurel; distributed in Portugal and Spain): The plants are shrubs or trees up to 6(15) m in height. Shoots and petioles are red. Leaves are shining, elliptical and 7-13 cm long. Flowers are white, 8-13 mm across. Fruits are dark purple, rounded cone-shaped, 8 mm long and very unpalatable.

P. laurocerasus (cherry laurel; distributed in Asia Minor and south east Europe): The shrub or tree is up to 6 m in height. Shoots and petioles are pale green. Leaves are more or less obovate oblong, (5)10-15 cm long with more or less serrate margin. Flowers are white and 8-9 mm across. Fruit is purplish black, rounded, cone-shaped, about 8 mm long and is palatable.

Table 23.5. Subgenera and sections frequently involved in interspecific hybridization with *Prunus* species (Rehder, 1940)

***Prunus* species**	**Subgenera and sections involved in interspecific hybridization**	
	Major	**Minor**
European plum (*P. domestica*)	*Prunophora*	*Cerasus*
	Euprunus	*Microcerasus*
	Prunocerasus	*Amygdalus*
	Armeniaca	*Euamygdalus*
Damson plum (*P. institia*)	*Prunophora*	
	Euprunus	
Cherry plum (*P. cerasifera*) and	*Prunophora Euprunus*	*Cerasus*
Japanese plum (*P. salicina*)	*Prunocerasus*	*Microcerasus*
	Armeniaca	*Amygdalus*
		Euamygdalus
American plum (*P. americana*)	*Prunophora*	*Cerasus*
	Euprunus	*Microcerasus*
	Armeniaca	*Amygdalus*
Apricot (*P. armeniaca*)	*Prunophora*	*Cerasus*
	Euprunus	*Microcerasus*

	Prunocerasus	*Amygdalus*
	Armeniaca	*Euamygdalus*
Peach (*P. persica*)	*Amygdalus*	*Cerasus*
	Euamgdalus	*Microcerasus*
	Chamaeamygdalus	*Prunophora*
	Prunophora	*Prunocerasus*
	Euprunus	*Armeniaca*
Almond (*P. dulcis*)	*Amygdalus*	*Prunophora*
	Euamygdalus	*Euprunus*
	Chamaeamygdalus	*Armeniaca*
Sweet cherry (*P. avium*)	*Cerasus*	*Cerasus*
	Microcerasus	*Lobopetalum*
Sour cherry (*P. cerasus*)	*Pseudocerasus*	*Mahaleb*
	Eucerasus	*Padus*

Interspecific crosses within *Prunus* have led to new fruits such as plumcot, pluot and aprium. Hybridization involving the subgenera and sections of *Prunus* species have been most frequently achieved (Knight, 1969; Rehder, 1940). As given in Table 23.5, for the purpose of genetic transfer *Amygdalus* and *Prunophora* form one group but, within this group, almonds and damson plums are somewhat isolated from the main stream of genetic transfer. Although this may be merely as a result of less attention by breeders rather than intrinsic isolation. Transfer between the *Amygdalus-Prunophora* group and the sweet and sour cherry group is only rarely direct but is usually via the *Microcerasus* section of *Cerasus*. The *Amygdalus* part of the group seems to be more loosely connected to the *Microcerasus* bridge than the *Prunophora* portion of the group. The subgenus *Padus* is only very weakly linked to other *Prunus* (via *Cerasus* and *Amygdalus*) if the number of hybrids between *Padus* and other species is considered as a guide. Using this criterion, the subgenus *Laurocerasus* appears to be even more isolated from the other subgenera.

Almond
(***Prunus dulcis*** (Mill.) D.A.Webb. syn. ***P. amygdalus*** Batsch.; ***P. communis*** (L.) Arcang.) n=16)

The almond originated in Asia and is cultivated in the Middle East since antiquity and apparently introduced in Spain in the 8th century during the incursions of Arabs. The plants are subtropical, deciduous, hardy and heat and drought resistant and require dry period during fruit ripening. The trees are similar to those of peach but the leaves are smaller and narrower. The branches are reddish on one side and green on the other. It is the first one to bloom amongst the stone fruits. Most of the crop is borne on short spurs. The fruit buds are simple and without any leaves. Each bud produces one flower. The flower is solitary, large, showy and white. The fruit is a compressed drupe with dry endocarp, mesocarp and hairy exocarp. All the commercial cultivars are self sterile. Some are also cross compatible and thus specific pollinizers are required.

The wild species of almond have been classified into 5 sections: section Eumygdalus, section Spartioides, section Lycioides, section Chameamgdalus and section Leptopus. The important cultivars are Non Pareil, Drake, Ne Plus Ultra,

Jordanolo and Merced. The cultivars vary in taste of the kernels (bitter and sweet), and texture of the shell (hard-shelled, standard, soft-shelled and paper-shelled). The bitterness in the kernels is due to high amygdalin content. Immature almonds are also eaten in the Middle East.

Cultivars

Ne Plus Ultra: The tree is vigorous and spreading having rough bark, long and medium wide branches and large and flat leaves. It bears alternately and irregularly. The hull is light green with some dark green spots. The nut is irregular ovate having pointed apex, very soft shell, medium to large kernel, not well filled with 14-17% double kernel.

Non Pareil: The tree is vigorous, spreading and medium in size and flowers in mid season having medium productivity. It is self incompatible but compatible with Drake, Ne Plus Ultra and Marcona. The shell is soft and light coloured and has high suture opening. The nuts ripen early. The nut is medium-sized, flat and has smooth surface. It is cordate oblong having very thin shell, 65-70% shelling and very few double kernels. The kernel is light coloured that shrivels slightly.

Texas: The tree is upright, vigorous and bears both on spurs and laterally on one year old shoots. It is self incompatible but its pollen is compatible with Cristomorto and Ferragnes. The cultivar is medium to high cropper and has very late fruit maturity. The nut is elliptic oblong having semi-hard shell with about 40% double kernel. The kernel is dark.

Merced: It is hybrid of Texas x Non Pareil. The tree is of medium size, vigorous, upright and very high in productivity. It is cross compatible with Non Pareil. The nuts are well-sealed, medium, bold, slightly flattened, paper-shelled and in colour lighter brown than Non Pareil. The kernel forms 58-63% of the nut.

Peerless: The plants are fast growing with spreading branches and give moderate nut yield. The cultivar is mid season to late. Flowers appear mostly on spurs and also on one year old shoots. It is self incompatible, but its pollen is compatible with Non Pareil and Ne Plus Ultra. It has hard shell with good integrity, smooth surface and no suture opening. The nut is medium-sized, wide with fairly wrinkled surface. The nut is elliptic having semi-hard shell, about 40% shelling and nearly 10% double kernel. The kernel colour is intermediate.

Tuono: The tree is vigorous with spreading branches. It bears only on spurs. It is a self compatible cultivar. Its pollen is also compatible with Ferranges and Filippo Ceo. It flowers late in the season and thus escapes spring frost injury. The maturity period being short, the nuts are picked early. The cultivar is regular and heavy producer. The nuts are light coloured, oblong elliptic, medium thick and hard having well sealed shell and nearly 30% nuts with double kernel. The kernel is nearly 40% of the nut.

Filippo Ceo: The tree is moderately upright having semi-spreading branches. It is a self compatible mid season cultivar with high productivity. Bearing is only on spurs. It is compatible with Genco and Tuono. Flowering is very late and thus escapes spring frost damage. The nuts are elliptic in shape with well sealed and hard shell with 40-45% double kernel. The kernel is light brown, slightly wrinkled and constitutes 35-37% of the nut.

Makhdoom: It is a seedling selection. Trees are large and spreading. It is a mid season cultivar giving 5 q/ha yield. The fruit is semi-soft having medium size nuts and kernels having 38-40% shelling. Nuts are brown, soft shelled, broad shouldered with bold and slightly curved apex.

Parbat: It is a clonal selection. It is a mid season cultivar giving 5 q/ha yield. It has 49% shelling.

Waris: It is a clonal selection. Trees are upright in growth and medium in vigour. Nuts are brown to creamy whitish, soft shelled, medium in size, bold and bulged at shoulder with sharply pointed apex. It is a mid season and soft shelled cultivar giving 6-7 q/ha yield.

Shalimar: It is a clonal selection. Trees are medium in vigour and spreading. Nuts are long and bold with curved pointed apex. Nut colour is creamy brown slightly whitish and soft shelled. It is a mid season cultivar having high shelling ability, attractive plump nuts of white colour giving 5 q/ha yield.

Drake: Trees have low vigour and are spreading. Nuts are small to medium in size, bold and roundish with pointed apex, light creamy whitish brown in colour and semi-soft shelled. It has mid season blooming and maturity.

Primorskij: Trees are moderate in vigour and are spreading. Nuts are of medium size and brown and flattened to bulged. Kernel is medium to large and papery shelled. It has mid season blooming and fruit maturity.

California Paper Shell: Trees are spreading and moderately vigorous. Nuts are medium to large, slightly flattened and brown in colour. Kernel is medium to large, soft and paper-shelled. It is mid to late blooming cultivar and has late season maturity

I X L: Trees are spreading and intermediate in vigour. Nuts are medium, bold and brown in colour. Kernel is medium and soft shelled. It has mid season blooming and mid to late maturity.

Carmel: It has soft shell with good integrity and fair suture opening. The nut is medium sized, narrow and has slightly wrinkled surface.

Butte: It has light coloured semi-hard shell with smooth surface and low suture opening. The nut is small, short, plump and has wrinkled surface.

Padre: It has hard shell with good integrity and no suture opening. The nut is small, short wide and has wrinkled surface.

Monterey: It has hard shell, smooth surface and low suture opening. The nut is large, long narrow and has deeply wrinkled surface.

Sonora: The shell is soft, dark brown with rough surface and high suture opening. The nut is large, long and narrow and has light colour and smooth surface.

Fritz: The cultivar has semi-hard shell and good integrity and low suture opening. The nut is small, medium plump and has fairly wrinkled surface.

Price: The cultivar has soft, dark brown shell and rough surface and high suture opening. The nut is small, short, narrow having fairly wrinkled surface.

Mission: It has hard shell with good integrity and no suture opening. The nut is small, short, wide and has deeply wrinkled surface.

Peach and Nectarine
(*Prunus persica* (L.) Batsch.) (2n=16)

The peach and the nectarine are the most important stone fruits. In Asia, peaches are considered as a symbol of longevity. Nectarine (*Prunus persica* var. *laevis; P. laevis; P. persica* var. *nucipersica*) is a peach with smooth fuzzless skin. It is considered to have developed by a single mutation from peach. It is not a plum x peach hybrid as considered by some people. A reference to peach is found in Confucius' book which dates back to 1000 BC. It is native to warm areas of China. It is a warm temperate zone fruit, except for the two races which are subtropical.

The trees are low spreading with a broad top. The leaves are usually borne in pairs. These are elliptic lanceolate, acuminate and broadest above the middle. The petioles are 1.25 cm or less in length with closely toothed margin and rounded teeth. The glands are reniform at the base of the lamina. Glandless cultivars are resistant to leaf curl virus. The winter buds have terminal bud. The leaves in the bud are folded. The fruit buds are simple with one flower borne laterally on one year old shoot. There are no spurs. The flowers are solitary or in pairs. These are pink in colour. Ovary is nearly always downy. The buds are borne on the nodes in groups of 3, which are simple, only the central one being vegetative. The fruit is a drupe having a rough and compressed stone. The commercial cultivars are self fruitful except J. H. Hale which is male sterile. Major problems of peaches are cottony flesh texture and chilling injury. Peach and nectarine tend to be susceptible to peach leaf curl and brown rot.

Horticultural races

Odordonk and Price have divided the peaches into the following 4 horticultural races, and since these races breed freely with each other their mixtures are also found:

1. Spanish: The trees are small and compact. Fruit ripening is late. The fruits are small, round, brown, streaked or mottled with red. The flesh is yellow, white or red with flavour having a suggestion of the aroma of pineapple. None of the cultivars are commercially valuable.

2. North China: The trees are very vigorous, broad headed and open. The leaves are large, flat and dark green. The fruits are very large, usually cream white with a beautiful blush. The flesh is predominantly white. The fruit quality is good. It is an early maturing race. The important cultivars are Chinese Cling, Elberta and Belle of Georgia.

3. South China: Most of the subtropical peaches belong to this race. These require a long growing season. The trees are small, compact and are susceptible to cold. It is very productive. The fruits are small to medium in size, oblong oval tapering at the apex into a nipple. The fruit is creamy white with a red attractive blush and a distinct suture. The flesh is white and sweet with slight bitterness. These are free stone type with nearly red flesh near the pit.

4. Peento: These are referred to as *P. persica* var. *compressa* and are suitable for the tropics. The trees are tender to cold, very vigorous having drooping branches. The leaves are long and narrow. The fruits are small, flattened into a peento shape, creamy white with a red blush. The flesh is white and slightly bitter.

5. Persian; Most of the cultivated types belong to this race. It includes several types having distinct characters.

Cultivar classification

Peaches have a wide variety of fruit shape and flesh colour from yellow to red. There are basically two types of peaches based on flesh texture; melting and rubbery. The types having rubbery flesh are cling stone and are principally used for processing into juice and sliced or diced products and some are dried. The cultivars are usually classified on the basis of adherence of flesh with the stone and colour of the flesh.

i. Adherence of flesh: When classified on the basis on how firmly the flesh attaches to the pit, these are classified as clingstone, freestone or semi-freestone.

a. Clingstone: The flesh clings stubbornly to the stone or pit. In the Northern hemisphere, this type ripening from May through August is the first to be harvested. The flesh is yellow with bright red touches closest to the stone. The pulp has soft texture and is juicier and sweeter and is thus perfect for desserts. These are used for jellies, jams, and canning. Although these are tasty and eaten fresh, but are seldom found in the local market as the industry uses them for canning in various levels of syrup. The popular cultivars are Santa Rosa and Red Beauty.

b. Freestone: The stone does not stick to the flesh and is easily removed making the fruit a good choice for eating fresh. Harvest begins in late May and continues until October. This is the type most commonly found in the local market. The fruits tend to be larger than those of cling stone and have a firmer and less juicy texture, yet still sweet to acidic in taste. The skin is creamy yellow with varying range of red blush or mottling. These are excellent for canning and baking purposes. The popular cultivars are Glowhaven, Cresthaven and Redhaven.

c. Semi-freestone: This is a hybrid of the clingstone and freestone. It is good for general purposes, both fresh and canned.

ii. Colour of the flesh: When classified on the basis of flesh colour, these can either be yellow-fleshed or white-fleshed.

a. Yellow-fleshed: The peaches have the pit in the centre of the flesh. The pulp is more acidic than that of white-fleshed peaches. The skin colour is mostly red over a bright yellow ground. The fruiting season is from May through September. The popular cultivars are Reliance and Sweet Scarlet.

b. White-fleshed: The fruits with white flesh are very sweet with low acidity and appear smoothier. The fruiting season is from May through August. The skin has soft texture and creamy or yellow colour with red or pink colour near the pit. The popular cultivars are Spring Snow and Sugar May.

Cultivars have also been classified based on chilling requirement:

1. Low chill (350-550 hours): Cultivars Flordadawn, Flordacrest, Flordaking, Flordasun, Flordared, Ventura, Bonita, Rochan, Early Amber, Florda Belle, Shan-e-Punjab, Flordared and16-33 (Shan-e-Punjab).

2. Medium-high chill (600-1050 hours): Cultivars Redhaven, Queencrest Flvorcrest, June Princess (Nectarine), Junegold, Snow Queen Nectarine, Snow Zee Nectarine, Fairlane Nectarine, May Crest, July Elberta and Dixi Red.

Cultivars of peach

Alexander: The fruits are large, round, greenish white with red blush. The flesh is greenish white and the pit is semi-cling. It is a prolific bearing and early cultivar.

J.H. Hale: The fruits are very large, round, yellowish with red blush, freestone, fuzzy skin and red at the pit. The flesh is firm and of good quality.

Sharbati: The fruit is oblong with a roundish beak. The flesh is white, slightly bitter and has a mottled skin.

Early Rivers: The fruits are large, oblong to round and straw coloured having delicate pink patches. It is a prolific bearer.

Gujrati: The leaves are glossy green and attractive. It is resistant to diseases particularly blight and is used as a rootstock.

Elberta: It has remarkable climatic adaptability. It is the most commonly grown cultivar in the world. The fruits are large, freestone of medium quality with some bitterness and yellow flesh. It is good for canning.

July Elberta: It originated in California. Its parentage is not known. The trees are vigorous, hardy and productive. It is very fruitful and requires 750 chill hours. It has early to mid season maturity. The fruit is freestone, round, medium to large in size, greenish yellow overlain with dull red blush or streaks. Pubescence is dense. The flesh is firm, yellow and faintly red at the pit and is of very good quality. The stone is small and free.

Honey: It has a beak.

Flordared: It was developed from the cross, Southland x Hawaiian. It has very low chilling requirement (50-100 hrs). The flowers are large and showy. The fruit is small, reniform, medium round having about 50% skin blushed with red. The flesh is white, somewhat firm and has free stone.

Flordasun: The tree is medium tall and spreading. It requires 300 chill hours to break dormancy and is self fruitful. The flowers are showy. The fruit is small, round, yellow and slightly blushed. The flesh is medium firm, uniformly ripen, yellow in colour and red at the pit, almost freestone but not of very good quality.

Sunheaven: The tree is vigorous and large. It has high chill requirement (900 hrs) and is self fruitful and productive. It is a late maturing semi-freestone cultivar. Its fruits ripen early and are medium to large, uniformly round, bright red over yellow having soft and short pubescence. The flesh is of firm and fine texture, yellow, freestone having excellent flavour and does not brown. It is good for fresh market.

Starking Delicious: It is a bud mutant of July Elberta. Most of the tree, flower and leaf characters are similar to the parent cultivar. The flowers are pink and small. The fruit ripens almost 15-20 days earlier than that of July Elberta. Flesh is yellow and freestone.

Maya and Vesna: These cultivars were evolved at Beograd, Yugoslavia from self pollination of Glohaven. These are self fruitful and tolerant to peach mildew scab and brown rot diseases. The plants are more vigorous than of Standard. The plants of Maya are more productive (20 t/ha). The fruits are large, roundish and firm having 60-70% area blushed red over yellow ground colour. The flesh is firm, freestone and yellow and resists browning and has very good flavour. The fruits of Maya have excellent table quality even after processing. The fruit of Vesna is good to very good for fresh market and superior as a processed fruit.

Pant Peach 1: It is a seedling selection. The fruit is medium sized, clingstone and having red pigmentation on skin surface.

Fantasia: Tree is vigorous, fruits are large ovate in shape, bright yellow with red blush over the major part of fruit skin and have early to mid season maturity.

Pratap: The fruits mature in the third week of April are yellow with red blush. Flesh colour is also yellow with red colouration. It has better firmness and keeping quality than Prabhat and Flordasun. The average yield is 70 kg/plant.

Shan-e-Punjab: It matures in the first week of May. Fruits are very large, yellow with red blush, juicy, sweet, and excellent in taste and freestone. Since fruits are firm in texture, they can withstand transportation. These are suitable for canning. The average yield is 70 kg/plant.

Florda Prince: Its fruits ripen in the last week of April. Fruits are semi-clingstone, medium to large, round with little or no tip, red blush with yellow ground colour, melting and yellow flesh with some red colour. On an average it yields 100 kg/plant.

Early Grande: It ripens in the first week of May. Fruits are large with red blush. Flesh is yellow and firm with some red colour next to pit, semi-freestone when fully ripe. The average yield is 95 kg/tree. The fruits have excellent shipping qualities.

Prabhat: It is early maturing (mid April). Fruits are medium in size, roundish with an attractive red blush. It is white fleshed when fully ripe. The average yield is 50 kg/tree.

Red June: Trees are medium in vigour. Fruits are freestone, large, roundish with rounded beak, distinct suture, yellow with red blush on the shoulder. It has early maturity.

Cresthaven: It produces top notch freestone fruits with golden yellow skin and flesh. It blooms late and is a mid to late season cultivar. The fruits keep well on the tree and are excellent for freezing and canning.

G10 Heaven: A large peach with yellow, freestone flesh, milder flavour and has mostly red skin with no fuzz. It is excellent for canning and fresh eating.

Snow Queen: Trees are spreading and vigorous. Fruits mature during mid June and are cling stone, small to medium in size having bright red colour on cream white background and smooth surface. Flesh is white.

Sun Red: Trees have low vigour. Fruits are small to medium in size with bright red skin and semi-freestone flesh. The cultivar is early maturing.

Cultivars of nectarine

Juneglo: The cultivar is very precocious and sets fruits in cool and wet weather. Sixty per cent of the fruit is red wth some russeting. It has 10 to 15 per cent split pits and varying fruit size. The flesh is semi-freestone when ripe.

Harko: The cultivar is solid red, clingstone nectarine having good quality and flavour. It is a consistent producer with no split pits. It tends to overbear and thus must be heavily thinned in order to get good fruit size. The tree is vigorous with a twiggy habit making the pruning operation more time consuming than in other cultivars.

Redgold: The cultivar is freestone and has 80 to 90 per cent red fruit skin. Fruit set is modest and fruit size is large. The flesh is firm with good flavour and high quality. The tree is vigorous and its pruning is time consuming.

Fantasia: The cultivar is freestone having solid red fruits with flesh of excellent quality, flavour and firmness.

Sunbest: The cultivar has yellow, melting flesh and semi-freestone pit. It develops 90–100% bright red blush over a yellow ground skin colour, and has fruit development period (FDP) of 85–90 days earlier than the standard 'Sunraycer' cultivar. It is a good replacement for 'Sunraycer'.

UFRoyal: The cultivar is yellow flesh, non-melting with a FDP of 85 days. The fruit is large with 100% red skin and a semi-clingstone pit. It is symmetrically oval and ripen approximately 1 week before 'UFQueen'. The flesh has excellent firmness and flavour with excellent shipping potential.

UFQueen: The cultivar is early and regular bearer in north central Florida having large fruits with an FDP of 95 days. The trees are semi-upright and are easily pruned to an open vase system. The flesh is yellow, non-melting with clingstone pits. The fruits are slightly oval with a slight tip and develop 80–100% red skin over a yellow background.

UFSun: The cultivar is early season and bears heavy annual crops of medium-sized fruits. The flesh is yellow with clingstone pits. The fruits are uniformly symmetrical and develop 50–60% red skin with darker red stripes.

Sunraycer: The cultivar has vigorous and semi-spreading trees that respond well to open centre pruning system. It produces oval, large, fruits with no sharp tips or suture bulges and 85 day FDP and develops 80–100% brilliant red blush over bright yellow ground colour. The flesh is melting, semi-clingstone with good firmness. The cultivar has good resistance to bacterial spot.

Sunbest: The cultivar is semi-freestone and resists bacterial spot well.The trees are semi-upright and vigorous responding well to open centre pruning system. The fruit having FDP of 85–90 days develops 90–100% bright red blush over a yellow ground colour. It is a good replacement for 'Sunraycer' because of its larger and more attractive fruits.

Sunmist: The cultivar has highly vigorous trees with a spreading growth habit. The cultivar is early ripening having large fruits of 85 days FDP having white, melting, semi-freestone flesh. The fruit develops nearly 100% red blush and is uniformly symmetrical. The trees and fruits are highly resistant to bacterial spot.

Suncoast: The cultivar has vigorous and semi-spreading trees. The fruits are slightly oblong with no sharp tips or bulges and tend to be tart and develop 80–90% red blush over a yellow ground colour and FDP of 77 days. It is a melting flesh, semi-clingstone nectarine. The flesh is yellow.

Apricot
(*Prunus armeniaca* L.) 2n= 16

Apricot was named *P. armeniaca* as it was supposed to have originated in Armenia. However, Vavilov (1951) gave 3 important regions as origin of apricot:-

a. Chinese centre (China and Tibet).

b. Central Asian centre (from Tien-Shan to Kashmir).

c. Near Eastern centre (Iran, Caucasus, Turkey).

Based on the presence of cultivated types and absence of wild forms, he reported that the Near Eastern centre could be secondary gene centre. The pattern of spread of the apricot diversity originating from Central Asia to Middle Asia and Caucasia and later to Europe, North America and rest of the world has been explained by the following three views:

1. The dried fruits and stones of natural apricot flora in Fergana Valley which is at the border of Uzbekistan, Tajikistan, and Kyrgyzstan and piedmont of Hind Kush and Tian Shan mountains were brought to Anatolia by soldiers in Iran and Transcaucasus during the Asia campaigns by Alexander in BC 334 and these were later moved to Europe during the Roman-Persian wars in BC 1 (Layne *et al.*, 1996).

2. The apricot was brought to Anatolia by merchants from China and Central Asia on famous Silk Road and then Roman soldiers carried it to Italy (Bailey and Hough, 1975).

3. The Romans moved apricot to the west during their expeditions to seize the Near East (Syria, Iran and Caucasus) in BC 2 (Layne *et al.,* 1996). It gradually spread to Africa and Mediterranean countries and Middle East. It was also carried to Balkans by Ottomans in 15th and 16th centuries (Suranyi, 1999). Apricot was taken to southern Europe from eastern Europe (Asma, 2011) and to England in 1524 or 1548 from Italy. It was taken to the American continent by the Spanish in 1626 (Faust *et al.*, 1998).

Apricot is a temperate and subtropical fruit. The tree is a hardy plant of warm temperate zone. It is fairly resistant to cold and heat. Morphologically, it is between peach and plum. It hybridizes freely with both peach and plum, e.g. plumcot (peach x apricot). The tree is large with arching branches. The bark of young shoots is entirely coppery red as in plums. Winter shoots have a terminal bud (as in peach) and have conspicuous oval lenticels. The leaves are cordate ovate (appear similar to small leaves of *Ficus benghalensis*), 7.5-10 cm long, short-pointed and hairy on the lower surface. The petioles are downy. The buds are round and plump. Most of the crop is borne on spurs which are slender and lobed. The flower is simple, solitary, somewhat large, about 2.5 cm across and pale pink eventually turning almost white, sessile and borne on stalkless umbels. Two to five flowers are borne on one spur. The calyx is reddish. It is self fertile. The fruit is round, 3 cm or more across, yellowish with red cheek, nearly glabrous, smooth stone with a thickened and furrowed edge. The semi-dried fruit is principally consumed fresh and is also canned, usually sulfured to maintain colour and longevity. The major processing industry is located in southwest Turkey (Malatya). In some cultivars, the seeds are also consumed as almonds.

Eco-geographical groups

Wide variations emerged in apricots because of seed propagation and growing in different ecological areas. This resulted in the following 8 eco-geographical groups (Mehlenbacher *et al.* 1990; Kostina, 1969; Bailey and Hough, 1975) and 13 regional subgroups:-

1. Dzhungar-Zailij eco-geographical group: The group is represented by selections of Volkova (1978) from Dzharskent, Taldy-Kurgan, Kazakhstan and Xinjiang regions (Mehlenbacher *et al.,* 1990; Layne *et al.*, 1996; Faust *et al.,* 1998) and mostly bears small fruits. The group has the following regional subgroups (Mehlenbacher *et al.,* 1991):
   i. Dzhungar
   ii. Zailij
2. Central Asian eco-geographical group: Central Asia being the oldest and the primary genetic source of apricot, this group is the richest in diversity which includes local types from Central Asia, Xinjiang, Afghanistan, Baluchistan, Pakistan and Northern India (Kashmir). This group is mostly self incompatible and characterized by medium sized fruits having a tendency to bloom in late spring. The group has the following regional subgroups (Bailey and Hough, 1975):
   i. Fergana: Cultivars Boban, Kandak, Kech-pshar, Khurmai, Mirsandshali, Supkhany and Isfarak.
   ii. Upper Zeravshan: Cultivars Sadifak, Iska-dari, Tuliaki, Khosravashi, Badami, Akhori and Arzami.
   iii. Samarkand Shahrisyabz: Cultivar Samarkandski Samji Rannii.
   iv. Horezm: Cultivars Kizil-Nukul, Ak- Nukul and Kizil-Palvan.
   v. Kopet-dag: Cultivar Ashkhabad.
3. Irano-Caucasian eco-geographical group: The group extends from Armenia, Georgia, Azerbaijan, Dagestan, Iran, Iraq, Syria and Turkey to North Africa and even to Spain and Italy is the secondary gene centre. These apricots are mostly the cultivated ones and are generally self incompatible but, on the contrary, produce large fruits and bloom earlier

than the Central Asian and need lower chilling hours. The group has the following regional subgroups (Mehlenbacher *et al.,* 1991):

   i. Irano-Caucasus: Cultivars Erevani, Sateni, Spitak, Malayar, Damavand and Hacihaliloglu.
   ii. Dagestan: Cultivars Hekobarsh and Honobah.
   iii. North Africa: Cultivars Hamidi, Bedri, Bakour and Amor Leuch.

4. European eco-geographical group. The group consists of North American, South African and Australian apricots originated from Armenia, Iran, Turkey and other Arab countries. These are self compatible, fruits are more precocious and the trees require low chilling. The group has the following regional subgroups (Layne *et al.*, 1996):
   i. West European: Cultivars Canino, Rouge de Rousillon and Moniqui.
   ii. East European: Cultivars Hungarian Best and Ananassa.
   iii. North European: Cultivar Ukarainian 'Zherdeli'.
5. North-Chinese eco-geographical group: The group includes forms of *P. mandshurica* and *P. sibirica.*
6. Tibet eco-geographical group: The group includes forms of *P. armeniaca* var. *holosericea.*
7. Northeast China eco-geographical group: The group includes cultivars and types of *P. armeniaca, P. sibirica* and *P. mandshurica* (Bailey and Hough, 1975).
8. Eastern China eco-geographical group: It includes the species *P. armeniaca* var. *ansu.*

Genetic diversity

The genetic diversity research in apricot was traditionally based on describing pomological, morphological and phenological characteristics (Guerriero and Watkins, 1984). Leaf characteristics were accepted as the most important criterion for apricot systematics. Bailey (1916) examined the leaves emerging from dormant buds. Rehder (1940) used leaf shape and pubescence for classification of species. Loudon (1838) mentioned wild apricots having different shades of pink flowers that had been used for ornamental purpose for centuries. While Chinese botanists utilized leaves, Japanese researchers considered flower and branch colour and flower size for classification of Japanese apricot (*P. mume*), an ornamental plant (Mega *et al.*, 1988; Horiuchi *et al.,* 1996). The characterization is now done based on UPOV and IPGRI criteria using a common descriptor. In the last two decades, molecular studies have been integrated into the conventional germplasm characterization of genetic diversity (Rao *et al.,* 2008; Yilmaz, 2008; Akpinar *et al.*, 2010).

Restriction fragment length polymorphism (RFLP) and PCR based markers such as randomly amplified polymorphic DNA (RAPDs), sequence-related amplified polymorphism (SRAP), single nucleotide polymorphism (SNPs), micro-satellites or simple sequence repeats (SSRs) are mostly used marker systems to characterize the apricot cultivars belonging to diverse eco-geographical groups. Microsatellites are most promising to clear genetic relations among the apricots and their travel routes (Romero *et al.,* 2003; Maghuly *et al.,* 2005). In AFLP molecular markers assesment for genotyping 118 commercial apricot accessions and some related apricot species (Geuna *et al.,* 2003), the apricots were clustered into four groups corresponding to their geographic distribution; (1) Mediterranean apricots, (2) Chinese apricots, (3) apricots of continental Europe and (4) Europe-North American apricots. The data confirmed the migration of apricot from the East to West and also showed that *P. sibirica* and *P. mandshurica* are different from *P. armeniaca*, but group together with Chinese accessions (Geuna *et al.*, 2003). Romero *et al.* (2003) using of SSR markers, observed that Western European and North American subgroups clustered together with agreement of their common origin from the ancient European cultivars (Kostina, 1969; Bailey and Hough, 1975; Badanes *et al.*, 1996). However, Hungarian cultivars were placed closer to the Central Asian group than to the other European cultivars.

Hayashi *et al.* (2008) studied *P. mume* and reported genetic diversity and relationships among 127 Japanese apricot germplasms assessed by SSR markers and supported the two hypotheses that Japanese apricot cultivated in Japan had been introduced from China and that fruiting cultivars had been selected from the flower ornamentals. Yilmaz (2008) and Uzun *et al.* (2010) using RAPD, ISSR, SRAP and SSR markers reported high genetic diversity in Turkish apricots. Four high chill requiring cultivars originated from eastern Turkey clustered apart from the rest. European, South African, North American and other Turkish cultivars were not clearly grouped with regard to their geographic districts and therefore, it was suggested that these cultivars, despite their different geographic origins, have similar genetic background.

China, the Irano-Caucasian region (Turkey and Iran), Central Asia, Europe and North America are the main apricot producing regions in the world. Central Asia is the oldest and the primary genetic source. Thus the maximum diversity is in the Central Asian and Irano-Caucasian groups and also in Turkish and Iran cultivars. The European and apricots that originated from Irano-Caucasia including cultivars grown in North America, Australia and South Africa exhibit relatively narrow genetic diversity (Mehlenbacher *et al.*, 1991; Halasz *et al.*, 2010). The diversity observed between apricot cultivars is probably due to crosses between wild and cultivated apricots and cultivars from different eco-geographic origin (Uzun *et al.,* 2010). Microsatellite analyses suggested that European cultivars might have originated through hybridization among Irano-Caucasian genotypes and also most of the European cultivars have originated by hybridization with genotypes from the Irano-Caucasian group (Maghuly *et al.,* 2005; Faust *et al.,* 1998; Kostina, 1969). The heterozygosity of the apricot genotypes narrowed during their movement from China to Europe. Pedryc *et al.* (2009) showed that Middle European and Chinese apricots are distantly related.

Like the other *Prunus* species, apricots show gametophytic self incompatibility controlled by a single locus with multiple genes, S-haplotypes (De Nettancourt, 2001). The S-haplotype contains a female determinant (S-RNase) encoding for a ribonuclease enzyme (McClure *et al.,* 1989) and the male determinant, S-haplotype-specific F-box gene (Entani *et al.,* 2003; Romero *et al.,* 2004; Halasz *et al.*, 2010).

Cross incompatibility frequently occurs between a pair of cultivars of self incompatible species. Cross incompatibility was observed among the North American cultivars, Goldrich, Hargrand and Lambertin No. 1 (Egea & Burgos, 1996) and also among giant-fruited Hungarian apricots (Szabo & Nyeki, 1991; Halasz *et al.*, 2010). Halasz *et al.* (2010) found 12 cross incompatiblity groups between Irano-Caucasian eco-geographical (Turkish apricots) and European eco-geographical (Hungarian and North American apricots) groups.

Twenty one S-RNase alleles are known in European apricots, 20 of which (S1-S20) code for self incompatibility and one (Sc) allowing self compatibility (Burgos *et al.*, 1998; Halasz, 2007; Halasz *et al.*, 2005, 2007) and it was confirmed that SC haplotype is a pollen part mutant of S8 haplotype (Halasz *et al.,* 2007). Besides, some additional S-alleles have also been identified in Chinese cultivars (Wu *et al.,* 2009; Halasz *et al.,* 2010). A gradually decreasing allele number was detected in apricot landraces from China to Western Europe, with some allelic exclusivity occurring in certain geographic areas (Halasz, 2007; Halasz *et al.,* 2010).

Classification

The classification of apricot species by different authors has been summarized (Table 23.6) by Yilmaz and Gurcan (2012).

Table 23.6. Apricot systematics (Yilmaz and Gurcan, 2012).

Bailey (1916) (Ledbetter, 2008)		**Rehder (1940)** (Ledbetter, 2008)	
Genus	*Prunus*	Genus	*Prunus*
Subgenus	*Prunophora* (plums, prunes & apricot)		Subgenus *Prunophora*
Prunus armeniaca	var. *pendulata* Dipp. var. *variegata* Hort.	sections	Euprunus (European/Asian plums)
	var. *sibirica* Koch var. *mandshurica* Maxim. var. *ansu* Maxim.	Armeniaca (apricots)	Prunocerasus (North American plums) *Armeniaca* (apricots)
P. mume Sieb. & Zucc.	var. *goethartiana* Koehne.		*P. brigantina* Vill.
	var. *albo-plena* Hort.		*P. mandshurica* Maxim.
Other wild forms	*laciniata* Maxim.		*P. sibirica* L.
	microcarpa Makino		*P. armeniaca* L.
	viridicalyx Makino		*P. mume* Sieb. & Zucc.
	cryptopetala Makino		*P. dasycarpa* Ehrh.
P. brigantiaca Vill.			*P. armeniaca* L.
P. dasycarpa Ehrh.			*P. armeniaca variegata* Schneid.
Lingdi & Bartholomew (2003) (Ledbetter, 2008)			*P. armeniaca pendula* Jaeg.
Family	*Rosaceae*		*P. armeniaca ansu* Maxim.
Subfamily	*Prunoideae*	*P. mume* Sieb. & Zucc.	*P. mume alba* Rehd.
Genus	*Armeniaca* (apricots)		*P. mume Alphandii* Rehd.
	A. vulgaris L.	**Bortiri *et al.* (2002)** (Ledbetter, 2008)	
	var. *vulgaris* L.	sections	*P. fremontii* S. Wats.

var. *zhidanensis* Qiao & Zhu	*Penarmeniaca*	*P. andersonii* A. Gray.
var. *ansu* Maxim.	*Penarmeniaca*	
var. *meixianensis* Zhang		
var. *xiongyueensis* Li		
Armeniaca limeixing Zhang & Wang	**Hayashi *et al.* (2008)**	
A. sibirica L.	Traditional Japanese classification (Mega *et al.*, 1988; Horiuchi *et al.*, 1996)	
var. *sibirica* L.		
var. *pubescens* Kostina	*P. mume*	
var. *multipetala* Liu & Zhang	For fruit production	
var. *pleniflora* Zhang	For ornamental "kei"	
A. holosericea Batal.	Yabai	Yabai subgroups
A. hongpingensis Li		Naniwa subgroups
A. zhengheensis Zhang & Lu		Benifude subgroups
A. hypotrichodes Cardot		Aojiku subgroups
A. dasycarpa Ehrh.	Koubai	
A. mandshurica Maxim.		Koubai subgroups
var. *mandshurica* Maxim.	Bungo	
var. *glabra* Nakai		Bungo subgroups
A. mume Sieb. & Zucc.		Anzu subgroups
var. *mume* Sieb.		
var. *pallescens* Franc.		
var. *cernua* Franc.		
var. *pubicaulina* Qiao & Shen.		

P. armeniaca, P. mandshurica, P. x dasycarpa (2n = 16); *P. mume* (2n = 16 or 24)

Cultivars

Commercial production areas of apricots are still limited to a small number of cultivars, although these are spread over a wide area of the world. The cultivars are of the following two types:–

i. Ordinary or European: These are commercially grown in Europe, North America, South Africa and Australia. The important cultivars are Baracca, Bergeron, Callatis, Ceglédi, Comandor, Gönci Magyar, Hungarian Best, Polonais, Goldrich, Nugget, Perfection and Senetate.

ii. Russian: Important cultivars are Alexander, Budd, Alexis and Catherineas.

Zardalu: It is indigenous to India and is from the Kumaon hills. The fruits are small having firm flesh of yellowish orange colour. It is good for canning. It is also used for oil extraction.

St. Ambroise: It is particularly successful at higher elevations of 1800-2100 m. The trees as well as their leaves are large. It is a medium to late season cultivar. The fruits are freestone, much larger than of other cultivars and are oblong oval, large, orange yellow with tiny dots of pink. The flesh is orange or deep yellow, firm, juicy and sweet and is of good quality. It is a late season cultivar ripening at the end of June to first week of July. It is not suitable for lower midhills.

Royal: It is a very popular cultivar of midhills. Most of its characters resemble those of Blenheim. It tolerates high heat. Fruits ripen by middle of June. The fruits are medium to large, roundish oval, light orange yellow tinged with red. The flesh is firm, light orange yellow, sweet and juicy and the stone is always free. The kernel is bitter. It is good for canning.

Blenheim: It is a clingstone cultivar. The fruits are roundish and similar to those of Royal but the flesh and skin colour is slightly deeper.

Kaisha: It is commonly found in the hills. Trees are vigorous, spreading and extremely prolific. The fruit is sweet, delicious and freestone, of medium size with roundish flattened shape and prominent suture and yellowish skin with a red blush. The flesh colour is orange yellow. It ripens in early June and gives fairly good yield. It has a bitter kernel.

New Castle: The cultivar is very popular especially for its consistent regular bearing and wide adaptation extending as a popular dessert cultivar for warm locations. Trees are vigorous and spreading. Fruits ripen early by May end and are roundish, medium to large in size having prominent sutures and pubescence and yellow deep orange colour. It is a highly coloured cultivar. The pit is spherical. The flesh is yellow orange, sweet and juicy with partially freestone.

Moorpark: It is a mid season cultivar and a shy bearer. The fruit ripens in the first week of June. The fruit is large, usually more than 5 cm in diameter, roundish and deep orange with brown dots. The skin is light orange with a light red blush. The flesh is deep orange, juicy, sweet and excellent in flavour. The kernel is bitter.

Safeda (Safaida): It is an exotic cultivar well adapted to the cold arid conditions. Fruits are large and round having glossy, smooth and light yellow skin. The flesh is soft, maize yellow cream in colour, very sweet and less acidic with pleasing flavour. The stone is small and oval with pointed apex having one ridge on both sides. The fruit has 72% shell and 28% kernel. The kernel is sweet. It is a poor shipper.

Charmaghaz: It is from Afghanistan where it is used primarily for drying. The cultivar has high chilling requirement and hence is suitable for cultivation at higher altitudes. It is also found growing in the cold arid regions. It is a self incompatible cultivar and needs a pollinizer like Turkey and is a shy bearer. The fruit is medium in size and roundish flat in shape. The skin is straw yellow having attractive pubescent surface. The flesh is firm and quite dry with light yellow white flesh which is very sweet and highly flavoured. It is suitable for both dessert and drying. It is used as dessert and for drying being rich in sugar content. The kernel is sweet.

Halman (Tibetan name meaning grafted): This is perhaps a local seedling selection. This is the most popular cultivar widely grown in cold arid regions with maximum area in Leh and Kargil districts of Ladakh. It has mid season maturity. The tree is spreading and vigorous. The fruit is medium in size and round having compressed pedicel, distinct suture, smooth skin and orange red colour. The pulp is orange red, thick, sweet and mild acidic with pleasant flavour. It has the highest TSS among popular cultivars. It is used primarily for drying since it is less juicy with high TSS. The stone is free, medium, round oval, pointed towards the apex having rough surface and prominent ridges on both sides. It has 72% shelling and 28% kernel. Its kernel is sweet and is used as almond.

Rakchey Karpo ('Karpo' means white and 'Rakchey' means stone): The cultivar is indigenous to Ladakh region, probably a seedling selection. This is a very popular table cultivar due to the juicy and pleasant aromatic pulp and its sugar/acid blend. It is an early cultivar ripening during end of July to middle of August. The fruits are of medium to large, round with compressed pedicel end, glossy and pale yellow skin with red rose blush on the side exposed to sun. The pulp is light pale, juicy, sweet and mild acidic with pleasant flavour. The stone is medium, free, round to oval with sharp ridges, creamy white colour, 68% shell and 32% kernel.

Tokpopa: This is an indigenous cultivar of Leh district used for table purpose as well as for drying. The fruits ripen late and are available during August. The fruits are of medium size, round, compressed and with smooth dull yellow skin having juicy and acidic to sweet taste. The stone is free, medium, round and rough. The shell is 68% and sweet kernel is 32%.

Rogan: This is a very early table cultivar, ripening by middle of July and grown in limited area of Leh district. Fruits are very small (perhaps the smallest among the popular cultivars) and round having glossy straw yellow skin and very soft, highly juicy and slightly acidic sweet pulp. The stone is small, free, oblong ovate having prominent ridges on both sides. The shell is 62% and kernel is 38%. The kernel is sweet.

Nari: This exotic cultivar has been well adapted in the cold arid region of India. It is a late cultivar that ripens after middle of August. The fruits are medium, oblong elliptical with truncate base, greenish to light yellow skin with red blush towards the side exposed to sun. The pulp is light yellow having good sugar/acid ratio and pleasant flavour. The stone is free, small, round oval having 70% shell and 30% kernel. The kernel is sweet. The cultivar is suitable for table purpose as well as for drying. It gets dehydrated even on the tree, if not harvested.

Australian: The cultivar has been introduced in the cold arid region of India. It ripens during end of July to late August. The fruit size is very large, the largest among the cultivars grown in cold arid region of India, round in shape with acute apex, distinct suture, mild flavour having medium sweet and acidic pulp. It is not liked as a table fruit but is good for processing. Stone is big, free, round and compressed. Shelling percentage is about 72 and kernel is 28%. The kernel is sweet.

Shakarpara: This cultivar is from Afghanistan. The fruits ripen from late July to middle of August. These are sweet, medium in size and round having pleasant aroma, glossy and creamy yellow skin with rosy blush. It can be used for table purpose. The pulp is soft, light yellow, sweet and less acidic having pleasant flavour. The stone is small and ovate having pointed apex and one ridge on the two sides, 78% shell and 22% kernel. The kernel is sweet.

Shipleys Early: It has performed exceptionally well in the foothills as an excellent early ripening dessert cultivar. The fruit ripens during the middle of May. The fruit is of medium size and creamy white overlain by light pink to red blush on the cheeks. The flesh is firm, white to creamish, very sweet and juicy and the kernel is bitter.

Nugget: The cultivar is highly adapted in midhill region and has gained popularity for its regularity in bearing heavy crops and high fruit quality (Chadha, 2001). The fruits are medium large and round having thin and soft pubescence, shiny surface and dark yellow to orange with bright red blush. The flesh is firm, deep orange, sweet and juicy having fine texture and very good quality. The kernel is sweet.

Harogem: The cultivar was evolved in Canada. The tree is medium in vigour having open and spreading crown and long petioles with number of glands. It is a self fruitful mid season cultivar and produces consistently. The flowers are white. The fruit is round ovate having compressed sides and bright red blush on attractive orange background. The flesh is orange, firm, free stone with moderate juice, good flavour and very good keeping quality (Chadha, 2001). The fruits can be stored at room temperature for several weeks.

Chaubattia Alankar: It was developed by inducing mutation in bud wood of the hybrid, Kaisha x Charmaghaz, by gamma rays. It is an early, regular bearing and low chilling cultivar. The fruits have good keeping quality.

Chaubattia Madhu: It was developed by inducing mutation in bud wood of the hybrid, Turkey x Charmaghaz, by gamma rays. It is an early, regular bearing and highly productive cultivar.

Chaubattia Kesri: It was developed by inducing mutation in bud wood of St. Ambroise x Charmaghaz with gamma rays. It is a mid season cultivar having good quality fruits.

Harcot: Trees are upright to spreading and vigorous. Fruits are medium to large with roundish heart shape. Skin is yellow orange and red blushed. Kernel is sweet. The fruits have early to mid season maturity.

Turkey: The trees are vigorous and spreading. Fruits are medium in size and almost round in shape having deep yellow skin with brownish orange dots, freestone and sweet kernel and mid season maturity.

CITH-1 Apricot: It is a self fertile and mid season blooming cultivar. Fruits are very large (79 g) having round symmetrical and smooth distal end, yellowish orange and reddish blemishes. It is an early maturing cultivar tolerant to major pests and diseases.

CITH-2 Apricot: It is a self fertile and early to mid season blooming and early maturing cultivar. Fruits are very large in size, oblate, asymmetrical with slightly pointed beak, yellowish orange with reddish blush on exposed surface. It is tolerant to leaf curl and stigmina blight.

CITH-3: It is a self fertile and early to mid season cultivar. Fruits are medium in size, oblate in shape, asymmetrical with slightly pointed beak and yellowish orange with very little reddish tinge and of good quality. It is tolerant to major pests and diseases.

Plums
(2n= 16, 32, 48)

Plums represent a diverse group of fruits including European (*P. domestica* L., *P. cerasifera* Ehrh., *P. spinosa* L., *P. institia* L.), Asian (*P. salicina* Lindl., *P. simonii* Carr.) and American (*P. americana* Marsh., *P. nigra, P. angustifolia* Marsh., *P. hortulana, P. munsoniana*) species. The principal economically important species are *P. domestica* and *P. salicina*.

The leaves of plums are small to medium and are lanceolate to elliptic. The fruit buds are simple with 1-3 flowers per bud, but the American species have more than 3 flowers. Fruiting takes place on previous season's growth, usually on short spurs. The flowers are small, usually pure white. Ovules are 2 in each ovary but generally one of these aborts. Most of the cultivars are self sterile and some are cross sterile. The fruit is sulcate (grooved on one side). The stone is compressed and smooth, winged on one side and grooved on the other. While plums are mostly consumed as a fresh or processed fruit, the prune type plums (French prune or "Agen") are used to produce a well known product called prunes or dried plums.

Key to the classification of plums (after Hedrick, 1911)

A. Flowers are single or in twos (3 in *P. salicina*) ....Old world plums

B. Leaves are drooping .... *P. domestica, P. institia, P. cerasifera, P. salicina*

C. Shoots and pedicels are pubescent ....*P. domestica, P. institia*

D. Fruits are large, more than 2.5 cm in dia., shape is variable. Branches are glabrous or nearly so from the beginning...*P. domestica*

DD. Fruits are small, less than 2.5 cm in dia., usually oval or ovoid. Flowers are in twos. The shoots are hairy at first. Pistil is glabrous ....*P. institia*

CC. Shoots are glabrous or soon become so; pedicels are glabrous ....*P. cerasifera, P. salicina*

D. Flowers are in singles. Leaves are hairy along the midrib on the underside ....*P. cerasifera* (Myrobalan or cherry plum), *P. divaricata*

DD. Flowers are in threes. Leaves are glabrous.. *P. salicina (P. triflora)*

BB. Leaves are upright, peach-like, glabrous, veins are very conspicuous, underside is barbate (having long weak hairs in tufts at axils of veins), conspicuous by large, flattened, brick red fruits... *P. simonii* (apricot plum)

AA. Flowers in clusters of 3 or more. Plants are trees .... American plums

B. Leaves are broad mostly ovate or obovate.

Leaves are long ovate or long obovate.

Flowers are white. Leaf serrations are glandless, acute; petiole usually glandless. Stone is turgid, large, pointed at the apex .... *P. americana*

BB. Leaves are lanceolate ovate, folded upwards.

Fruit is large, 2.5 cm in diameter. Petioles have 1-6 glands. Stone is compressed and pointed at both the ends .... *P. munsonia*

Asian plum

(***Prunus salicina*** Lindl.; ***Prunus triflora*** Roxb.; Japanese plum) (2n=16,32)

It is a diploid (2n = 16). It has great climatic adaptability and is suitable for warm climate. Heat is required for fruit maturity. It is comparatively free from diseases but is susceptible to brown rot. Its wood is not so dark brown as that of European plum. The European plum bears fruit largely on spurs while Japanese plum bears largely on lateral or axillary buds formed on one year old shoots. The shoots are dark, glabrous or nearly so right from the beginning and are smooth, somewhat similar to those of peach. Longitudinal bark striations are present. The leaves are doubly rounded, toothed, sharp pointed and downy in the axils of the veins on the lower surface. Unlike the European plum, most of the bearing is on last season's lateral growth. There are no spurs. Three buds are present on one node and 3 flowers emerge per bud (Fig. 23.4). The pedicels are smooth. It is very productive and very early. The tree starts bearing fruits at a very early age. The fruit is cordate or rounded with a sharp cavity on the stalk end. It is never bluish purplish in colour and has very little bloom. It has fairly good shipping quality. The most commonly cultivated plums in India belong to *P. salicina.*

Fig. 23.4. Terminal and lateral twigs of Japanese (*P. salicina*) and European (*P. domestica*) plums (Source: Zielinski, 1955).

Cultivars

Methley: It is a Japanese plum. The tree is vigorous, upright and hardy, requires low chilling and is self fruitful and productive. The fruit ripens early in the season and is small to medium, round having purple skin blushed with red. The flesh is red, soft, very juicy and sweet having pleasant flavour and good quality. It is a good pollinizer.

Santa Rosa: It is a hybrid that retains most of the characteristics of the Japanese plum. The trees are large, vigorous and upright. It has early to mid season maturity. It is self fruitful and is a prolific and regular bearer and requires very little fruit thinning. The fruit is large, round to oblong conical in shape with a slight beak-like tapering at the base, red skin colour with purple bloom, juicy, cling stone and sweet having heavy whitish bloom, thick skin, prominent suture and a characteristic aroma when fully ripe. The flesh is golden yellow, red near the skin, sweet, acidic near the seed and juicy. Its shipping quality is not so good. It acts as a pollinizer.

Wickson: The tree is spreading. The fruit is medium to large, heart shaped, yellow with moderately sweet and translucent flesh. There is little or no tartness in the skin or near the pit.

Burbank: It is a *P. salicina* x *P. simonii* hybrid. Trees have low vigour and are somewhat drooping. The cultivar has early to mid season maturity. The fruits are large, heart-shaped, cherry red with amber colour, very juicy having deep yellow aromatic flesh. It is a high yielding and regular bearing cultivar.

Satsuma (Blood Plum): It is a product of Burbank. Trees are upright and vigorous. The cultivar has mid season maturity. The fruits are medium to large in size, roundish cordate in shape with dark reddish and thick skin and semi-freestone and intensely red flesh. It does well in transport.

Mariposa: It is a Japanese plum originated as a chance seedling. The tree is upright and vigorous. It needs cross pollination for good fruit set and has mid to late season maturity. The fruit is large, heart-shaped, freestone and of good quality. The colour of the skin is greenish yellow to maroon but it is similar to Satsuma from inside. The flesh is thick, red, firm and juicy having sweet flavour.

Beauty: It is an early bearing, self fruitful and prolific cultivar. Trees are upright and medium in vigour. The fruits are of medium size, clingstone with round shape and deep red colour. It requires heavy fruit thinning.

Kelsey: The plants of this Japanese plum are upright with moderate growth. The cultivar has low chilling requirement. It bears moderately and regularly and is a prolific bearer. The fruit is large, roundish oval heart shaped having distinct apex and deep suture towards the stem end. The skin is greenish with bright red blush and greenish dots. The flesh is juicy, sweet subacidic and yellowish with firm texture, best flavour and semi-clingstone. It has good keeping quality.

Alucha; It is a very prolific bearer. The cultivar is more acidic near the stone.

Pant Plum 1: It is a seedling selection. The tree is dwarf. The fruit is yellow and subacid. It is a good rootstock for other plum cultivars.

Grape (contd...)

Himrod

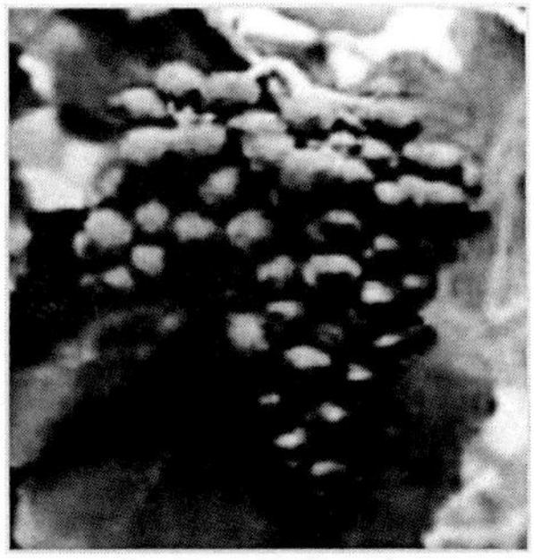

Einset Seedless

Arka Neelmani

Bangalore Blue

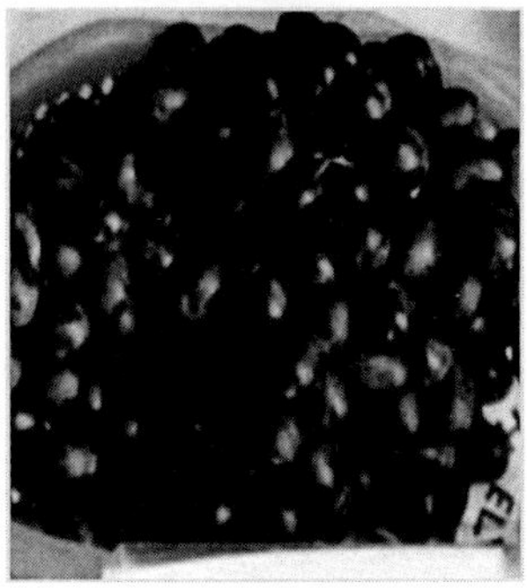

Sharad Seedless

Crimson Seedless

Pear

Conference

Winter Nelis

Anjou

William Bartlett

Comice

Apple

Red Delicious

Golden Delicious

Jonathan

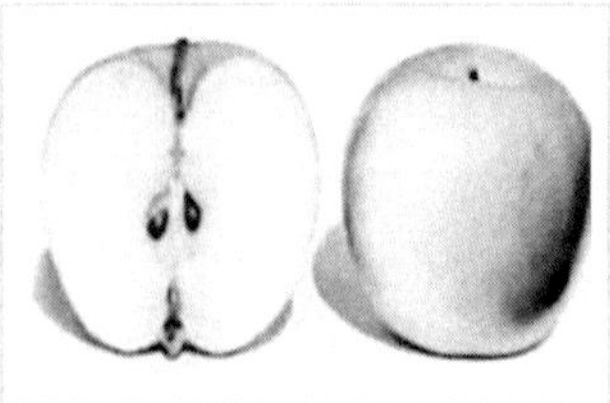

Granny Smith

Anna Apple

Royal Kinnaur

Peach

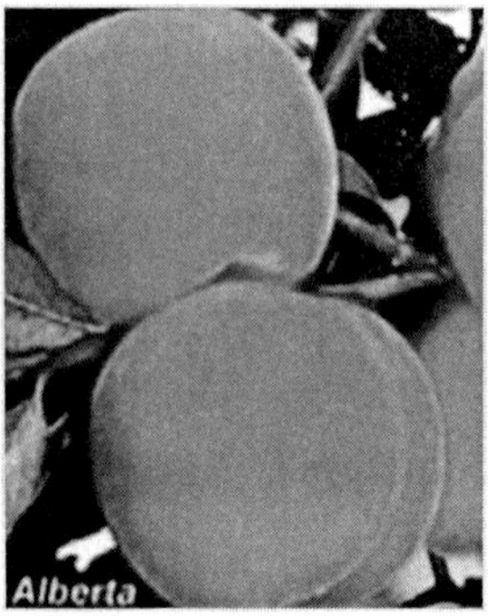

Alberta

July Elberta

J. H. Hale

Plum

Santa Rosa

Frontier

Avalon

Plum

Jubilee

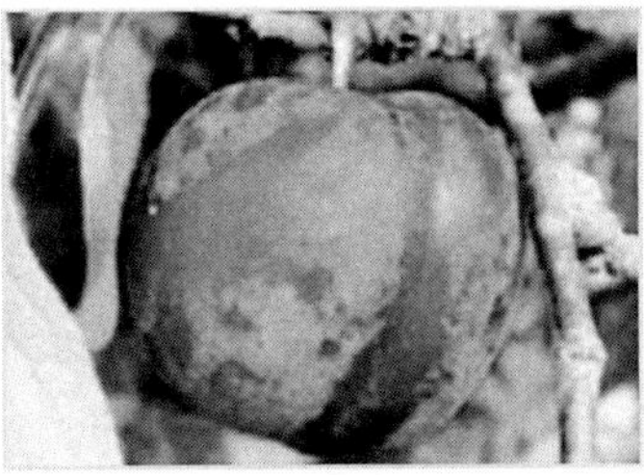

Excalibur

Damson Plum

Apricot

Blenheim

Moorpark

Cherry

Early Rivers

Bing

Bigarreau Napoleon

Stella

Ber (CIAH, Bikaner)

Gola

Seb

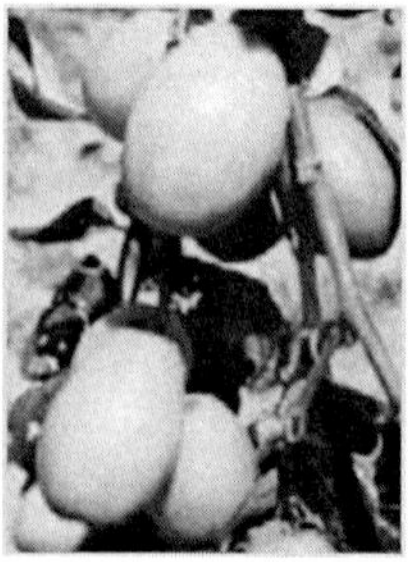
Umran

Banarsi Kadaka

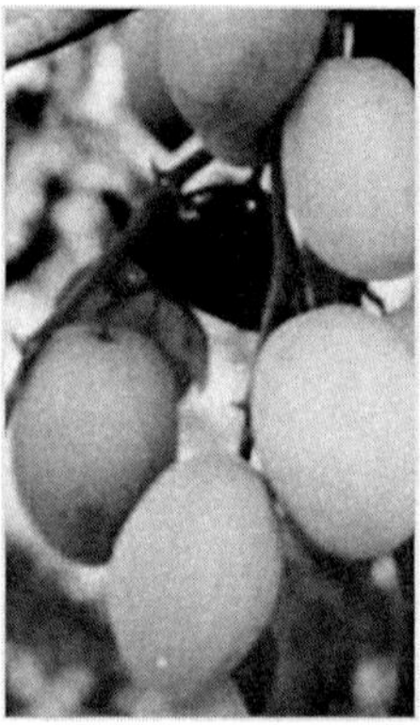
Kaithali

Mundia

Illiachi

Katha Phal

Chinese Jujube

Jackfruit

Koozha Chakka of Kerala

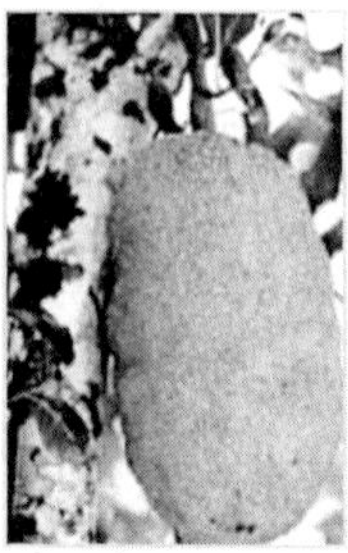
Malaysian J31 (NS1)

Fla 12: It is a seedling selection and an exotic type. The fruit is much larger than Titron or Jamuni.

Au-Rosa: The cultivar is high yielding (10.1 t/ha). Fruit has 19.3°B TSS. It is recommended for cultivation in temperate regions.

Frontier: Trees are upright and vigorous. Fruits are large, rounded, slightly heart shaped having red purple skin at the base and yellowish flesh colour and freestone. The cultivar has mid season maturity.

Red Beauty: Trees are medium to high in vigour. Fruits are medium in size, globose in shape having bright red skin colour and yellow flesh. It has very early season maturity.

Kanto-5: It is a high yielding (6.44 t/ha) cultivar recommended for cultivation in temperate regions. The fruit has 8.3°B TSS.

Kublo: It is a high yielding (6.5 t/ha) cultivar recommended for cultivation in temperate regions. The fruit has 8.3°B TSS.

Satluj Purple: The fruits are quite large, bright crimson with thick flesh, excellent shipping and possessing quality. The fruits ripen in the second week of May giving average yield of 30 kg/tree. It is self incompatible and thus has to be planted with Kala Amritsari.

Kala Amritsari: It is the most popular cultivar in Punjab, its fruits are of medium size, round shape and dark brown at maturity, moderately juicy and excellent for jam making. The fruits ripen during mid May giving average yield of 40.5 kg/tree.

European plum
(*Prunus domestica* L.) (2n=48)

It seems to have been in cultivation in Europe for at least 2000 years but no distinctly wild form is known. The fact that its seeds were not found under the ash of Pompeii indicates that it is of relatively recent origin. It is a hexaploid (2n= 48) probably originated as a hybrid between the diploid *P. cerasifera* (2n= 16) and the triploid *P. spinosa* (2n= 32). Evidence suggests that it arose by spontaneous doubling of a sterile triploid hybrid of *P. cerasifera:*

P. cerasifera (2x) x *P. spinosa* (4x) → 3x → doubling → *P. domestica* (6x).

It is by far the most important plum species worldwide.

Old trees do not have rough bark although transverse striations may be present. The branches are dark brown. Young shoots are glabrous. Terminal bud is vegetative but the winter shoots do not have terminal buds. One bud is present at each node (Fig. 23.4). The buds are small and glabrous. The leaves are bluntly toothed, often doubly crenate or serrate, large, obovate oval, thick and firm and pubescent on the lower surface. The petioles are also pubescent and are tinged red and have 0-2 glands. Fruiting is mostly on spurs. The pedicels are also pubescent. The flowers are borne on fascicled umbels and there are 1-2 flowers per bud. The fruit is oblong or rounded, reddish to bluish in colour and is often necked. The flesh is yellow. *P. domestica* has 6 races that require cold climate. Four of these are as follows:

1. **Reine Claude (Green Gage)**: The trees are low headed and have compact crowns. Their bark is dark in colour and the stems are short and pubescent. The shoots are thick and do not lose their pubescence. The leaves are thick, broad, wrinkled, loosely crenate and sometimes doubly serrate. The fruit is rounded and has shallow suture, thin bloom and is sweet, greenish or yellow or golden having excellent quality. Cultivars include Reine Claude, Bavay, Jafferson, Yellow Gage, Washington, Imperial Gage and Hand. The fruits are used for canning and in fresh market.

2. **Prunes:** These are plums having sugar content high enough to permit drying without removing the stones. The fruit is large, oval and has one side straighter than the other and is usually much compressed on sides and has a shallow suture. The fruits are usually necked and have heavy bloom. The colour of the fruit is blue to purple. It is a freestone plum with firm flesh and high sugar content. The fruits are used for drying, canning and fresh market. Cultivar Pozegaca is used for brandy in Yugoslavia. Important cultivars are Agen (French), Stanley, Sugar, Imperial, Enterprise, Italian (Fellenberg), Genan and Tragedy.

3. **Yellowish Egg Plum:** The trees are large, tall, upright spreading and vigorous and are very handsome but are tender to cold. The fruit is more or less necked, yellow or purple with firm flesh and usually of poor quality. It is a small group having plums used for canning. The main cultivars are Yellow Egg, Red Magnum Bonum and Golden Drop (Silver Prune).

4. **Lombard**: It is a group of large, oval, red or pink plums of good quality valuable mostly for fresh market. The most important fresh market cultivar in western Europe is Victoria. Other cultivars are Pond (incorrectly called Hungarian), Bradshaw and Lombard.

Cultivars

Greengage: It is a famous European cultivar of the Reine Claude group. The tree is medium in growth with round top. Flowering is mid season to late. The fruit is small, round with vivid greenish yellow skin mottled with red and has the finest flavour amongst plums. The flesh is firm, greenish yellow, very juicy, tender, sweet and partly clingstone. The stone is round and thick.

Early Transparent Gage: It is of the Reine Claude group. The tree is dwarf having compact growth and oval leaves that are initially brownish. Flowering occurs early. It is a self compatible and regular bearing cultivar. The fruit is small and roundish having flat ends and green colour with primrose bloom and red dots. The flesh is yellow, juicy, very sweet having the characteristic gage flavour. The cultivar is very good as dessert and excellent to make jam and for canning.

Victoria: It is has high chilling requirement and gives regular medium to heavy yields. The tree is small having spreading branches. The fruit is oval having deep sutures, round apex and straw green skin colour that turns pink to red with green dots when ripe. The flesh is deep red, firm, juicy, sweet acidic, freestone and of good quality. It has good storage quality and excellent canning quality.

The plum cultivars developed at East Malling Research Station, England are **Excalibur** (Count d'Althans Gage open pollinated; Selection WJ4) and **Avalon**

(Reeves open pollinated; Selection WJ10). The rootstock cultivars from East Malling Research Station are **Myrobalan B, Damas** C, **St Julien** A and **Pixy** (St. Julien d'Orleans open-pollinated; Selection E340/4.6).

American plums (2n=16)

There are at least 5 American species; *P. americana* Marsh. (American red plum or common wild plum), *P. nigra* Ait. (Canada plum), *P. angustifolia* Marsh. (chickasaw), *P. hortulana* Bailey (hortulana plum) and P. *munsoniana* Wight and Hedr. (wild goose plum). *P. americana* is cold hardy and good for dry and cold climate. The trees are slow growing, 3-3.6 m in height and have arching branches and smooth twigs. The winter shoots are without terminal buds. The leaves are roundish ovate, 7.5-10 cm long with a slender apex and a rounded base, hairy on the lower surface only on the axils of the veins having downy and up to 7.5 cm long glandless petioles. The flowers are white, 2-5 in stalkless umbels. The fruit is nearly round and yellow to red having yellow flesh.

Cherries
(2n=16, 32)

Cherry is the common name of several *Prunus* species including the commercially important sweet cherry (*P. avium)*, tart or sour cherry (*P. cerasus*) and Duke cherries (natural tetraploid hybrids between the diploid sweet cherries and the tetraploid sour cherries).

Key to the classification of cherries

A. Few flowered branching clusters. Leaves are much longer than broad.

B. Leaves are large, long, oblong ovate, soft, taper pointed ....*P. avium* (sweet cherry; Mazzard)

BB. Leaves are small, short, ovate or obovate, short pointed, glabrous and not hanging down .... *P. cerasus* (sour cherry)

AA. Many flowered umbel like clusters. The leaves are small, very broad, nearly rounded, firm, shiny and perfumed, short petioles ....*P. mahaleb* (Mahaleb cherry)

Sweet cherry
(***Prunus avium* L.**; Mazzard) (2n = 16)

Sweet cherry is native to the Caucasus but is restricted to the regions having cooler climate. The trees are upright and tall. Branches are thick and the young shoots are smooth. The bark is dark and peels off in horizontal rings. The leaves are downy on the midribs below. They are 7.5-12.5 cm long (longer than broad), oval to ovate and slender pointed. The petiole is very long (5 cm). The buds are roundish, solitary and axillary (Fig. 23.5). The inflorescence is without leafy bracts, in few flowered umbels (5-7 flowers) and without stalk. The flowers are white and 2.5 cm across. Pedicels are 2.5-3.75 cm long. The fruit is sweet and neither sulcate nor bloomy. The stone is swollen or nearly globose.

Cherry is consumed fresh as a gourmet fruit and also in soups, tarts, pies and candies, often covered with chocolate and as an almost artificial product called *maraschino*. The fruit is used to prepare liqueurs and wines. The wood is used for furniture and veneers.

Cultivar groups

Mazzard: The fruits are small of various shapes and colours. It is used as a rootstock for both sweet and sour cherries.

Hearts or Geans or Guiganes: Fruits are heart shaped. The flesh is soft. The main cultivars are Governor Wood, Round or Black Tartarian, Chapman and Bing.

Bigarreaus or Bigarreaux: Fruits are heart shaped and light coloured. The flesh is firm. The main cultivar is Napoleon (called Royal in America).

Cultivars

Bing: Trees are upright to spreading, vigorous and mid season flowering. The fruits are very large with roundish to slightly heart shape and maroon or deep red skin. These are of good quality ripening uniformly and hang well on the tree.

Chapman: It is a very early cultivar and is attacked by birds. The fruits are small, blackish having soft flesh of excellent quality. It is not important commercially.

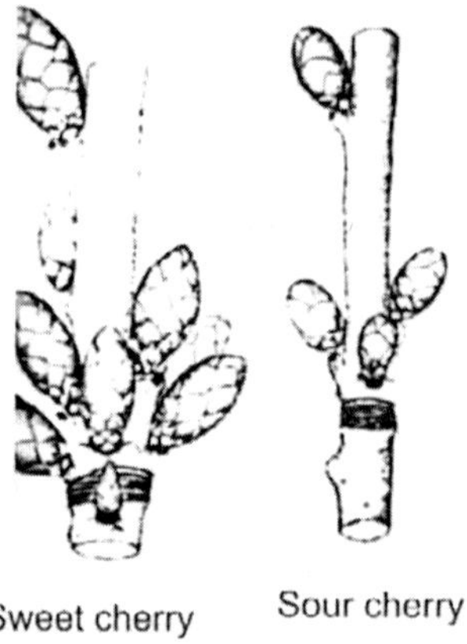

Fig. 23.5. Bud arrangement on sweet and sour cherries (Source: Zielinski, 1955).

Napoleon: It is a very productive and late maturing cultivar. The fruits are large, red and are often prone to cracking. The keeping quality of the fruits is good.

Bigarreau Napolian (Double): Trees are medium to vigorous having early season flowering and early to mid season maturity. The fruits are longish, medium to large and heart shaped and have creamy red yellow skin colour.

Lapins, Stella, Van, Black Heart, Compact Stella, Bigarreau Noir Groosa (Mishri): Trees are medium to large. The fruits have obtuse heart shape and dark red skin colour which finally changes to blackish purple. It has mid to late season maturity.

Dukes (sweet cherry x sour cherry): It is sometimes put under sour cherries but resembles sweet cherries in most of the characters such as tree growth habit and flower and leaf characters. The fruits are heart-shaped and have acidic juice and hardly any viable seed.

Early Rivers: It is an early and prolific bearing cultivar with large and black fruits.

Black Heart: The trees are vigorous. It is mid season flowering with early to mid season maturity. The fruits are medium in size, heart shaped with compressed apex and deep shiny blackish purple skin colour.

Guigne Noir Gross: Trees are medium to large. The fruits are medium in size, roundish obtuse, heart shaped having dark red skin colour and early season maturity.

Guigne Noir Hative (Makhmali): The trees are medium to vigorous, late flowering and mid to late season maturity. The fruits are very large with ovoid obtuse heart shape, shining dark blackish brown to black skin and small stone.

Lambert: Trees are medium in vigour, mid season flowering and mid to late season maturity. The fruits are large, round in shape with deep ruby red blackish skin. It is susceptible to cracking as a result of rainfall.

Stella: Trees are medium spreading and precocious and have mid to late flowering and mid to late season maturity. The fruits are very large with heart shape and are dark red turning black at maturity. The stone is small.

CITH Cherry-01: The cultivar was selected from Bigarreu Napoleon (Double). Trees are semi-spreading, precocious, regular and prolific bearing. Fruits are large, ovoid in shape, attractive, dark red and with long pedicels. The fruits have high TSS and good acid/sugar blend.

CITH Cherry–02: It was selected from the local cultivar Mishri. Trees are upright, precocious and prolific and regular bearer. Fruits are large having attractive red colour and higher TSS than those of Mishri. The fruits mature 10 days earlier than those of Mishri.

Tart or sour cherry
(***Prunus cerasus*** L.) (2n = 32)

Sour cherry is hardier than sweet cherry and the fruits require a longer season to mature. The branches are not so thick. Young shoots are smooth. The leaves are glabrous, 5.0-7.5 cm long (longer than broad), elliptic to ovate, abruptly sharp pointed and have fine teeth. The petiole is short, 1.25-5.0 cm long. The buds are plump, spherical and solitary and are borne in the axils (Fig. 23.5). The inflorescence is usually with leafy and persistent bracts in few flowered umbels (5-7) and is without stalk. The flowers are white or pinkish and 2.5 cm across having 1.25-1.88 cm long pedicels. The fruits are small, pale red, sour and are borne laterally on the shoots. Their use is restricted to processing, mainly as a filling for pies and pastries. However, it is now becoming popular as a dried fruit and as a source of health promoting syrup. The fruits are suitable for canning.

Cultivars

The cultivars fall into the following three groups:-

1. Amarelles: The fruits are pale red in colour and are flattened at one end having colourless, less bitter and acidic juice. The main cultivar is Montmorency.

2. Morellos or Griottes: The trees are small and more compact. The branches are more horizontal. The leaves are smaller, thinner and pendent. The fruits are dark, more spherical or cordate, smaller in size having reddish juice. Important cultivar is Schattenmorelle.

3. Marasca: It grows wild in South Europe. The fruits are extremely small, blackish from which an alcoholic liquor is prepared. The cultivar has also given rise to a *P. cerasus* x *P. marasca* hybrid designated as *P. cerasus* var. *marasca.*

The trees are more vigorous having finer serrated leaves and longer stipules. The inflorescence is more compact and the fruits are much smaller, deep red or almost black with intensely red, acidic and bitter flesh.

The following cherry cultivars were developed at East Malling Research Station, England:-

Penny (Colney x Inge; Selection C73-5).

Wildstar™ (Timber cherry; Clones 1-3 *Prunus avium* 1/3 open pollinated, Clones 4-8 wild *P. avium* accessions were collected in England; Selection Malling clones 1-8).

Cherry rootstock cultivars developed at East Malling Research Station, England are **Colt** *(P. avium* F299/2 x *P. pseudocerasus*; Selection FB2.58-21), **Charger** *(P. avium* F1/3 open pollinated; Selection FD1-57-4-13), **Cob** *(P. avium* F299/2 x *P. pseudocerasus*; Selection FB2-58-17) and **F12/1.**

Family Elaeagnaceae (oleaster and seabuckthorn)

It is a small family of about 3 genera and 50 species (Heywood *et al.*, 2007). The plants are multi-branched shrubs, woody climbers or small trees, often thorny and densely covered with silver, gold or brown peltate scales and/or stellate hairs. The leaves are deciduous or evergreen, leathery, alternate, opposite or whorled, simple and entire without stipules. The flowers are axillary, solitary in clusters, racemes or spikes, bisexual (*Elaeagnus*) or unisexual (plants monoecious in *Elaeagnus*, dioecious in *Shepherdia* and *Hippophae*) and strongly perigynous. The perianth is in 1 whorl, 2 to 4-lobed, rarely more, often petaloid with a tubular hypanthium, often constricted above the level of the ovary (erroneously giving the appearance of an inferior ovary), sometimes flat in male flowers. The stamens are inserted on the hypanthium throat, 4 in a single whorl, alternating with the perianth segments or 5 in 2 whorls (1 alternate and 1 opposite), 2-locular with longitudinal dehiscence. A nectary disk is often present on inner hypanthium surface. The ovary is superior, 1-locular and 1 anatropous ovule and basal placentation. The style is long with a basal to capitate stigma. The fruit is a single-seeded achene or drupe-like. The seeds have little or no endosperm.

Genus *Hippophae* L.

The plants are dioecious. Leaves are usually alternate, rarely in whorls or subopposite. Flowers are odourless and emophilous having valvate calyx with 2 lobes, 4 stamens, alternate to and opposite with the sepals. Fruit has longitudinal ribs in several species.

Seven species, four of which have been recognized in temperate areas of Eurasia. *Hippophae rhamnoides* L. (seabuckthorn) is the most widespread species with fragmented range from central China to the coast of Europe (Kubitzki, 2004). *H. rhamnoides* has been divided into nine subspecies, *H. rhamnoides* subsp. *carpatica* Rousi, *H. rhamnoides* subsp. *caucasica* Rousi, *H. rhamnoides* subsp. *gyantsensis* Rousi, *H. rhamnoides* subsp. *mongolica* Rousi, *H. rhamnoides* subsp. *sinensis* Rousi, *H. rhamnoides* subsp. *turkestanica* Rousi, *H. rhamnoides* subsp. *yunnanensis* Rousi, *H. rhamnoides* subsp. *rhamnoides* and *H. rhamnoides* subsp. *fluviatilis* Rousi. The other important species are *H. salicifolia* D. Don., *H. tibetana* Schlechdt. and *H. neurocarpa*.

Seabuckthorn
(***Hippophae rhamnoides*** L.; sirma; kalabisa; chuma)

It is a native of temperate zone of Europe and Asia. It is mentioned in the writings of ancient scholars such as Dioscorides and Theophrastus. It is widely distributed in the Eurasian continent (27-69°N latitude) throughout the temperate zones of Asia and Europe and at high altitudes of the subtropical zone of Asia. It is found growing wild in Europe, west and north China and northwestern Himalayas. It is cultivated in China, Mongolia and former USSR. It grows between a few to 5200 m altitudes (Rongsen, 1992). In India, seabuckthorn grows in high altitude areas of Himachal Pradesh, Jammu and Kashmir and Uttar Pradesh (Singh, 1998).

Seabuckthorn is a fast growing deciduous and spinescent shrub or small tree growing up to 12 m in height having rough brown bark. Branches are gray in colour and are usually spiny. Leaves are small, linear lanceolate covered with silvery scales. Seabuckthorn is dioecious. Flowers are very small, greenish or yellowish appearing with new leaves. The male flowers are borne in axillary clusters while the female ones are solitary. Fruit is enclosed by a succulent receptacle (calyx tube) and is ovoid subglobose, 5-8 mm long and orange yellow in colour. One hundred fruits weigh 20-80 g. Seeds are light to dark brown. But the seeds of *H. tibetana* are white (Singh, 1998). One hundred seeds weigh 0.7-1.3 g. The seed is surrounded by a parchment-like ovarian wall. It is ovate oblong, 4-7 x 2.5-3 mm in size and has 1.6 to 2.2 mm thickness. The skin of the seed is grayish brown or dark brown, leathery and lustrous (Anon., 1990; Rongsen, 1992).

Genus *Elaeagnus* L.

The plants are polygamous or monoecious. Leaves are alternate. Flowers are 4-merous, often scented and entomophilous and have quadrangular perianth and equal number of stamens alternating with the sepals. Fruit usually has eight longitudinal ribs. About 20-45 species occur worldwide, mostly in Eurasia and up to North America (one species, *Elaeagnus commuta*), 3 in Kazakhstan and through tropical

SE Asia and Malaysia to North Queensland. The most widespread species is *E. angustifolia* with discontinuous range from China and Central Asia to Europe (Kubitzki, 2004). Most of the species are found in temperate latitudes, except for a few that grow in the subtropics of Asia and the Mediterranean region. The important edible species is *E. angustifolia* L. (oleaster). The other species is *E. philippensis* Perr. syn. *E. latifolia* L. (lingaro) which grows mainly in Turgai forest along the banks and in valleys of desert rivers, among alluvial shrubs, forest borders, sands, borders and lower sides of sandy hills and steppes.

Oleaster
(*Elaeagnus angustifolia* L.; Russian olive; narrow-leafed oleaster; trebizond date)

It is a native of temperate Asia (Wickens, 1998). Oleaster is a temperate plant species. It is drought resistant, light demanding, air pollution resistant and tolerates soil salinity. It is a shrub or small tree, 3 to 10 m tall with an open silvery crown. The trunk and older branches have reddish brown and glossy bark. The shoots and buds are covered with silvery scales. Leaves are alternate, lanceolate, oblong lanceolate, acuminate elliptical, 2.5 to 7 cm long, 0.4 to 1.5 cm wide, grayish green on the upper side and silvery white on the lower side. It blooms in May and matures fruits in July to August. Fragrant flowers are borne in the axils on short (2 mm long) pedicels and have silvery yellow colour. The fruit is edible, spherical to oblong, drupaceous, 7 to 14 mm long, 5 to 10 mm wide, yellow or reddish bluish having sweet mealy flesh.

Family Rhamnaceae

The family comprises 58 genera and about 900 species. The plants are mostly trees, shrubs or climbers and rarely herbs, which are sometimes scandent and are often spiny. The leaves are stipulate, simple, alternate and rarely opposite with small caducous stipules. The flowers are small, usually borne in cymes or corymbs, perfect or rarely polygamous or dioecious, if polygamous then monoecious, or unisexual by abortion of one of the essential whorls. An intrastaminal disk is often present. Sepals (4-5) are connate in tubular 4-5 lobed calyx and the lobes are valvate, usually ridged internally. Petals are small, 4-5 or rarely absent, inserted on the calyx tube, free, usually clawed and hooded enclosing the anthers at flowering. The family is characterized by the 4-5 stamens, which are opposite to and often embraced by the petals and inserted along with the petals at the margins of the fleshy disc. The anthers are 2-locular, opening lengthwise, disc is mostly present, perigynous, sometimes lining the calyx tube. The carpels form a 3-celled, sometimes 2 or 1-celled ovary. The ovary is sessile, free or sunken into the disc, 2-4 celled with one or rarely 2 ovules in each cell, erect from the base, anatropous with two integuments and the style is shortly lobed. The fruits are of various types, often a dehiscent or indehiscent drupe with one to several pits or winged fruit or capsule. Seeds mostly have copious endosperm and a large straight embryo.

Sussenguth (1953) divided the family into five tribes; Rhamneae having a berry or schizocarp fruit with thick testa, Zizipheae having drupe with papery thin testa, Ventilagineae having winged indehiscent fruit or capsule, Colletieae having capsule or schizocarp with thick testa, and Gouanieae having fruit with wing-like expansion of carpellary portions with massive testa. The tribe Zizipheae contains the genus *Ziziphus*.

Genus *Ziziphus* Mill. (x=12; 2n=24)

The generic name *Ziziphus* has been derived from 'Zizouf', the Arabic name of *Z. lotus*. The plants are erect or straggling, small to medium sized trees or shrubs having stipules modified into spines, which may be solitary or in pairs, usually one straight and the other curved. The plants are deciduous or evergreen. Leaves are alternate, or rarely subopposite with extra-petiolar stipules. The leaves are simple and coriaceous or membranous, acuminate, toothed or not and strongly 3(-5)-nerved from the base. The branchlets have stipular spines. The flowers are 5-merous, actinomorphic and hermaphrodite. The flowers are borne sometimes solitary or 2-3 together in axillary cymes or in umbels or racemes arranged in terminal panicles or thyrses. The inflorescences may be pedunculate or sessile. The calyx has triangular acute lobes up to 2 mm long, dentate, valvate and keeled on the inside and the tube is obconical. The petals are 5, occasionally absent, small, about 2 mm long, unguiculate at the base, deflexed with the expanded parts about 1.5 mm wide and clasp the stamens or filaments. Stamens are 5, slightly adnate to the base of petals, usually longer than the petals and the filaments are inserted under the edge of the disc. The ovary is subinferior, sunk into the flat or pitted disc but not coherent with it. The disc is 5 or 10-lobed, with a free margin and confluent at base. Stigma is small and papillose. The ovary is superior, 2-4 celled with 2-4 styles that are distinct or more or less connate. When 2-celled, usually only one produces a seed. Hypanthium is shallow, patelliform to hemispherical and flat disc.

The fruits are usually drupes, may be pilose when young, subglobose, ovoid or oblong. These are 1-4 celled and 1-4 seeded but the drupes contain only one seed. The flesh is usually juicy, but rarely may be relatively dry. The genus is pantropical and has about 100 species centred in tropical America and South East Asia (Kubitzki, 2004) and is divided into the following two sections:

Section 1. *Ziziphus*: Plants glabrous with deciduous fruiting branchlets and mainly distributed in temperate zones .... *Z. jujuba* Mill., *Z. acidojujuba* C.Y. Cheng et M. J. Lui

Section 2. *Perdurans*: Plants with at least two kinds of pilose organs and without deciduous fruiting branchlets; distributed in tropical and subtropical areas (M. J. Liu et C.Y. Cheng)

Series Cymosiflorae: Axillary cymes, glabrous ovary and fruit, thick and hard endocarp, widely distributed in tropical and subtropical areas .... *Z. mauritiana* Lam., *Z. oenoplia* Mill., *Z. cambodiana* Pierre, *Z. spina-christi* (L.) Willd., *Z. nummularia* (Burm. f.) Wight & Arn., *Z. horrida* Roth., *Z. incurva* Roxb., *Z. lenticellaria* Merr., *Z. lotus* Lam., *Z. apetala* Hook., *Z. glabrata* Heyne ex Roth., *Z. abyssinica* Hochst. ex Rich., *Z. mucronata* Willd., *Z. truncata* Blatt. et Hall., *Z. guatemalensis* Hemsl., Chen et P. K. Chou, *Z. xiangchemgensis* Y. L., *Z. mairei* Dod., *Z. montana* W. W. Smith, *Z. publinervis* Rehd., *Z. laui* Merr. and others.

Series Thyrisflorae: Terminal or axillary thyrse, pilose young fruit and (or) ovary, thin and fragile endocarp, concentrated in South and South East Asia .... *Z. rugosa* Lam., *Z. calophylla* Wall., *Z. attopensis* Pierre, *Z. hoaensis* Pierre, *Z. kunstleri* King, *Z. borneensis* E. D. Merrill, *Z. javanensis* Bl., *Z. fungii* Merr. and others

The number of species reported under the genus *Ziziphus* varies from 18 (Hooker, 1875), 40 (Rendle, 1959), 60 (Ridley, 1922), 80 (Evreinoff, 1964), 86 (Johnston, 1972) and 135 (Bhansali, 1975) to 271 (in Floras published until 1994) and, considering the synonymy, have been reduced to 170 by Liu and Cheng (1995). A key for classification of *Ziziphus* species (Pareek, 2001) is given below:

Plants glabrous, fruiting branchlets deciduous .... *Z. jujuba* Mill.

Plants having pilose organs, fruiting branchlets are not deciduous; Axillary cymes, glabrous ovary and fruit, hard endocarp:

Trees:

Leaves glabrous on both sides:

Leaves broadly ovate, many flowered cymes .... *Z. joazerio* Mart.

Leaves elliptic or ovate elliptic, armed trees ....*Z. spina-christi* (L.) Desf.

Leaves elliptic, unarmed trees .... *Z. trinervia* Roxb.

Leaves glabrous above, tomentose beneath:

Leaves oblong ovate or orbicular, obtuse or acute, base rounded oblique, nearly asymmetric....................... *Z. mauritiana* Lam.

Leaves ovate, acuminate, base very asymmetric ....*Z. abyssinica* Hochst. ex Rich

Leaves tomentose on both sides, oval, minutely serrulate ....*Z. mistol* Griseb.

Shrubs:

Leaves smaller than 2 cm:

Leaves oblong, sharp shining spines, cyme 2-4 flowered.. *Z. hamur* Engl.

Leaves suborbicular or elliptic to ovate, tomentose beneath and less so above, flower solitary or 2-3 ....*Z. lotus* L. subsp. *saharae Maire*

Leaves ovate, tomentose on both sides, long spines pilose when young, cyme 10-20 flowered..................................... *Z. nummularia* Wight & Arn.

Leaves elliptic to obovate, glabrous, sessile cyme ....*Z. parryi* Weberb.

Leaves larger than 2 cm:

Leaves glabrous on both sides:

Leaves oval, acuminate, wooly branchlets .. *Z. napeca* Willd.

Leaves ovate oblong, prickly shrub .... *Z. lotus* Lam.

Leaves truncate, downy branchlets,
2 pricklets .... *Z. truncate* Blatt & Hall.

Glabrous branchlets, solitary spines or
unarmed .... *Z. glabra* Roxb.

Leaves glabrous above and tomentose beneath:

Elliptic or ovate elliptic, subentire, several flowered
cyme *Z. spina-christi* var. *microphylla* Hochst ex. A. Rich.

Oval elliptic, entire, glands at
edges .... *Z. mauritiana* var. *serticola* Chevalier

Oval oblong, entire or slightly denti-
culate ... *Z. mauritiana* var. orthacantha (DC.) Chevalier

Semi scandent shrub:

Leaves glabrous above and tomentose beneath:

Leaves lanceolate oval, unequal sided, only one spine
developed .... *Z. oenoplia* Mill.

Plants having terminal or axillary thyrse, pilose young fruit and (or) ovary,
thin and fragile endocarp:

Fruit woody, inedible, trees................................*Z. xylopyrus* Willd.

Fruit edible:

Shrubs, leaves smaller than 2 cm, long
petioles ....*Z. oxyphylla* Edgew.

Climbing shrubs:

Petals 0

Leaves glabrous above, dense fulvous tomentose to
glabrous beneath ....*Z. rugosa* Lam.

Petals 5

Leaves elliptic oblong, glabrous except on nerves
tomentose beneath...............................*Z. kunstleri* King

Leaves ovate acuminate, glabrous above, Branches and
cyme pubescent ....*Z. elegans* Wall.

Climbers:

Glabrous branchlets and cyme, vigorous climber .. *Z. affinis* Hemsl.

Cyme densely tomentose, vigorous climber ..... *Z. calophylla* Wall.

Branchlets and cyme pubescent, slender
climber .... *Z. horsfieldii* Miq.

Branchlets and cyme sparingly pubescent, slender
liana ....*Z. elegans* Wall.

Scattered hair on branchlets, leaves <2 cm, slender woody
creeper ....*Z. pernettyoides* Ridl.

Chinese jujube
(*Z. jujuba* Mill. non Lam. syn. *Z. vulgaris* Lam., *Z. sativa* Gaertn., *Z. flexuosa* Wall., *Z. nitida* Roxb., *Z. sinensis* Lam., *Z. chinensis* D.C., *Z. chinensis* Watt, *Z. officinarum* Medicus, *Z. mairei* Dode): x = 12; 2n = 24

The Chinese jujube is native to temperate Asia, particulatly China and the neighbouring areas of Mongolia and the central Asian Republics. Its cultivation is spread westwards to the Mediterranean, throughout the Near East and the South West Asia and eastwards to Korea and Japan.

Deciduous shrubs or small trees are up to 6-10 m high with rigid spreading boughs and stiff zigzag branches producing a gnarled shape. Winter buds are small. Branches of young plants are armed with very short, paired spines, one straight, 2.5 cm long, the other much shorter and recurved. Older trees are usually unarmed. Branchlets are flexuous, green and glabrous when young. The flowering shoots are about 15-20 cm long, often fascicled on dwarf branches and are caducous leaving a knob-like structure at the nodes. The leaves are 2.5-5 cm long, oblong ovate to ovate lanceolate, rarely ovate, acute or obtuse, glabrous, crenate serrate, oblique, 3-veined. Petioles are 2.5-7.5 cm long and stipules form spines. The spines and leaves are also caducous. Flowering takes place in spring. The flowers are in few flowered axillary clusters, borne on smaller lateral branches. Petals are clawed with truncate tips. The disc is lobed. Styles are 2, connate to the middle. The ovary is 2-4 celled but generally 2-celled and sunken into a disc. The fruit ripens in autumn. It is an ellipsoid drupe, 1.5-2.5 cm long with a pointed stone. The stone is oblong or ovoid.

Cultivars

The National Jujube Germplasm Repository, Pomology Institute of Shanxi Academy of Agricultural Sciences, China has two species and 530 cultivars (170-248 characterized). Muzao, a group of cultivars is widely distributed and cultivated in the Canyon of the Yellow River between Shanxi and Shaanxi Provinces.

Sihong Dazao: The trees are resistant to drought, water logging and diseases. It is an early cultivar maturing fruits from mid March to late September. The fruits are very large weighing up to 65 g and 50-60 g on an average, elongated round in shape with purplish red skin and light green, crisp, juicy and very sweet pulp having 30-36% TSS.

Li Zao: The trees are drought resistant and bear early giving high and stable yields. The fruits are of good quality and contain 23.1% sugar, 0.37% organic acids and 287.9 mg/100 g ascorbic acid.

Dongzao: The trees are adaptable to soil pH of 5.5 to 8.5. It is an extra late cultivar. The fruits are large, weighing about 13.3 g on an average reaching 37.3 g, round, glossy and brownish red. The pulp is plump, fine, tender and acid-sweet having 35-38°B TSS, 30.3% sugar, 3.3% protein, 0.3% oil and 352 mg/100 g ascorbic acid.

Wolchul Daechu: The trees are spreading and vigorous. It is similar in growth and flowering habit to the popular cultivars Moodeung and Geumsung. The fruit is large 10.1 g in weight having 29.8°B TSS and is suitable both for fresh eating and drying.

JMS 3 (male sterile Jujube No 3): Anthers in unopened buds are small, shrunken and dingy yellow and become brown after anthesis. No surviving pollen is observed in the flower.

Cultivars introduced in California

Frank Meyer introduced cultivars Li and Lang at the Plant Introduction Station Chico, California. The other cultivars, based on fruit ripening time in southern California are:-

i. Early ripening

Li: Tree is narrow, upright and many-branched. Fruits ripen in mid August, may be picked at yellow green stage and are round and large, up to 86 g.

ii. Mid season

Ed Hegard: Very similar to the Lang and Thornless.

GA-866: An outstandingly sweet selection. Fruit is large and elongated.

Jin: The fruit is elongated and very chewy when allowed to dry on the tree.

Lang: Tree is upright and virtually spineless. Fruit is large, pear-shaped and is best for eating when fully coloured. Fruits are best to let dry on the tree.

Redlands #4: Very large, sweet and round fruit.

So: The tree is somewhat dwarf and has beautiful shape. Branching is zigzag.

Sugar Cane: The plants are spiny. The fruits are small to medium, round to elongated and extremely sweet.

Thornless: The plants have no or very few thorns. The fruit is very similar to the Lang.

Cultivars **Globe** and **Honey Jar** are new introductions.

iii. Late ripening

Admiral Wilkes: Fruit is elongated and ripen in mid to late November.

Chico (GI 7-62): Fruit is round but flattened on the bottom and looks like small apple. These are excellent both fresh or dried.

GI-1183: Fruit is large and sweet.

Sherwood: It is a seedling plant. Tree is very narrow and upright with leaves of weeping habit. The fruit is very dense and sweet.

Silverhill: The tree is virtually spineless. Fruit is elongated.

Tigerstooth: Very similar to Silverhill.

Topeka: The fruit is excellent.

Sour jujube
(***Z. acidojujuba*** C. Y. Cheng et M. J. Liu; ***Z. spinosa*** Hu.)

It is a direct ancestor of *Z. jujuba* Mill., originated in China and widely distributed in most northern provinces. It is very important because of its wide adaptability and use as a rootstock. Besides, the species is of great value for its medicinal uses and for juice making from its high vitamin C rich acidic fruits. There is a rich diversity with fruit weight varying from 0.14 to 6.33 g, colour from orange, red to dark red and shape from oblate, globose, oblong globose to ovoid.

Ber
(***Z. mauritiana*** Lamk. syn. ***Z. jujuba*** (L.) Lam., ***Z. jujuba*** Lam. non Mill., ***Z. insularis*** Smith, ***Z. sororia*** Roem. and Shult., ***Z. tomentosa*** Poir., ***Z. rotundata*** DC., ***Z. aucheri*** Boiss., ***Z. jujuba*** (L.) Gaertn., ***Z. jujuba*** (L.) Gaertn. var. ***stenocarpa*** Kuntze, ***Z. jujuba*** (L.) Gaertn. forma ***aequilaterifolia*** Engl.)

The species is distributed throughout the warm subtropics and tropics of South Asia. Its cultivation is spread eastwards through Malaysia and Indochina and southern China. It is widespread in Africa and southern Arabia. The plants vary from shrubs to small, medium-sized or large trees which may be erect, semi-erect or spreading and vary in height from 3 to 16 m or more, sometimes 20 m. The trees are much branched. The bark has deep longitudinal furrows and is grayish brown or reddish in colour. The branches and branchlets are armed with short stipular spines, generally twin, one straight and the other bent, either equal or one wanting, or entirely unarmed. The branches are erect and spreading, becoming flexuous and dull brown gray. Branchlets are densely white pubescent, especially when young and tend to be zigzag. Fruiting branches are not deciduous. The branches are evergreen and may shed their leaves during the summer. The branches may also drop off.

The leaves are elliptic to ovate or nearly orbicular, 1.3 to 12 cm long and 0.4 to 6.5 cm wide. The apex is rounded, obtuse or subacute to emarginate. The base is rounded, sometimes cuneate, mostly symmetrical or nearly so. Margins are minutely serrulate. There are 3 marked nerves almost to the apex with more or less prominent lateral nerves, the nerves being depressed in the upper, light or dark green, glabrous surface. The lower surface is whitish due to the persistent dense hairs but may be buff coloured. Occasionally the lower surface is glabrous. The leaves are petiolate, 1.1-5.8 mm long and the stipules are mostly in the form of spines, sometimes not developed into spines. In each pair of spines, usually one is hooked and the other is straight or both may be hooked.

Flowering takes place during autumn. The flowers are greenish yellow, on short stalk or subsessile or in short pedunculate cymes. The hairy pedicels are longer than peduncles. Calyx lobes are keeled to the middle and wooly outside The petals are unguiculate with an oblong, concave or hood-shaped lamina. The disk is fleshy, 10-lobed and 10-sulcate. Styles are 2, thick, conical and connate to the middle. The fruit ripens in late winter or late spring. The fruit is round to oval to ovoid oblong drupe generally about 1.25-1.9 cm long, on the stalk about half its length, dark brown, orange or red when ripe. The kernel is irregularly furrowed, mostly 2-celled with a hard, thick and bony shell and more acidic.

Cultivars

Originated as selections from the natural variability at different locations, over 300 cultivars are under cultivation of which only a few are commercially important. Pareek (2001) has listed about 180 named cultivars that vary in vegetative and fruit characteristics. Singh *et al.* (1971, 1972) prepared two keys to classify 39-40 cultivars, one on the basis of vegetative characters (length/width ratio and width of leaf, branching habit of the tree and shape and type of leaf) and the second on the basis of fruit characters (shape and apex of fruit, presence of cavities in the pericarp, type of base of fruit and the presence of styler scar and its colour, fruit size and colour of developing fruit and markings). Vashishtha and Pareek (1989) prepared the following key to classify 59 cultivars using both vegetative and fruit characters simultaneously:

A. Tree form erect
B. Fruit round
C. Leaf oval
D. Style end flat with apple like depression .... **Seb**
CC. Leaf oblong
DD. Style end obliquely beaked ....**Khatti**
BB. Fruit oblong
C. Leaf oval
D. Styler end obliquely beaked ....**Gobindgarh Selection**
CC. Leaf oblong
D. Style end round
E. Leaf apex acute.......................................**Kaithli**
EE. Leaf apex sub-acute ....**Lam**
DD. Style end bluntly tapering.................................**Nimaj**
BBB. Fruit ovate
C. Leaf oval
D. Style end straight pointed
E. Leaf apex round...................................... **Tikadi**
EE. Leaf apex acute **Sanaur-1**
CC. Leaf oblong...**Sua**
BBBB. Fruit oval
C. Leaf oval.. **Thornless**
CC. Leaf oblong
D. Style end bluntly pointed.....................................**Narma**
DD. Style end round
E. Leaf apex sub-acute
F. Pulp cavity at both ends .... **Chhuhara**
FF. Pulp cavity at stem end..........**Narikeli**
BBBBB. Fruit oblate

C. Leaf cordate .... **Illaichi**

AA. Tree form semi-erect
- B. Fruit oblong
  - C. Leaf oval
    - D. Style end obliquely pointed .... **Banarasi Pebandi**
    - DD. Style end bluntly tapering .... **Dandan**
  - CC. Leaf cordate .... **-Bahadurgarh**
  - CCC. Leaf oblong
    - D. Style end round .... **Mundia**
    - DD. Style end bluntly tapering
      - E. Leaf apex subacute
        - F. Pulp cavity at stem end
          - G. Leaf base broad .... **Jogia**
        - FF. Pulp cavity at both ends .... **Pathan**
    - DDD. Style end obliquely beaked
      - E. Leaf apex acute .... **Chonchal**
      - EE. Leaf apex subacute .... **JS II**
    - DDDD. Style end obliquely pointed .... **Triloki**
- BB. Fruit oval
  - C. Leaf oblong .... **Banarasi Karaka**
  - CC. Leaf oval
    - D. Style end round
      - E. Leaf apex subacute
        - F. Pulp cavity at stem end.... **Umran, Ajmeri, Katha**
  - CCC. Leaf cordate
    - DD. Style end obliquely round .... **Chencho**
    - DDD. Style end round .... **Madhuri**
- BBB. Fruit obovate .... **Deedwana**
- BBBB. Fruit round
  - C. Leaf oval .... **Jalandhari**
  - CC. Leaf oblong **Vikas-2**

AAA. Tree form spreading
- B. Fruit oblong
  - C. Leaf oval
    - D. Style end round with depression **Sanaur-2**
    - DD. Style end obliquely beaked
      - E. Leaf apex subacute
        - F. Pulp cavity at both ends
          - G. Leaf base broad...... **Kala Gola**
          - GG. Leaf base tapering .... **Noki**

CC. Leaf cordate

DDD. Style end beaked .... **Maharwali**

DDDD. Style end obliquely beaked .... **Wilayati**

CCC. Leaf oblong

D. Style end obliquely tapering

E. Leaf apex subacute

F. Pulp cavity at stem end .... **Mirchia**

FF. Pulp cavity at both ends.......................... **Pebandi Alwar**

BB. Fruit round

C. Leaf cordate.. **Gola**

CC. Leaf oblong..

D. Style end flat.. **Gola Gurgaon**

DD. Style end flat with depression................. **Popular Gola**

DDD. Style end round.................................... **Kakrola Gola**

CCC. Leaf oval

D. Style end round.................................... **Gola Gurgaon-1**

DD. Style end flat with depression

BBB. Fruit obovate

C. Leaf oblong

D. Style end flat with depression

E. Leaf apex subacute

F. Pulp cavity absent .... **Akhrota**

FF. Pulp cavity at stem end .... **Gola Gurgaon-3**

DD. Style end round... **Kheera**

EE. Leaf apex subacute

F. Pulp cavity at stem end

G. Leaf base tapering............ **Kali**

GG. Leaf base broad.. **Kathaphal**

CC. Leaf oval

D. Style end round with depression

E. Leaf apex subacute

F. Pulp cavity at stem end

G. Leaf base broad........... **Aliganj**

GG. Leaf base tapering..... **Laddu**

CCC. Leaf cordate

D. Style end round.................................... **Jhajjar Selection**

DD. Style end flat with depression................. **Safed Rohtak**

BBBB. Fruit oval

C. Leaf oval

D. Style end round
E. Leaf apex acute.................................... **Meharun**
EE. Leaf apex obtuse
F. Pulp cavity at both ends
G. Leaf base broad......... **Bagwadi**
GG. Leaf base tapering........... **Rewa Selection**
BBBBB. Fruit ovate
C. Leaf cordate... **Sanaur-3**

Umran (Katha, Kotho, Ajmeri, Chameli and Madhuri): The trees are semi-erect. The leaves are oval, broad having length/width ratio of 1.3, subacute apex, curved margin, broad base. The petiole is light green and has purple tinge on both surfaces and is 1.5 cm long. Anthesis occurs during 13.00 to 14.30 hrs. The fruits mature late. The fruits are fairly large, 33-39.8 g, oval, styler end round, stem end round and ridged having yellow, smooth and glossy skin and cavity at stem end in pericarp. The pulp is white, sweet, hard and brittle having 17.9°B TSS. Pulp/stone ratio is 25.2. Fruit yield is about 195 kg per tree. It has good keeping quality.

Goma Kirti: It is similar to Umran except that the fruit maturity is about 3 weeks earlier and is about 25% more productive.

Kaithli: The tree is erect. The leaves are oblong having length/width ratio of 2.2, acute and slightly curved apex and tapering base. The petiole is light green with purple tinge on dorsal and light green on ventral surface and is 1.5 cm long. Anthesis occurs between 13.00 and 14.30 hrs. The fruits mature in mid season. The fruit is oblong, 29.5 g in size having 32.1 pulp/stone ratio, round styler end, shallow stem end, yellowish skin and cavity in pericarp on both ends. The pulp is soft, white and of excellent quality having 15.3°B TSS. The fruit yield is about 123 kg per tree. It does not transport well.

Bagwadi: The trees are spreading. The leaf is oval and broad having length/width ratio of 1.3, obtuse and flat apex, broad base. The petiole is light green on both surfaces, densely pubescent and is 1.9 cm long. Anthesis occurs between 13.00 and 14.30 hrs. The fruits mature in mid season. The fruit is oval, 19.5 g in size with round styler and stem ends with a shallow notch and ridges on stem end having 27 pulp/stone ratio. The skin is yellowish green and smooth. Pulp cavity is present in pericarp at both ends. The pulp is white and soft having 14.8°B TSS.

Banarsi Kadaka: The trees are semi-erect. Leaf is oblong with 1.5 length/width ratio, curved margin, tapering base.The petiole is light green with purple tinge on dorsal and light green on ventral surface having 1.4 cm length. Anthesis occurs between 13.00 and 14.30 hrs. The fruit matures in mid season. It is oval having obliquely pointed styler end, round, narrow and slightly ridged stem end, cavity in pericarp at stem end and pulp/sione ratio of 31. The skin is light yellow, smooth and glossy with streaks. The pulp is light cream, soft having 16.7°B TSS.

Banarsi Pebandi: It has almost similar characters as Banarsi Kadaka except that the fruits are slightly larger having cavity in pericarp only at stem end with semi-soft pulp of about 13.7°B TSS.

Gola: The trees are spreading. The leaf is cordate and broad having 1.1 length/width ratio, obtuse apex, round base. The petiole is light green on both surfaces and is 1.2 cm long. Old leaves are curved towards ventral side. Anthesis occurs between 13.00 and 14.30 hrs. The fruits mature early. The cultivar is suitable for extremely dry areas. The fruits are 21.4 g in size, round with flat styler end, round stem end, bright yellow, smooth and glossy skin, cavity in pericarp at stem end and 14.3 pulp/stone ratio. The pulp is white and soft having 21.1°B TSS. It is an early cultivar.

Jogia: The trees are semi-erect. Leaf is oblong and broad with 1.3 length/width ratio, subacute apex slightly curved at margin and apex, round base. The petiole is light green on both surfaces. The petiole is 1.4 cm long. Anthesis occurs between 07.00 and 08.30 hrs. The fruit matures early and is oblong, 24 g in weight, yellowish green in colour with surface having coarse ridges, styler end bluntly tapering, ridged stem end and cavity in pericarp at stem end. The pulp/stone ratio is 24. The pulp is white, semi-soft having 14°B TSS.

Maharwali: The trees are spreading. Leaf is oval and broad with 1.2 length/width ratio having obtuse and curved apex, tapering base. The petiole is with purple tinge on dorsal and light green on ventral surface. The petiole is 1.7 cm long. Anthesis occurs during 13.00 to 14.30 hrs. Fruit maturity is late. The fruit is oblong and 17.7 g in size having beaked styler end and rising shoulders at stem end and yellowish green and smooth skin. The cavity in pericarp is at both ends. The pulp is white and hard having 14.9°B TSS.

Mundia: The trees are semi-erect. Leaf is oblong and long with 1.5 length/width ratio, subacute apex, curved margin and tapering base. The petiole is light green with purple tinge on dorsal and light green on ventral surface. The petiole is 1.6 cm long. Anthesis occurs between 13.00 and 14.30 hrs. Fruit matures early and is oblong bell shaped, 39.9 g in weight having round styler end, narrow stem end with a notch and yellowish green and smooth skin with depressions and cavity in pericarp at stem end. The pulp is white and soft having 19.9°B TSS.

Seb: The trees are erect. The leaf is oval and broad with 1.2 length/width ratio, subacute and slightly curved apex and broad base. The petiole is light green with purple tinge on dorsal and light green on ventral surface. The petiole is 1.8 cm long. Anthesis occurs between 07.00 and 08.30 hrs. The fruit matures early and is 24.6 g in size and round resembling crabapple in shape having round styler end with a depression at the centre and broad and deeply grooved stem end. The pulp/stone ratio is 14.4. The skin is yellowish green with brown specks, slightly rough. The pericarp has cavity at stem end. The pulp is white and hard having 16.8°B TSS. It is an early cultivar suitable for extremely dry areas.

Thornless: The trees are erect. Leaf is oval and long with length/width ratio of 1.9, acute apex and tapering base. The petiole is light green with purple tinge on dorsal and light green on ventral surface. The petiole is 1.3 cm long. Anthesis occurs between 13.00 and 14.30 hrs. Fruit matures in mid season and is oval, 16.3 g in weight having round and smooth styler end, round and slightly ridged stem end, greenish yellow, smooth and glossy skin with cavity in pericarp at both ends. The pulp is white and soft having 14.9°B TSS.

Illaichi: The trees are erect. Leaf is cordate and broad with 1.2 length/width ratio, obtuse apex and flat and broad base and light green on both the surfaces. The petiole is light green and 1.8 cm long. Anthesis occurs between 07.00 and 08.30 hrs. The fruit matures in mid season. The fruit is oblate having flat and ridged styler end and rounded stem end with prominent ridged stripes, yellowish green, smooth and streaked skin colour, 8.5 g in weight, cavity in the pericarp at stem end. The pulp/stone ratio of 18.4. The pulp is white and soft having 20°B TSS and 138 mg vitamin C per 100 g.

Dandan: The trees are semi-erect. The leaf is oval and broad with 1.2 length/width ratio, obtuse and slightly curved apex and broad base. The petiole is light green with purple tinge on dorsal and light green on ventral surface and 1.5 cm length. The fruit matures in mid season. The fruit is 27.6 g in weight and styler end bluntly tapering with ridges giving a tooth-like apex and the stem end slightly ridged. The pulp/stone ratio is 17.4. The skin is yellowish green, smooth and streaked. The fruit has cavity in pericarp at both ends and soft, granular, light cream and sweet pulp having 17.2°B TSS.

Chonchal: The trees are semi-erect. Leaf is oblong and broad with 1.4 length/width ratio, acute and flat apex and tapering base, light green with purple tinge on dorsal and light green on ventral surface. The petiole is 2.7 cm in length. Anthesis occurs between 07.00 and 08.30 hrs. The fruit matures in mid season. The fruit is 24.9 g in weight, oblong with styler end obliquely beaked and stem end narrow and necked having light yellow, smooth and streaked skin surface, pulp/stone ratio of 19 and cavity in pericarp at stem end. The pulp is soft and white having 19.8°B TSS. The fruit is longer than of any other cultivar and has sharply pointed apex and sweet and juicy pulp.

Seedless: It is found in Gujarat but is not of good quality.

Dodhia: It is found in Andhra Pradesh and is reported to be resistant to fruit fly.

Thar Sevika (Seb x Katha): Early maturing and high yielding cultivar. Fruits are juicy, sweet with a TSS of 22-24°B. Fruits do not cause throat soaring after consumption, which is common in other cultivars.

Thar Bhubraj: It is a selection from Bhusavar, Bharatpur in Rajasthan and is an early maturing and high yielding cultivar. Fruits are very juicy and sweet.

Narendra Ber-1: Trees are spreading type, heavy yielder. Fruits are obovate and yellowish green in colour.

Narendra Ber-2: Trees are medium in height and semi-spreading. Fruits are obovate having yellowish green skin.

Jharber

(***Z. nummularia*** (Burm. f.) Wight & Arn., syn. ***Z. rotundifolia*** Lamk.)

The plants are small and spiny bushes. The fruits are small, round, yellow to red and are usually acrid in taste.

Genus *Hovenia* Thunb.

The plants are deciduous and unarmed trees or shrubs. Leaves are long petiolate. Flowers are borne in axillary or terminal, 3 to several-flowered cymes having obconical to dish-shaped hypanthium, fleshy, plane and tomentose disc filling the hypanthiun and half inferior and 3-locular ovary. Fruit is a 3-seeded nut, peduncles and pedicels becoming fleshy and juicy at fruit maturity. It is distributed in the region from India to Japan. Seven species occur but are restricted in East Asia (Kubitzki, 2004).

Japanese raisin tree
(***Hovenia dulcis*** Thunb.; raisin tree)

It is native of China. It is distributed in China, Korea, Japan and the hills of northern India. It is found throughout the sub-Himalayan tract from Chamba in HP to Bhutan including North Bengal, Assam and in Khasi and Garo hills.

It is a medium or large sized deciduous tree growing from 9 to 30 m in height. The bark of young trees is smooth, pale ashy or whitish and that of old trees is pale brown, rough with deep and regular vertical fissures. The leaves are alternate, long stalked, broad ovate, acuminate, 10-18 cm long and 5-8 cm broad, green, glabrescent above and hairy on the nerves beneath. The flowers are bisexual, small and greenish white and borne on pedunculate, many flowered axillary or terminal cymes. The fruit is 8 mm in diameter, gray brown, globose, succulent, obscurely 3 lobed and embedded in the peduncle. On ripening, the fruit becomes reddish brown on the fleshy swollen peduncle and later falls to the ground. The seeds are hard. The dried stalks taste like raisins (Anon., 1959; Bailey, 1971).

Family Moraceae

It is large family of woody plants having 37 genera and 1050 species (Heywood *et al.,* 2007). The family has 5 tribes. The tribe Moreae has 8 genera of woody plants in tropical to northern temperate region having mostly racemose inflorescences with inflexed stamens in bud and reflexing abruptly at anthesis (as in Urticaceae). The tribe Dorstenieae has 8 genera and 130 species in tropical Africa and America, rare in Asia, mostly herbaceous with bisexual inflorescences and strongly reduced flowers. The genus *Dorstenia* has 105 species. The tribe Castilleae has 7 genera and 50 species (*Naucleopsis* with 20 spp.) of woody plants, mostly neotropical and few from Africa to Asia and Australia having unisexual capitate and involucrate infloresences. The tribe Ficeae has one genus *Ficus* with 700-750 of woody plants, pantropical but mostly in Asia to Australia having invaginated inflorescences enclosing the flowers. The tribe Artocarpeae has 10 genera and 80 species (*Artocarpus* with 47 spp.) of woody plants, pantropical but mostly in Asia and America having unisexual inflorescences, the male ones are spicate to racemose.

The plants are herbs, shrubs, trees and sometimes vines having laticifers and milky sap present in the parenchymatous tissues. Cystolyths, usually globose, are present often with tannins. The leaves are mostly alternate, usually simple, often with 3-5 basal palmate veins, stipules 2, small and lateral or each pair forming a cap over the bud. Buds are naked or scaly. Inflorescence is basically cymose but often greatly modified (head, spikes, discs or hollow receptacles as syconia). The flowers are small, inconspicuous, regular, monoecious or dioecious. Pistillate flowers are with or without perianth. Perianth (2-6), is 4-lobed in two whorls with the same number of stamens opposite the sepals. The anthers are 2-celled and versatile. The ovary is generally superior with basal placentation, basically bicarpellate with one carpel usually aborting. Ovules are usually 1 or 2 and 1 or 2 stigmas. The fruit is basically a drupe, often multiple (*Morus*) or connate with perianth and axis (*Artocarpus*) or achene with a fleshy receptacle (*Ficus*). The seeds are usually endospermic. The embryo is usually curved.

The principal plants are fig, mulberry, breadfruit, jackfruit and hop (*Humulus*). The other plants of interest are osage orange (*Maclura*), paper mulberry (*Broussonetia*), banyan (*Ficus benghalensis*), climbing fig (*F. pumila*) and rubber plant (*F. elastica*).

Subfamily Moroideae

Genus *Morus* L. (x=14; 2n=28-308)

The genus has about 110 species but only 10-12 are cultivated. Some of these are *Morus alba* L. (white mulberry), *M. cathayana* Hemsl. (Chinese mulberry) and *M. atropurpurea* Roxb. (guangdong mulberry) native of China, *M. alba* and *M. rubra* (red mulberry) naturalized in Europe and North America, *M. nigra* L. (black, English or Persian mulberry) native of North America and *M. indica* L. syn. *M. australis* Poir. (Korean mulberry or common mulberry), *M. laevigata* Wall. ex Brandis (tut) and *M. serrata* Roxb. (Himalayan mulberry) found wild in Himalayan region of India. Hybrid forms between *M. alba* and *M. rubra* also exist. Ten to 15 species occur mainly in temperate to subtropical regions of the Northern hemisphere, some in montane habitats in the tropics and one in tropical lowlands in Africa (Kubitzki *et al.*, 1993). Morphological characters of some *Morus* species are given in Table 23.7.

The plants are temperate and subtropical, dioecious or monoecious, thornless trees and shrubs. The trees are deciduous. Leaves and shoot apices are deciduous. The branches are drooping. The bark is usually scaly and the buds have 3-6 imbricate scales. The leaves are distichous, large, lanceolate, alternate and usually undivided or lobed, serrate or dentate with 3-5 nerves at base. The lobed and unlobed leaves can be seen on the same branch. Stipules are free and almost lateral. The fruit buds are located laterally on the current season's growth. The plants may be monoecious or dioecious. The flowers are small and are borne on male or female catkins. The male catkins are long and cylindrical and the female ones are short and thicker. Staminate inflorescence is spicate having 4, (almost) free and imbricate tepals and 4 stamens. Pistillate inflorescence is short spicate to capitate having (almost) free tepals, ovary and two (sub)equal stigmas. The perianth is 4-lobed and persists until the fruit ripens and becomes succulent. At this stage, the perianth completely covers the achene. The fruit is a syncarp, a nutlet enclosed in a juicy perianth and fleshy indehiscent exocarp. It is an compressed achene, covered by the succulent white to black calyx aggregating into an ovoid to cylindric syncarp superficially resembling a blackberry. The seed is albuminous and the cotyledons are oblong. There are three types of mulberry but variation is frequent within them and as a result both white and black fruits may be found on the same tree.

Table 23.7. Morphological characters of some *Morus* species.

Characters	*Morus alba*	*Morus laevigata*	*Morus serrata*	*Morus nigra*	*Morus rubra*
Bud colour	Brown	Brown	Dark brown	Dark red	Black
Bud size (mm^2)	16.5-39.9	34.10-79.55	19.4-79.2	18.0-75.1	15.5-38.0
Branch colour	Gray or grayish yellow	Gray or grayish yellow	Gray	Dark	Dark
Branching	Erect	Semi-erect	Semi-erect	Semi-erect	Erect
Leaf lobation	Lobed to unlobed	Lobed to unlobed	Lobed to unlobed	Lobed to unlobed	Lobed to unlohed
Leaf colour	Pale green	Dark green	Dark green	Dark green	Dark green
Leaf surface	Smooth	Rough	Rough	Smooth	Rough
Leaf margin	Large round serration	Shallow lobed	Large round serration	Large round serration	More pointed serration
Leaf length (cm)	10-15	28-32	20-25	10-15	Pointed serration
Inflorescence length (cm)	3-4	5-12	2-5	3-5	--
Fruit colour	White red	White red	Red	Dark black	7-10
Petiole groove	Present	Present	Absent	Present	2-4
Lenticel size (mm^2)	0.41-2.00	0.70-2.25	1.44-8.00	1.40-7.50	Red

White mulberry
(***Morus alba*** L.) 2n = 28, 42.

The tree is deciduous. It is of moderate size growing up to 15 m in height and has a spreading and umbrella-shaped crown, gray to yellow branches, smooth bark and slender young twigs. The leaves are thin, small, 5-15 cm in size, broadly ovate cordate, frequently 3-lobed, 7.5-20 cm long and 5-12.5 cm wide, sometimes almost orbicular or triangular. The leaves are nearly smooth on the upper surface and are light yellow. Whitish hairiness is found only along the veins on the lower surface. There are 3 basal veins prominent on the lower surface. The margin is coarsely toothed and the teeth are large. The leaves are used for rearing silk worms. The trees are monoecious or dioecious and spicate. Male flower has 4 sepals, which are imbricate, and four stamens inflexed in the bud. Female flower has 4 decussate, accrescent and succulent sepals and one-celled and two partite or two-fid ovary having pendulous ovule. The fruits are borne on short stalks that are as long as the fruits. These are globose, 2 cm in diameter and white to pinkish purple but usually become red when ripe. Seed is subglobose with copious and fleshy albumen and the embryo is incurved (Anon., 1962; Hocking, 1993).

M. alba has several botanical varieties named on the basis of mode of branching and shape of leaves. These are:

i. *M. alba* var. *pendula* Dipp.: It generally has slender and drooping branches.

ii. *M. alba* var. *pyramidalis* Ser.: The branches give the tree a pyramidal form.

iii. *M. alba* var. *laciniata* Beissn.: It is called skeleton leaved mulberry. The leaves are uniformly divided into narrow lobes.

iv. *M. alba* var. *tartarica* Loudon (Russian mulberry): It is dwarf having bushy top and bears black insipid fruit. It is raised from seeds and can be used as a very hardy rootstock. The tree is very ornamental.

v. *M. alba* var. *japonica* Audib.: The leaves are large and fruits are pointed oval and red.

vi. *M. alba* var. *multicaulis* Perr.: The tree is vigorous in growth and has large pointed unlobed leaves and sweet fruits. It is grown in China for silk worms.

vii. *M. alba* var. *celtidifolia* HBK: The tree is medium sized of 7 m height having small, smooth and less lobed leaves and globular fruits.

viii. *M. alba* var. *indica*: It is dioecious. The bark is smooth and ash coloured. The leaves are long and taper pointed.

ix. *M. alba* var. *mongolica*: It is from Mongolia and is like *M. alba*. The teeth end in short and stiff hair.

x. *M. alba* var. *venosa*: It has very prominent white veins.

xi. *M. alba* var. *tartarica* (Russian mulberry): The trees are extremely hardy. The fruit is black and insipid. The leaves are small and much lobed.

Cultivars

Most of the white mulberry types are grown as ornamental trees or for rearing silk worms. But some cultivars like Downing's Everbearing, New American, Wellington, Trowbridge, Thorburn, Ramsey White, Victoria, Munson and Merrit are grown in USA for fruit.

Black mulberry

(***Morus nigra*** L.) 2n = 308.

It is the real fruit mulberry. The tree is deciduous, small, spreading growing up to 10 m in height. Young twigs are thick, dark brown with a velvet like hairy covering. The shoots are also downy (hairy). The leaves are thick, alternate, 5-20 cm long, ovate with deeply cordate base and abruptly acute apex, dull surface, dark green and rough above but are shining and slightly hairy beneath with coarsely and sharply toothed margin. The leaves are broader than in *M. alba* and are not usually lobed but sometimes 2-5 lobes may be present. There are 5 basal veins. No teeth are present. Flowers are similar to those of *M. alba*. Fruits are long, black and juicy and are more or less sessile, dark purple, about 2 cm in diameter and acidic and become sweet and good in quality only when completely ripe. Black Persian is an important cultivar. It has plump, black, juicy fruits of 4 x 2.5 cm size with a rich and subacid flavour.

Red mulberry
(*Morus rubra* L.)

The trees are deciduous and very large growing up to 20 m in height with wide and spreading crown. But *Morus rubra* var. *tomentosa* remains shrub-like and spreading. Red mulberry is used for both fruit and timber. On young shoots, both lobed and unlobed leaves may be seen on the same branch. The leaves are alternate, longer than those of *M. alba*, 8-20 cm in size and ovate to oblong. These are broad and deeply lobed. The upper surface is rough. The lower surface is densely pubescent. The leaves are closely toothed. The teeth are of small or medium in size and may be blunt or rounded. The sinuses of the leaves are very oblique (asymmetrical) and are rounded at the base where the margin is without teeth. Flowers are similar to those of *M. alba.* The fruit is almost black, globose, 3-4 cm in diameter, reddish purple and is very sweet (Bailey, 1971; Singh *et al.,* 1963).

Superior selections of red mulberry made in USA are Johnson, Hick's Everbearing, Stubbs, Lampasab, Townsend, Tehama, Riveria, Travis and Illinois Everbearing (Ottman, 1987).

Subfamily Artocarpoideae

It contains the genera *Ficus* and *Artocarpus.*

Genus *Ficus* (x = 13; 2n=26)

The plants are tropical and subtropical, usually trees and shrubs and sometimes woody climbers. The trees are deciduous growing 10 m in height with stout and glabrous branches. The leaves are thick, leathery, deciduous or persistent, 3-5 lobed, rarely divided, 10-20 cm long and about as broad, usually cordate at base, palmately nerved. The lobes are usually obovate and obtuse at base and irregularly dentate, scabrous above and below with stout, stiff hairs and 2-5 cm long petioles. The inflorescence is a syconium. The flowers are unisexual, staminate or pistillate, may be present in the same syconium or in different syconia. The individual fruit is a multiple fruit and the fruitlets are achenes or nutlets that are small, dry and indehiscent borne axillary and solitary and are 5-8 cm long greenish or brownish violet and pear shaped at maturity. The important species that yields fruits used fresh or after dehydration or canning is *F. carica*. The other species are *F. roxburghii* having brick coloured fruits and huge leaves, *F. palmate* and *F. hispida* having leaves with entire margin and the evergreen *F. retusa. F. glomerata* is resistant to nematodes and has unlobed leaves and poor quality fruits that are dried and used to prepare flour.

Fig
(*Ficus carica* L.) (x=13, 2n=26)

The fig has been described in old Egyptian literature. It is subtropical and is resistant to both heat and drought. It requires a rain free period for proper fruit maturity and has little chilling requirement. The trees are hardy, deciduous, round topped and shrub-like. The trunk is short and thick and the young growth is pithy.

The suckers are reddened. The leaves are large, thick, leathery, rough or pubescent and generally 3-7 lobed. Some of the leaves are deeply lobed, which is the characteristic of the species. The fruit buds are borne in the axil of the leaves of previous season's growth which give a spring crop called 'breba'. But the main crop comes later and is borne on current season's growth.

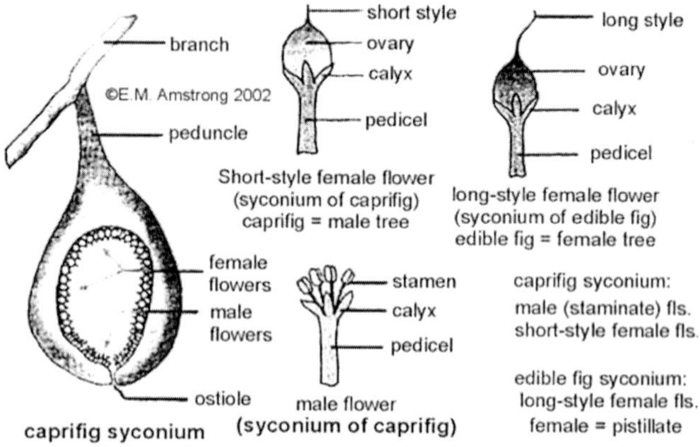

Fig. 23.6. Floral morphology in caprifigs and edible figs (Armstrong, 2006).

The flowers are unisexual, small, numerous, greatly reduced to the essential organs and are borne in the syconia. The pistillate flowers are of two types – i) with short styles, and ii) with long styles. The edible cultivars have long style flowers and these are not capable of being fertilized (Fig. 23.6). The staminate flowers are found in the syconia containing only the short style flowers and are located near the ostiole end of the syconium. The short style and long style pistillate flowers do not occur in the same syconium.

On the basis of pollination requirement, the figs are of three types:

i. Completely parthenocarpic (the Adriatic or common fig), e.g. Mission, Brown Turkey.

ii. Those that require pollination for both the crops (Smyrna type), e.g. Calimyrna.

iii. Those that require pollination for the second crop and not for the spring crop (San Pedro type), e.g. San Pedro, King and Gentile.

Pollination is carried out by the insect *Blastophaga psenes* that are found in the caprifig or the goat fig. The caprifig may belong either to *F. carica* or *F. pseudocarica* or *F. palmata*. Thus the caprifigs are of three types: i) those corresponding to the spring crop (Profichi), ii) those corresponding to the summer crop (Mammoni), and iii) those corresponding to the winter crop (Mamme).

Cultivars

Adriatic syn. **Verdone**: The cultivar is from California. Fruit is small to medium, green to yellow green, having light pink to pink pulp and rich mild berry flavour. It is used as fresh fruit or for dehydration. Pollination is common type.

Alma: The cultivar is from Texas, USA. Fruit is small and yellow having amber to pink pulp with caramel flavour used as fresh fruit or for preserves. Pollination is common type.

Black Bursa syn. **Bursa Siyahi**: Fruit is large, striped violet brown green to purplish black having red pulp with rich berry-like flavour and is used as fresh fruit or for dehydration. Pollination is Smyrna type.

Brown Turkey: The cultivar is from California and Israel. Fruit is very large, violet brown having amber pulp with mild caramel flavour and is used as fresh fruit. Pollination is common type.

Celeste syn. **Malta**: The cultivar is from southeast USA. Fruit is very large, violet bronze having amber to pink pulp with caramel flavour and is used as fresh fruit and in preserves. Pollination is common type.

Cuella Dama Blanco syn. **Col de Dame**: The cultivar is from Spain and Chile. Fruit is medium, green, having red pulp with berry-like flavour and is used as fresh fruit. Pollination is common type.

Donato syn. **Kadota**: The cultivar is from Italy, California, Chile. Fruit is medium, green to yellow having green to yellow amber pulp with honey flavour and is used as fresh fruit. Pollination is common type.

Kalomon syn. **Kalamata**: It is from Greece.

King syn. **Desert King**: The cultivar is from California. Fruit is medium to large, greenish purple having amber to light pink pulp with mild caramel flavour and is used as fresh fruit or for dehydration. Pollination is Smyrna type.

Lampiera: The cultivar is from Portugal. Fruit is large, greenish brown, having rose pulp with rose flavour and is used as fresh fruit. Pollination is San Pedro type.

Masui Dauphine syn. **Masui Dolphin**: The cultivar is from Japan. Fruit is very large, violet brown to purple having pink pulp with mild caramel flavour and is used as fresh fruit. Pollination is San Pedro type.

Mission syn. **Franicscana, Brebal**: The cultivar is from California and Spain. Fruit is large purplish black skin, amber to light pink pulp with berry rich flavour and is used as fresh fruit or for dehydration. Pollination is common type.

Panachee syn. **Striped Tiger**: The cultivar is from USA. Fruit is medium, dark pink to red having amber to light pink pulp with berry-like rich flavour and is used as fresh fruit or for dehydration. Pollination is common type.

Safi Lop syn. **Calimyrna Lob Injir, Sarlop**: The cultivar is from Turkey and California. Fruit is large, light yellow to golden yellow having amber to light pink pulp with caramel rich flavour and is used as fresh fruit or for dehydration. Pollination is Smyrna type.

Sierra: The cultivar is from California. Fruit is medium large, green to yellow having amber to light pink pulp with caramel rich flavour and is used as fresh fruit or for dehydration. Pollination is common type.

Sultani syn. **Fayouni, Ramadi**: The cultivar is from Egypt and Tunisia. Fruit is medium large, green and brown having green and brown pulp with rich flavour and is used as fresh fruit or for dehydration. Pollination is common type.

Zidi: The cultivar is from North Africa. Fruit is very large, purplish black, having pink to red pulp with berry-like rich flavour and is used as fresh fruit or for dehydration. Pollination is Smyrna type.

Conadria: The cultivar is from California. Trees have moderate vigour. Fruits are produced parthenocarpically. The fruit is large, weighs about 50 g, pyriform and yellowish green with purplish tint having very small eye, light pink to bright red pulp with honey flavour, 18ºB TSS and white meat, and resists cracking. The fruits are good for table and drying purposes. Pollination is common type.

Flanders: The fruit is globose in form with thick neck, yellowish green in colour having amber white, very small and tight pulp. Splitting occurs in unfavourable conditions. The fruit dries well.

Excel: The cultivar is from California. The trees have short stature and compact canopy. The fruit is small in size (35 g), light yellow and ovoid to globose having pale yellow to amber pulp having 20ºB TSS, white meat and the eye neither tight nor too loose. Fruits are produced parthenocarpically. Splitting of fruits does not occur. The fruits are very good for fresh eating, drying and canning.

Gulbun: It is a good cropper. The fruits are large, 65-80 g, light yellow in colour, round flat having light pink to white pulp and the eye as that of Excel. Fruits have some splitting.

Evrem: It is a high yielding mid season cultivar. The fruit is somewhat small, weighs 35-50 g, attractive, light yellow and round flat having somewhat greenish meat, white pulp and medium tight eye. The fruits do not split.

Deanna: The cultivar is from USA. Trees are vigorous and produce parthenocarpically. Fruits are pyriform, large (80 g) having golden yellow skin, medium tight eye and straw yellow pulp with 18ºB TSS. Fruits are suitable for drying.

The well known cultivars were not grown in India perhaps because the soils are infested with nematodes. The types that are grown in India are probably hybrids with the species such as *F. glomerata*.

Poona Fig: It has bell shaped and light purple fruit. The flesh is rosy.

Black Ischia: The cultivar is from Lucknow.

YCD 1 (timla fig): The trees bear fruits throughout the year except during winter. It is high yielding (4000 fruits/tree). Fruit is attractive, reddish purple, large, 7 cm in diameter and 100-200 g in weight.

Genus *Artocarpus* J. R. and G. Forster

About 50 species are native of Asia and Australasia. Two species, *A. altilis* (Parkinson) Fosb. and *A. heterophyllus* Lam., are cultivated throughout the tropics. Two distinct subgenera are subgen. *Artocarpus* with spirally arranged leaves and amplexicaul stipules and subgen. *Pseudojaca* with distichous leaves and lateral stipules (Kubitzki *et al.*, 1993). The related species are *A. altilis* 'Seminifera' (breadnut), *A. integer* (Thunb.) Merr. (chempedak), *A. lacucha* Buch.-Ham. (lakoocha), *A. odoratissimus* Blanco. (marang), *A. kemando* Miq. (pudau) and *A. hirsutus* Lamarck (aini-maram), *A. mariennensis* Trécul, *A. lanceifolius* Roxb., *A. gomezianus* Wall ex.

Trécul, *A. hypargyreus* Hance, *A. lowii* King, *A. anisophyllus* Miq., *A. nitidus* Trécul and *A. glaucus* Blume, *A. hirsutus* and *A. rigidus* Blume are used as rootstock.

The trees are monoecious. The leaves are enrolled in bud stage. Leaves are spirally arranged or disitchous, penninerved or rarely sub-triplinerved having free, intrapetiolar or lateral stipules, amplexicaul or not. The intrapetiolar stipules unite and form a cap over the bud. Inflorescences are capitate head, cylindric to clavate, obovoid ellipsoid or globose, occasionally ramiflorous or simple and entire to pinnatifid (rarely pin-cauliflorous). Flowers are numerous. Staminate flowers free, usually mixed with peltate to clavate interfloral bracts, tubular, entire or 2-4-lobed perianth, and one stamen. Pistillode is absent. The stamens are straight. Pistillate flowers are at least distally connate with each other and/or with interfloral bracts having tubular perianths, thin-walled below and thick-walled above, the apices either completely fused forming an areolate surface or free forming variously shaped processes on the surface. Ovary is free with one or two, equal or unequal stigmas. Fruit is a syncarp, at least the lower part of the perianth (the middle layer of the syncarp) becoming fleshy, sometimes the entire head.

Key to classification of genus *Artocarpus*

1. Leaves distichous with paired stipule scars. Syncarps are velvety globose and 5-8 cm wide. Male heads are 1 cm wide and globose ....1. *A. gomezianus* Wall ex. Trécul

1. Leaves spirally arranged with annular stipule scars. Syncarps are warted or somewhat spinous, larger. Male heads cylindric, larger

2. Cauliflorous with massive syncarps. Leaf is 4-10 cm wide and entire.. 2. *A. heterophyllus* Lamarck

2. Not cauliflorous, Leaf larger

3. Leaf is pinnatifid and very large. Cultivated trees....................... 3. *A. incisus*

3. Leaf is entire (lobed in sapling). Wild trees..................4. *A. nobilis* Thwaites

Jackfruit

(*Artocarpus heterophyllus* Lamk. syn. ***A. integrifolius*** non L.f., ***A. integra, A. integrifolia***) (2n=56)

The jackfruit originated in the rain forests of Western Ghats in India and has a long history of cultivation in the country. It is hardier than the breadfruit. The trees are evergreen and large growing up to 25 m in height. The young tree is pyramid shaped but develops a broad crown when mature. The leaves are entire, fairly oblong or oval or elliptic, elliptic obovate or obovate, large, 10-15 cm long and leathery with their upper surface more glossy and shiny than the lower. The tree is monoecious and starts bearing when 4 to 8 years old. Both male and female inflorescences are borne on the same tree on short lateral branches arising from the main trunk and large branches. Flowers are unisexual, composite, oval and have dull green surface. These are about 5 cm long and 2 cm in diameter. The male spike is produced singly and appears as a solid, elongated structure, has many densely crowded flowers, which may be sterile or fertile. Female spikes, on the other hand, are either solitary or paired but are larger and bright green having a segmented surface. Each flower has a pair of perianth lobes and a single pistil. The ovary is oblong, compressed or coalesced. The multiple fruit (syncarp) is large, having tuberculate surface and varies from 4 to 30 kg in weight; flavour, seediness and shape depend on cultivar. The fruit is ovoid to oblong with a green rind composed of hexagonal fleshy spines, containing 100 to 500 seeds. Seeds are oblong ellipsoid, 2-4 x 1.5-2.5 cm is size, 1-7 g in weight enclosed by horny endocarps and sub-gelatinous exocarps (FAO, 1982; Morton, 1987; Acedo, 1992).

Cultivars

Owing to seed propagation, protandry and cross pollination, great variability exists in the natural population with respect to growth and fruit characters including period of maturity, precocity and quality. Elite types have been selected from the variability and developed as cultivars. These have been grouped into two major types based on softness and quality of pulp. The cultivars of the first type generally have thin, fibrous, soft and mushy pulp which is acidulous to very sweet and emit a strong odour on ripening, e.g. Koozha Chakka of South India, Vela of Sri Lanka, Khanum Lamoud of Thailand and Nangka Bubur of Indonesia and Malaysia. The cultivars of the second type have thick, firm or crisp and less odorous pulp, e.g. Koozha Puzham of South India, Varaka of Sri Lanka, Khanum Nang of Thailand, Nangka Salak of Indonesia and Nangka Bilulang of Malaysia. The second form is more palatable and commercially more important.

The cultivars may be divided into following three groups:-

1. Form having firm, hard, crisp and sweet pulp with flesh varying in sweetness.
2. Form having soft and more acidic pulp. The fruit yields to the pressure of fingers when ripe. The soft and very juicy pulp has taste varying from insipid (flat taste), sweet acidic to very sweet.
3. Form having small fruits having less spiny and smooth surface.

Indian cultivars

There are two types of cultivars in India, one having soft flesh and the other with firm flesh (Mitra and Maity, 2002).

Koozha Chakka: It is small, fibrous, soft and mushy, but has very sweet carpels of high quality known as Varika. It is commonly grown in the southern Indian state of Kerala. This is known in different areas by other names such as Barka or Berka (soft, sweet and can be broken open with hands).

Koozha pazham: It is commercially more important than Koozha Chakka due to its crisp carpels. This is known in different areas by other names such as Kapa or Kapiya (crisp and has to be cut open with a knife).

Khuja or Karcha: It is green, hard and smooth with pale brown or occasionally pale green rind and pulp as hard as that of an apple having juicy pulp and small seeds.

Ghila or Ghula: It is usually light green, occasionally brownish and has soft pulp, sweet or acidulously sweet and large seeds.

Rudrakshi: The cultivar is small-fruited and is widely grown in Sri Lanka and South India but is considered inferior.

Hazari: It is similar to Rudrakshi and has relatively smooth rind and the flesh of inferior quality. An early maturing cultivar is known that starts bearing very early, about 18 months after planting at low elevations and after about 30 months at higher elevations. Its fruit is a hard fleshed Varikka. Fruit size is as that of the common jackfruit The fruits are round having smoother rind compared to that of jackfruit. The pulp is fleshy and of inferior quality.

Palur 1 Jack (PLR 1): It is a clonal selection from Panikkankuppam Local in Tamil Nadu. The trees are of medium height and less spreading and are suitable for high density planting. Fruits normally mature during April-June besides off season crop during November-December. It gives higher yield than Panrutti and Singapore. Annual yield is about 900 kg (80 fruits). Average fruit weight is 12 kg having 115-120 carpels.

PPI 1 Jack: It is a clonal selection from Mulagumoodu Local in Tamil Nadu. The trees are medium tall and bear during April-June and November-December giving yield of 107 fruits (1818 kg), 41% higher than the local type. The fruit has high quality crisp carpels rich in TSS and ascorbic acid.

PLR (J) 2: It is a clonal selection from Pathirakkottai Local. The trees are high yielding (95-110 fruits) with fewer incidence of pests and diseases. The fruit is of good quality, large size having highly palatable flakes. The keeping quality of fruits is good.

Swarna: It is a very good yielder and bears fruits in bunches on the trunk and primary as well as secondary branches. Fruits are medium in size (6.8 kg). The fruitlets are golden brown in colour, juicy with 25-26°B TSS having thick flakes and very thin rind (<1 cm).

Konkan Prolific: It gives average yield of 420 kg/tree (73 fruits each weighing 5- 6 kg).

Singapore or Ceylon: It is a remarkably early cultivar bearing fruits in 18 to 30 months after transplanting. This was introduced into India from Ceylon and planted extensively. The fruit is of medium size with small, fibrous carpels which are very sweet. The equivalent types in Thailand are known as Kha-nun nang (firm; best) and Kha-nun lamoud (soft) and as Vela (soft) and Varaka or Waraka (firm) in Ceylon.

Peniwaraka or honey jackfruit: It has sweet pulp and has been claimed as the best of all jackfruits.

Kuruwaraka: It has small rounded fruits with dark green rind in contrast to the golden yellow pulp when ripe.

Thirty five superior clones have been identified from eastern India (mainly West Bengal).

Malaysian cultivars

Some of the recommended cultivars for commercial planting are J29 (formerly MART11-N), J31 (formerly MART08-N) or NS1, NS4, NS9 and Mastura.

Cultivar Na 2: It has large, roundish fruit, which always splits at maturity and has yellow green, sweet to slightly acid and coarse pulp of hard texture emitting little odour but has poor storability.

J29: It is a popular cultivar. The fruit is round, medium to large (11-15 kg) with yellowish green skin having coarse spines and well spaced bulbs inside. The bulb (flesh) is medium to thick, yellow orange having fine texture and strong and sweet aroma. It gives flesh recovery of 36%. The fruits contain little latex and have good edible quality. It is suitable for canning.

J31: The cultivar produces medium sized (8-12 kg) and elongated and long stalked fruits with green skin of moderate thickness containing much latex. The flesh is yellow, of medium thickness, crispy, sweet with fine texture and strong aroma. It also gives flesh recovery of 36%. It is suitable for canning. The cultivar is susceptible to *Erwinia* bacterial dieback.

Some other important cultivars originated from Malaysia are J2, J27, J28 and J30. These are suitable for canning.

Indonesian cultivars

The Mekasari Fruit Garden of Indonesia has a rich collection of *Artocarpus* species from different regions of the Archipelago (Tirtawinata, 2000). More than 30 cultivars have been planted in Java, Indonesia. The popular ones are Kandel, Mini and Tabouey.

Cultivars from Philippines

The important cultivars are J Torres, $J0_1$ and $J0_2$.

West Indies

The Vela type predominates in the West Indies.

Cultivars from Florida, USA

Many new superior cultivars were imported by Fairchild Tropical Garden. Of the 22 cultivars in collection, Black Gold, Golden Nugget, J 31, Honey Gold and Lemon Gold are considered the most precious.

Black Gold: It was selected in Queensland, Australia. The tree is vigorous with a dense and highly manageable canopy. The tree maintained at a height and spread of 2 to 2.5 m by annual pruning gives consistent heavy production of 55 to 90 kg. The fruit is medium-sized of 6.7 kg average weight having edible flesh content of 35%. The exterior of the fruit is dark green and has sharp fleshy spines. The spines do not flatten or open upon maturity. This makes proper judging of harvest time and maturity difficult. The deep orange flesh is soft with a strong, sweet flavour and aroma. The flesh is more easily removed from the fruit compared with other cultivars.

Golden Nugget: It was selected in Queensland, Australia. The tree is fast growing with a distinctive dark green and rounded leaf. It forms a dense, spreading canopy which is maintained at a height and spread of 2 to 2.5 m. The fruits are small, green and rounded with sharp and fleshy spines on the skin. The spines flatten upon maturity to smooth golden yellow. The fruit weighs 3.2 kg and has excellent edible flesh content of 41%. The deep orange flesh is soft to medium firm depending on fruit ripeness. The flavour is excellent and the flesh has no fibre. Its fruit often splits open prior to ripening if there are heavy rains. Fruit yield is 60 to 80 kg per tree per year.

Breadfruit

(***Artocarpus altilis*** (Parkinson) Fosb.: syn. ***Artocarpus communis*** Forst.) (2n=56)

It has tropical climatic requirement. The tree is large, 9-12 m in height and contains a milky sap. The leaves are very large, pinnately lobed and shining with extremely prominent white veins. The trees are monoecious. The flower catkins are enclosed in a large hood-like bract. The male catkins are longer than the female ones and are produced throughout the year. The female catkins are produced in two distinct seasons, March-April and August-September. The fruits are produced on the extremities of the branches only. The fruit has tuberculate surface and is rich in starch. The fruits are used for culinary purpose.

Cultivars

Dang Rasimi: The cultivar originated in Thailand. The tree is vigorous and spreading and must be pruned to check its height. The vigorous growth makes it suitable for marginal areas. It is very productive and high cropper. The fruit is green to light yellow and has uniform skin with sharp spines and does not flatten or open at maturity. The pulp is dark orange, firm, mild in sweetness with pleasant flavour.

Tabouey: The cultivar originated in Indonesia. The tree has rounded top, dark green and shiny leaves. The cultivar is a moderate producer giving 50-70 kg fruits per tree. Fruit is yellow, usually thin, long tapering at stem end, often misshapen and has bright yellow coloured, blunt and irregular spines. The pulp is pale yellow in colour having pleasant taste and no aroma.

Black Gold: The cultivar originated in Queensland, Australia. The tree has medium growth and is spreading. The tree can be maintained to a height of less than 3 m by pruning. The cultivar is regular and consistent heavy bearer giving 55-90 kg fruit yield per tree. The fruit has dark and fleshy spines that do not flatten. This makes the harvesting operation difficult. Fruit weight varies between 6 and 7 kg having about 35% pulp and 200 seeds. The pulp is deep orange, soft to somewhat firm and sweet with strong aroma. The flesh separates more easily from the ray than in other cultivars.

Cheena: The cultivar originated in Malaysia from the cross between jackfruit and chempedak. The tree is low growing and spreading and can be kept at 2.5 m height by annual pruning. It is a regular producer giving fruit yield of 50-70 kg per tree. The fruit is small, 2.5 kg in weight, uniform in shape, somewhat long and narrow having about 30-40 seeds, green skin and blunt spines that turn yellow on maturity. The pulp is orange to deep orange, fibrous and soft having high aromatic flavour. It separates easily from the pulp which constitutes 33% of the fruit.

Honey Gold: The cultivar originated in Queensland, Australia. The tree is slow to moderate in growth having spreading branches and open and spreading top. The height can be maintained at 2.5-3 m by annual pruning. The tree produces 35-50 kg fruits. The fruit is dark green, blocky and weighs about 4.5 kg having small, sharp and usually open spines that turn yellow at maturity. The pulp is dark yellow to orange and has sweet aroma, very rich flavour and comprises nearly 36% of the fruit weight having about 40 or more seeds (5% of total weight).

Ma'afala: The cultivar originated in Polynesia. The fruit is small, 0.8 kg in weight, oval in shape, seedless, occasionally with one or two seeds having white flesh.

Maopo: The cultivar originated in Polynesia. The fruit is 2.5 kg in weight, oval to broad ovoid in shape, seedless having pale white or creamy flesh.

Puou: The cultivar originated in Polynesia. The fruit is 1.9 kg in weight, round, oval or heart shaped, seedless, occasionally with one or two seeds having creamy pale yellow flesh.

Meinpadahk: The cultivar originated in Micronesia. The fruit is seedless, 1.1 kg in weight and oval to asymmetrical in shape having light yellow green flesh.

Yellow Heart: The cultivar is Caribbean. The fruit is seedless, 2 kg in weight and oval in shape having creamy yellow flesh.

Some selections such as J-30, J-31 NS-1 have also been made in Malaysia. These are cultivated in a number of South East Asian countries.

Key to classification of close relatives of *Artocarpus* (Zerega *et al.*, 2005)

1. Leaf margin entire or with three to seven lobes in the distal third of leaf; leaf blade with abundant appressed reddish brown hairs on midrib and abaxial veins; infructescence with dark green surface, oblong or irregularly shaped .... *A. mariannensis*

1. Leaf margin typically pinnately lobed, rarely entire with a praemorse apex; leaf blade glabrous to pubescent with colourless to pale white spreading and erect hairs on veins or veins and blade; infructescence with yellowish green or rarely pink surface, globose to oblong.

    2. Leaves densely pubescent with spreading or erect rough walled straight white hairs, and smooth walled uncinate white hairs; numerous achenes (commonly called seeds) with dull, light brown, thin, flexible walls; infructescence surface echinate, with anthocarp apices narrowly conical and 5–12 mm long . ...*A. camansi*

    2. Leaves glabrous to moderately pubescent with spreading or erect rough walled straight pale hairs, juvenile leaves may be densely pubescent; achene (commonly called seeds) development often aborted but when present has dull light brown or shiny dark brown hard walls; infructescence surface flat to bumpy, with anthocarp apices rounded and barely protruding, or echinate with anthocarp apices conical and up to 5 mm long. . ... *A. altilis*

Monkey jack
(*Artocarpus lakoocha* Roxb. syn. *A. lacucha* Buch.-Ham.)

Monkey jack or *barhal* or *lakuch* is indigenous to the humid sub-Himalayan region of India and is also found wild in Assam, UP, Western Ghats and in the sub-Himalayan areas of India and Malaysia (Anon., 1985; Verheij and Coronel, 1991). It has been in cultivation in India as mentioned in early medical works, *charaka samhita* and *sushruta samihita*.

Monkey jack is a large deciduous tree with a clear straight stem, generally 6 to 9 m in height and up to 2.5 m in girth having dark brown bark exfoliating in small round woody peels exposing the reddish inside colour. Leaves are alternate, simple, large, leathery, 13-37 x 6-21 cm in size, entire and ovate elliptic in shape. Monkey jack is monoecious and bears male and female flowers on separate drooping catkins. Male catkins are more profuse. Male flowers are small, elongated, yellow and taste like tamarind. Female flowers are borne on shorter and thicker peduncles compared to male flowers. Fruit is round, irregular shaped multiple fruit, 5-12.5 cm wide, velvety, dull yellow tinged with pink and sweet-sour pulp. Seeds are endospermic, white and are bold in size (Anon., 1985, 1990). The seeds are edible.

The chempedak
(*Artocarpus integer* (Thunb.) Merr. syn. *A. champeden* Spreng., *A. polyphema* Pers.; jahona jack) (2n=56)

The chempedak (pronounced "chem-pe-dak") can be distinguished from the jackfruit by its smaller fruits with thinner rind and more juicy flesh, which becomes darker yellow when ripe (Jarrett, 1959). It is native of South East Asia (Martin *et al.*, 1987) and is widely distributed in Myanmar, peninsular Thailand and Malaysia, Sumatra, Borneo, Moluccas and Irian Java. It is cultivated commercially in peninsular Malaysia (Verheij and Coronel, 1991) and used as rootstock.

In peninsular Malaysia, distinction is made between the wild (bankong) and cultivated (cempendak) trees, being respectively classified as var. *silvestris* Corner and var. *integer*. The wild trees are glabrous to variously hairy having green to yellowish withering leaves whereas chempedak has hairy trees with deep yellow to rich orange leaves. In Sarawak (Brunei), chempedak is preferred since it produces larger fruits having thicker and dark orange flesh.

The chempedak tree is evergreen, monoecious and of medium height of 18-20 m. The trunk is straight with smooth and grayish bark. New shoots, including petioles and pedicels, are covered with thin, brown and wiry hair, which makes it distinguishable from the jackfruit. The leaves are about 5 to 25 cm long and 5 to 10 cm wide and alternate with short petioles, sometimes three lobed, but on older trees these are obovate or elliptic and entire. The upper side of the leaf is green and shiny and almost glabrous and the lower side is covered with long brownish and short white hair. The small flowers are borne in dense spikes. Male and female flowers are borne on different inflorescences, the female on large branches on the trunk itself. The large multiple fruit is similar in appearance to the jackfruit except that it is more cylindrical and smaller. The fruit is edible and has an odour similar to that of durian. It is 35 cm in length and up to 15 cm in diameter having dark yellow and thinner rind and more juicy flesh. The fruit has 30 or more large seeds embedded in the pulp (Morton, 1987; Verheij and Coronel, 1991).

Cultivars

In Malaysia, high yielding selections CH 29 (attractive orange flesh), CH 19 (moderate yielder, yellow flesh with strong aroma), CH 26 (Paya Jaras), CH 27 and CH 28 have been made. Hybrids between jackfruit and chempedak are called Nangka chempedak and one of them has been named as CH/NA (Page, 1984; Verheij and Coronel, 1991). Collection of germplasm of chempedak has been done at Selangar, Malaysia. There is scope to develop superior quality clones.

Marang
(***Artocarpus odoratissimus*** Blanco)

Marang is native of South East Asia and the Philippines (Martin *et al.,* 1987). Its trees are evergreen growing up to 25 m tall with 40 cm trunk diameter. Twigs are 4-10 mm thick having long, yellow to red, spreading hairs and stipule scar rings. Leaves are broadly elliptic to obovate and 16-50 x 11-28 cm in size with both surfaces roughly hairy, entire or shallowly crenate margin, often 3-lobed upper half and 2-3 cm long petioles. The tree is monoecious. Inflorescences are solitary and borne in leaf axils. Male heads are ellipsoid to ovate and 4-11 x 2-6 cm in size. Female heads with pubescent and peltate bracts that mostly shed and simple styles are exerted 1.5 mm. Fruit is syncarp, subglobose, 16 x 13 cm in size, green yellow and densely covered with stiff, hairy processes of about 1 cm length having white, juicy and fragrant flesh and 5-14 cm long peduncle. Seeds of about 12 x 8 cm size are ellipsoidal in shape.

Genus *Treculia* Decne

The plants are trees or shrubs and may be dioecious or monoecious. Leaves are usually distichous, simple and pinnately veined with free amplexicaul stipules. Inflorescence is bracteate, ±globose, with numerous involucral bracts having pedicellate flowers immersed in cavities formed by the connate lower parts of the interfloral bracts, 2-4(-5)-lobed perianth and 2-4 stamens. Pistillode is usually absent in staminate flowers. In pistillate flowers, perianth is lacking and ovary is free having 2 stigmas. Fruit is a syncarp, covered with the indurate tips of the interfloral bracts. Three species occur in tropical Africa, one of them extending to Madagascar (Kubitzki *et al*., 2003).

African breadfruit
(***Treculia africana*** Decne.; African boxwood; mozinde; okwa)

It is a native of tropical West Africa (Martin *et al*., 1987) and is found growing in Guinea, Ivory Coast, Gold Coast, Nigeria, Cameroon, Sierra Leone and Ghana. The trees are dioecious, medium to large and are of 27 m height and 3 cm girth. Leaves are alternate, simple, glabrous, elliptic to ovate elliptic and 20-25 x 7.5-12 cm in size. Male and female flowers are borne on separate inflorescences. Male flower heads are globular, 5 cm in diameter, brownish yellow, very short pedunculate with 3 stamens. Fruit is spherical, 45 cm in diameter and 12-16 kg in weight, borne sub-sessile on the trunk and main limbs and is covered with coarse, spine-like tubercles. It becomes yellow brown and soft on ripening. Seeds are numerous, smooth, ellipsoid, 1.25 cm long and brown in colour (Duke, 1989).

Genus *Malcura* Nutt.

The genus includes the inedible Osage orange used as mosquito repellant. It is found throughout USA as a hedge plant.

Che

(***Maclura tricuspidata*** (Camere) Bureau syn. ***Cudrania tricuspidata*** Bur. ex Lavallee; Chinese che; Chinese mulberry)

The che is native to many parts of eastern Asia from the Shantung and Kiangson Provinces of China to the Nepalese sub-Himalayas. It is deciduous. The tree grows to about 7.5 m in height but often remains as a broad, spreading bush or small tree. Female trees are larger and more robust than the male trees. The leaves are alternate, smaller and thinner and pale yellowish green in colour. The typical form is distinctly trilobate with the central lobe sometimes twice as long as the lateral ones. As the plant grows, the tendency seems towards larger leaf size having entire margin with indistinct or irregular lobing. The general form of leaves vary from oblong to lanceolate. The male flowers turn yellow as the pollen ripens and is released. The fruit is 2-5 cm in diameter. The ripe fruit becomes attractive red or maroon red with a juicy, rich red flesh and contains 3 to 6 small brown seeds (Hendrickson, 1981).

Genus *Broussonetia* L'Hér. ex Venten.

The plants are dioecious unarmed trees, shrubs or climbers. The leaves and shoot apices are deciduous. The leaves are distichous to subopposite, simple or palmately lobed and pinnately veined to tripliveined. Stipules are free and laleral. Staminate inflorescences are spicate to subcapitate having a distinct sterile strip abaxially, interfloral bracts, 4 valvate tepals, connate below and 4 stamens. Pistillate inflorescence is capitate to slightly elongate having interfloral bracts longer than the flowers, utricular perianth with 2-4 small lobes or teeth, free ovary with one or 2 unequal stigmas. Fruit is an indehiscent syncarp having enlarged and membranous perianth and fleshy exocarp. Out of 8 species, 7 occur in tropical and subtropical Asia and one in Madagascar.

Paper mulberry

(***Broussonetia papyrifera*** (L.) Vent. syn. ***Morus papyrifera*** L.; tapa cloth tree; toot)

The paper mulberry is native to Asia distributed in China, Japan, Korea, Laos, Cambodia, Thailand, Burma and India. The plant is a deciduous shrub or tree usually growing 10-20 m tall, but at times 35 m. The leaves are variable in shape, lobed or unlobed, but usually have toothed edges, lightly hairy, pale undersides and a rough texture and 15-20 cm long. It is dioecious. The staminate inflorescence is a 8 cm long catkin with fuzzy male flowers. The pistillate inflorescence is a spherical 2 cm wide head with greenish female flowers trailing on long styles. The infructescence is a 2-3 cm wide spherical cluster containing many red or orange fruits (drupe). The fruits and cooked leaves are edible. The fruit, leaves and bark have been used in traditional medicine.

⑧ ⑧ ⑧

Chapter 24

FAGALES

The order differs from the related orders in its highly specialized dichasial inflorescences, much reduced flowers and in its chalazogamy. The plants are trees or rarely shrubs, evergreen or deciduous. Buds are covered with imbricate scales or are naked very rarely. Vessels are opposite, intermediate or alternate with scalariform and simple or more often only simple perforations and lateral pitting. Fibres are with bordered or simple pits. Rays are homogeneous or slightly heterogeneous. Axial parenchyma is diffused or in thin bands. Sieve element plastids are of S-type and contain non-dispersive P-protein bodies. Nodes are trilacunar. Leaves are alternate or very rarely verticillate in whorls of 3, simple, pinnately veined, entire to deeply lobed and crenate. Stipules are present and are caducous. Stomata are anomocytic and/or encylocytic.

Flowers are small, inconspicuous and usually unisexual, monoecious or rarely dioecious, apetalous, anemophilous or secondary entomophilous in variously modified and frequently very reduced dichasia, which are often arranged in "catkins" with the dichasia sometimes reduced to solitary flowers. Male flowers are in more or less reduced dichasia that are arranged into catkins or sometimes small heads. Sepals are (4-) 6(-9), scale like, imbricate, more or less connate or calyx is much reduced and sometimes completely absent. Stamens are (4)6-12(-90) having filiform, mostly free filaments having tetrasporangiate, dorsifixed or basifixed anthers, opening longitudinally. Tapetum is secretory. Microsporogenesis is simultaneous. Pollen grains are 2-celled, from 3-colpate to 2-7-porate. Pistilodia are sometimes present. Female flowers are 1-7-(-15) at base of male inflorescences or in separate axils, subtended individually or collectively, surrounded or completely covered by an involucre that develops into a cupule. In the integrated dichasial inflorescence, the outer (ultimate order) axes of the dichasium are modified into cupule valves. In a few species of *Nothofagus* from New Guinea the cupule is reduced to two minute loose flaps or may even be entirely absent. Staminodia are present or absent. Gynoecium is of 2(3) or sometimes 6-9 or more (up to 15 in *Lithocarpus*) united carpels, with distinct or nearly distinct stylodia. Ovary is inferior with as many locules (at least in the lower part) as carpels and two pendulous ovules in each locule. Ovules are anatropous to hemitropous, bitegmic or seldom unitegmic and crassinucellate. Female gametophyte is of *Polygonum*-type. Fertilization is chalazogamous. Endosperm is nuclear. Fruits are 1-seeded nuts subtended by accrescent cupule. Seeds are with large embryo and without endosperm. Plants are strongly tanniniferous with gallic acid and also proanthocyanidins and flavonols (quercetin and less frequently kaempferol). Crystals of calcium oxalate are commonly present in some of the cells of the parenchymatous tissues. It contains 7 families, members of which are largely monoecious and wind pollinated.

Family Fagaceae (chestnut family; beeches, oaks, and sweet chestnuts)

The Fagaceae has a long fossil record, suggesting its origin at least by the middle Cretaceous, about 90 million years ago. The plants are found mostly in the northern hemisphere with a few species crossing the equator in South East Asia. Beeches (*Fagus*), oaks (*Quercus*) and sweet chestnuts (*Castanea*) figure prominently and are frequently the dominant members of the broad leaved forests that cover vast areas of North America and Eurasia at the mid-latitudes. Evergreen oaks are important members of the forests around the Gulf of Mexico, in southern China and southern Japan. In South East Asia, the structure of the mixed mountain forest is largely determined by the evergreen members of the family, particularly oaks. It contains 8 genera and 620-750 species (Heywood *et al*., 2007).

The plants are hardwood deciduous or evergreen trees, rarely shrubs with edible fruits and ornamentals. Tannins are present. Hairs are simple or stellate, often also glandular scales. These may be deciduous or evergreen. Leaves are alternate (rarely whorled) simple, entire to pinnately lobed and scarious, usually with deciduous stipules. The flowers are unisexual (plants monoecious) and usually arranged in catkins or small spikes that may comprise only flowers of one sex as in oaks, or may have female flowers at the base of otherwise male inflorescences as in chestnuts. The perianth is bract-like with 4-7 lobes. The male flowers have as many or twice as many stamens as perianth segments, occasionally up to 40, with free filaments, with or without a pistillode. The female flowers are in groups of 1-3, each group being surrounded by a basal involucre.

The other features, such as pollen and a strongly scented inflorescence, suggest that insect pollination is the ancestral condition in the family and this is retained in most members except *Fagus* and the temperate oak species. The familiar acorn "cup" is one example of the great variety of forms shown by the cupule, surrounding one or more fruits, which is a unique feature of the family and the origin of which has caused controversy. Only with the discovery of *Trigonobalanus* in 1961, restricted to Sulawesi, northern Borneo, Malaysia and northern Thailand, it has been possible to firmly suggest that the cupule is derived from 3-lobed extension of the pedicel below each flower, which has been variously fused around single flowers or groups of flowers. It is possible that the cupule provides a link with the pteridosperm ancestors of the flowering plants. The tremendous diversity of scales and spines in the cupules appears to be derived from the branched spines (Heywood *et al*., 2007). The ovary is inferior with 3 or 6 styles and locules and 2 ovules in each locule. The fruits are single-seeded nuts, in groups of 1-3(-15), surrounded or enclosed by an often hardened cupule having one seed filling the nut. Endosperm is not apparent at maturity. The seeds are animal dispersed and have a short viability.

Genus *Castanea* Mill. (x = 12; 2n = 24)

The name "*Castanea*" is probably derived from the old name for the sweet chestnut, either in Latin or in ancient Greek. The *Castanea* species are native of western Asia, Europe and northern America originating over a wide area of the northern temperate zone in southern Europe from Italy to Iran, northwards to Hungary and up to North Africa besides in western Asia and northern America (Vavilov, 1951). The species are divided into 3 sections of the genus:

1. *Eucastanon*: The section includes the four main commonly known chestnut types; viz. the European sweet chestnut (*Castanea sativa* Mill. syn. *C. vesca* Gaertn., *C. vulgaris* Lam., also called Spanish chestnut and Italian chestnut in USA) of European group, naturalized, extensively planted and cultivated commercially in Spain, France and Italy and successfully introduced to the Himalayas and other temperate parts of Asia; the chestnuts of Asiatic group such as Japanese chestnut (*C. crenata* Sieb. & Zucc.) planted in Japan and Korea; Chinese hairy chestnut (*C. mollissima* Blume syn. *C. formosana* (Hayata) Hayata, *C. sativa* var. *formosana* Hayata, *C. bungeana* Blume), Seguin's chestnut (*C. seguinii* Dode) and *C. davidii* Dode planted in China; and the American chestnut, *C. dentata* (Marsh.) Borkh. of American group planted in North America (Table 24.1).

Table 24.1. Characteristics of *Castanea* species

	C. crenata **Sieb. & Zucc.**	***C. dentata*** **Borkh.**	***C. mollissima*** **Blume**	***C. sativa*** **Mill.**
Common name	Japanese chestnut	American chestnut	Chinese chestnut	Spanish chestnut, Portuguese chestnut and "marron" (French for chestnut).
Origin	Japan, South Korea	Northern America	China, Taiwan, Korea. Commercially cultivated in China, Korea and USA	Europe and Asia Minor
Tree height (m)	10-15	30	20	20-35
Tree girth (m)		3		2
Leaf size (cm)	8-19 x 3-5	14-20 x 7-10	10-20 x 4.5-8	16-28 x 5-9
Leaf serrations		Toothed (saw teeth)	Toothed margins	Boldly toothed
Catkins	Upright (7-20 cm long), male flowers in upper and female in lower part, appear in summer	15-20 cm (male), female flowers at the base, near twig, appear in spring-summer, self incompatible	4-20 cm long, female flowers at the base and male on the rest	Upright (10-20 cm long), male flowers in upper and female in lower part, appear in June-July. Male catkins are pale buff and the female catkins are green, spiny, partly hidden by the leaves.

Cupule	Spiny, contain 3-7 nuts, shed in October	Spiny, green lined in tan velvet, contain 3 nuts	4-8 cm long each having 2-3 glossy brown nuts	Spiny, contain 3-7 brownish nuts, shed in October
Others			Softly downy shoots on young trees	Bark has net-shaped (retiform) pattern with deep furrows or fissures running spirally in both directions up the trunk

2. *Hypocastanon*: The section includes the Chinese chinkapin, also called Henry's chestnut, Willow leaf or pearl chestnut (*C. henryi* (Skan) Rehd. & E. H. Wils.) of the Asiatic group planted in China.

3. *Balanocastanon*: The section includes the chestnuts of American group, viz. American Allegheny chinkapin or dwarf chestnut (*C. pumila* (L.) Mill. var. *pumila*) planted in southeast USA and Ozark chinkapin (*C. pumila* (L.) Mill. var. *ozarkensis*) planted in Arkansas and Oklahoma, USA besides *C. ashei (*Sudw.) Ashe (Ashe chinkapin) and *C. floridana* Ashe (Sarg.) (Florida chinkapin) planted in southeast USA and *C. paupispina* Ashe and *C. alnifolia* Nutt. (creeping chinkapin) planted in southern USA (Alabama, Florida, Texas, Lousiana).

The other related species that produce edible nuts are *C. costata* (Blume) A. DC., *C. inermis* Benth., *C. lucida* Soepadmo, *C. malaccensis* Gamble and *C. wallichii* King ex Hook. f.

Chestnuts

The *Castanea* species produce nuts, called the "chestnuts". The name is derived from an earlier English term "Chesten nut", which descends from the Old French word "*chastain*". These belong to about 12 *Castanea* species that occur in the temperate regions of the northern hemisphere (Kubitzki *et al.*, 1993). The chestnut species are native of western Asia, Europe and northern America originating over a wide area of the northern temperate zone in southern Europe from Italy to Iran, northwards to Hungary and up to north Africa besides in western Asia and northern America (Vavilov, 1951).

Chestnut trees are tall long lived, deciduous with a spreading and rounded top and trunk having characteristic spirally ridged bark. Chinese chestnut trees have moderate growth rate. The American and European species are fast growing. The mature height of trees varies from the smallest and often shrubby chinkapins to the giant American *C. dentata* that could reach 60 m followed by the European chestnut around 30 m, the Chinese chestnut about 15 m and the Japanese chestnut 10 m on an average (Table 25.1). The Chinese and more so the Japanese chestnuts are often multi-leadered and wide spreading, the European and especially American species tend to grow very erect with little tapering columnar trunks, which are firmly set and massive. They spread on the sides and develop broad, rounded, dense crowns at maturity. The foliage of the European and American species has striking yellow autumn colouring. The bark of young trees is smooth. It is of a vinous maroon or red-brown colour in American chestnut and gray in European chestnut. With age, the bark of American species becomes gray and darker, thick and deeply furrowed; the furrows run longitudinally and tend to twist around the trunk as the tree ages. It sometimes reminds one of a large cable with twisted strands. Branches of Chinese chestnut are glabrous whereas the branchlets are covered with dense pubescence of coarse spreading hair. The branchlets are without terminal bud. The buds have 3-4 scales. The leaves are simple, ovate or lanceolate to elliptic oblong, 10–30 cm long and 4–10 cm wide, glossy green in colour with sharply pointed, widely spaced teeth with shallow rounded sinuates between. These are 2-ranked, serrate with numerous parallel veins. There are 10-20 deep serrations on each side.

The trees are monoecious. The flower buds are mixed and are produced laterally on previous season's growth. These open following the leaves, appearing in late spring or early summer or into July to form shoots which bear male catkins at the base and mixed male and female catkins slightly further up the shoot. Inflorescences are unisexual or androgynous and spike-like. Staminate flowers are borne on axillary or terminal erect cylindrical catkins that are about 20 cm in length with 6-parted calyx and 6-20 stamens (8 in European and 10-12 in *C. mollissima*) in the axils of small bracts with or without rudimentary ovary. The ripe pollen carries a heavy, sweet odour that may be too sweet or unpleasant. Other catkins have these pollen bearing flowers, but also carry the twigs from which emerge small clusters of female or fruit producing flowers. The pistillate flowers are borne on the lower part of the upper staminate catkins, rarely on separate catkins, usually 1-3 in a prickly symmetrical involucre with branched spines and scaly bracts, about 5 mm long and densely hirsute 6-9 styles and incompletely 6-9 celled ovary, sub-spherical cupule, dehiscing into 4 valves and enclosing 3 nuts or 2-valved cupule enclosing one nut. Two or three flowers together form a four-lobed prickly calybium, which ultimately grows completely together to make the brown hull or husk covering the fruits. Most of the trees are self sterile, although some self compatibility appears to exist. Chestnut flowers are not self compatible. Therefore, two trees are required for pollination. Pollination occurs through wind and by insects. All *Castanea* species readily hybridize with each other.

The fruit is contained in a spiny (very sharp) cupule, 5–11 cm in diameter, also called bur or burr. The burr is up to 6 cm thick with long, very stout, strongly pubescent spines and the nut has thin skin that peels off readily from the kernel (Duke, 1989). Around the time the fruits reach maturity, the burrs turn yellow brown and split open in two or four sections. They can remain on the tree longer than they hold the fruit, but more often achieve complete opening and release the fruits only after having fallen on the ground. Opening is partly due to soil humidity. The burrs are often paired or clustered on the branch and contain 1-7 nuts according to the different species and cultivars. The nuts are flattened to sub-globose, large,1-3 cm in diameter and brown with a large pale scar at the base. The nut excels in sweetness and general palatability. It is eaten raw, boiled, roasted and cooked with meat and is also used to make confections, powders and candy or is dried whole (Duke, 1989). It is a folk remedy for diarrhoea, dysentery, epistaxis, nausea and thirst (Duke, 1989).

The fruit has two cotyledons inside with a creamy white flesh throughout. Cotyledons are undulate ruminate. In some cultivars there is only one cotyledon whose episperm is only slightly or not intruded at all. Usually, these cultivars have only one large fruit per burr, well rounded (no flat face) and which is called marron

(*marron de Lyon* in France, *marron di Mugello* in Italy, or Paragon). Thus, chestnut has two forms with respect to fruiting; in the form Marrons the burr in a large spiky husk normally has a single more aromatic and sweeter nut and the other form Chataignes, more common among the seedlings, has 2-3 smaller nuts in the husk (Duke, 1989).

The chestnut fruit has a pointed end with a small tuft at its tip (called flame in Italian), and at the other end is the hilum, a pale brown attachment scar. In many cultivars, the fruit is flattened on one or two sides. It has two skins. The first one is a hard shiny brown outer hull or husk, the pericarp or peel. Underneath the pericarp is another thinner skin called the pellicle or episperm (the paper membrane between the kernel and shell). The pellicle closely adheres to the seed itself, following the grooves usually present at the surface of the fruit. These grooves are of variable size and depth according to the species and cultivar. Chestnut fruit has no dormancy and germinates right upon falling to the ground in the autumn, with the roots emerging from the seed right away and the leaves and stem the following spring. Because the seeds lack a coating or internal food supply, they lose viability soon after ripening and must be planted immediately.

Cultivars

The superior cultivars of European chestnuts have good size, sweet taste and easy-to-remove inner skins. American chestnuts are usually very small (around 5 g), but sweet tasting with easy-to-remove pellicles. Some Japanese cultivars have very large nuts (around 40 g) with typically difficult-to-remove pellicles. Chinese chestnut pellicles are usually easy-to-remove, and their size varies greatly according to cultivars, although these are usually smaller than the Japanese chestnut.

The important cultivars of northern America are Marron Combale, Marron Nousilland, Marron Queen, Numbo, Paragon, Abundance, Nanking, Kuling, Meiling, Carr, Orrin, Crane, Sleeping Gaint, Hemming, Willoka, Jersey Gem, Marron de Saint Vincent and Kuling. Seedlings of selected trees such as Hemming from Maryland and Peter from Georgia are most promising. The important cultivars in Spain are Amarelante, Blanca, Famosa, Garrida, Inxerta, Longal, Loura, Luguesa, Negral, Parade, Presq, Raigona, Rapada, Ventura and Verde (Pereira-Lorenzo and Fernandez-Lopez, 1995). Important cultivars of Chinese hairy chestnut are Abundance, Kuling, Meiling, Nanking and Carr. Kelsey and hybrids like Sleeping Giant (*C. mollissima* x (*C. crenata* x *C. dentata*) have been developed and a natural hybrid Stoke (Japanese x Chinese chestnut) has been identified (Duke, 1989).

Orrin: It originated in Lockhaven, Maryland. The tree is vigorous, upright spreading, precocious, prolific bearer and resistant to blight having short growing season and is thus considered suitable for more northern areas. It has early season blooming. Each burr has 2-3 nuts of uniform thickness that are not wedge-shaped and have very good keeping quality compared to that of other cultivars. Nut is medium to large, the shell is dark mahogany to almost black, shiny, attractive but with some pubescence at tip. It has mid to late season maturity.

Tourney: The cultivar evolved from a complex cross between *C. crenata, C dentata* and *C. mollissima*. The plants are fast growing and upright. It is Chinese type but is not very fruitful. The nuts are of medium size, variable shape and fair in flavour.

Jersey Gem: It evolved from a cross, Orrin x Nanking. The tree has moderate vigour having round top and is very productive. The nuts are of medium size having spherical shell of shiny red mahogany colour. The seal is good. The kernel is sweet in taste, crisp, crunchy, yellow with very good flavour and the pellicle separates easily. The nuts mature late and all drop off in short time.

Revival: The trees are upright, vigorous with upper branches spreading. Foliage is dark green and shiny. It crops regularly every year and responds to harvesting by shaking. Nut is large, dark reddish brown, about 25 g in weight. Nuts per burr are 2-3. Pellicle separates easily from kernel which is sweet in taste.

Au-Cropper: The cultivar originated at Auburn University Alabama. Plant is Chinese type, resistant to chestnut blight and gives high yields consistently. It has mid season maturity. The nuts are dark chocolate brown in colour with 2-3 nuts per burr that open well. Each nut weighs about 10-12 g.

Colossal: It is a hybrid between *Castanea sativa* and *C. crenata*. It is similar to French hybrids but is not from France or Spain. It is from the foothills of the High Sierra in California. It produces excellent yields of large nuts. The tree grows very rapidly and starts producing within 3 years after planting, sometimes in the second year. The tree is vigorous, pollen sterile and susceptible to chestnut blight. The nut can be round or triangular depending on its position in the burr. The hilum is very large. The nut can seem lumpy from the outside. The point is very prominent and can be hard and sharp. It is large to very large, 15-20 g. Nuts mature in early October. Peeling is poor and can have pellicle pinched within the nut. Double embryos are common. It is slightly bitter if eaten off the tree. After curing (slightly drying in cooler), it develops sweet flavour. When peeled and frozen, it tastes as good as any Chinese chestnut.

Bouche de Betizac: It is a French hybrid (between *C. sativa* and *C. crenata*). The tree is pollen sterile and vigorous with upright growth. This cultivar produces big nuts that taste good and are easy to peel. It survives winters and is stated to be resistant to *Phytophthora* root rot. It is reported to be resistant to the Asian gall wasp and leaf anthracnose. It ripens in mid October just after Colossal. The nut is elliptical triangular, large to very large, 15-20 g, reddish brown quickly turning dark brown, very good peeling and of high quality.

Precoce Migoule: It is a French hybrid (*C. sativa* and *C. crenata*). The tree is vigorous with upright growth and produces copious early pollen that synchronizes with Colossal and the nuts mature at least two weeks earlier than Colossal making it suitable for areas where frost damages the nuts before harvest. The nut is medium to large, 15-20 g, slightly flattened, brown with dark stripes having extremely large hilum spot. It has very good suitability for peeling.

Michigan Early: It is a selection from a mother tree of about 50 year age and has multiple trunks with upright growth. It may have Korean genes (probably *C. crenata*). It is a prolific early pollen producer and sheds pollen for three weeks, which should help pollinate the early flowering European/Japanese cultivars like Colossal. The cultivar is a good producer of mature nuts in the second and third weeks of September. The nut shape is variable, oval to triangular, dark brown with shades of red. The nut is of large size, 20-30 g, very sweet having very good peeling. The tree may be resistant to chestnut blight.

Norman J65 aka J65: The tree is similar to Labor Day and was selected from mother tree of about 50 years age having multiple trunks with upright growth. It may be Korean or have some Korean genes (probably *C. crenata*). It has early nut production like Michigan Early and the size and quality of the nut are good. The cultivar also produces large amounts of pollen. The tree shows slow upright growth and the burrs are big and thick. The nuts show different sizes when there are 3 nuts in the burr. The nut has a tendency to split when there is a wet fall. It is a medium yield producer. Nuts start dropping by about 20 September through the first week of October. The nut is 40-45 g in size with light red colour, good flavour, quality and peels extremely well. The nut produces about 20% double embryos. The cultivar may be resistant to Chestnut blight.

Nankings: Trees are vigorous and spreading. Nuts are medium to large and dark brown. It is a mid season cultivar.

Meiuing: Trees are vigorous, upright and spreading. Nuts are medium to large and dark brown.

Kashmir Seedling Selection: It is a seedling selection made in Kashmir valley and is found to be very promising with respect to nut quality and blooming period (March to April with duration of 25-34 days).

Crane (named in honour of Dr. H. L. Crane): It originated in Maryland by selection made from seedlings of *C. mollissima*. The trees are vigorous, spreading and precocious. It is a mid season cultivar, slightly protandrous and cross compatible with Nanking. The nuts are small to medium in size having dark cherry red shell, almost completely shiny and the seal is good. The kernel is light in colour and has firm crisp excellent eating quality and keeps well compared to that of other cultivars.

Manoka: It originated in British Columbia, Canada from open pollinated seedlings of *C. mollissima*. The tree is very hardy, more timber type. Nuts are medium in size having small and thin husk, dark brown shell and good quality and flavoured yellow kernel.

Kelsey: It originated at Connecticut from the seedlings of *C. mollissima*. The tree is Chinese type, i.e. having light coloured scaly bark, silvery twigs and rough bark of large branches that are free of blight. The nuts are like small squares and very dark brown in colour. Pellicle separates readily. Kernel is yellow, sweet, firm, crisp and crunchy.

Benton Harbor: It is a selection from seedling trees of *C. mollissima*. The mother tree is larger than Colossal and produced regular high yields (30-40 kg) of high quality nuts. The tree is resistant to chestnut blight and has more vigour than most Chinese chestnuts but this makes it extremely vulnerable to wind damage. It produces very large quantities of pollen starting in early July. The nuts are of medium size (20-30 g) and dark red purple colour having characteristic Chinese chestnut shape with flat top without double embryos or splits and have very good flavour and very good peeling. Its maturity overlaps with that of Colossal.

Everfresh: It is a selection from 15 year old *C. mollissima* tree that produced regularly when most Chinese chestnut cultivars were frosted during the growing season. The tree is slow growing and produces lots of pollen. The flowers set in groups resulting in clumps of burrs at the ends of the branches. The nuts have typical Chinese shape, deep reddish brown colour, medium size, 20-30 g, very good peeling and high quality. The nuts have a unique characteristic of extremely long shelf life for months without molding with good flavour.

Peach: It is a selection from *C. mollissima* . Like Benton Harbor it can produce large yield of nuts. The cultivar appears to be vulnerable to very low temperature that slows the growth lowering the yield potential. Being a Chinese chestnut, it grows slowly, produces a lot of pollen after the first week of July, which synchronizes well with the other Chinese cultivars. Nut shape is typical having medium size (20-30 g) and very good peeling. The cultivar gets its name from the "peach" fuzz found on the shell of the nut. The nuts have reddish brown colour, average or flat flavour having a tendency to split. Nuts stay attached to the burr and when it detaches, a yellow line forms around the edge of the hilum spot which often vanishes upon storage. The nuts have medium shelf life. It may be resistant to Chestnut blight.

Norman J26 aka J26: It appears to be pure *C. mollissima* selected from 60 years old tree. The mother tree is very large with a round shape producing about 10-20 kg nuts. It is also a good pollen producer. The size of the nut is large (40-50 g), because it usually produces only one or two nuts in a burr with double embryos and low percentage of three nuts. Nuts start dropping by 5 to 20 October. The nut has also the tendency to split with a wet fall. But in general the nut has good flavour and peels well. The skin colour is light red.

Genus *Fagus* L.

The plants are deciduous trees having numerous male flowers in slender pedunculate heads with 4-7-lobed calyx, 8-16 stamens, usually 2 female flowers surrounded by 4-partite pedunculate involucres and 3 slender, recurved styles. The fruit is an ovoid triangular nut, (1-) 2 in a 4-valved woody cupule which on the outside is covered with prickly or bract-like or rarely short and deltoid appendages. About 10 species occur in temperate regions of northern hemisphere (Kubitzki *et al.*, 1993).

American beechnut
(*Fagus grandifolia* Ehrh.)

It is native of northeastern America. The related edible species is *F. sylvatica* (European beech) found growing east to the Caucasus in central and southern Europe. It is found growing especially at higher elevations in eastern USA from Allegheny Hills to Florida and Texas (Wickens, 1995).

American beechnut is a slow growing tree and has a life span of 400 years or more (Rosengarten, 1984). It grows with a round top up to a height of 30-40 m and trunk diameter of 1 m. The tree is deciduous and monoecious. Leaves are alternate, simple, short petioled, ovate oblong to obovate or elliptical, 6.5-12.5 cm long, sharply serrate to denticulate, densely silky when young becoming glabrous above and dark bluish green and usually silky pubescent beneath and turning yellow at fall. Flowers appear along with the leaves. Staminate flowers appear in drooping heads with small calyx and 8-16 stamens. Pistillate flowers occur in 2-4 flowered spikes, usually in pairs at the end of a short peduncle. The fruit is a woody burr, 2- 2.5 cm in diameter dehiscing into 4 valves, partially opening at maturity. The nuts are triangular, up to 2 cm long, 2 or 3 in each burr. The brown seed coat is removed from the kernel before eating. Three distinguished botanical varieties are:

1. *F. grandifolia* var. *grandifolia*: It has prickles of burr, 4 to 10 mm long, erect and spreading or recurved with leaves usually sharply serrate. It grows in rich upland soils from Nova Scotia to Minnesota, in south to Virginia and Kentucky and in mountains to North Carolina, Illinois and southeastern Missouri.
2. *F. grandifolia* var. *caroliniana* (Loud.) Fern. and Rehd.: It has prickles of burr, 1 to 3 mm long and usually abruptly reflexed from near base with leaves more acuminate and often merely denticulate. It is found in moist or wet lowland forests on or near coastal plains of Massachusetts to Florida and Texas and in the Mississippi valley to southern Illinois and Ohio.
3. *F. grandifolia* var. *pubescence* Fern. and Rehd.: It has leaves that are soft pubescent below. It is found growing in Kentucky and other mountainous areas where both red and white beech occur. Abrams and Abundance are the important cultivars of beech, which produce superior nuts (Duke, 1989).

Family Myricaceae

It is a small family having 3-4 genera and 57-62 species (Heywood *et al.*, 2007) found on all major land masses except Australia and New Zealand. Most species are temperate or subtropical with the main centre of diversity in southern Africa.

The plants are small trees or shrubs, usually aromatic, often evergreen. The roots often have nitrogen fixing nodules. The leaves are alternate, simple or pinnatifid and have entire, serrate or irregularly dentate margins. The inconspicuous flowers are unisexual (plants monoecious or dioecious) borne on axillary catkin-like spikes. The male flowers usually have 2 bracteoles, (2)4(-20) stamens with the filaments sometimes joined at the base, sometimes with a disk at the base. The female flowers have 2-4 bracteoles and no disk and the ovary is superior, comprising 2 fused carpels that form a single locule with 1 erect ovule with basal placentation. The 2 styles are distinct or fused at base with short style branches. The fruit is a small, rough and often waxy drupe with a hard endocarp and seed with little or no endosperm and straight embryo.

Genus *Myrica* L.

The plants are evergreen or deciduous and dioecious or monoecious. The leaves are exstipulate. The spikes are compound or simple having flowers with or without perianth, subtended by a bract and 2 bracteoles. Female flowers sometimes have additional bracts. Male flowers have 2-8 (-20) stamens and rudimentary pistil.

The fruit is drupaceous, often covered with variously shaped protuberances, sometimes with a fat exudate, infrequently with glandular dots. The genus has 4 subgenera; subgen. *Morella* (Lour.) Engl. that bears fruits covered with numerous fleshy emergences having 7 species distributed from Malesia to India, subgen. *Cerophora* having emergences of fatty exudates and 45-50 species in the Old and New World, subgen. *Faya* having 3 species in eastern USA and Atlantic Islands, subgen. *Myrica* having 2 species that bear smooth fruits flanked by accrescent, fleshy bracteoles and *M. gale* L. having fleshy circumboreal bracteoles (Kubitzki *et al.*, 1993).

Kafal

(***Myrica esculenta*** Buch.-Ham. syn. ***M. sapida*** Wall., ***M. nagi*** (Hook. f.) non Thunb.; box myrtle)

It is indigenous to India. It is an evergreen tree of small or moderate size growing up to 15 m in height and 1.5 m in girth. Its bark is dark brown or blackish, rather rough, exfoliating in irregular small woody scales. The leaves are lanceolate or oblong obovate, acute, undulating, dark green above, rather glossy on both the surfaces and dotted beneath with minute resin. Flowers are minute, unisexual borne on axillary brown tomentose spikes. Male and female flowers are 1.25-2.25 cm long. The fruit is an ellipsoid or ovoid drupe of the size of a cherry, tubercled, reddish or cheese coloured when ripe with rugose seeds, which are 9 mm long and 5 mm in diameter (Anon., 1962; Parmar and Kaushal, 1982).

Much variation with respect to size and colour of fruit, taste of pulp and pulp/ stone ratio is seen in the produce brought to the local markets harvested from the wild trees. Protected trees in the courtyards produce sweeter fruits with less waxy surface.

Family Juglandaceae (walnut family; walnuts, hickories, pecan nut)

It contains 8 genera and 60 species chiefly of north temperate regions (Heywood *et al.*, 2007). Some species are subtropical and a few are tropical. The trees are aromatic having tannins. Hairs are often stellate. Peltate scales with glandular and swollen head contain various aromatic oils and/or resins. The plants are usually deciduous, sometimes evergreen. Terminal and lateral buds and leaf scar arrangements vary in butternut, walnut and hickory (Fig. 24.1). The leaves are alternate, rarely opposite and pinnate, usually aromatic and without stipules. The flowers are bracteate and unisexual (plants monoecious). Male flowers are usually borne in catkin-like, pendulous inflorescences produced laterally on twigs of previous season's growth having one flower per 2-5 bracts and 3 to many stamens, usually 3-40 in 2 or more series with short filaments and 2-locular anthers opening longitudinally usually with a 2-5-lobed calyx adnate to ovary. The perianth is typically 4-lobed but is often reduced or absent. Pollination is by wind. The female flowers are solitary or in smaller erect or long pendulous (*Pterocarya*) spikes on current season's growth close to the terminal end with 2 bracts and usually a 4-lobed calyx adnate to the ovary. The ovary is inferior, incompletely 2-4-celled of 2 fused carpels forming a single locule containing one erect orthotropous ovule attached at the base, lacking endosperm. The style is short with 2 stigmas. The fruit is a drupaceous nut or 3-winged samaroid, tightly enclosed by the coriaceous or fibrous husk developed from the perianth, bracts and bracteoles, dehiscent in most species of *Carya* and *Juglans*. The characteristic boat shaped walnut halves, obtained on cracking do not correspond to the 2 carpels as the suture is along their midribs. It is of considerable importance in the walnut and the pecan. In addition to the genus *Juglans* (walnuts), the family includes *Carya* (pecans and hickories), *Pterocarya* (wing nuts), *Platycarya, Engelhardia, Alfaroa* and *Oreomunnea.* The cotyledons are often contorted.

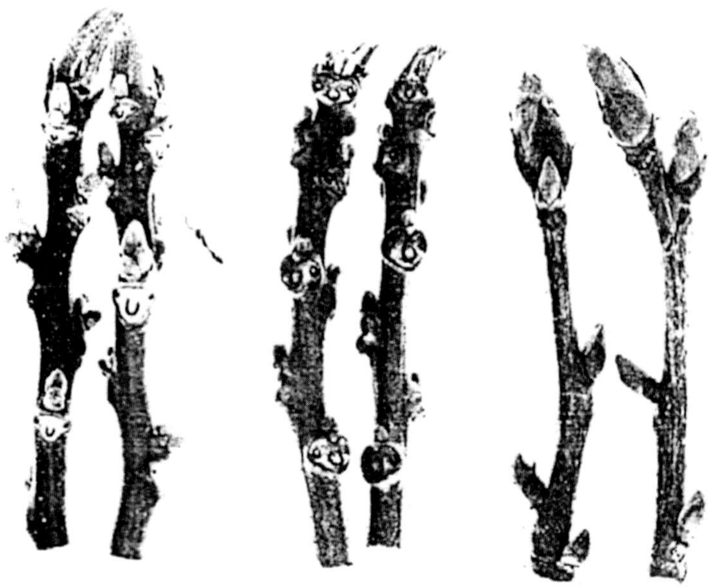

Fig. 24.1. Terminal and lateral buds and leaf scar arrangements in butternut, walnut and hickory (Source: Zielinski, 1955).

Genus *Carya* Nutt. (x = 16; 2n = 32, 64)

The trees are deciduous having branches with continuous and solid pith and buds protected with scales. The buds are thin, long and scaly The leaves are asymmetrical, alternate, odd-pinnate and exstipulate. The leaves are pubescent only in the young stage. The number of leaflets is 8-17, opposite and serrated or rarely entire. The species is monoecious. The staminate flowers are slender, 3-branched catkins borne in the axil of 3-lobed bract with 3-10 stamens. The pendulous catkins are placed below the pistillate inflorescence. Pistillate flowers are sessile in terminal to 10-flowered spikes enclosed by 4-lobed involucre fused to ovary with tips exposed at top. Sepals are absent, but appear below stigmas as stigmatic disk. The carpels are transverse with 2, commissural stigmas. The ovary is unilocular. The plants fall into two groups, viz. self fruitful and self unfruitful (owing to protandry). Wind pollination takes place. The fruit is globular to oblong, thin-shelled with husk separating more or less completely into 4 parts. The nut is smooth or slightly rugose, often angled, 4-celled at base and 2-celled at apex with cotyledons remaining enclosed in the shell. Germination is hypogeal. The nuts contain 70 per cent fat.

The genus *Carya* is divided into 3 sections, *Rhamphocarya, Apocarya* and *Carya.* About 20 species are found in North America and 2 in East Asia (eastern China, extending into southern Mexico, northern Vietnam and eastern Pakistan). The important native American species are *C. cordiformis* (Wang.) K. Koch (bitternut), *C. glabra* (Mill.) Sweet. (pignut), *C. laciniosa* (Michx.) F. Loud. (big shellbark hickory), *C. ovalis* (Wang.) Sarg. (sweet pignut), *C. ovata* (Mill.) K. Koch (shagbark hickory) and *C. illinoensis* (Wang.) K. Koch (pecan). Many of these are useful for their timber and ornamental value while from some others oils and resins are obtained.

Shagbark hickory nut

(***Carya ovata*** (Mill.) K. Koch; shagbark hickory; scaly bark; white heart; red heart; upland hickory)

It is native of northeast America. It is found growing from southeastern Canada and eastern USA to the Mississippi except for Florida and the coastal plains of the southern States. It prefers the upland plains (Rosengarten, 1984; Wickens, 1995). The relatively higher proportion of shell than in the other better known nuts probably restricts its long distance marketing prospects (Wickens, 1995).

It is a deciduous tree and grows to more than 30 m in height with trunk up to 60 cm in diameter. The bark exfoliates in long narrow plates but remains attached by the middle. Leaf is imparipinnate and consists of 5-7 leaflets. The leaf is oblong having 10-15 cm long leaflets. Nut is ellipsoidal, somewhat flattened laterally with four prominent longitudinal ridges, 2.5 cm long and thin but hard shell and the light tan kernels are deeply divided into two longitudinally ridged halves (Menninger, 1977). The angular nut is enveloped in green and fleshy outer husk that turns black, dries and splits open on maturity.

Pecan

(***Carya illinoinensis*** (Wangenh) K. Koch syn. ***Juglans illinoinensis*** Wangenh, ***C. pecan*** (Eng.) Graeb., ***C. oliviformis*** Nutt.) (2n=32)

It is native of southeastern USA. The trees are large, up to 50 m in height with 35 cm trunk diameter. The trees are deciduous. The long tap root system makes its transplanting difficult. The leaves are alternate, odd pinnate, exstipulate with 3-17 leaflets, opposite with serrate margin. It is monoecious. Pistillate flowers are borne terminally on current season growth whereas the staminate catkins are borne at the base of new shoots and sometimes on 2-year old shoots. Staminate flowers are borne axillary, usually on ternate pendulous catkins, each in the axil of a 3-lobed bract and have 3-10 stamens. Pistillate flowers are sessile, borne on terminal 2-10 flowered spikes having 1-celled ovary enclosed by a 4-lobed involucre and short stigma. The fruit is globose to oblong with a husk separating it into 4 valves, more or less completely. The nut is smooth or slightly rugose, often angled, 4-celled at base, 2-celled at apex and the cotyledons remain enclosed in the shell. Flowers are dichogamous. Pollination occurs through wind. Nuts appear in clusters of 2 to 8 (Duke, 1989; Wickens, 1995).

Cultivars

Important cultivars of pecan grown in USA are Stuart, Ukulinga, Mohawk, Pawnee, Western, Cheyenne, Curtis (resistant to scab), Desirable, Elliott, Success, Mahan, Moneymaker, Schley, Moore, Wichita and Kennedy (Fig. 25.2). In New Zealand, the most common cultivars are Mahan, Desirable, Mohawk, Candy and Wichita (Rathore, 1991). The other important cultivars are Barton, Burkett, Caspiana, Clark, Dependable, Farley, Ideal, Monarch, Sabine, San Saba, Squirrel, Stevens, W. Schley, Western, Cheyenne, Pawnee, Moreland and Ukulinga (Duke, 1989).

Mohawk: It is of hybrid origin (Success x Mahan). The tree is vigorous having spreading branches and large leaves. The catkin sheds pollen when pistillate flowers are receptive. It is an early maturing cultivar. The nuts are large, somewhat elongated having thin and attractive shell with conspicuous markings, 60% shelling, septum separating easily from the kernel. The kernel surface is smooth having shallow and parallel grooves and of very high quality.

Mahan: Its parentage is unknown. The plants have vigorous upright growth. Bearing is heavy and starts early. The nuts are long and extra large and oblong cylindrical with flattened base and moderately pointed apex, uneven and brown shoulder with dark stripes at the apex. Kernels are amber brown in colour and easily removable from the grooves. The shell is thin and gives nearly 60% shelling. Filling is poor on old trees.

Shawnee: The cultivar was developed from the cross Schley x Barton. The tree is medium tall, vigorous and having dark green leaves. It is a very productive and early bearing cultivar. The flowers are protogynous. The nuts are somewhat elongated, rounded at the centre and base having flat or short pointed apex, thin and light brown shell with dark stripes and loose septum. The kernel is smooth, bright in colour having very good keeping and eating quality and excellent flavour.

Stuart: It is a very old and famous cultivar that takes long time to start bearing. The trees are moderately vigorous and the leaves are of medium size. The nuts are large in size and light brown with light brown kernel of high quality and constitutes 45-50% of the nut. The cultivar is very good for shell trade. Being protogynous it has to be planted with protandrous cultivar to obtain good yields.

Desirable: This cultivar is of hybrid origin (Success x Jewett). Plants being small and compact are amenable for high density plantation. It starts bearing early and produces regularly and prolifically. It is resistant to scab. The nuts are larger than those of Stuart. The kernel quality is very good and average shelling is 52% of the meaty nuts.

Burkett: Trees are upright with medium vigour. Nuts are more or less round in shape having flattened to pointed base, pointed apex, even and grayish shoulder with black stripes around the apex. Kernels are dark brown to chrome yellow and moderate in ease to remove the kernel.

Nellies: Trees are upright and medium in vigour. Nuts are oblong in shape, cylindrical and tapering towards the end, light brown in colour with dark stripes at base. Kernels are amber in colour, moderately filled and easily removable from shell.

Schley: Trees are medium and compact in vigour. It is a self pollinated cultivar. Nuts are medium in size, oblong cylindrical in shape with evenly pointed apex and base, even and dark brown shoulder with prominent black stripes around the apex. Kernels are light brown having moderate removal from grooves and of good quality.

Cheyenne: Trees are medium and compact in vigour. It is protandrous cultivar. Nuts are medium in size and oblong with a slightly pointed apex and brown colour. The kernels are light brown, loosely filled and easy to remove from the grooves.

Excel: It is suspected to be a hybrid (Pierce x Success). It gives nuts of 10 g weight with 49% kernel. The cultivar has a unique combination of large nut size with excellent scab resistance and early harvest (October). Kernels are bright, but kernel content is only moderate as shells are thick. Yields are high, but alternate bearing and overbearing may be a problem in older trees.

Gafford: The cultivar produces 8.1 g moderate quality nuts with 50% bright kernels having occasional speckling. Nuts are medium-sized and harvest is mid season. It has excellent resistance to scab and foliage pests. It is one of the most pest free selections.

Headquarters: The cultivar produces 7.6 g nuts with 54% kernel. The tree is like an Elliott seedling. Its nuts have similar quality but are larger and rounder than in Elliott. Scab resistance is excellent and harvest is mid season.

Kanza: It is a Major x Shoshoni cross released by USDA. The cultivar produces nuts of 7 g having 49% kernel. It has excellent scab resistance and cold hardiness unlike Elliott. Similar to Elliott, it bears alternately but maintains good quality in on years. Kernel brightness is less than in Elliott or Headquarters. Harvest is very early in mid to late September.

Amling: It has the prettiest trees with good tree vigour and excellent foliage among the selections, good for home use and for landscape but not useful for commercial orchards. The cultivar produces 7.6 g nuts with 53% kernel. Scab resistance is excellent. Nut quality is very good.

Adams 5: Like Amling, this selection is outstanding for homeyard and landscape. The cultivar produces 5.6 g nuts having 53% kernel. It is the most scab resistant cultivar. Nut quality is good but nut size is too small for commercial use.

Miss L: The cultivar produces 5.3 g nuts with 52% kernel. It stands out because of pest resistance, good yields of excellent quality and good tasting nuts. It is suitable only as yard tree as the nuts are too small.

Prilop: The cultivar produces 5.4 g nuts with 54% kernel. The selection produces excellent quality small nuts. It is a good choice for home plantings.

Gloria Grande: The cultivar produces large nuts having 47% kernel and good and consistent yields. But it is extremely susceptible to black aphids.

Jenkins: It produces excellent quality nuts of medium size with 53% bright kernels. As the tree gets older the nut size becomes larger but of offgrade and fuzzy. It is also susceptible to aphids, sooty mold and zonate leaf spot.

Ellis: The cultivar produces 10.3 g nuts with 57% kernel. This selection has scab resistance similar to Sumner and combines several highly desirable traits. It has exhibited a remarkable and exceptional ability to produce excellent quality even when the nuts are large and crop is heavy. It is early to mid season cultivar and harvest is a few days earlier than Desirable.

Eclipse: The cultivar produces 7.6 g nuts with 55% kernel. Molecular profile established that it is same as USDA selection 1963-16-182, a Mohawk x Starking Hardy Giant cross, a full sib of Pawnee. The cultivar is extremely early with harvest, two weeks earlier than Pawnee. The nuts are smaller than Pawnee and are longer and more slender. The nut is about 7.6 g with 55% kernel. Kernels are similar to those of Pawnee with bright colour and occasional flecking. Yield is greater than Pawnee with less alternate bearing. Scab resistance is much better than in Pawnee and Sumner.

McMillan: The cultivar produces 8.6 g nuts with 51% kernel. This cultivar is mid season and consistently highly productive. Scab resistance is similar to Sumner. Kernels are somewhat dark and like Pawnee and have ugly dark kernel markings.

Baby B: The cultivar produces 6.8 g nuts with 50% kernel. The trees have large leaves and in full canopy even in years with heavy pressure from diseases and insects. Yields are heavy and consistent. Nuts resemble Elliott, but harvest is very early, similar to Pawnee and Kanza. Scab resistance is good. Nut quality is not as good as Elliott, but yields are far higher.

Elliott: The cultivar produces 6.3 g nuts with 51% kernel. It is an old cultivar and has good scab resistance. Owing to development of new fungal strains the usual scab resistance has weakened. It is now susceptible to foliage diseases and is quite susceptible to yellow aphids and sooty mold. Alternate bearing is severe. It usually maintains high quality with excellent bright kernels even in on-years. Early bud break makes it quite susceptible to spring freezes. It gives lower yields on young trees compared to selections like Baby B and Headquarters.

Sumner: The cultivar produces 9.1 g nuts with 50% kernel. It is a productive cultivar with good kernel quality, high and consistent yields, large nuts and good scab resistance. Like Gloria Grande, it is highly susceptible to black aphids. It is late in harvest, about 11 days after Stuart.

Mandan: The cultivar produces 9.1 g nuts with 57% kernel. This cultivar is very early, several days ahead of Pawnee. Kernel quality and appearance are unattractive.

Caddo: The cultivar produces 6.5 g nuts with 54% kernel. The small, football shaped nut is well filled with bright kernels. The nut has good cracking qualities and is suited to shelling. It is a very prolific and consistent bearer. The cultivar can be susceptible to fungal leaf scorch and black pecan aphids. Harvest is mid season.

Giftpack: The cultivar produces 7.4 g nuts with 56% kernel. This cultivar, likely a Schley seedling, has kernel quality similar to Sioux and Schley. Kernels are bright and the nut is thin-shelled. It is earlier than Schley. Yields are very good and consistent. Scab resistance is mediocre. Black aphid damage is less than in Schley. As in Schley, bird predation of the thin-shelled nuts is a problem.

Apalachee: The cultivar produces 5.7 g nuts with 57% kernel. It has consistently exhibited remarkable yield and early harvest of high quality nuts. In addition to small nut size, problems include alternate bearing and black aphid susceptibility. Kernels can be dark, especially if left on wet ground. Bird predation is a serious problem.

Creek: The cultivar produces 8.4 g nuts with 50% kernel. The trees are small, compact and can be used for high density planting. The cultivar is a very dependable producer of high yields of good quality nuts if intensively managed including control of scab.

Desirable: The cultivar produces 9.9 g nuts with 53% kernel. This is an old standard cultivar but requires scab control and should not be planted in low wet areas. The cultivar is well known for large nut that shells well and bright kernels and yields the most consistently. It is not as susceptible to aphids or sooty mold as most cultivars. In addition to scab susceptibility, the trees have weak limb structure and susceptibility to pecan leaf scorch mites.

Pawnee: The cultivar produces 8.3 g nuts with 54% kernel. The nuts are highly valued because of the early harvest (September), large size, and excellent quality. It is very susceptible to scab and requires intensive cultural management otherwise quality can be poor. Alternate bearing is very severe.

Genus *Juglans* L. (x = 16; 2n = 32)

The plants are deciduous monoecious trees or large shrubs possessing twigs with lamellate (chambered) piths, large aromatic compound leaves, staminate catkins and female flowers. The trunk is smooth or with furrowed bark. The buds are with few scales and sessile, rarely short-stalked. The leaves are alternate, pinnate, large, aromatic and exstipulate. The leaflets are 3 to 23, opposite and serrate or entire. Flowers appear before the leaves. Staminate flowers are generally borne in solitary pendulous catkins one year old wood and have 6-40 stamens and 2-4-lobed perianth. The pistillate flowers are borne on the current season's growth in small racemes covered by 3-lobed involucre. The calyx is 4-lobed. The ovary is inferior, unilocular with two carpels. The style is divided into 2 plumose stigmas. The fruit is a large thick walled (husked) indehiscent drupe or is incompletely 2-4-celled and dehiscent, finally separating into 2 valves. It is morphologically a 2-chambered true nut. The husk consists of the involucre and the flower tube. The husk is indehiscent. It may be leathery or fibrous. The seed has 2-4 lobed embryo with very large cotyledons that are wrinkled and are without endosperm.

The genus comprises about 21 extant species native to parts of North America, the Andean region of South America and the mountain ranges traversing central Asia (Fig. 24.2). These are spread over North and South America to southeastern Europe, eastern Asia and Japan (Manning, 1978) and exhibits disjunct distributional patterns between eastern Asia and eastern North America. The distribution of the cultivated species, *J. regia* extends beyond its natural range. A fossil species is also reported from the West Indies (Descourtilz, 1829; Manning, 1960). All species produce edible nuts, although size and extractability differ considerably. Most of the species are highly regarded for their timber. *J. nigra* L. (eastern black walnut or black walnut) is the most important North American species valuable mainly for fine hard wood (Fig. 24.4). *J. cinerea* L. (butternut) and *J. sieboldiana* Maxim (Japanese walnut) are also planted for their nuts. *J. hindsii* Jeps. and hybrids have been used as rootstock for *J. regia*. *Juglans* species appear to hybridize when grown in the same location. The genus is divided into four sections: *Juglans, Trachycaryon, Cardiocaryon* and *Rhysocaryon*; based mainly on fruit morphology, wood anatomy and foliage architecture (Dode, 1909a,b; Manning, 1978).

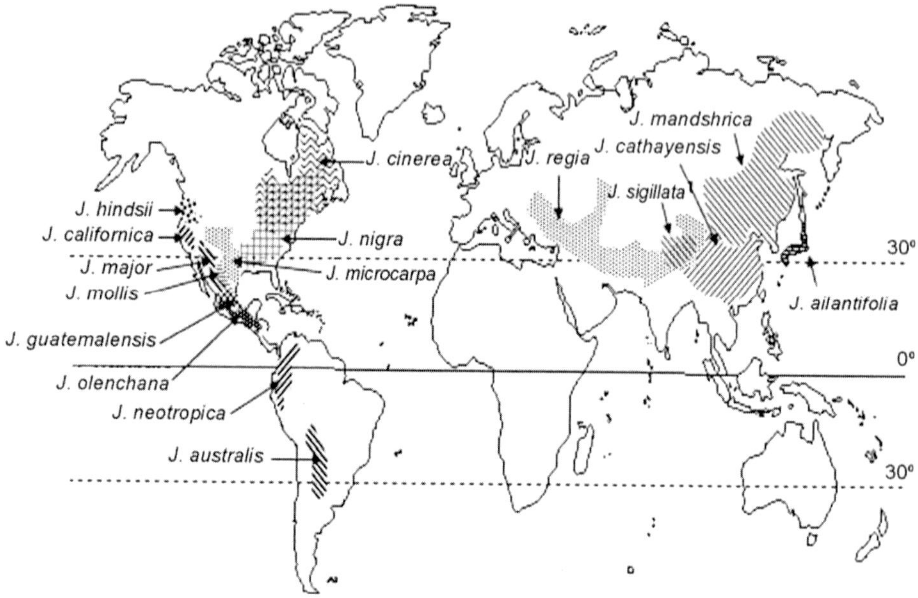

Fig. 24.2. Distribution of *Juglans* taxa (after McGranahan and Leslie, 1991).

1. Section *Juglans* (x=16, 2n=32)

The section includes two taxa: the cultivated Persian or English walnut, *J. regia* L., occurring naturally from southeastern Europe to China and the Himalayas (the Balkan, north Iran, Turkey, south Caspian region, central Asia, the Himalayas and China). Persian walnut bears four-chambered nuts generally singly or in pairs, occasionally three nuts, with smooth, thin nutshells and papery septa and a dehiscent husk that separates easily from the nut. It is cultivated throughout the subtropical regions of the World. The second one is called iron walnut, *J. sigillata* Dode, which is restricted to southern Chinese province of Yunnan and Tibetan regions and bears thick rough-shelled nuts and the characteristic dark-coloured kernels (Dode, 1909 a,b), and often considered as an ecotype of *J. regia*, but some botanists have treated it as a separate species.

Persian or English walnut
(*Juglans regia* L.)

The typically large tree grows to a height of about 30 m. The bark is smooth. The pith is laminated. The buds are very large, the largest amongst the *Juglans* species. Its seedlings have two rows of buds immediately above the cotyledons and below the spirally arranged compound leaves. The number of leaflets is 5-13. It produces large, relatively smooth and generally thin-shelled nuts. It is characterized by the four celled nut and the husk that separates from the nut at maturity. The fruit has slight pubescence on the husk. There is some tendency towards protandry. Protogyny is also found. The horticultural races are: (i) hard shell group, (ii) paper shell group, (iii) soft shell group (e.g. Santa Barbara), (iv) French group, (v) kaghazi group and (vi) Bijou or Klondyke group.

Cultivars

Hartley: It is a seedling selection and commercial cultivar of California. It performs well under drained and irrigated soil conditions. Trees are moderate to large. Leaf opening takes place 12-15 days after Payne. Bearing starts late and production increases with age of tree. The nuts are large having broad base and pointed apex and are light coloured, thin and well sealed with endocarp or shell. The kernel is light in colour. The cultivar is tolerant to codling moth and blight.

Payne: It originated as a seedling selection and is a popular cultivar in California. The tree is round topped and has moderate vigour. It is very productive because the lateral buds are fruitful. Since pollen and stigma mature together, it can be grown in a single block. The nuts are small to medium and well sealed. The cultivar is susceptible to codling moth and blight.

Franipiette: It is an old commercially grown cultivar of France. The trees are upright and large. The laterals are unfruitful. It is late in leafing out, bearing and maturity. It escapes spring frost. The nuts are small, shell seal is good and the kernels are of light colour and good quality.

Ashley: It is Persian walnut type. It is a seedling selection of unknown parentage and is high yielding. The trees are smaller, have medium chilling requirement and start bearing early. Ninety per cent of its lateral buds are fruitful. Pollen shedding coincides with stigma receptivity of pistillate flowers. The nuts ripen early and are large and ovoid having fair shell seal. The kernel is light tan in colour and plump with about 54% of the nuts of good quality and flavour.

Chico: It is Persian walnut type. It originated from a cross, Sharkey x Marchetti. Plant growth is moderate. About 80% of lateral buds produce pistillate flowers. Pollen shedding is late and does not synchronize with stigmal receptivity of its pistillate flowers. The cultivar is early to mid season in maturity. The nuts are round, small to medium and fair to good shell seal. The kernel is about 49% of the nut and is light in colour and of excellent quality.

Serr: It is Persian walnut type. It originated in California. It adapts well to warmer areas and is resistant to sun burn. The trees are very vigorous and grow very fast when young with leafing out about one week after Payne. About 50% lateral buds produce pistillate flowers. It is an early or mid season cultivar. The nuts are large, thin-shelled having fair to good seal and good cracking quality. The kernel is light coloured and is of good quality.

Chandler: It is a moderately vigorous and high yielding cultivar having lateral bearing. The fruit is oval, smooth, of light colour having thin shell that becomes stronger in older trees, 49% kernel, weighing 6.5 g and extra light in colour with easy removal in halves that are not well filled. It is the most common cultivar having excellent colour and halves, fewer pest problems but is relatively late in harvest (leafing by 4 April and harvest by 10 August). The pollinizers are Cisco, Franquette and Fernette.

Cisco: It is a smaller, moderate yielding cultivar more precocious than Franquette and having terminal bearing. The fruits have good shell seal and strength, 44% kernel, weighing 14.8 g, variable in colour but generally medium light. Leafing is by 14 April and harvest by 10 December. It is a pollinizer cultivar for Chandler and Howard.

Eureka: It is a vigorous and fair yielding cultivar having terminal bearing. The fruit is elongated and round at both ends having solid shell and seal, 49% kernel, weighing 7.4 g and poor in colour. It is an old mid season cultivar with distinctive elongated nut shape (leafing by 28 March and harvest by 29 September).

Fernette: It is a moderately vigorous and high yielding cultivar having lateral bearing. The fruit has good shell strength having 50% kernel weighing 7 g of light and extra light colour. It was developed in France and is abundant pollen producer and more precocious than Franquette. It is used as a pollinizer for Chandler. The cultivar is relatively late in harvest (leafing by 15 April and harvest by 13 October).

Forde: It is a moderately vigorous and high yielding cultivar having lateral bearing. The shell is strong having good strength and size. Kernel is 52% weighing 8.1 g and is plump and of light colour and can be easily removed. The females bloom before the catkins and the hulls do not open well before maturity. Leafing starts by 30 April and harvesting is done by 10 August. The pollinizer cultivars are Ivanhoe, Howard and Tulare. The cultivar is resistant to blight.

Franquette: The trees are large and vigorous having terminal bearing and give fairly good fruit yield. The shell is medium thin with good seal. Kernel is 50% weighing 5.5 g and is of good quality having light and extra light colour. It is an old cultivar giving late harvests and is primarily a pollinizer for Chandler. Leafing starts by 23 April and harvesting is done by 17 October.

Gillet: It is a moderately vigorous and high yielding cultivar having lateral bearing. The shell is strong having good strength and size. The shell is good and large and the seal can be weak. Kernel is 51% weighing 7.7 g and is of light colour and can be easily removed. It is a mid season cultivar having large nuts. Leafing starts by 25 March and harvesting is done by 27 September. The pollinizer cultivars are Payne, Vina and Serr. The cultivar is resistant to blight.

Howard: It is not as vigorous as Chandler and is very high yielding cultivar having lateral bearing. The shell is strong and large and the seal is good but can be slightly rough. Kernel is 51% weighing 7.2 g and is of light colour but darkens in storage. The cultivar has large nuts often marketed as in-shell. Leafing starts by 4

February and harvesting is done by 28 September. The pollinizer cultivars are Cisco, Franquette and Fernette. The cultivar faces limb breakage.

Ivanhoe: The tree is fairly small to moderate in size, very precocious having lateral bearing giving good fruit yield. The shell is smooth and thin. Kernel is 57% weighing 7.3 g and is of extra light colour and can be removed easily. The pistillate flowers bloom before the catkins. The cultivar gives very early harvest of excellent coloured fruits. Leafing starts by 17 March and harvesting is done by 13 September. The pollinizer cultivars are Payne and Serr. The cultivar is not resistant to blight.

Poe: The trees are large having terminal bearing and give fairly good fruit yield. The shell is thick and is not well filled. Kernel is 41% weighing 5.6 g and the small kernels have marketable flavour. Leafing starts by 4 April and harvesting is done by 4 October. No pollinizer cultivar has been recommended. The cultivar is unique and grown in California for its flavour.

Robert Livermore: The trees are of moderate size similar to Chandler having lateral bearing and give good fruit yield. The shell is solid, moderately small and dark. Kernel is 50% weighing 6.4 g and has distinctive uniform red skin colour. Leafing starts by 3 April and harvesting is done by 29 September. The pollinizer cultivars are Cisco, Franquette and Fernette.

Sexton: The tree has densely branched canopy. It has an unusual forked branching habit and cluster flowering. Fruit bearing is precocious and in lateral clusters giving good yield. The shell is large, round and smooth having good strength. The kernel is 53%, large, weighing 8.3 g, light in colour and is easy to remove from the shell. Leafing starts by 26 March and harvesting is done by 1 October. For pollination, it coincides well by Chandler, Howard and Tulare.

Solano: The trees are upright and of moderate size similar to Chandler having lateral bearing and giving high fruit yield. The shell has good strength and appearance and suitable for in-shell use. Kernel is 54% weighing 7.9 g having light and extra light colour and good removal. Leafing starts by 28 March and harvesting is done by 24 September. The pollinizer cultivars are Chandler, Howard and Tulare.

Sunland: The trees are vigorous having lateral bearing and variable fruit yield. The shell is large, oval, solid and well filled. The kernel is 55%, oval, large and plump weighing 9.8 g and of good quality. Leafing starts by 30 March and harvesting is done by 27 September. The pollinizer cultivars are Chico, Tehama and Tulare. The cultivar has potential for high productivity but has oil-less nuts and is susceptible to nut drop.

Tehama: The trees are vigorous having lateral bearing and give heavy fruit yield. The shell is solid and can have weak seal. The kernel is 48% weighing 6.8 g and of light colour and not well filled. Leafing starts by 31 March and harvesting is done by 25 September. The cultivar is primarily used as a pollinizer for Serr.

Tulare: The trees have upright canopy and vigorous growth having lateral bearing and give heavy fruit yield. It is a mid season cultivar. The shell has medium texture and strength. The kernel is 53% weighing 7.6 g and of light colour and good fill. Leafing starts by 1 April and harvesting is done by 28 September. The cultivar is often planted with no pollinizer. It is susceptible to low fall and winter temperatures.

Vina: The tree is of moderate size and does not have upright growth. It has lateral bearing with a tendency to overbear giving heavy fruit yield. The shell has good strength and good seal. It can be used in-shell. The kernel is 49% weighing 6.2 g and often having inadequate colour. Leafing starts by 26 March and harvesting is done by 23 September. The pollinizer cultivars are Chico, Chandler, Tehama and Howard. The cultivar is highly productive but has inadequate kernel colour and poor branch structure.

Hamdan: It is a clonal selection. Trees are vigorous and spreading. The cultivar is mid to late blooming, protandrous and terminal bearing. Nuts are medium to large in size, oblong to ovate in shape, attractive, smooth in texture, of 14 g weight having shelling of 54%. Kernels are medium creamy, light brown and soft shelled.

Suleman: It is a clonal selection. The cultivar is precocious, mid season blooming and protandrous, terminal bearing with mid season maturity. Trees are spreading and vigorous. Nuts are roundish, medium to large in size, of 20 g weight having smooth shell surface and 50% shelling. Kernels are medium creamy, light brown and soft shelled.

CITH Walnut–1: The cultivar is suitable for export as well as domestic market. Nuts are bold, long trapezoidal in shape having light shell colour and easy to remove kernel halves giving good kernel recovery (47%). Kernels are large having light colour.

CITH Walnut–2: Nuts are large, ovate having medium shell texture and colour, strong shell seal, intermediate shell strength and complete shell integrity. Kernels are of light colour, well filled, plump and have satisfactory flavour. Kernel halves are easy to remove.

CITH Walnut-3: Nuts are large, round having medium shell texture and colour, strong shell seal and strength and complete shell integrity. Kernel is well filled, plump, has satisfactory flavour and is of light colour. Kernel halves are difficult to remove.

CITH Walnut-4: Nuts are large, ovate having rough shell texture, light shell colour, strong shell seal, intermediate shell strength and complete shell integrity. Kernel is thin, well filled, and moderately plump having satisfactory flavour and light colour. Kernel halves are very easy to remove.

CITH Walnut-5: It is a high yielding cultivar having extra light kernel colour suitable for export market. The nut is large (19 g) and ovate having light shell colour giving good kernel recovery (48.9%). Kernel is of 9.5 g. Removal of full kernel halves is moderate.

CITH Walnut-6: Nuts are large, ovate having medium shell colour, intermediate shell seal and shell strength. Kernel is well filled and moderately plump having satisfactory flavour. The kernel halves are easy to remove.

CITH Walnut-7: The cultivar matures in 155-160 days after full bloom. The nuts are of medium size and ovate having medium shell texture and colour, intermediate shell seal and shell strength. Kernel is well filled, plump having satisfactory flavour. Removal of kernel halves is moderate.

CITH Walnut–8: The nuts have 20.4 g weight, long trapezoidal shape, light shell colour, rough shell texture, strong shell seal and strength and give good kernel recovery (54%). Kernel has light colour and 11.01g weight. Kernel halves are very easy to remove.

CITH Walnut–9: The nuts are medium in size, round in shape, light in colour having strong shell seal and intermediate shell strength. The kernel is well filled and plump. Removal of kernel halves is moderate.

CITH Walnut–10: It is a heavy bearing cultivar. Nuts are small, round having smooth shell texture, medium colour, intermediate shell seal and shell strength. The kernel is well filled, plump and has satisfactory flavour. The kernel halves are easy to remove.

Pratap: The trees are large, vigorous end heavy bearer. The nuts are large, oblong, smooth and light amber in colour. Kernels are light in colour and very easy to remove and semi soft-shelled.

Kotkhai Selection-1: The trees are vigorous and good yielder. The nuts are medium in size, smooth and light in weight. The kernels are light in colour, well filled, thin-shelled and early maturing.

Chakrata Selection: The trees are vigorous and spreading. The cultivar is mid bloomer and protandrous. Nuts are small to medium in size, round ovate or short trapezoidal, thin-shelled and have early maturity.

Iron walnut
(***Juglans sigillata*** Dode)

It is a type from southern China and Tibet with a very thick rough shelled nut, an adherent hull and very dark coloured kernels. The iron walnut is sometimes considered as an ecotype of *J. regia.* It is the most distinctive of the variations within *J. regia.* It is accepted as a separate species with support by isozyme analysis data. This has been cultivated for a long time in Yunnan Province for its oil. Several cultivars have been developed.

2. Section *Trachycaryon*

The section appears to be very closely related to the Asian section *Cardio-caryon.* It has only one North American species. *J. cinerea* L., the butternut, characterized by a two chambered nut (resembling the members of section *Cardiocaryon*) with thick, rough shells and septa exhibiting eight prominent sharp ridges and furrows on the shell and an indehiscent and persistent husk borne in clusters of 2-3 nuts on long stalks. The seedlings exhibit few, if any, scale buds imm-ediately above the cotyledons resulting in a long naked area on the lower seedling stem whereas other species typically produce scale leaves. The nuts are borne in clusters of several nuts on a long stalk and the husks are conspicuously four ribbed.

Butternut
(***Juglans cinerea*** L.; white walnut; oil nut)

It is a native of the eastern USA and southeast Canada and is distributed from southern New Brunswick to Ontario, Michigan, southern Minnesota, South Dakota, southern and eastern Virginia, central and northern Kansas, northern Georgia,

Alabama and western Tennessee (Duke, 1989). It is the hardiest cultivar to cold among the North American walnuts (Rosengarten, 1984). This species is often found on river bottoms in mixed hardwood forests and tolerates high water table. The trees are seldom found in pure stands.

Butternut tree is shorter and more spreading than that of *J. nigra*. The tree also has relatively shorter life span, seldom living longer than 80-90 years. The tree is deciduous growing up to 35 m in height with 0.6 to 1 m trunk diameter and round topped canopy. Butternut wood is not as strong or durable as that of black walnut but is used for furniture, box and toy construction. The branchlets are dark and hairy. Leaves are imparipinnate, 35 to 75 cm long with stout pubescent petioles and 11 to 17 oblong lanceolate leaflets. The leaflets are 5-7.5 x 5 cm in size, finely serrate, sticky, yellow green and rough above and pale pubescent beneath. The leaves are pubescent on both sides. Species is monoecious. Staminate flowers are borne in thick 1.2 to 5 cm long spikes. Calyx is 6-lobed and light yellow to green. Bract is rusty pubescent, acute at apex. Stamens are 8 to 12 with nearly sessile dark brown anthers and slightly lobed connectives. Pistillate flowers are borne in 6-8 flowered spikes, constricted above the middle, coated with sticky glandular hair and about 1.3 cm long red stigma. Fruits are borne in drooping clusters of 3 to 5, obscurely 2 or 4 ridged, 3 to 6 cm long with thick husk, ovoid oblong and covered with rusty clammy hair. The nut is elongated, ovoid, deeply ridged with 4 prominent and 4 less prominent ribs, light brown, 2-celled at the base and 1-celled above the middle. Kernel is white to cream, sweet, very oily and soon becomes rancid (Duke, 1989; Rosengarten, 1984).

American butternut bears two-chambered nuts with thick, rough shells featuring distinct sharp ridges and furrows on the surface, indehiscent and persistent husk and borne in clusters of 2–3 nuts on long stalks. About 25 cultivars have been selected from the native seedling population considering their cracking characteristics, shell thickness and nut yield. The kernels are large in the selected cultivars and can be cracked in halves. A few of these are cultivated but do not have significant commercial use. Butternut canker is a serious disease.

3. Section *Cardiocaryon* (Asian or Oriental butternuts)

The section contains three taxa: *J. ailantifolia* Carr., *J. mandshurica* Maxim., and *J. cathayensis* Dode, all native to East Asia. The species produce two chambered nuts with thick shells and septa, four to eight prominent ridges and indehiscent husks and borne in long racemes of 5 to 25 nuts. Seedlings exhibit five rows of scale buds immediately above the cotyledons which merge in small, alternate and compound leaves higher on the stem. Members of this section are native of eastern Asia where their nuts and timber are used but their susceptibility to walnut bunch disease is a limiting factor.

Japanese or siebold walnut
(***Juglans ailantifolia*** Carr.; heart nut)

The tree reaches a height of 25 m having leaves very pubescent on the lower surface and bears nuts in long racemes in clusters of up to 20 nuts. This species is native to Japan where its trees are generally found along streams and in moist plains. The nuts are typically difficult to crack. Its seedling variant, known as the heart nut, *J. ailantifolia* var. *cordiformis* (Maxim.) Rehd., bears heart shaped nuts that crack more easily and from which kernels can be removed whole.

Manchurian walnut
(***Juglans mandshurica*** Maxim.)

The tree grows up to 30 m in height and attains 50 cm diameter. Nuts are borne in clusters of five to seven on short, 10-15 cm long pendulous racemes. It is native to northeastern China, Manchuria and Korea and is the hardiest to cold among the *Cardiocaryon* but the nuts are difficult to extract. The species is used in China mainly for timber, furniture and as rootstock in cold areas. The nuts are variable in size and shell thickness.

Chinese walnut
(***Juglans cathayensis*** Dode.; Chinese butternut)

The tree or shrub is vigorous growing up to 25 m in height. The small edible nuts having very hard shells are produced on pendulous or erect, 8-15 cm long spikes which bear 6 to 13 flowers each. This species is native to much of central and eastern China and is thought to be botanically very close to *J. mandshurica,* perhaps a geographical and ecological variant. *J. cathayensis* var. *jormosana* Hayata, native to Formosa and the southern portions of the *J. cathayensis* range, has a smoother shell. *J. cathayensis is* reportedly a commonly used rootstocks in regions of China along the Yangtze valley.

4. Section *Rhysocaryon* (black walnuts)

The section is endemic to the New World, comprises 6 North American temperate taxa: *J. californica* S. Wats., *J. hindsii* (Jeps.) Rehder, *J. nigra* L., *J. major* (Torr. ex Sitgr.) Heller, *J. microcarpa* Berl. and *Juglans mollis* Engelm. ex Hemsl.; 3 Central American subtropical taxa: *J. olanchana* Stadl. & L. O. Williams, *J. steyermarkii* Mann. and *J. guatemalensis* Mann.; and 4 South American tropical taxa: *J. australis* Griesb., *J. boliviana* (C. DC.) Dode, *J. neotropica* Diels, and *J. venezuelensis* Mann., mainly occurring in the highlands. Black walnuts typically bear four chambered nuts with thick nutshells and septa with thick, indehiscent and adherent husks borne singly or in pairs but the sutures are not widened or winged and shells are ridged or striate but are not completely smooth. Five rows of scale leaves at the base of seedling stems merge into small, spirally arranged compound leaves farther up the stem.

The species are found in much of the eastern USA and in localized portions of the west and southwest. Latin American members are found mostly in the mountains of Mexico, Central America and the Andean region of South America with little overlapping distribution ranges of the species (Manning, 1960). The species are so closely related and similar that it is often difficult to distinguish them and to group into separate species. Incomplete collection, considerable loss of the collected material and difficulty in reaching their remote mountainous native areas are the reasons that have seriously impeded the study of taxonomy and economic characteristics of these species.

Eastern black walnut
(*Juglans nigra* L.; black walnut)

It is native to the deciduous forests of eastern USA and Canada as one of the most valuable natural forest trees frequently in mixed stands on bottom lands and lower slopes with moist and well drained soils. It requires warm temperate climate. The species is distributed from Kansas eastwards to the Atlantic seaboard, from Minnesota to Texas in the west and from New England to northern Florida in the east (Reid, 1990).

Black walnut is the largest of the North American walnuts. The tree is straight, often unbranched and deciduous growing up to 30-45 m in height with trunk diameter of 1.3 to 2 m. It is very hardy and has small buds, the terminal one being flat. The bark is rough and brown. The branchlets are pubescent. Leaves are compound, 30 to 60 cm long with pubescent petioles and 13 to 23 leaflets, which are 7.5-8 x 2.5-3 cm in size, sharply serrate, yellow green, glabrous above and pubescent beneath. Black walnut is monoecious. Staminate flowers have near orbicular calyx with 6 concave lobes that are pubescent on outer surface, triangular bracts with rusty brown tomentum and 20 to 30 stamens in many series. Pistillate flowers are borne on 2 to 5 flowered spikes having bracts with pale glandular hairs, ovate and acute calyx lobes, puberulent on outer surface and glabrous or pilose within. Fruits are usually produced in clusters of 2 to 3 and are borne on the terminals of current season's growth. Fruit is a drupe like nut, 3 to 5 cm in diameter surrounded by an oval oblong, fleshy and 3-3.5 cm wide indehiscent exocarp. The nut has a rough and furrowed hard shell that protects the edible seed. It has stronger flavoured kernels than those of *J. regia.* The irregular grooves and ridges on the shell separate it from the other species native to USA that produce evenly grooved to nearly smooth nuts. The seed has sweet oil that soon becomes rancid (Duke, 1989).

Its high quality wood is prized for furniture and gunstocks and is the most valuable hardwood produced in the USA. Eastern black walnut is planted in Europe both for timber and rootstock. The nuts are used for candies, bakery and ice cream and are generally more expensive than those of the Persian walnut. Almost all eastern black walnuts are harvested from the wild trees without the aid of mechanical harvesters but the kernel yield is only 8-25%.

Cultivars

Considerable genetic variation has been observed in the wild plantations with respect to hardiness to summer heat, resistance to diseases and insect damage, nut quality, blooming date, leafing date, age of first bearing and growth rate response to length of growing season. From this variability, over 400 cultivars have been selected. The highest quality walnuts have thin outer shell with no internal convolutions protruding into the nutmeat and very thin inner shell partition between the kernel valves to allow easy removal of the kernel. The best cracking black walnuts are the single lobed sports, sometimes called peanut type, which have only a half nut and can be extracted whole, e.g. Throp, Blaettner and Worthington. Selections exhibiting lateral bud fruitfulness and up to 36% kernel content have been made. Deming Purple has reddish shade in its foliage and a purple pellicle. Laciniata is a variant with deeply indented foliage. Most of the thin-shelled black walnut cultivars yield over 30 per cent kernel.

The important cultivars of black walnut are Thomas, Synder, Cornell, Wiard, Huber, Cochrane, Sparrow, Stambaugh, Elmer Myers, Ohio and Myers (Duke, 1989). Cultivars that bear nuts on lateral branches and produce nuts with more than 30 per cent kernel content are Cranz, Football II, Spark 127, Clermont, Kwik-Krop and Sparrow, which are also noted for their consistent productivity. The cultivars Ohio and Thomas are resistant to anthracnose disease (Reid, 1990). The other cultivars are Stabler and Ten Eyck. The hybrids are Paradox (black walnut x Persian walnut) and Royal (black walnut hybrid).

North California black walnut
(*Juglans hindsii* (Jeps.) Rehder)

It was once considered to be a variety of *J. californica* S. Wats., but is now regarded a separate species. It is very similar to *J. nigra.* The tree grows to a height of 30 m, has small buds and produces round, smooth, hard shelled nuts which vary considerably in size and quality but are generally smaller and less strongly flavoured than those of *J. nigra.* The shell is thick and practically smooth. At the time of European settlement, it existed only in a few small groves in northern California but now the species is a common shade tree in the region. Many of the existing trees may be hybrids with other species. The most important use of *J. hindsii* or of the hybrid Paradox (*J. regia* x *J. hindsii)* is as a rootstock.

Family Betulaceae syn. Corylaceae (Alders, birches, hazels and hornbeams)

The family consists of two subfamilies, Coryloideae and Betuloideae. The first includes hazelnut (*Corylus*) along with *Ostryopsis*, *Carpinus* and *Ostrya*, while subfamily Betuloideae includes alder (*Alnus*) and Birch (*Betula*). It contains 6 genera and 130 species (Heywood *et al.*, 2007) occurring mainly in arboreal and cool temperate regions. Some species grow on tropical mountain ranges through Central America and the Andes to Argentina.

The plants are small anemophilous trees or shrubs, often with smooth bark exfoliating its large thin layers. The leaves are simple, alternate, 2 to 3-ranked and deciduous and with stipules and the lamina sometimes lobed and the margins dentate to nearly entire. The flowers are unisexual (plants dioecious), clusters adhering to their bracts. The staminate flowers are in pendulous, conspicuously bracteate, cylindrical catkins comprising 1 to 3-flowered clusters. The pistillate flowers are borne on a stiff axis in erect to pendulous and bracteate catkins or in 2 to 3-flowered clusters subtended by a leafy involucre. The perianth, when present, is in variable number of scale-like segments. The staminate flowers have (1-) 4-6 (-12) stamens and 2-celled anthers, and without traces of vestigial carpels. The pistillate flowers are highly reduced, consisting of a single inferior ovary of 2 fused carpels and completely lacking vestigial stamens. The fruit is a single seeded nut maturing in late summer or fall, which is often winged suited for wind dispersal. The seed has no endosperm. It has a straight embryo.

Genus *Corylus* (x=11; 2n=22)

Ten *Corylus* species are commonly recognized and these are distributed throughout the northern hemisphere. All are diploids (2n=2x=22) and produce edible nuts that are gathered from the wild. Based on morphology, DNA sequence comparisons and success in interspecific crosses, these species have been assigned to 4 subsections, but the status of the paperbark tree hazel remains uncertain. subsection *Corylus* includes *C. avellana, C. americana* Marshall and *C. heterophylla* Fisch. These have leafy, bell-shaped husks (involucres). Subsection *Columae* includes 3 tree species including *C. chinensis* Franch. Subsection *Siphonochlamys* includes 3 species with bristle covered tubular husks: *C. cornut*a Marshall, *C. scalifornica* Marshall and *C. sieboldiana* Blume. The tree hazel *C. ferox* Wall., distinct from the other species in having the nuts enclosed in a burr-like husk, is placed in subsection *Acanthochlamys*.

The plants are mostly deciduous shrubs and rarely trees usually having obtuse, rarely acute, buds with many imbricate scales. The leaves are generally ovate, usually doubly serrate and more or less pubescent and conduplicate in bud. The staminate catkins are cylindric, pendulous and naked during winter. The flowers are without perianth, each bract with 4-8 stamens, bifid filaments and pilose anthers at apex. The pistillate inflorescence is head like enclosed in a small bud with only the red styles protruding with the ovary having 1, rarely 2 ovules per cell and the bifid style to the base. The fruit is a subglobose or ovoid nut having ligneous pericarp borne in clusters at the end of the branchlets. The cotyledons are thick and fleshy remaining enclosed in the nut. Flowers appear before the leaves in winter and the nuts mature in autumn. About 15 species occur in North America, Europe and Asia.

Hazelnut and cobnut

European hazel or cobnut (*Corylus avellana* L.) and European or Turkish filbert (*Corylus maxima* L.) are important nut crops having their origin in the centre of Anatolia. "Cob" refers to the nuts in which the husk is as long as the nut whereas in "hazel" the husk is much shorter than the nut (Menninger, 1977). European hazel is found throughout Europe and eastward through West Asia to Syria and Iran (Table 24.2). It is also cultivated in North America. Turkish filbert is found growing in Balkan Peninsula and cultivated in many countries (Wickens, 1995). Their commercial strains are probably the hybrids of the European cobnuts and filberts. Ninety five per cent of the world's production is from the Black Sea area of Turkey, Italy and Spain. It is also cultivated in USA, France and Greece.

Other important species are *C. americana* (American filbert), *C. colurna* (Turkish filbert), *C. chinensis* (Chinese tree hazel), *C. heterophylla, C. cornuta, C. sieboldiana, C. jacquemontii* (Indian tree hazel) and *C. ferox* (Tibetan hazel).

Table 24.2. The hazelnut species and their geographic distribution

Species	Geographic distribution
C. avellana L. (includes *C. maxima* Mill. and *C. pontica* C. Koch)	Europe from Portugal and Ireland to the Ural Mountains, the Caucasus Mountains, Iran, Syria, Lebanon
C. colurna L. (syn. *C. byzantina* Hort.)	Balkan Peninsula, Turkey, northeastern Iran
C. jacquemontii Decne. [syn. *C. colurna* L. var. *lacera* (Eall.) A.DC.]	Afghanistan, northern Pakistan, northern India, Nepal
C. chinensis Franch. [syn. *C. colurna* L. var. *chinensis* (Franch.) Burkill]	Southeastern China (Yunnan, Sichuan, Guizhou, Hubei)
C. ferox Wall.	Nepal, Sikkim, and Southeastern China (Tibet, Yunnan, Sichuan, Guizhou)
var. *thibetica* (Batal.) Franch. (syn. *C. thibetica* Bata.)	China (Gansu, Shaanxi, Sichuan, Yunnan)
C. sieboldiana Blume [includes *C. mandshurica* Maxim. et Rupr., syn. *C. sieboldiana* Blume var. *mandshurica* (Maxim.) C. Schneid.	Japan, Korea, Soviet Far East, and China (Heilongjiang, Jilin, Liaoning, Hebei, Shanxi, Henan, Shandong, Gansu, Shaanxi, Sichuan)
C. heterophylla Fisch.	Japan, Korea, Soviet Far East, and China (Hellongjiang, Jilin, Liaoning, Inner Mongolia, Ningxia, Gansu, Shaanxi, Shanxi, Hebei, Henan, Shandong)
var. *sutchuensis* Franch. (syn. *C. kweichowensis* Hu)	China (Henan, Shaanxi, south Gansu, Sichuan, Hubei, Hunan, Jianxi, Anhui, Zhejiang)
var. *yunnanensis* Franch. (syn. *C. yunnanensis* A. Camus)	China (Yunnan, Sichuan)
C. americana Marsh.	Eastern North America
C. cornuta Marsh. (syn. *C. rostrata* Alt.)	Northern and eastern North America
var. *californica* (A.DC.) Sharp [syn. *C. californica* (A.DC.) Rose]	Western North America (California, Oregon, Washington, British Columbia)

Filbert (*Corylus maxima* Mill.) is a hazel native to southeastern Europe and southwestern Asia, from the Balkans to Ordu in Turkey. It is a deciduous 6-10 m tall shrub with 20 cm thick stems. The leaves are rounded, of 5-12 x 4-10 cm size with a coarsely double-serrated margin. The flowers are borne on catkins produced in late winter. The male catkins are pale yellow and 5-10 cm long, while the female catkins are bright red and only 1-3 mm long. The flowers are wind pollinated. The nuts are produced in clusters of 1-5. The fruit is a 1.5-2.5 cm long nut fully enclosed in a 3-5 cm long tubular involucre (husk). It is similar to the common hazel (*C. avellana*) differing in having the nut more fully enclosed by the tubular involucre as in the beaked hazel (*C. cornuta*) of North America and the Asian beaked hazel (*C. sieboldiana*) of eastern Asia. The nut is edible. It is mainly used as filler along with peanuts in the containers of mixed nuts. The purple leaved *C. maxima* (Purpurea) is a popular ornamental shrub.

Cobnut (*C. avellana* L.) is a type of hazel nut grown in Britain mainly in southern England where these were introduced in the 19th century and are often referred to as Kentish Cobnuts. When young, the green cobnuts have a taste very similar to coconut. Mature nuts become golden and much sweeter and juicier. Cobnuts are very distinctive in their pretty, downy cover which is easy to remove. The shell toughens on drying.

C. colurna grows much taller and has a tendency to sucker. The trees are deciduous. The leaves are generally ovate, usually double serrate and more or less pubescent. Flower buds are simple and are borne laterally on previous season's growth. The flowers are monoecious and dichogamous. Male flowers open earlier than the female flowers. Staminate flowers are without perianth, each bract with 4-8 stamens, bifid filaments and pilose anthers at the apex and are borne on staminate pendulous catkins. Pistillate inflorescence is head like, enclosed in a small scaly bud with only red protruding styles. Ovary is with 1, usually 2, ovules per cell and bifid style to the base. Male catkins shed pollen from June to September. Female flowers remain receptive for several weeks but the pollen has short life. Pollination is carried out by wind. Fruit is a subglobose or ovoid nut with ligneous pericarp included or surrounded by a large leafy and variously toothed or dissected involucre, which is often tubular and in clusters at the end of the branchlets. The cotyledons are thick and fleshy remaining enclosed in the nut (Duke, 1989; Wickens, 1995).

Cultivars

The most important cultivar developed at Oregon (USA) is Barcelona, besides Butler and Ennis. Tondo Romana and Tondo di Griffoni are the Italian selections, which successfully pollinate each other. The other important cultivars are Duchilly (good pollinizer), White Aveline, Montebello, Brix Nut, Halls Giant (good pollinizer), Tombul (important cultivar of Turkey), Negreta (important cultivar of Spain), Nooksack, Tondo Gentile delle Langhe (important cultivar of Italy), Istariki Dagutyasti, Northampton, Ana Self Husker (free husker), Skinner and Tondo Gentile Tomanu (Jackson, 1986; Sharma, 1991). Important cultivars of Netherlands are Gustav's Zeller, Mortarella, Pauetet, Riccia di Talanico, Tondo di Giffoni and Willamette (Wertheim, 1997). Main cultivars for green nut market are Lang Tidlig Zeller and Lambert Filbert (Kentish Cob or Longue D' Expagne) (Wertheim, 1997). Oregon State University, USA has released cultivar Willamette for blanched kernel market (Mehlenbacher, 1995).

Barcelona: It is known as Fertile de Coutard hazelnut in France. Its large plantations exist in Europe. It is a late maturing (mid September) high yielding cultivar but is sometimes erratic in bearing. Percentage of empty nuts is very high if there is cold during June and is damaged by frost. It is a good pollinizer for Segorbe and is effectively pollinated by Segorbe, Butler and Merveilte de Bollwiller cultivars respectively at the beginning, full bloom and towards the end of flowering.

Butler: It is a seedling selection but the parentage is not known. The cultivar is very productive and is highly compatible with Segorbe and number of other cultivars but shows pronounced biennial bearing.

Ennis: It is a seedling selection but the parentage is not known. The plants are fast growing and resistant to cold. It is a high cropper with lesser tendency towards biennial bearing as compared to Barcelona. The nut is large, of about 4-5 g, light brown with very small husk and borne singly or in pairs. Small male catkins produce large quantity of defective pollen which is not compatible with Barcelona.

Skinner: The cultivar is a hybrid, Dropmore x Italian Red seedling. The tree is very hardy. It is a late cultivar ripening by end of September. The nuts are large, wider than long having quite thick and smooth shell of chestnut colour. The kernel is sweet, plump and crisp resembling that of Barcelona and has very pleasant flavour.

Tonda Giffoni: Trees are medium in vigour. Stone is hard and kernel weight is 1.8 g. The nut is flat with brownish colour prominent towards stem end and brown streaks towards the tip.

Tonda Romana: Trees are medium in vigour. Stone is moderately hard and kernel weight is 1.98 g. Kernel filling is partial with dark brownish colour at stem end turning brownish towards the end.

Gentile Delle Langhe: Trees are medium in vigour. Stone is comparatively soft and kernel weight is 2.4 g with complete kernel filling. Kernel colour is creamy white with prominent brownish streaks and pointed beak.

Kashmir Selection: The trees are mostly large and vigorous and single to multi-branched. Kernel weight is 0.43-0.53g.

⑧ ⑧ ⑧

Chapter 25

CUCURBITALES

The plants are perennial or annual herbs, rarely soft wooded lianas or less often shrubs and trees. Vessels are with scalariform or simple perforations. Rays are heterogeneous. Axial parenchyma is paratracheal. Sieve element plastids are of S-type. Nodes are trilacunar. Leaves are alternate, usually palmately lobed, sometimes palmately compound with three or more leaflets, stipulate or less often exstipulate. Stomata are mostly anomocytic.

Flowers are in axillary or less often terminal inflorescences, sometimes reduced to a usually actinomorphic solitary, nearly always unisexual (monoecious or dioecious), rarely bisexual. Calyx is (3-)5(6-8)-lobed, imbricate or open. Corolla is more or less deeply (3-)5(6-8)-lobed, valvate or induplicate valvate. Stamens are less often 5(1-5) or numerous, free or sometimes more or less connate having tetrasporangiate or disporangiate and extrorse anthers opening longitudinally or rarely by pores. Tapetum is secretory. Microsporogenesis is simultaneous. Pollen grains are 2-celled and of various types, the most primitive ones are 3-colpate or 3-colporate. Nectaries are commonly present in both male and female flowers. Gynoecium is of (3-)4-5(-8) united carpels or rarely secondary monomerous. Stylodia is usually more or less united into a style. Ovary is inferior or very rarely semi-inferior, basically 1-locular. Ovules are numerous or rarely solitary, anatropous, bitegmic and crassinucellate. Female gametophyte is of *Polygonum*-type or of *Allium*-type. Fruits are berries or pepos, less often dry or fleshy capsules. Seeds are usually numerous, rarely solitary, mostly with thick, woody exotesta and papery endotesta, commonly compressed and sometimes even winged. Embryo is straight with two large flat cotyledons. Endosperm is wanting or vestigial. Bitter substances known as cucurbitacins (oxidized triterpenes) are widespread. It contains 8 families.

Family Cucurbitaceae (gourd or pumpkin family)

It contains 120 genera and 750-850 species (Heywood *et al.*, 2007). It is well represented in the moist and moderately dry tropics of both Old and New World, particularly in rain forest areas of South America and woodland, grassland and bushland areas of Africa. Some species occur as semi-desert or even desert vegetation.

The plants are usually climbing perennial herbs with a swollen tuberous subterranean or wholly or partly superficial roots, formed by swelling of the hypocotyls, sometimes annual, occasionally soft woody liana, rarely shrub or tree

(*Acanthosicyos, Dendrosicyos*). The stems are characterized by bicolateral vascular bundles with internal as well as external phloem. The leaves are alternate, simple or sometimes ternate, or palmately compound with 3 or more leaflets, palmately veined and usually lobed, sometimes pinnatifid (*Citrullus*), rarely absent (*Seyrigia*), usually coarsely hairy. In most species a solitary, branched or simple tendril arises at each side of the petiole base, the tip coiling round any suitable nearby object, such as a plant stem, the rest of the tendril then coils in a spring-like manner, drawing the stem close to its support; or the tip is adhesive. The inflorescences are usually axillary, of solitary flowers or cymes, racemes or panicles. The flowers are actinomorphic, nearly always unisexual (plants monoecious or dioecious). The sepals and petals are usually 5, borne at the top of a cup or tube-like expanded hypanthium. The petals are often more or less united at the base. The androecium is complex, with 1-5 stamens, commonly 3, 2 of which are with 4 pollen sacs each, and one with 2 pollen sacs inserted on the lower part of the hypanthium, united in various ways and sometimes the filaments are more or less completely fused into a single central column. The anthers are bent twisted or convoluted with longitudinal dehiscence. In the pistillate flowers, the ovary is inferior of 3 fused carpels, 1-locular, usually with parietal placentation, or 2 to 5-locular by intrusive placentas each having one to many anatropous ovules. The seeds are without endosperm, usually large and more or less flattened. The fruit is berry, sometimes firm walled (such as the melon), pepos or fleshy or dry capsules that may be explosively dehiscent (*Ecballium, Schizopepon*) or are leathery and indehiscent.

Genus *Telfairia* Hook.

The plants are dioecious, large and woody liana growing up to 30 m long with strong and fleshy tuberous roots. The leaves are petiolate, pedately (3-)5-7-foliolate having elliptic leaflets, apically 2-fid tendrils and tubular probracts (nodal stipules) with nectaries. Flowers are large, showy, sweet scented and diurnal; male flowers in racemes and female flowers solitary (rarely in pairs). Receptacle tube is short campanulate. Sepals are triangular, acuminate and dentate and 2 cm long. Petals are distinct, white, purplish or pink. Stamens are fringed, 5 or 3, inserted halfway up the tube with distinct filaments, five anthers, 2-thecous or 3-thecous. Pollen are large and 3-colporate and reticulate. Ovary is ribbed having many horizontal ovules and 3 stigmas. Fruit is fleshy, ellipsoid, up to 60 cm long and 25 cm in diameter, weighing up to 12 kg, ribbed, with or without an expanded and basal collar with white waxy surface when young, dehiscing apically by 8-10 longitudinal valves. Up to 200, large, broadly ovate seeds are 3.5-5 cm in diameter, ±compressed in yellowish white pulp and covered by fibrous sheath containing edible oil. The seeds are yellowish to pale or dark reddish brown having smooth or ±verrucous testa (Kubitzki, 2011). Three species occur in tropical Africa in lowland rainforest, often cultivated in the vicinity of villages for its leaves and oily seeds.

Oyster nut

(***Telfairia pedata*** (Sm. ex Sims) Hook. f.)

Oyster nut is native of tropical East Africa. It is also known as Zanzibar oil vine, kweme nut and Mkweme. It is cultivated in East and Central Africa at elevations up to 100 m. It requires tropical hot climatic conditions and is tolerant to drought and shade. It can grow on a wide range of soils including high pH, poor laterite soil (Duke, 1989).

It is a perennial woody vine growing about 30 m in length. The stem is stout and woody having 2-branched tendrils. Leaves are alternate, digitate and 5 to 7 foliate. The leaflets are 13 x 6 cm in size, lanceolate, elliptic or narrowly ovate or obovate, penninerved and obscurely minute toothed. It is dioecious. Male flowers are borne on racemes of 20 cm length having purple mauve petals with frilled margins. Female flowers are solitary having red petals, green at base, and white stigma. The fruit is a large pepo, 45-60 cm in length, 20 cm in diameter and weighing up to 15 kg having 10-12 deep longitudinal ridges with its fruit stalk constricted near the attachment. Seed is circular, flattened, 38 x 12 mm in size, yellow or brown with no obvious rim and covered with a network of fibrous material. Each fruit contains 60 to 200 seeds having two shells of which the outer can be peeled or removed by burning and the inner one splits with a blow. The shells protect the kernel.

Telfairia nut
(*Telfairia occidentalis* Hook. f.)

Telfairia nut is native of tropical West Africa. It is also known as fluted pumpkin, fluted gourd and calabaza costillada. It is extensively cultivated in Nigeria, Ghana and Sierra Leone.

It is a vigorous fast growing perennial vine growing up to 10 m in length. The stem is five angled and ridged. Petioles and leaf blades are covered with multicellular hair. Stem is stout and woody having tendrils branched with the coiled tips. Leaves have 3-5 palmately arranged leaflets and 2-3 cm long petioles. The terminal leaflet is asymmetrical and the remaining pairs are symmetrical, ovate and shortly acuminate. The terminal leaflet is up to 15 cm in length and the lower epidermis is sometimes scabrid. The plant is dioecious. Flowers are small and white with dark purple mark at the inside base of the five petals borne in racemes with 7-10 cm long pedicels. Male plants produce smaller leaves. Male inflorescences project conspicuously from the stem on 5-25 cm long peduncles. Female flowers are solitary and short stalked produced in the axils of leaves and are often screened by the leaves. Corolla lobes are cream or white having dark purple basal area with short stiff bristles. Fruits are pale green with waxy deposit, strongly ribbed (10) at maturity, up to 25 cm in diameter, 3-6 kg in weight with light yellow and fibrous flesh. There are 30-70 dark red flattened seeds per fruit, 35-49 mm in diameter attached by a slight projection to the placenta (Duke, 1989; Okolia and Mgbeogu, 1983).

Genus *Sicana* Naudin

The plants are monoecious, annual or perennial and herbaceous growing up to 15 m long. Leaves are ovate to sub-orbiculate, palmately 3-9-lobed, often with diskoidal glands at the leaf base, 24 cm long having 3-5-fid tendrils, with apical adhesive pads. Flowers are solitary, medium to large sized and showy having obconical or campanulate receptacle tube, triangular lanceolate, reflexed or less often ascendent sepals, campanulate corolla, divided in the upper ¼ yellow petals, stamens inserted close to the mouth of the tube, short, distinct or ±connate filaments, two 2-thecous anthers, one 1-thecous, thecae duplicate. Pollen is large. Ovary is elliptical with 3 placentae, many horizontal ovules with short style, 3 stigmas and 0, 3 or 5 staminodes. Fruit is a globose, ellipsoid or cylindrical smooth pepo, up to 60 cm long. Seeds are many, compressed, ovate with distinct margin, sometimes narrowly winged (Kubitzki, 2011). About 4 species occur in the Caribbean Islands and Central America in rainforest and secondary scrub.

Cassabanana

(***Sicania odorifera*** (Vell.) Naudin syn. ***Cucurbita odorifera*** Vell.; silkana; musk cucumber) n = 20

It is a native of Brazil. The plants are also found in Bolivia, Paraguay, Brazil, Venezuela and tropical part of Central America. It is widespread throughout the tropical America. Historical evidences show that it was cultivated in Ecuador in pre-Hispanic times. The European writers mentioned that it was cultivated in Peru. It is a widely cultivated vegetable and is also grown for its fruit in Cuba, Puerto Rico and Mexico.

⑧ ⑧ ⑧

Chapter 26

OXALIDALES (CONNARALES)

The plants are small trees, shrubs, woody lianas or less often herbs commonly with mucilage canals and/or tanniniferous secretory cavities and indumentum of multicellular or unicellular glandular hairs. Vessels are with simple perforations and alternate lateral pitting. Fibres are septate with simple pits. Rays are homogeneous or heterogeneous, all uniseriate or occasionally biseriate for part of their length or some of them up to five cells wide. Axial parenchyma is typically absent or scanty paratracheal. Sieve element plastids are of Pcs or Pcfs-type. Nodes are trilacunar (Oxalidaceae) or pentalacunar (Connaraceae).

Leaves are alternate, imparipinnate with two or more pairs of leaflets or less often trifoliate or unifoliate with coriaceous, entire or rarely lobed, very rarely peltate leaflets, commonly exstipulate. Stomata are paracytic, anisocytic and anomocyclocytic. Flowers are small, in terminal or axillary panicles or racemes, bisexual or very rarely unisexual (plants dioecious), actinomorphic, rarely slightly zygomorphic, 5-merous or seldom 4-merous. Sepals are free or rarely basally connate, imbricate or valvate, usually persistent and often embracing base of the fruit. Petals are free or rarely slightly connate, imbricate or valvate, sometimes loriform and circinate. Stamens are 10 or 8, in two cycles, the inner ones sometimes staminodial having slender and free filaments, shortly connate at the base and short, dorsiflxed, tetrasporangiate, introrse or extrorse anthers opening longitudinally. Tapetum is secretory. Microsporogenesis is simultaneous. Pollen grains are 2-celled, mostly 3-colporate, sometimes 3-colpate and rarely 4-colpate. Nectary disc is poorly developed or wanting. Gynoecium is of 5 or 1 carpels, rarely of 3, 7-8 carpels, free or only basally connate. Ovary is superior. Ovules are anatropous, hemitropous or more often orthotropous, bitegmic, crassinucellate or tenuinucellate, sometimes (*Connarus*, *Jollydora*, and *Averrhoa*) with an endothelium. Female gametophyte is of *Polygonum*-type or very rarely of *Allium*-type. Endosperm is nuclear. Fruit capsules are indehiscent. Seeds are mostly arillate, without or with fibrous exotegmen. Embryo is straight. Endosperm is copious and oily to scanty or none (Takhtajan, 2009). It contains 7 families.

Family Oxalidaceae (wood sorrel, bermuda buttercup, oca, star fruit)

It contains about 5 genera and 800-900 species (Heywood *et al.*, 2007). Although dominated by the weedy genus *Oxalis* the family is known for the star fruit

(*Averrhoa carambola*). It is native to the tropics with many species at high altitudes, some are subtropical or temperate. Two species are probably native of America.

The plants are small trees, shrubs, climbers and usually perennial herbs (rarely annual) and often with underground bulbs, tubers or fleshy roots having high levels of soluble and crystalline oxalates. Plants are often clump forming or spreading by stolons. The leaves are alternate and spiral, sometimes forming a basal rosette, pinnately or palmately compound or reduced and trifoliate or unifoliate, often with prominent pulvini and showing sleep movements, entire, often emarginate with palmate to pinnate venation and usually the stipules are lacking. The petioles are sometimes woody and persistent or rarely succulent. Inflorescences are determinate, often umbel-like, sometimes reduced to a single axillary flower. Flowers are bisexual, radial and heterostylous having 5 distinct sepals, 5 distinct or very slightly connate, usually convolute petals, 10 stamens with basally connate filaments, outer smaller than the inner. Pollen grains are tricolpate or tricolporate. Carpels are 5, connate with superior ovary with axile placentation. Styles are 5, distinct capitate or punctate stigmas. Ovules are several in each locule with thin megasporangium wall. Nectar is produced by base of filaments or glands alternating with petals. Fruit is a loculicidal capsule or berry, often lobed or angled. Seeds are sometimes arillate, the outer part of the testa often elastically turning inside out ejecting the seed.

Genus *Averrhoa* L.

The two well known species are *A. carambola* L. and *A. bilimbi* L., probably of Indo-Malaysian origin and distributed throughout the tropics (Kubitzki, 2004). The plants are trees and shrubs. The leaves are alternate, pinnately compound and plurijugate. Terminal leaflet is absent. Inflorescence is thyrso-paniculate. The flowers are small, downy, purple streaked, regular in panicles that are much branched or in cyme. Sepals are 5 and contorted. No glands are present. Stamens are 10, united at the base, all perfect or 5 staminodes. Ovules are 3-7 per locule. The fruit is a baccate, 5-lobed berry. The seeds are naked or sometimes arillate.

Carambola
(***Averrhoa carambola*** L.; star fruit) (2n=22, 24)

It is believed to have originated in South East Asia, probably in Indonesia where it has been reported to occur in a wild state (Martin *et al.*, 1987). It is a much branched, small and slow growing evergreen tree, up to 10-15 m in height with drooping branches. The bark is light brown, smooth or finely fissured. Leaves are alternate, imparipinnate with 3-6 leaflets that are entire, ovate or ovate lanceolate, acute, glabrous and glaucous (with bloom) on lower surface. The flowers, borne on axillary or cauliflorous panicles, are perfect, pentamerous and heterotristylous with coherant petals, much larger than the 8 mm long pink sepals with purple or red heart and 10 stamens of which 5 are sometimes rudimentary (Shiesh *et al.*, 1985). Ovary is superior, 5-celled with 5 styles. The fruit is yellowish green, smooth and shiny and large, ovoid to ellipsoid berry, 6-13 cm in size with five prominent longitudinal ribs, stellate in cross section and seeds having fleshy aril (FAO, 1982; Verheij and Coronel, 1991).

Cultivars

Some attributes of a good cultivar are: i) sweet and less tart with >11°Brix and low oxalic acid content, ii) yellow to golden yellow colour, iii) strong, broad ribs to withstand bruising, iv) good shelf life, v) fruit yield >40-60 mt/ha, and vi) withstand low temperatures.

There is no well defined cultivar, but two recognized types are:

i. Sweet (popular in China).

ii. Sour (popular in India).

The cultivars have also been grouped on the basis of length of style (Watson *et al.*, 1988):

i. Short style cultivars-- B-2, B-8, B-10, Fwang Tung, Lu Tho, Wheeler, Sri Kembangsaan and Kara.

ii. Long style cultivars-- B-1, B-6, B-11, B-16, Starting, Maha, Arkin and Kary.

The important cultivars of Malaysia are Maha 66, B1, B17, B2, B10 and B11. In Thailand, the two important cultivars are Thai Knight and Bangkok Noi besides Fwang Tung. Taiwan has developed cultivars such as Two Forest, Light Green and Think, Slant Tail, Malay, TaiFarm #1. The cultivars namely, Tao (P.I. No. 272065) were introduced in 1963, besides Dah Pon, Mih Tao, and Tean Ma. Cultivar Icambola is important in Colombia. The cultivars Arkin, Fwang Tung, Golden Star, Hoku, Kaiang, Maha, Srikembanquan, Wheeler, Thayer, Newcombe, Kary and Kera are important in Florida. The cultivars introduced into Australia include Leng Bak and Jurong from Singapore, Thai Knight (ex Thailand) from Florida and Kona Beauty, Hart, Kajang and Seremban (both ex Malaysia) from Hawaii. The others are Fuang-Gung, Kembangen, B_1, B_4, B_6 and B_{16}. The local selections include Giant Siam, Jungle Gold, BCP-1, Hosie, Chujuba. The cultivars introduced from Malaysia are B2, B17 and B10.

Arkin: The tree is partially self fertile. The cultivar bears fruits from December to March in California where it is the leading commercial cultivar. The fruit is uniform, 10 to 12.5 cm long, 90-200 g in weight, golden yellow at maturity and becomes yellow orange when fully ripe. It has thick ribs and large apple with very sweet, juicy, firm and crisp flesh having yellow orange texture, 6.0-11.5°B TSS and good flavour (rating 4.9/9) and few seeds. It is used as fresh fruit and for processing. It keeps and ships well.

Golden Star: The cultivar originated in Homestead, Florida, USA. The fruit is large, 100-200 g in weight, deeply winged and golden yellow when fully ripe. It has thick ribs and large apple with crisp, fibreless, very juicy and sweet flesh. The fruit has high carbohydrates and vitamins A and C content. It is a self incompatible cultivar.

Sri Kembangsaan Karry: The cultivar is grown in Florida, USA (collected in Malaysia selection Karry). The fruit is 150-200 g in weight and lemon yellow when fully ripe. It has slightly crisp flesh texture with 7.0-13.0°B TSS and very good flavour (rating 6.5/9).

Kaput: The cultivar is grown in Indonesia.

Lang Bak: The cultivar is grown in Singapore.

Cheng Tsey (Chum Choi): The cultivar is grown in Taiwan. The fruit is up to 315 g in weight, light green at maturity and becomes orange in colour when fully ripe. It has slightly crisp flesh texture with thin ribs and sharp apple.

B-2 (Maha 66): The cultivar is grown in Malaysia. The tree is slow growing. The fruit is elongated and narrow, medium to large in size (100-200 g), greenish yellow at maturity and becomes yellow when fully ripe. It has deep furrow ribs and sharp apple with fine crisp texture and 7-8ºB TSS and good aroma. The fruits do not keep well and soften easily. These are susceptible to injury during handling and cold storage owing to narrow ribs.

B-10 (Ching Sing Keow): The cultivar is grown in Malaysia. The tree is vigorous. It has moderate resistance to fruit fly. The styles are short. The fruit is large in size (100-315 g), greenish yellow at maturity and becomes yellow to golden reddish orange when fully ripe. It has more compact ribs than of B-2 and slightly rounded apple with juicy and sweet flesh of fine crisp texture and 9-12ºB TSS. The fruits are used fresh as well as for processing.

B-17 (Cristal Honey or Honey Carambola): The cultivar is grown in Malaysia. The cultivar is said to produce better quality fruits than B2 and B10 (Rao and Ramanatha Rao, 1998). The fruit is golden yellow when fully ripe with broad wings. The flesh is firm, fairly good textured having large ribs of very sweet (15-18ºB TSS) and good flavour (rating 5.3/9). It requires a pollinizer like B2 to obtain satisfactory fruit set.

Fwang Tung: The cultivar is grown in Thailand. The fruit is large, 9.5-20 cm long, 100-300 g in weight, golden yellow when fully ripe with few seeds. It has large ribs with crisp texture, 9.2-12.6ºB TSS and good flavour (rating 5.3/9). The firm flesh when cut its slices present beautiful star shape. Fruits are susceptible to injury during handling and cold storage owing to narrow ribs (Martin *et al.*, 1987; Morton, 1987; Verheij and Coronel, 1991).

Hoku: It was selected at the University of Hawaii. The fruit is 12.5–15.0 cm long with bright yellow skin and flesh. The fruit has juicy, firm and sweet flesh having rich flavour and few seeds. The fruit slices are attractive star shaped.

Wheeler: It has medium to large, elongated fruit with orange skin and flesh. The fruit has mildly sweet flavour. The tree is a heavy bearer.

Thayer and **Newcombe:** These are two of the known tart cultivars.

Bilimbi

(***Averrhoa bilimbi*** L.; cucumber tree; tree sorrel)

Bilimbi is native to Moluccas. It is an attractive, long-lived and small tree growing to 5-10 m height and has a short trunk that generally separates into a number of upright branches. Leaves are compound, alternate, imparipinnate, 30-60 cm long with 11-37 alternate or sub-opposite, ovate or oblong leaflets having rounded base, pointed tip, downy and medium green upper surface and pale underside. Flowers are small, fragrant, 5-petalled, yellowish green or purplish marked with dark purple, borne in small hairy panicles emerging directly from the trunk and the oldest and thickest branches. Fruit is an ellipsoid berry, obovoid or nearly cylindrical, faintly 5-sided, 4-10 cm long, about 2.5 cm in diameter, capped at the apex by a thin star shaped calyx. The fruit skin is glossy, very thin and soft and tender and the flesh is green, jelly-like, juicy and extremely acidic. There may be a few, flattened disc-like arillate seeds which are about 6 mm wide, smooth and brown (Morton, 1987; Verheij and Coronel, 1991).

Family Elaeocarpaceae

It contains about 15 genera and 400-600 species (Heywood *et al.*, 2007). It is often tropical and subtropical. The plants are trees, ericoid shrubs and herbs with glandular or rarely star shaped hairs. The trees are sometimes with buttresses. The leaves are alternate, spirally arranged, opposite or rarely whorled, simple (but rarely pinnate or pinnatisect in juvenile plants) with entire or serrate margins with stipules or mucilaginous hairs. Inflorescence is compound or simple, racemose or cymose, axillary or terminal, sometimes of solitary axillary flowers (*Tremandra*). The flowers are regular, mostly hermaphrodite and have 3-5 usually valvate sepals, free or partly united. The petals are 4 or 5, or absent (*Sloanea* spp.), usually free, valvate, but sometimes overlapping at tip, often fringed or lacerated at their tips. The stamens are 4 to numerous and free and the anthers have 2 locules that release pollen through 2 apical pores. The receptacle is sometimes swollen and glandular, lobed between the stamens and petals. The ovary is superior and contains 2 to many locules each containing 1 to many pendulous ovules. The style is simple and sometimes lobed at the tip or may be slender. The fruit is a capsule or drupe with 1 to many seeds per locule.

Genus *Elaeocarpus* L.

The name *Elaeocarpus* is derived from the Greek 'elaia' meaning olive and 'karpos' meaning fruit. The genus has about 350 species (8 in Madagascar, 30 in Ceylon and India, 18 in Thailand, 20 in China, 2 in Japan, 30 in Peninsular Malaysia, 15 in Java, 70 in Borneo, 40 in Sulawesi, 50 in Philippines, 85 in New Guinea, 29 in New Caledonia, 25 in Australia, 1 in Lord Howe Island, 2 in New Zealand and 22 in Fiji and Hawaii) (Kubitzki, 2004). South Asia has 7 species (*E. serratus*, *E. amoenus*, *E. coriaceus E. montanus, E. subvillosus, E. glandulifer* and *E. zeylanicus*).

The plants are shrubs to large trees. The leaves are spirally arranged to distichous, very rarely opposite. Stipules are minute to large, linear to foliaceous, sometimes early caducous. Inflorescence is a raceme, rarely short racemose or paniculate. Flowers are usually bisexual, sometimes unisexual (on monoecious plants) having petals expanded or sepaloid, sometimes small, variously lobed and/or labiate or entire and ±sepaloid, rarely entire and expanded, with or without pockets at base, disk variously tall or low, sometimes resembling a cog-wheel or lobed, sometimes merely annular with minute teeth, rarely pulviniform. Stamens are 5-200, inserted on disk surface and/or at ovary base. Filaments are straight to sigmoid, shorter than, equaling or exceeding anthers, sometimes ±0 and anther connective extension is often present as awn or absent, apical setae sometimes present (but never surrounding apical pore), dehiscing by a single apical confluent extending down sides sometimes to base. Ovary is 2-9-locular with 2-16 ovules per loculus and one style. Fruit is a drupe with woody and often sculptured endocarp usually separable from the mesocarp, sometimes with ±persistent fibres as in *Aceratium*. Seeds are 1-5 (-7)/fruit, at the most 1 per loculus and without sarcotesta or appendages, straight with broad to curved or narrow cotyledons.

Ceylon olive
(*Elaeocarpus serratus* L.)

Ceylon olive is an evergreen, small to medium sized tree growing about 20 m high with a spreading canopy and about 30 cm bole diameter. Flowers are borne on numerous 4-8 cm long racemes that emerge from the axils of leaves. The flower has 4-6 mm long, lanceolate, acute, fine pilose or glabrous sepals, about 5-6 mm long white petals, 25-35 stamens and 3-celled hairy ovary. Fruit is about 3-4 cm long, ovoid bluntly pointed, smooth, dull and greenish yellow drupe having a light to dark green edible pulp with copious acid. Stone is ovoid oblong, thick, bony, strongly tubercled, 1-celled and 1-seeded. It is not cultivated. The fruits are collected either from wild trees or from home gardens mostly in wet and intermediate zones of the country. It is also found in India, Bangladesh, Brazil, Thailand, Malaysia and Australia.

Indian olive
(*Elaeocarpus floribundus* Blume)

Indian olive or jalpai is an evergreen, moderate sized tree with spreading crown and clean bole of 12-16 m height. It occurs in evergreen forests of northeast India, up to 1500 m altitudes. Leaves are ovate elliptic, thinly leathery, varying from 6.5 x 3 to 19 x 8.5 cm with pointed tips and toothed margins. White flowers are borne in the leaf axils on many flowered 2.5-12 cm long racemes. The flowers are 5-merous, 0.5 cm long comprising 25 stamens. There are 5 sepals and 5 white petals divided into many frilly segments. Flowering takes place in July-August. The fruit is a light green 2-5 cm long and 1.5- 2.5 cm wide drupe. Both the ends of the fruit are pointed having smooth outer surface and fleshy and pleasantly acidic mesocarp. The stone is 3-celled, each cell having spindle shaped seed. It is often planted in home gardens in northeast India for its fruits that have medicinal value and are used for making pickle.

⑧ ⑧ ⑧

Chapter 27

MALPIGHIALES

The plants are trees, shrubs, subshrubs or herbs, sometimes woody lianas. Vessels are with simple perforations having alternate lateral pitting. Fibres are with simple or bordered pits. Rays are narrow, heterogeneous or homogeneous. Axial parenchyma is apotracheal or paratracheal, sometimes wanting. Sieve element plastids are of So-type. Nodes are unilacunar or sometimes trilacunar. Leaves are alternate, opposite or verticillate, simple and usually entire with stipules present or absent, sometimes modified into spines or glands. Fibrous exotegmen and toothed leaves are with teeth having a single vein running into a congested and often deciduous apex (i.e. teeth violoid, salicoid or theoid). Leaf mesophyll cells contain oil bodies. Stomata are mostly paracytic. Flowers are borne in different types of inflorescences. These are bisexual, actinomorphic or more or less strongly zygomorphic, basically 5-merous or less often 4-merous. Sepals are free or nearly free, imbricate or valvate. Petals are free and often clawed or basally connate or only some of them are connate. Nectary disc is present or absent. Stamens are 1-10(-15), often some of them staminodial. Filaments are free or often variously connate having tetrasporangiate or rarely disporangiate and mostly basifixed, introrse anthers opening in various ways. Tapetum is secretory. Microsporogenesis is simultaneous. Pollen grains are 2 or 3-celled, very diverse but mostly 3-colporate or pantoporate. Gynoecium is of 3-5, less often 2 or up to 8 united carpels. Many families are predominantly three carpellate. Stylodia are free or only basally connate or more often connate into a terminal style and many have dry stigmas. Ovary is usually superior, commonly plurilocular with axile placentas, seldom unilocular and with two parietal placentas or with 1 or 2, rarely 2-16 pendulous sub apical ovules and sometimes pseudomonomerous. Ovules are epitropous, anatropous to hemitropous, bitegmic and crassinucellate. Female gametophyte is of *Polygonum*-type or *Penaea*-type, less often of *Allium*-type. Fruits are of diverse types. Seeds are testaltegmic, exotegmic or endotestal, often with fibres. Embryo is straight or more or less curved. Endosperm is present, sometimes copious or lacking or nuclear (Takhtajan, 2009). It has 37 to 42 families.

Family Euphorbiaceae (spurge family)

It is cosmopolitan, with the greatest diversity in the tropics, often abundant at low to medium altitudes and dominant in some ecosystems. It is a large and diverse family with unisexual flowers, superior syncarpous ovaries, and one ovule per locule.

The plants are trees, shrubs, herbs, climbers or succulents with hairs ranging from simple to dendritic and T-shaped to stellate and lepidote, urticating in *Cnidoscolus* and in the unrelated tribe *Plukenetieae*. It is chemically diverse having alkaloids, di- or triterpenoids, tannins and cyanogenic glucosides, often latticifers containing clear or milky latex. The latex is usually white or red. The white milky latex of subfamily Euphorbioideae is usually caustic or toxic. Also notable is the secretion of resin from floral bracts in *Dalechampia*. The leaves are simple or palmately compound, entire to toothed or deeply lobed. Stipules are generally present, not always, and can be from minute and caducous to large and foliaceous. Leafless succulent species are often spiny, resembling the cacti. Inflorescences are diverse. The tribe Euphorbieae is characterized by highly specialized pseudanthia infloresences (cyathia), consisting of bracts subtending 4-5 staminate inflorescences (reduced to a single stamen) and a terminal pistillate flower (reduced to gynoecium). The flowers are unisexual (plants monoecious or dioecious). Sepals, petals, disks, staminodes and pistillodes may be absent or present. The stamens range from 1-1000 (variously branched in *Ricinus*) and are free or variously fused. Styles are usually 3, each usually bifid or divided several times with various stigmas. The ovary is superior, of (1-(2-5(-20) fused carpels, forming as many locules, each with a single apical axile, anatropous and epitropous ovule provided with an obturator. The fruit is characteristically an explosive schizocarp with typical dehiscence and persistent columella. In many taxa, the fruit is indehiscent and in critical taxa such as Peroideae, it is typically nonexplosive (Heywood *et al.*, 2007).

Genus *Schinziophyton* Hutch ex Redcl.-Sm.

It is a monotypic genus having large, spreading trees found on wooded hills and amongst the sand dunes and is associated with the sandy soils with distinctive hand-shaped leaves and pale yellow wood similar in characteristics to balsa (*Ochroma pyramidale*), being both light weight and strong and with yellowish flowers that are slender and occur in loose sprays.

Mogongo nut
(***Schinziophyton rautanenii*** (Schinz.) Radcl.-Sm.
syn. ***Ricinodendron rautanenii*** schinz.; mongongo nut)

It is a native of northern South Africa and is distributed in Botswana, Zimbabwe and Mozambique. It is found on wooded hills and amongst sand dunes and is associated with the Kalahari sandy soils. The related species, *Ricinodendron heudelotti* Pierre, known as manketti nut, essang nut or juk nut also produces edible nuts and is found growing throughout tropical Africa (Duke, 1989; Peters, 1997).

Mogongo nut is a large, spreading and deciduous tree, up to 24 m in height and 1 m diameter. Wood is pale yellow and similar to balsa, being both light weight and strong. The leaves have distinctive hand-shaped. Leaves are alternate, stipulate, digitately compound with 3 to 7 pubescent leaflets having 15 cm long petioles. Leaflets are broadly lanceolate to ovate, 5-13 x 2.5-9 cm in size, dark green above and pale yellow on the underside. The tree is dioecious. The yellowish flowers emerge in slender loose sprays. Male flowers borne in slender loose panicles are whitish whereas female panicles are shorter and few flowered. The fruit is plum shaped, 4 cm long and is hairy when small. The stone is exceedingly hard containing one or two light coloured kernels (Duke, 1989; Wickens, 1998).

Genus *Caryodendron* H. Karst.

It includes the species *Caryodendron amazonicum, C. angustifolium* and *C. orinocense* (Inchi tree).

Castanha de porco
(***Caryodendron amazonicum*** Ducke)

It occurs in the Amazonian lowland of Brazil adjacent to *C. orinocense*.

Orinoco nut
(***Caryodendron orinocense*** Karst.)

Orinoco nut is native of Colombia, Ecuador and Venezuela. It is also known as palo de nuez, cacay or inche. It is also found in humid tropical parts of Brazil and Ecuador. The other related species are *C. amazonicum* Ducke (castanha de porco) found in Ecuador and Colombia, *C. grandifolium* found in Brazil, and *C. angustifolium* found in Panama. Efforts have been made to cultivate this nut in Costa Rica, Colombia and Ecuador.

The tree is large, of 20 m height having yellowish trunk, which produces watery and pinkish yellow latex. Leaves are alternate, glabrous, elliptic or obovate, 12-25 x 4-10 cm in size and biglandular at the base of the blade. Both monoecious and dioecious trees occur. Flowers are unisexual and are borne on separate inflorescences. Male flowers are borne on terminal racemes with 3 cm long concave sepals, 4 conical and glabrous stamens and white disk. Female flowers have 5 to 6 ovate sepals, trilocular ovary, short and trilobate stigma and annular disk. Fruit is a globose oblong and 3-seeded nut, 5-6 x 4-5 cm in size. Seed kernel is 3 x 1.7 cm in size (Reckin, 1983; FAO, 1986; Brücher, 1989).

Genus *Tetracarpidium* Pax syn. *Plukenetia* L.

It comprises one species distributed in Africa.

Conophor nut
(***Tetracarpidium conophorum*** (Müll. Arg.) Hutch. and Dalziel
syn. ***Plukenetia conophora*** Müll. Arg.; African walnut; Nigerian walnut)

It is a perennial climber found in the moist forest zones of sub-Saharan Africa (Oke, 1995). It is known as ukpa (igbo) in southern Nigeria, as awusa or asala (yoruba) in western Nigeria and as kaso or ngak in the littoral and the western Cameroon (Dalziel, 1937). It occurs in Uyo, Akamkpa, Akpabuyo, Lagos, Kogi, Ajaawa-Ogbomoso and Ibadan.

This is a woody climber, 6-18 m long with large stem which can be up to 16 cm in girth. The young stem is green and glabrous and becomes dark gray when old. The root is fibrous. The leaves are alternate, 10 cm long and 5 cm broad, simple, crenulate and ovate with a serrated margin and abruptly acuminate and rounded at the base. The plant is monoecious. The male flowers are in narrow raceme like panicles about as long as the leaves with 1-2 female flowers near the base. The flowers are arranged alternately on the axis of the raceme. The style is stout and quadrangular with four spreading stigmas. The stamens are about 40 in number. The fruit is a four winged ribbed capsule containing subglobose seeds with a thin brown shell and yellowish kernel. Each seed loculus ends in a wing thereby creating ridges in between the wings. The seed is about 2.5 cm in diameter. The fruit (7 cm across) is light green to brown when ripe. The seeds are round and dark brown at maturity (covered with a hard testa). Sometimes all the seeds do not develop in which case the fruit has fewer wings (Isawumi, 1993).

The economic importance of the species lies in the edibility of its oil rich seeds, which are cooked and consumed as snacks along with boiled corn by various populations in Nigeria, Sierra Leone and the lower Congo region. It grows along the African coastline and is thought to have originated in southwestern Nigeria. A biscuit-like snack has been developed from the nut. It has significance as oilseed. The nut contains 48-50% oil, which is liquid and golden yellow in colour with taste and odour resembling those of linseed oil.

Family Phyllanthaceae

The plants are trees, shrubs and herbs but rarely climbers, succulents or aquatics. Latex is absent although resinous exudate is rarely present. Stipules are free or rarely intrapetiolar, entire or rarely laciniate, sometimes foliaceous and rarely spinose. The leaves are simple (compound only in *Bischofia*), rarely absent in mature plants (phyllocladous species of *Phyllanthus*), alternate, spiral, subopposite, more rarely fasciculate, whorled or opposite. The blades are symmetrical or rarely asymmetrical with pinnate venation and usually entire margins. Inflorescences are axillary, more rarely cauline or terminal. *Uapaca* has pseudanthia with large coloured bracts. The flowers are actinomorphic, unisexual (plants monoecious or dioecious) except for 4 bisexual *Aporosa* species. The sepals are 3-8. The petals are (2-) 4-6 or absent. A disk is often present and in staminate flowers may be divided, extrstaminal annular, rarely intrastaminal or have the stamens inserted in cavities of the disk. The pistillate disk is divided or annular. The stamens are 3-10(-19) with the filaments free or variously fused and the anthers longitudinally dehiscing (rarely appearing oblique or horizontal) or rarely poricidal. The thecae are sometimes separate and the connectives are enlarged. A pistillode may be present. Bur staminodes are rare. The ovary is superior with (1)2-5(-15) carpels and locules with 2 ovules per locule, often only one ovule developing into a seed. The ovules are anatropous or hemitropous, apical axillary and have art obturator. The styles are usually bifid, sometimes entire or rarely multifid, and the stigmas ±terete or sometimes flattened. The fruits are explosively dehiscent (schizocarp), tardily dehiscent or idehiscent (drupes or berries). The seeds are ecarunculate (minutely carunculate in *Celianella*) but sometimes with a brightly coloured sarcotesta or endosperm is usually present in mature seeds, and the embryos usually have thin cotyledons. Exalbuminous seeds with plicate or fleshy cotyledons occur in some genera.

Genus *Phyllanthus* L.

The number of species in this genus varies from 750 to 1200. It has remarkable diversity of growth forms including annual and perennial herbs, shrubs, climbers, floating aquatics and pachycaulous succulents. Some plants have flattened leaf-like stems called cladodes. It has a wide variety of floral morphology and chromosome numbers and has one of the seed plant genera having the widest range of pollen types.

Aonla

(***Phyllanthus emblica*** L. *syn.* ***Emblica officinalis*** Gaertn., ***Averrhoa acida*** L.; emblic; Indian gooseberry; myrobalan)

Aonla is a small to medium sized deciduous tree, reaching 8 to 18 m in height. It is well known for its edible fruit. The tree has crooked trunk and spreading branches. The leaves are simple, nearly stalkless and closely set along the slender branchlets (Fig. 27.1). The leaves are often mistaken for leaflets of pinnate leaf. Thus the branch looks like a compound leaf. The genus name *Phyllanthus* is derived from the Greek words meaning leaf flower, an illusion apparent from flower bearing pattern on the leaves. The flowers have both sexes and short pedicels (Fig. 27.2). Corolla is missing. Disc is present. There are no rudimentary ovaries in the staminate flowers. Stamens are 3. Ovary is 3-celled with 2 ovules in each cell. Styles are connate. Sepals of staminate flowers are 5-6. Filaments are conical. The anthers open vertically. The fruit is a smooth, rounded berry, 2.5-5.0 cm in diameter having very firm flesh. The fruits are very rich in vitamin C.

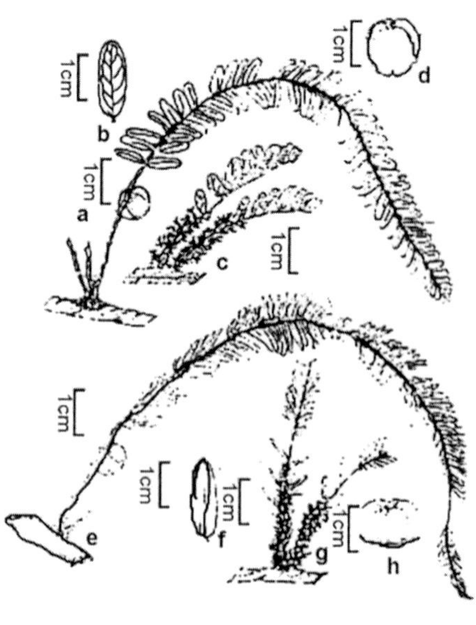

Fig. 27.1. Leaf arrangement in *Phyllanthus indofischeri*: a. branchlet with a fruit, b. leaf, c. flowering branch, d. fruit of *P. emblica* (e-h), e. branchlet with a fruit, f. leaf, g. flowering branch, h. fruit (Source: Pathak, 2003).

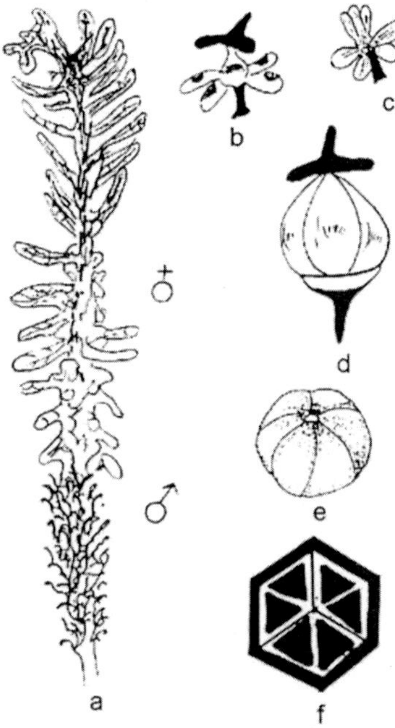

Fig.27.2. Determinate shoot of aonla showing male and female flowers (Source: Pathak,, 2003).

Cultivars

Banarasi: The plants have upright growth habit usually with three branchlets emerging from a node. It is shy bearing owing to less number of female flowers and self incompatibility. The fruits mature early. These are large in size, triangular and slightly conical at apex having green to straw yellow and smooth skin, distinct and raised 6 segments in three pairs that are easily separated. Keeping quality of fruits is poor. Sometimes the segments split on boiling while making preserve. The flesh is light whitish yellowish green, nearly fibreless and soft but stands transportation and is very rich in ascorbic acid.

Chakaiya: The tree has spreading growth habit and bears profusely. Female flowers are more than 4 per branchlet. It is a late maturing cultivar and is free from necrosis. The fruits are small to medium, flattened round and light greenish having six segments that are difficult to separate and smooth skin that gets russeted at maturity. The flesh is whitish green, hard, crisp and fibrous, ideally suitable for making pickle and other products. Keeping quality of the fruits is good.

Francis (Hathi Jhool): Tree is erect tall having drooping branches. The cultivar is mid season and medium cropper. The fruits are large, oblong (thick at upper side and thin at the basin) and greenish yellow having both ends flattened, easily separable six segments and smooth skin. The flesh is whitish green, soft, nearly fibreless and does not keep for very long. The cultivar is highly susceptible to necrosis which makes the fruits unsuitable for preserve making.

Kanchan: It was selected as a chance seedling of Chakaiya. The tree is tall and spreading. It is heavy and regular bearer. The fruits mature late and are free from necrosis. The fruits are small to medium, yellowish and oblong having smooth, light green and flattened skin surface. The fruit has six segments that are difficult to separate. The flesh is fibrous and hard having good keeping quality and is ideally suitable for pulp extraction and for manufacturing products such as pickle. It has 9.5°B TSS, 2.11% acidity and 422.70 mg/100g vitamin C.

Krishna: This is a chance seedling probably of Banarasi from Pratapgarh, Uttar Pradesh. Tree is semi tall with spreading growth habit. It is a shy bearer, having early fruit maturity (October - November) and no evidence of necrosis. The fruits are large, triangular and somewhat angular with flattened apices and papillate basin having whitish green to apricot yellow, smooth and shiny skin with red blush on sides exposed to sun and six easily separable segments. The flesh is pinkish green yellowish, less fibrous, highly astringent and hard having moderate keeping quality. It can stand transportation. The fruit has 11°B TSS, 2.32% acidity and 549 mg/100 g vitamin C. It is an ideal cultivar for making preserve, candy and juice.

Neelum (NA 7): It is a selection from open pollinated seedlings of Francis. The tree has tall and semi spreading growth habit. Number of female flowers per branchlet is 10. It is a precocious, prolific and regular bearer mid season cultivar. Fruits are medium to large, conical in shape, semi-translucent, yellowish green, having smooth skin and six easily separable segments. The flesh is almost fibreless and soft having moderate keeping quality. It contains 10.33°B TSS, 2.15% acidity and 527 mg/100 g vitamin C. The fruits are free from necrosis. This is an ideal cultivar for processing.

Agra Bold or Balwant: It is believed to be a chance seedling from cultivar Banarasi. The tree is semi-tall and has semi-spreading growth habit. The leaves are oblong with obtuse apex. It is a moderate bearer having 4.6 female flowers per branchlet. It is early maturing. The fruits are flattened round with roundish stylar end and medium in size having rough yellowish green skin. The flesh is slightly fibrous, whitish green, soft, juicy and highly astringent having good keeping quality. The fruits are moderately susceptible to necrosis. It has heavy bearing capacity and is suitable for dehydration and pickle making.

NA 6: It is a selection from open pollinated seedlings of Chakaiya. The tree is semi-spreading having brownish gray trunk. The leaf is large and comparatively wider, oval oblong with obtuse apex. The cultivar is prolific bearer having 10 female flowers per branchlet. The fruits are attractive and shining, small to medium and oval in shape and semi-translucent, smooth, and light green skin. The flesh is semi-hard. The seeds are small and light brown. The fruits have low fibre conent making them suitable for preserve and candy. Keeping quality of the fruits is good. Fruits are free from necrosis.

NA 9: It is selection from open pollinated seedlings of cultivar Banarasi. The tree is tall with semi-spreading growth habit. It is a shy bearer and early maturing cultivar. The fruit is large, flattened round and light green in colour having smooth skin, soft and moderately fibrous flesh with moderate keeping quality. It is susceptible to necrosis. The pulp contains 11.50°B TSS, 2.52% acidity and 499 mg/100 g vitamin C.

NA-20 : This is a clone of Chakaiya cultivar. Trees are spreading and medium to tall in height. The fruits are bold and shining with very low fibre content.

BSR 1: It is a selection from Thimbam Local and is high yielding cultivar producing 155 kg fruits per tree. The fruits borne in clusters are medium-sized (27 g) and fleshy having 6 segments, 610 mg/100 g ascorbic acid and 18.1°B TSS.

Goma Aishwarya: It is a clonal selection from NA 7. The fruit yield is higher than NA 7. It is an early bearing and drought tolerant cultivar. The fruit has low fibre content and is suitable for processing and export.

BSR-1: The fruits are pinkish and small (12–14 g) having about 650 mg vitamin C /100g pulp. A five year old tree yields about 40–45 kg fruits per tree. The cultivar is considered suitable for pharmaceutical use.

Otaheite gooseberry

(***Phyllanthus acidus*** (L.) Skeels syn. ***P. distichus*** Muell. Arg., ***Cicca acida*** Merr., ***C. disticha*** L.; malay gooseberry; star gooseberry)

Otaheite gooseberry is an ornamental shrub or small tree growing up to 2-9 m in height with a spreading crown., Clusters of deciduous, greenish or pinkish, 15-30 cm long blanchlets are borne at the branch tips. The thin leaves are alternate, short petioled, ovate lanceolate, 2.0-7.5 cm long and green and smooth on the upper surface and blue green with a bloom on the underside. It is monoecious. Male, female and some hermaphrodite 4-merous rosy flowers are borne together in little clusters arranged in 5.0-12.5 cm long panicles. The fruit is oblate with 6 to 8 ribs, 1.0-2.5 cm in width and pale yellow to nearly white in colour when fully ripe. The fruit is waxy, fleshy, crisp, juicy and highly acidic. A hard and ribbed stone containing 4-6 seeds is tightly embedded in the centre (Morton, 1987; Verheij and Coronel, 1991).

Genus *Baccaurea* Lour.

The genus comprises over 100 species distributed from Indo-Malesia to the West Pacific.

Baccaurea species

A large number of *Baccaurea* species occur in the region extending from India to the Pacific with the centre of diversity in western Malaysia. But only the following 5 species are primarily grown for fruit and are cultivated in southern Sumatra and in parts of western Java -

1. *Baccaurea dulcis* (Jack.) Muell. Arg. (ketupa): It is native to South East Asia and is widely cultivated throughout peninsular Malaysia, Sumatra, Borneo, Java, Bali, Thailand and Philippines. The trees grow 5-15 m tall with bole diameter up to 50 cm. The leaves are obovate to elliptic, 14-18 x 8-13 cm in size, coariaceous, glossy, glabrous having 1-5 cm long petioles and ovate stipules. The trees are dioecious. Inflorescences are ramiflorous. Male racemes are 6-11 cm long with yellowish fragrant flowers, 4 sepals and 6 stamens. Female racemes are 5-14 cm long with flowers having 4-5 sepals, 3 locular ovary and 3 stigmas. The fruits are 3.5-4 cm in diameter and occur in clusters.

2. *Baccaurea motleyana* Muell. Arg. (rambai): It is native to South East Asia and is widely cultivated throughout peninsular Malaysia, Sumatra, Borneo, Java, Bali, Thailand and Philippines. The trees are slow growing, 15-25 m tall with 40 cm bole diameter and low and round crown. Leaves are evergreen, obovate lanceolate to elliptic, 20-35 x 8-17 cm in size with 3-10 cm long petioles. The trees are dioecious. Inflorescences are ramiflorous. Male racemes are 13-20 cm long with yellow flowers borne in fascicles of 2-5, having 4-5 sepals and 4-8 stamens. Female racemes are 25-60 cm long with flowers often in clusters having 4-6 sepals. The fruits are 2-4 cm in diameter, thinly puberulous and buff-coloured. The pulp is translucent, white and sweet to acidic having 3 to 5 segments which separate readily. Each segment contains a brown, flat seed, about 1.25 cm long and adherent to the pulp (Morton, 1987).

3. *Baccaurea racemosa* (Reinw. ex Blume) Muell. Arg. syn. *B. wallichii* Hook. f. (kapundung): It is native of Malesia and is cultivated in Java, Sumatra, Bali and peninsular Malaysia. The trees are 15-25 m tall with 25-70 cm bole diameter and dense and irregular crown. Leaves are ovate oblong to obvate, 7-18 x 3-7 cm in size, glandular having 0.5-4.5 cm long petioles. Inflorescences are borne on old branches or even on the trunk. Male racemes are 5-13 cm long composed of numerous 3-flowered, densely hairy cymes. Flowers are very small having 4-5 sepals and 4-8 stamens. Female racmes are 10-20 cm long having solitary or fascicled, rather large flowers with 5 sepals and 3-4 locular ovary. Two forms are distinguished, one with white fruit flesh (menteng) and the other with red flesh (bencoy). Both sweet and sour types are found. The fruits are 2-2.4 cm in diameter.

4. *Baccaurea ramiflora* Lour. syn. *B. sapida* (Roxb.) Muell. Arg. (Burmese grape, mafai): It is native to South East Asian region and is cultivated in India, Thailand, Mynamar and Malaysia. The trees are up to 25 m tall. Leaves are ovate to ovate lanceolate in shape and 10-20 x 4-9 cm in size. Inflorescences are borne on branches and on the trunk, which are tomentose. Male racemes are 3-8 cm long bearing flowers in fascicles on very short rachis. The flower has 4-5 sepals and 4-8 stamens. Female racemes are 14 cm long borne lower on the trunk with solitary flowers having 4-5 sepals, 3-locular ovary and 2 lobed stigmas. The fruit is 2.5-3 cm in diameter, glabrous, yellowish or pinkish to bright red. Lot of variability occurs in Burmese grape with regard to fruit colour (Verheij and Coronel, 1991).

5. *Baccaurea griffithii* Hook. f. syn. *B. macrocarpa* Muell. Arg. (larah, taban, rambai utan): It is native to Malayan Peninsula (Martin *et al.*, 1987; Verheij and Coronel, 1991). The trees are medium (10-15 m) in height. The trees are dioecious. Flowers are similar to those of other species and are borne on the trunk. The fruit is spherical, 2.5-6 cm in diameter having brownish external and white internal colour and borne in clusters of 3-5 (Verheij and Coronel, 1991).

Genus *Antidesma* L.

It is a genus of tropical plantain (Linnaeus, 1753). It is native to tropical Africa, South East Asia, Australia and Oceanic islands with the greatest diversity in South East Asia. The plants may be short and shrubby or tall and erect, approaching 30 m in height. The leaves are large, oval shaped, leathery and evergreen, up to 20 cm long and 7 cm wide. The flowers have a strong, somewhat unpleasant smell. The staminate flowers are arranged in small bunches and the pistillate flowers grow on long racemes which become the long strands of fruit. The fruits are spherical and less than 1 cm wide, hanging singly or paired in long, heavy bunches. They are white when immature and gradually turn red and then black. These have sour and astringent taste when white, sour when red and sweet and sour when black.

Bignay
(***Antidesma bunius*** (L.) Spreng.; salamander)

Bignay is native of South East Asia. It is also known as Chinese laurel (Martin *et al*., 1987). It is widespread from India and Sri Lanka to northern Australia and has been introduced into tropics but is not common outside Asia. It is cultivated extensively in many parts of Indonesia, particularly in Java and also in Indochina (Verheij and Coronel, 1991). A related species *A. dallachyanum* Baill., known as Herbert river cherry or woolmi, a native of Australia, also produces edible fruits (Morton, 1987).

The tree is tall (15-30 m), much branched and dioecious with dense crown. The straight trunk has smooth, flaky, dark gray bark with numerous fine splits and is usually branched near the base. The leaves are distichous, large, 19-25 x 4-10 cm in size, short-petioled, oblong lanceolate, coriaceous, shiny and glabrous above, yellowish green and shiny beneath with short tufts of hair. The inflorescence is terminal or axillary spike. The spikes are pubescent, 6-20 cm long and bear unisexual apetalous flowers with small ovate or obovate, 0.7-1 cm long bracts. The male flowers are sessile, pale green, later tinge red, 1-1.2 x 1.5-2 mm in size and have 3-4 stamens. The female flowers are large and stalked with ovoid ovary, 3-4 stigmas and small disk. The fruit is globose or ovoid drupe, 8.5-10 mm in diameter, dark red to light yellow and appear in clusters of 20-50. The seed is 6-8 x 4.5-5.5 mm in size, ovoid or ovoid oblong, slightly oblique with short, thick, reticulated ribs (Morton, 1987; Verheij and Coronel, 1991).

Genus *Uapaca* Baill.

It is the only genus in the subtribe Uapacinae having about 60 species of which 49 are confined to continental Africa. The genus has a chromosome number of 2n=26 and devoid of polyploidy. The genus includes 61 species but the number of distinct species is probably less. The greatest diversity occurs in the Zaire basin and further south in the Miombo region.

Wild loquat
(***Uapaca kirkiana*** Müll Arg.; masuku; mahobohoba)

It is a native of South Africa. It is found growing in lowland forests and up to 1900 m altitude. It requires tropical semi-arid or arid climatic conditions receiving 500-1270 mm annual rainfall.

The plant is small to medium-sized evergreen or semi-deciduous tree with spreading multiple branches forming a dense rounded crown. The trunk is short and stout, attaining a height of 5-12 m and diameter of 5-25 cm. The bark is dark gray or gray brown, thick and deeply fissured. The young shoots are covered with creamy brown hairs. Leaves are simple and alternately arranged in clusters concentrated at the ends of branchlets of 7-36 x 4-24 cm with secondary nerves parallel and quite prominent beneath. The young leaves are covered with curly hairs on the undersurface. Flower buds are globose. Flowers are pale yellow borne in short slender acicular and axillary peduncles. Trees continue flowering for several months. It is dioecious. Either insects, specifically bees or wind are possible pollinating agents. The male flowers are borne in dense clusters and the female flowers are solitary. Fruit is round, yellow brown, up to 3.3 cm in diameter having tough skin, yellowish, edible and sweet tasting flesh with a pear-like flavour. Fruit contains 3-4 seeds. The seeds are white, up to 2 cm long and 1.3 cm thick. Flowering occurs during the peak rainy season. Fruit development commences in the rainy season and extends through the dry season into the next rainy season over a 5-8 month period.

The fruit is consumed fresh. The sugary pulp forms 40 to 60% of the fresh fruit. The skin accounts for approximately 38% of the total fruit weight. The fruit is processed to produce a refreshing beverage, beer, wine, juice and jam in Malawi, Zambia and Zimbabwe. The fruit is low in fat and high in potassium.

Family Malpighiaceae

It contains about 75 genera and 1300 species (Heywood *et al.*, 2007). It is found in the tropics of the Old and New world but is mainly concentrated in tropical America with centre of diversity in Brazil.

The plants are trees, shrubs, subshrubs, herbs or climbers, often with unicellular and 2-branched "Malpighian hairs," rarely stellate. The leaves are simple, usually opposite, sometimes whorled, rarely alternate, entire, stipulate and often with glands. The flowers are in axillary or terminal racemose or paniculate inflorescences or are solitary. The flowers are usually bisexual, sometimes unisexual (plants dioecious or functionally dioecious), actinomorphic to obliquely zygomorphic. The sepals are 5, united, usually imbricate, rarely valvate with 2 (rarely 1) abaxial glands in neotropical species (much reduced or absent in Old World species). The petals are 5, usually imbricate, clawed at the base. The stamens are 10, sometimes fewer, in a single whorl. The filaments are distinct or connate at the base and the anthers are 2-locular dehiscing longitudinally. The ovary is superior, of (2)3(4) separate to united carpels, with axile placentation and one pendulous anatropous ovule per locule. The fruits are diverse, dry, usually schizocarpic splitting into 2-3 mericarps, which are often winged or fleshy drupe or berry. The seeds are without endosperm.

Genus *Malpighia* L.

It contains about 45 species of shrubs or small trees, all of which are native to the American tropics. The generic name is to honour a 17th century Italian physician and botanist, Marcello Malpighi. It grows tall with a dense and often thorny crown.

Barbados cherry

(***Malpighia emarginata*** DC. syn. ***M. glabra*** L., ***M. punicifolia*** L.,; acerola; West Indian cherry; Jamaican cherry; Puerto Rican cherry; Cereza; or French cherry) (2n= 20)

Barbados cherry is native to West Indies and South America (Martin *et al.*, 1987). Acerola is a dense, spreading, glabrous shrub or small tree growing up to 6-8 m in height. Leaves are simple, opposite, ovate, almost sessile, entire and 8.5 x 5 cm in size. Flowers are bisexual, zygomorphic, 1-2 cm in diameter, pinkish to reddish and regular, borne in groups of 2-4 in umbel like racemes. Calyx with 8-10 large sessile glands, 5, rosy red petals and stamens are united below. Fruit is 3-pyrenous drupe, red or scarlet in colour, depressed ovoid, slightly 3-lobed, small, 1-3 cm in diameter and acidic with thin skin. The fruits are very rich in vitamin C (10-32 g/kg^{-1} of pulp). Seeds are 3, subcordate, often somewhat 3-lobed, large, 1 cm long, angular, rugose and crested on outer surface (Page, 1984; IBPGR, 1986b; Morton, 1987; Verheij and Coronel, 1991).

Cultivars

Barbados cherry genotypes can be classified into two groups, sweet and acid. Sweet types have 10-20 kg fruit yield and the acid types yield up to 29 kg per plant. The sweet type cultivars are Manoa Sweet, Tropical Ruby and Hawaiian Queen whereas the acid types are Maunawili, J. H. Beaumont, C. F. Rehnborg, F. Haley and Red Jumbo (Nakasone *et al.,* 1968).

The important cultivars selected in Puerto Rico are B-17 (tart), A-14, A-21, B-6, B-7, B-8 and B-15 (high in vitamin C). Florida Sweet (K-7) is a selection made at Homestead, Florida and Selection Maunawili and Selection No. 4 have been made in Hawaii (Page, 1984; Morton, 1987).

Genus *Byrsonima* H.B.K

It is one of about 75 genera in the Malpighiaceae family and contains the locust berries (specifically Long Key locust berry, *B. lucida*). Another widely used common name is serrets or serrettes.

Nance

(***Byrsonima crassifolia*** (L.) Kunth. H.B.K. syn. ***B. cubense*** Juss., ***Malpighia crassifolia*** L.; golden spoon; manero; manteco; murci)

Nance is one of the popular Amazonian fruits. It is native of Mexico, Central and South America and West Indies (Martin *et al.,* 1987) and is found wild from southern Mexico through Pacific side of Central America to Peru and Brazil and also in Trinidad, Barbados, Curacao, St. Martin, Dominica, Guadeloupe, Puerto Rico, Haiti and the Dominican Republic and throughout Cuba and the Isles of Pines.

The nance is a slow growing large, evergreen shrub or tree of 10 m height varying in canopy form from round topped and spreading to narrow and compact. The trunk is short or tall and crooked or straight. Young branches are densely coated with russet hair. Leaves are opposite, ovate to elliptic or oblong elliptic, 3.2-17 x 4-7 cm in size, rounded or pointed at the apex, blunt or pointed at the base, leathery, usually glossy on the upper surface and more or less brown or gray hairy on the underside. The flowers are borne in thinly or conspicuously red hairy and erect racemes, which are 10-20 cm long and 1.2-2.0 cm wide. The petals are 5, yellow at first and then change to dull orange red. Fruit is aromatic, orange yellow, round, 8-12 cm wide with thin skin and white, juicy and oily pulp varying in flavour from insipid to sweet, acid or cheese like. Seeds are 1-3, white with fairly large stone (FAO, 1986; Morton, 1987; Brücher, 1989).

Family Chrysobalanaceae (Cocoa plum family)

The Chrysobalanaceae is a pantropical family of trees and shrubs some of which are important as fruit trees. It contains 18 genera and 520 species (Heywood *et al.*, 2007). The leaves are simple, alternate and entire, with stipules that are often caducous. Plants are monoecious The flowers are bisexual, rarely unisexual or polygamous, actinomorphic or zygomorphic, always with disk and markedly perigynous, on racemose, paniculate, spicate or cymose inflorescences. There are 5 sepals and usually 5 petals. The stamens are 2-100 (300 in *Couepia*) filiform filaments, free or connate at the base and the anthers dehiscing introrsely. The ovary is superior with 3 carpels, but usually only 1 developing, gynobasic, 1-locular with 2 erect basal ovules or 2-locular with one ovule per locule. The style is simple with a 3-lobed stigma. The fruit is a fleshy drupe, rarely dry with a hard, fibrous or thin and bony endocarp (stone). The seeds are without endosperm.

Genus *Chrysobalanus* L.

It is a genus of evergreen perennial shrubs to small trees, attaining a maximum height of 75-90 cm, native to subtropical and tropical climate. The plant is found wild in coastal areas throughout the tropical Americas and is frequently planted in gardens. It can form dense stands and become invasive owing to its low growing and sprawling habit.

Cocoplum
(***Chrysobalanus icaco*** L.; icaco)

The coco plum is a native of Central and South America and West Indies (Martin *et al.*, 1987). It is a small tree or shrub and grows up to 5-8 m tall and has numerous spines. The leaves are dark green, thick, leathery, alternate, 2.5-7.5 x 2.5-5 cm in size and elliptic or round turning upwards. The flowers are small, greenish white, borne in several clusters at leaf base. The fruit is elliptic or round, 2.5 cm long, pink, whitish or dark purplish drupe. It is longitudinally ridged with thin, fleshy and spongy and creamy white mesocarp with one large seed that is 5-6 ridged containing the edible white kernel. Its botanical variety, *C. icaco* var. *pellocarpus* L. produces oval, 2.5 cm long fruits having dark purple, soft, spongy and white flesh.

Genus *Licania* Aubl.

The plants are mainly shrubs and small trees. *L. caldasiana* appears to have gone extinct as a result of deforestation.

Sansapote
(***Licania platypus*** (Hemsl.) Fritsch syn. ***Moquilea platypus*** Hemsl.; sanzapote; zapote cabillo)

Sansapote is native of Central and South America (Martin *et al.*, 1987). It grows wild in dense forests from southern Mexico to Panama and in northern Colombia. It is planted as an ornamental and shade tree throughout central America. It is also grown in South America and the Philippines.

It is a handsome, erect tree reaching 30-50 m in height and has a rounded crown. Leaves are alternate, occasionally spiralled, elliptic to narrow lanceolate, pointed at both ends, 10-30 x 3-9 cm in size with thick midrib indented above and prominent beneath. New foliage is bronze or red purple and very showy. The fragrant flowers are borne terminally. Flowers are densely hairy with recurved petals and numerous protruding stamens. Only 1-3 fruits develop from each panicle. The fruit is obovoid or pyriform, 13-20 x 10-14 cm in size having a thin dark brown or reddish and warty rind covered with white lenticels. The average weight of fruit is 900 g. The flesh is somewhat pumpkin scented, yellow or orange yellow, soft, fibrous, dry or juicy and of subacid or sweet flavour. Usually, there is a single rounded or ovate oblong, flattened and 6-10 cm long seed (Morton, 1987).

Genus *Parinari* Aubl.

Parinari species are found in sub-Saharan Africa from Senegal to Sudan and Kenya and south to Namibia and Natal, in eastern Madagascar, from Indochina through Indonesia, New Guinea, northern Queensland and the southwest Pacific and in Central and South America from Costa Rica to Trinidad and southern Brazil.

Hissing tree
(***Parinari curatellifolia*** Planch. Ex Benth.; mupunda; parinaire)

Hissing tree is native of tropical Africa. It is found in the area from Senegal to Sudan, Zaire to Uganda and southwards through central and eastern Africa.

Genus *Couepia* Aubl.

These are tropical rainforest trees found in the amazon. The oil-rich nuts are used as food in rural South America, especially in Brazil. The nuts are useful for their oil.

Couepia
(***Couepia longipendula*** Pilg.; pendula nut)

Couepia is native of Brazil. It is found near the rivers Manaus, Negro and Purus spreading up to the city of Oriximina in the State of Para. It occurs throughout central and western Amazonia and western Guiana Shield. The related species that produce edible nuts are *C. edulis* Prance and *C. bracteosa* Benth. It is locally known as pendula nut, castanha de galinha or castanha pendula (FAO, 1986; Wickens, 1995).

Couepia is a large tree growing up to 30 m or more in height with a straight trunk up to 1.8 m in diameter. The leaves are alternate, simple, oblong elliptic to lanceolate, glabrous, dark green, lightly-veined, 16-16 x 3-7.5 cm in size with entire margin. Flowers are borne in groups of 10-20 and appear in pendulous panicles with slender, 30-60 cm long peduncles. The flowers are bisexual, white and asymmetrical. The receptacle is tubular obconical and 10-15 mm long and the 5 calyx lobes are rounded with 2 sessile exterior glands. The lobes obscure the 5 small white petals soon after falling. Stamens are more than 30, pinkish purple and 1-2 cm long. Fruit is obovoid to ellipsoid drupe, 5 cm long, 4 cm in diameter, 28 g in weight and shaped like a hen's egg, pubescent with up to 1 mm long brown hairs and the epicarp peels to reveal a hard, woody and fibrous, 6 mm thick pericarp. The seed contains a white to light green kernel that is 3 x 2 cm in size, 4-7 g in weight having a thin pubescent testa surrounded by a thin membrane (FAO, 1986; Clay and Clement, 1993).

Family Passifloraceae

It contains about 16 genera and 700 species. Many climbers of this family are famous for their extraordinary flowers and edible fruit. The plants are trees or shrubs (*Androsiphonia*, *Barteria, Paropsia, Viridivia*, some *Adenia*), woody or herbaceous climbers usually with tendrils (*Passiflora*, some *Adenia*), annual or perennial herbs (*Basananthe*), sometimes with a swollen tuber or large swollen trunk (some *Adenia*), sometimes spiny with alternate leaves. The poisonous leaves of *Passiflora* are well known as a food for *Heliconius* butterflies. Tendrils derived from the modified axillary inflorescences are present in climbing species. Tendrils are axillary, simple and unbranched. The leaves are simple or lobed, rarely compound, strongly 2-lobed in some *Passiflora*, petiolate and with small to large and foliose stipules. Extrafloral nectaries are often present on the petiole or stem. The inflorescence is usually axillary, rarely terminal or cauliflorous, one to many flowered cyme, rarely a raceme or fascicle. The flowers are actinomorphic, hermaphrodite varying in size and shape. The sepals are (3-(5(-8), petals equaling the sepals or rarely absent. A distinct five extrastaminal ring of filaments, the corona, usually forms a bright and showy structure between the petals and stamens borne on the apex and inner surface of the hypanthium. The stamens are (4)5 or 8(-10), on the hypanthium or androgynophore (*Passiflora*). The ovary is superior and of 2 carpels with parietal placentation, often borne on a gynophore, usually forming a many seeded berry. The aril is fleshy.

Genus *Passiflora* L.

About 500 species occur in the Americas and more than 24 in India and South China to Australia and Samoa (Kubitzki *et al*., 2007). The important edible species are *P. edulis* Sims., *P. mollissima* Bailey syn. *P. tomentosa* var. *mollissima* Tr. and Planch. (banana passionfruit, tacso, curuba, poka, parcha, curuba de castilla), *P. antioquiensis* Karst. (banana passionfruit), *P. laurifolia* L. (water lemon, yellow granadilla or bell apple), *P. ligularis* Juss. (sweet granadilla, curuba), *P. maliformis* L. (sweet calabash, curuba), *P. serratodigitata* L. (tagua, tagua-tagua), *P. quandra-ngularis* (giant granadilla), *P. incarnata* (Maypop) and *P. caerulea* L. (blue passionfruit).

The plants are herbaceous or woody vines with tendrils, rarely erect herbs, small trees or shrubs. Leaves are alternate, (sub-opposite in one Asian species) having often glanduliferous petiole, simple lobed or 7 unlobed lamina, pinnate, palmate, rarely pedate venation and minute to large foliaceous stipules. Flowers are axillary, solitary or in pairs, rarely in a cymose inflorescence, usually perfect, large and showy having minute to large bracts, patelliform, campanulate, funnelform or cylindric floral cup. Five sepals are often dorsally awned near the apex. Petals are 5, sometimes absent. Corona is in one to several series of filaments or tubercles, rarely tubular. Operculum (innermost coronal row) is membranous, flat or plicate, entire, lacerate or filamentous, rarely absent. Nectar ring is usually annular, sometimes lacking, limen is borne close to the base of the androgynophore, annular, cupuliform or cylindric, sometimes absent, 5(-8). The stamens are inserted on androgynophore below the ovary, rarely androgynophore is absent. Gynophore is very short. Stylodia are 3(4, 5), usually free. There are 3 parietal placentae and numerous ovules. Fruit is indehiscent or rarely irregularly dehiscent, globose, ovoid or fusiform and many seeded baccate berry. The juice is contributed by the arils.

The areas of origin and use of selected *Passiflora* species (Martin and Nakasone, 1970)

Passiflora alata Dryand: Originated in Brazil, Peru. It is used for fruit and as an ornamental plant.

P. antioquiensis Karst (banana passionfruit): Originated in Colombia. It is used as ornamental plant.

P. banksii Benth: Originated in Australia. It is used as an ornamental plant.

P. caerulea L. (blue passionflower): Originated in Brazil to Argentina. It is used for fruit and as an ornamental plant.

P. coccinea Aubl. (red granadilla flower): Originated in Venezuela to Bolivia.

P. edulis Sims. (purple granadilla): Originated in Brazil. It is used for fruit.

P. incarnata L. (wild passionflower, maypop, apricot vine): Originated in southern USA. It is used for fruit and as an ornamental plant.

P. laurifolia L. (yellow granadilla, water lemon, Jamaica honeysuckle): Originated in West Indies to Brazil and Peru. It is used for fruit and as an ornamental plant.

P. ligularis Juss. (sweet granadilla): Originated in Mexico to Bolivia. It is used for fruit.

P. maliformis L. (sweet calabash, sweet cup, conuch apple): Originated in West Indies to South America. It is used for fruit.

P. mollissima (HBK) Bailey (banana passionfruit, curuba): Originated in Venezuela to Bolivia. It is used for fruit.

P. quadrangularis (giant granadilla): Origin is not known. It is used for fruit.

P. vitifolia HBK: Originated in Nicaragua to Venezuela and Peru. It is used for fruit and as an ornamental plant.

Passionfruit
(***Passiflora edulis*** Sims.) (4n= 4x= 36)

It is indigenous to southern Brazil (Morton, 1987). There are two distinct forms, forma *edulis* (purple passionfruit), which occurs in cool environment at higher altitudes and forma *flavicarpa* (yellow passionfruit), which is found in the tropical lowlands. The comparative growth and fruit characters of the two forms (Knight, 1980) are given Table 27.1.

Table 27.1. Growth and fruit characteristics of *P. edulis* f. *edulis* and *P. edulis* f. *flavicarpa.*

***P. edulis* f. *edulis* Sims. (purple passionfruit) 2n=18**	***P. edulis* f. *flavicarpa* Deg. (yellow passionfruit) 2n=18**
Found on cooler high altitudes	Found on lower altitudes
Less vigorous vines	Vigorous vines
Small leaf	Large leaf
Flowers are small, fragrant, less protandry, anthesis in forenoon	Flowers are large, strong fragrance, strong protandry, anthesis in afternoon
Fruits are purple, small	Fruits are yellow, large
Mild acidic juice	Acidic juice
Ovules and pollen grains fully viable	Ovules and pollen grains fully viable
Normal meiosis	Normal meiosis
Self compatible	Self incompatible

Purple passionfruit
(*Passiflora edulis* f. *edulis* Sims.)

It is an important fruit in Australia. In India, it is found in Mysore and Nilgiri hills. It is a vigorous climber with a life span of 3-10 years forming thick woody stems supported by many spirally coiled and long axillary tendrils. The somewhat leathery and glabrous leaves are palmate and deeply three lobed, 10-20 cm wide with 5 cm long petioles. Large, solitary and showy flowers of 7.5-10 cm diameter are borne in the leaf axils on 5 cm long peduncles, which carry three, 1-2 cm long and ovate bracts. Calyx is tubular with 5 large sepals, which are 2-3 cm long and 1-2 cm wide. Five petals are white and elliptic. Corona is formed by two rows of wavy, sterile and thin filaments of different colours. These have several rows of purple tipped papillae at their bases, which enclose the androgynophore. Five fertile stamens enclose a gynophore with a superior ovary. There are 3 large horizontal styles. Nectar is secreted at the base of the androgynophore, which is self incompatible. Some protandry has been observed.

Honey bees, carpenter bees and humming birds carry out pollination. The vines are tender and require warm dry conditions for pollination. It is a subtropical species. The fruit is borne on new shoots. The fruit is a globose berry which is 5-9 cm long and deep purple or bright yellow. The pericarp is thin (5 mm) with greenish yellow mesocarp. The seeds are attached with short funiculi at the ovary wall surrounded by thin walled glabrous arils containing aromatic juice. Purple passionfruit has deep purple fruit, 4-5 cm in diameter, green tendrils and leaves (FAO, 1982; IBPGR, 1986b; Brücher, 1989).

Cultivars

There are a number of selections made in Brazil including Muico, Peroba and Pintado. The hybrids that have been developed are: Tainung No. 1 in Taiwan

(Nakasone and Paull, 1998), Australian Purple or Ned Kelly, Bali Hai, Black Purple, Common Purple, Crackerjack, Perfecta, Purple Gold, Lacey E-23 and M 2171 A in Hawaii, Florida and Australia and Kaveri in Bangalore (India).

Kaveri: It is a hybrid between purple and yellow passionfruit. The fruits are large (80-90 g), ovoid to round and purple dotted with 20-25% juice content. The juice is sweet with 11.5-12.0% total sugar and 3.0 3.5% citric acid. The cultivar is high yielding (16-20 kg per vine per year) and is tolerant to *Alternaria* leaf spot, *Fusarium* collar rot and nematodes.

Yellow passionfruit
(*Passiflora edulis* f. *flavicarpa* Deg.)

The yellow fruited form, f. *flavicarpa* is a chance mutant, inferior in flavour but resistant to *Fusarium* wilt and woodiness virus (Martin and Nakasone, 1970). It is a more tropical species and grows in the plains. The fruit has better flavour. It starts to bear fruits within a year after planting. Pollination is carried out by insects but hand pollination may be required in some areas. Protandry has been observed. The fruits are cenary yellow and 6-12 x 4-7 cm in size having reddish purple tinged tendrils, larger leaves and more showy flowers with deep purple coronas.

The important cultivars of yellow passion fruit are Brazilian Golden, Golden Giant, Waimanalo, Noel's Special (tolerant to *Alternaria* brown spot), Sevick Selection, Yee Selection, University Selection (B-74) (Hawaii) and Mirirn or Hawaiina (South America). There are a number of selections made in Brazil including Yellow Miram and Grande. In Colombia and Venezuela, Hawaiina is grown along with some Brazilian selections.

Purple: It is a prolific and heavy bearer with larger fruits. It is grown at higher elevations.

Yellow: It is tolerant to wilt, brown leaf spot, thrips and nematodes.

Giant granadilla
(*Passiflora quadrangularis* L.)

It is a native of South America. Wild population of giant granadilla occurs in Nicaragua and Colombia. It is distributed in the neotropics and has been introduced in other continents and is cultivated in West Indies, South and Central America, Hawaii, South East Asia and Australia (Page, 1984; Morton, 1987; Verheij and Coronel, 1991).

The plants are perennial and vigorous climbers with enlarged fleshy tuberous roots having a life of 5 to 10 years. The winged, sharp and quadrangular stem with large, ovate leaves distinguish it from the other *Passiflora* species. The leaves are alternate, large, 20-25 cm long and oval with typical pale green colour. The solitary pentamerous flowers are large, 10-12 cm in diameter with the characteristic structure of coloured fleshy 5 sepals and red and white 5 petals covered by the corona. Stamens are 5 with large anthers and 1-locular ovary on gynophores having many ovules, 3-5 styles and large stigmas. Its fruits are the largest among the *Passiflora* species, 15-30 x 10-15 cm in size weighing 2.8 kg and having four ridges, yellow green and soft with thin pericarp over a fleshy insipid mesocarp. The cavity of the fruit is filled with seeds surrounded by yellowish juicy arils. Seeds are flat, obovoid, 1 cm long and dark brown (Morton, 1987; Brücher, 1989; Verheij and Coronel, 1991). Several types/forms are found in nature. In Trinidad, some hybrids with other *Passiflora* species having better fruit taste have been produced.

Sweet calabash
(*Passiflora maliformis* L.; water lemon; ceioby cimarron)

It is a native of West Indies and South America and is found wild in Cuba, Puerto Rico, the Dominican Republic, Jamaica, Venezuela, Colombia and northern Ecuador. It is cultivated in Jamaica, Brazil and Ecuador (Morton, 1987).

Sweet calabash is an evergreen woody vine climbing up to 10 m or more on trees, walls and small buildings by means of tendrils arising from leaf axils. The leaves are ovate cordate or ovate oblong, fairly thin, light green, 6-15 cm long with a short recurved point at the apex and two round and flat glands at about the middle of the petiole. The peduncle bears 3 thin, ovate, pointed, 5 cm long bracts that enclose the unopened bud and form an ivory-hued background for the opened flower. The flower is fragrant, 5-6 cm wide with keeled, green, maroon dotted sepals and 5 small, greenish white petals dotted with red or purple. The corona is 3-ranked and variegated white, purple and blue. The fruit is oblate to nearly round oval or apple shaped. It is 4.5-5 cm long and 3.5-4 cm wide. The thin rind is yellow to brownish when the fruit is fully ripe and may be rather flexible and leathery to hard and brittle. The pulp is grayish or pale orange yellow, juicy, sweet or subacid and pleasingly aromatic containing many black, flat, ovate and pitted seeds (Morton, 1987).

Banana passionfruit
(*Passiflora mollissima* [Kunth] Bailey)

It is native of Andean valleys from Venezuela and eastern Colombia to Bolivia and Peru. It is believed to have been domesticated shortly before the Spanish Conquest. It is cultivated for its highly flavoured fruits. In USA, it is grown in California as ornamental plant and is known as soft leaf passion flower. It is grown to some extent in Hawaii, New Zealand, Ecuador and Colombia.

The vine is a vigorous climber growing up to 6-7 m in height with its nearly cylindrical stems densely coated with yellow hair. Leaves are deeply 3-lobed, 7-10 x 6-12 cm in size and finely toothed and downy above and grayish or yellowish velvety beneath. The stipules are short, slender and curved. The attractive blossom has a 7.6-10 cm long, gray green tube frequently blushed with red and is rarely downy. The tube has 5 sepals and deep pink petals flaring to a width of 5-7.5 cm and a rippled, tuberculated and purple corona. The fruit is oblong or oblong ovoid berry, 5-12 x 3.2-4 cm in size. The rind is thick, leathery, whitish yellow or dark green and minutely downy. Pulp (aril) is aromatic, salmon coloured, subacid to acid, rich in flavour and surrounds the small, black, flat, elliptic and reticulated seeds (Morton, 1987; Brücher, 1989; Verheij and Coronel, 1991).

The fruit size of the cultivars is smaller in Peru than in Colombia and Ecuador. A form called Curuba Quitena in Colombia is dark green externally even when fully ripe and its apex is abruptly pointed and furrowed. The pulp is dark orange or orange brown.

Maypop

(*Passiflora incarnata* L.; apricot vine; yellow-fruited Virginian passion flower)

It is native of southeastern North America where it is found growing wild (McGuire, 1999). Maypop is a perennial and herbaceous vine. The individual shoots are indeterminate and grow up to 10 m in length and are sometimes profusely branched. Leaves are alternate and subtended by two inconspicuous deciduous stipules. The petioles are up to 8 cm long and bear two sessile nectaries near the base of laminae. Leaves are moderately to deeply three lobed and 6-15 cm long. Flowers are borne singly on peduncles up to 10 cm long. Three bracts each bearing two nectaries enclose the base of the floral bud and the region of articulation is immediately distal to the bracts on the peduncle. Flowers are up to 9 cm wide and have the complex floral structure typical of *Passiflora*. The sepals and petals are white to pale lavender in colour. The prominent corona consists of five or six series of filaments of which the outer two are 10-20 mm long, white, pink, lavender and/or purple in colour and variously banded. The remaining series of corona filaments are much shorter, 2-4 mm long. The five stamens, ovary and three styles are elevated on a columnar gynophore. Flower shape and colour vary markedly even within a vine. The fruits are unilocular berries, ovoid or subglobose, up to 7 cm long and sometimes have three or six longitudinal sutures. Within the thin rind are three longitudinal parietal placentae and the fruit interior contains up to 120 seeds that are dark brown at maturity, 4-5 mm long and 3-4 mm wide and individually enclosed in arils. The arils of variable size contain the edible, aromatic and creepy yellow juice.

Cultivars

Cultivars such as Incense, Ruby Glow, Elizabeth, Lady Margaret, Red Inca and Medallion have been developed through interspecific hybridization. Selections can be made from the existing variability with regard to growth form, number of flowers per vine, days from flowering to fruit abscission, fruit shape and size and aril size. Interspecific hybridization with *P. incarnata* could yield desirable hybrids (McGuire, 1999).

Water lemon

(*Passiflora laurifolia* L. syn. *P. tinifolia* Juss.; yellow fruited passionfruit; yellow granadilla; vinegar pear; Jamaican honey suckle; belle pear; bell apple; sweet cup)

It is native of West Indies and South America (Martin *et al*., 1987. Originally wild in the West Indies, Venezuela and eastern Brazil, it is also found wild in Tonga, Fiji, New Guinea, Malaysia and East Africa (Morton, 1987; Brücher, 1989).

Water lemon is a tall climber and grows up to 10-15 m in height in tropical forests. Stem is terete having entire, ovate oblong or oblong, thick and 7.5 – 12 cm long leaves with acute or obtuse apex. The stipules are linear and about 0.3 cm long. The fragrant, solitary and 5-petaled flowers are 7.4-10 cm across when expanded, have bell shaped calyx, oblong, red or purple red sepals and petals. Corona filaments are 6 ranked, banded with red, blue, purple and white. The fruit is ellipsoid or ovoid,

5-8 cm long, 4-6 cm wide, orange yellow, clasped at the base by 3 large green, leaf-like bracts, toothed and edged with conspicuous glands. The rind is leathery, 3 mm thick, white and spongy within and becomes hard when dry. Pleasant rose-scented, translucent and white pulp is juicy and subacid in taste. Seeds are numerous, flat and minutely ribbed (Morton, 1987; Brücher, 1989). There is no standard cultivar of water lemon.

Sweet granadilla
(*Passiflora ligularis* Juss.)

It is native of Central and South America. The species is considered to be the finest of all passionfruits. It is found wild from central Mexico to Venezuela and from Peru to Bolivia at altitudes between 1000 and 3000 m. It has been introduced into many parts of the world and grows wild particularly in East Africa. It is widely cultivated throughout Central America, Hawaii, Africa and Australia (Martin *et al.*, 1987; Morton, 1987).

It is a vigorous and large climber and can grow up to 5 m high. Leaves are broadly heart shaped, pointed at the apex, 8-20 x 6-15 cm in size, conspicuously veined, medium green on the upper surface and pale green with a bloom on the underside. Glands spaced along the petiole are 4-6 in pairs or scattered, liguliform or filiform and 3-10 mm long. In the leaf axils, there are paired, leaf-like, ovate oblong 72.5 cm long and 1.25 cm wide stipules which are more or less finely toothed. Flowers are large, 4 cm wide and showy, white pink with sweet and musky odour, usually 2 to a node. The peduncle bears 3 leaf-like ovate oblong, faintly-toothed and pointed bracts that are 4 x 2.5 cm in size. The sepals are greenish white and lanceolate. The petals are pinkish white. The filaments in 2 rows are white and horizontally striped purple blue. Fruit is broad elliptic, 6-7.5 cm long and green developing purple blush on the sunny side. These are minutely dotted when unripe and become orange yellow with white specks when ripe. The rind is smooth, thin, hard and brittle externally and white and soft inside. The pulp (aril) is whitish yellow or more or less orange, mucilaginous, very juicy with sprightly aromatic flavour and encloses numerous black, flat, pitted, crisp but fairly tender seeds (Morton, 1987; Brücher, 1989).

Family Salicaceae (syn. Flacourtiaceae)

The plants are trees or shrubs, often with phenolic heterosides (salicin, populin) but usually lack cyanogenic glycosides, usually with tannins. Hairs are various. Leaves are deciduous, alternate, spiral or 2-ranked, simple, usually serrate to dentate. The teeth are salicoid (vein expanding at the tooth apex and associated with spherical glandular setae). Venation is pinnate to palmate, occasionally with pellucid dots or lines. Stipules are usually present. Inflorescences are determinate to indeterminate, sometimes in erect to pendent catkins, sometimes reduced to a solitary flower, terminal or axillary. Flowers are bisexual or unisexual (plants dioecious), radial, often reduced, subtended by a usually hairy bract. Sepals are usually 3-8, distinct to slightly connate, sometimes ±vestigial, forming a disk-shaped to cup-shaped structure. Petals are 3-8, distinct or lacking. Stamens are 2 to numerous having distinct to connate filaments, tricolpate, tricolporate pollen grains, or lacking apertures. Carpels are usually 2-4, connate. Ovary is superior to half inferior with parietal placentation, the placentae sometimes deeply intruded and then ovary appearing axile with usually 2-4, ±capitate to expanded and irregularly lobed stigmas. Ovules are one to numerous on each placenta, sometimes with only 1 integument. Nectar is a disk or of separate glands, sometimes lacking. Fruit is a loculicidal capsule, berry or drupe. Seeds are often arillate or with basal tuft of hairs. Endosperm is scanty or lacking (Heywood *et al.,* 2007).

Genus *Dovyalis* E. Mey ex. Arn.

It is a genus of shrubs and small trees. The 15 species are native to Africa (Ethiopia to South Africa) and southern Asia (India, Sri Lanka).

African dove plum
(***Dovyalis abyssinica*** (A. Rich.) Warb.;
Abyssinian gooseberry; African gooseberry; koshum)

It is native of Ethiopia and Kenya where it is most common in the forests. It is an evergreen dioecious, thorny shrub or tree, which grows up to 10 m in height. It is not spiny as the kei apple. Leaves are alternate, medium green, ovate, 5-7.5 cm in length, light green, glossy and wavy. Flowers are unisexual, greenish yellow, small and are borne axillary. Flowers have somewhat fleshy petals. Male flowers are covered with short soft hair and have dirty white stamens clustered in leaf axils. The female flowers are borne solitary. The fruit is ovoid, 2.5 cm in diameter, apricot or light orange in colour when ripe with yellow pulp and contains several small seeds (Martin *et al,* 1987; Morton, 1987; FAO, 1988). The other related species that produces edible fruits is *D. hebecarpa* Warb. (Ceylon gooseberry or kitembilla) besides the hybrid, *D. abyssinica* x *D. hebecarpa* (hybrid dovyalis, Florida gooseberry or tropical apricot).

Kei apple
(***Dovyalis caffra*** (Hook. f. et Harv.) Warb.; wild apricot; umkokola)

It is indigenous to southwestern Africa. It is an evergreen vigorous, large, dense and spiny shrub reaching 6 m in height. The axillary thorns are long, stiff and sharp. The leaves are oblong ovate, about 5 cm long, obtuse, entire and dark green and are often clustered around the thorn. It is a dioecious plant. The flowers are unisexual, greenish yellow and inconspicuous and are borne in the axils of the leaves. Female flowers are 3 mm long, light green, solitary or in groups of 1-3 on short stalks. Male flowers are borne in dense clusters. The fruits are oblate or nearly round, about 2.5 cm in diameter, solitary and bright golden yellow. The juicy, aromatic and acidic pulp surrounds 5-15 small, brown and flattened seeds (Morton, 1987; FAO, 1988).

Kitembilla
(***Dovyalis hebecarpa*** (Gardner) Warb.; kitembilla; Ceylon gooseberry)

The kitembilla is indigenous to Sri Lanka (Martin *et al.*, 1987). The related species, *D. abyssinica* (A. Rich.) Warb. (African gooseberry), is a native of Ethiopia and has better quality fruits than both kei apple and kitembilla. It has been widely introduced into the tropics but is not common outside its native home (Morton, 1987; Martin *et al*., 1987).

Kitembilla is an evergreen and arborescent shrub reaching a height of 4-6 m. It has long, slender, arching, spreading and spiny branches. The leaves are alternate, lanceolate to oval, 5-10 cm long, acute, entire or slightly toothed, light green and velvety when young. The trees are dioecious. The flowers are unisexual or sometimes perfect, axillary and inconspicuous. Flowers are greenish yellow and 1.25 cm wide. The fruits are nearly round, subglobose berry, 2.5 cm or less in diameter, solitary, maroon purple in colour and are covered with a velvety pubescence. The flesh is soft, purplish, subacid to acidic, juicy and having several small, soft and flattened seeds (Morton, 1987; Verheij and Coronel, 1991).

Genus *Flacourtia* Comm. ex L'Hér

The generic name is to honour Étienne de Flacourt (1607–1660), who was a governor of Madagascar. It contains 15 species of shrubs and small trees that are native to the African and Asian tropics and subtropics. Several species, especially *F. indica*, are cultivated as ornamentals and for their fruits. The trunks of small trees are often guarded by branching spines.

Governor's plum

(***Flacourtia indica*** Merr. syn. ***F. ramontchi*** L.'Her., ***F. sepiaria*** Roxb.; ramontchi; Madagascar plum; Mauritius plum; Indian plum; baichi)

It is a native of tropical Asia and Madagascar (Martin *et al*., 1987). It is a small, sprawling, shrubby, deciduous tree of 5-15 m height having a crooked, gnarly furrowed and low branched trunk. The young shoots are thin, finely pubescent and spiny. Later, these become nearly spineless. The cultivated forms are nearly or entirely spineless. The dark green leaves are 6-16 x 3-75 cm in size, alternate, oblong, ovate or elliptic having acuminate or obtuse apex and coarsely serrate crenate margin, shiny above and pale green and dull beneath. The tree is dioecious. The flowers are usually unisexual, rarely bisexual, small and borne in axillary, four to many flowered racemes having pedicels and 3-6 broadly ovate green sepals but no petals. The ovary of the female flower is large having 3 to 8 free styles with pubescent stigmas. The fruit is a subglobose or globose drupe, which becomes deep maroon on ripening. It is 2-2.5 mm in diameter and has yellowish white, juicy and acidic pulp. The flat and orbicular kernels are numerous, arranged in one or two superimposed rows (Morton, 1987). Cultivated forms of ramontchi vary in fruit quality. Some are sweet and flavourful and the others are tart or acidic.

Lovi-lovi

(***Flacourtia inermis*** Roxb.; tomi-tomi; martinique plum; batoko plum)

It is a deciduous spineless tree growing up to 5-15 m in height and has a gray or brown and smooth bark and a dense and rounded crown. The branches are thin and are covered with short pubescence. The leaves are alternate, ovate oblong with long, acuminate or obtuse apex, 8-20 x 4-12 cm in size and are glabrous on both surfaces.

The apetalous flowers are bisexual, borne on short axillary racemes, has 3-5 sepals covered with short hairs, 15-20 stamens and 4-5 celled ovary. The fruit is a berry, 2 cm in diameter, subglobose, dark red when ripe with yellow, sour or sweet pulp. The seeds are numerous and are placed in two superimposed rows (Morton, 1987). There are numerous local forms of which some are sweet and others are sour in taste. Sweet types become insipid on ripening.

Paniala

(***Flacourtia jangomas*** Raeusch. syn. ***F. cataphracta*** Roxb. ex Willd.; puneala plum; prunier malagache)

It is native of India. It is cultivated in tropical Africa and Asia especially in home gardens. It is found growing in northern districts of UP and in Bihar, Assam, Bengal, Orissa, Tripura and South India. The other related species that yield fruits are *F. indica* Merr. (kantal or governor plum) and *F. montana* Garh. *F. indica* is found throughout India whereas *F. montana* Garh. is mainly distributed in Western Ghats (Morton, 1987; Verheij and Coronel, 1991).

Paniala is a deciduous small shrub or a spreading tree. It grows up to 6-7 m in height with sharp decompound spines on the trunk. Leaves are alternate, glossy, ovate oblong and 5-11 x 2-5 cm in size. It is dioecious. Flowers produced in axillary racemes are unisexual, pale yellow and small and are borne in clusters on new branches. The fruits are round or ellipsoid, 1.5 to 3 cm in diameter with deep maroon skin and pleasant tart flavour. The flesh is firm, brownish green and fairly juicy. The fruit contains 4-10 small seeds (Morton, 1987; Verheij and Coronel, 1991).

Rukam

(***Flacourtia rukam*** Zoll. & Moritzi; Indian prune)

Rukam is a native of Philippines and Malay Archipelago (Martin *et al*., 1987). It has been introduced into Indochina, India, Fiji, Thailand and American tropics and subtropics (Verheij and Coronel, 1991).

Rukam is an evergreen, tall tree growing up to 10 m in height with twisted trunk. It closely resembles ramontchi (*F. indica* Merr.) except that it tends to be more upright and its leaves are narrower. Simple or branched woody spines, up to 10 cm in length, are present on the young stem and branches. Spines are usually absent in clonally propagated trees. Leaves are ovate oblong or elliptic to oblong lanceolate, 10-15 x 4-7 cm in size, glabrous or puberulous on the midrib and nerves, often shiny dark green above and brownish red and drooping when young with a coarsely toothed margin and 5-8 mm long petioles. Inflorescences are borne in few-flowered, short, axillary, fine, pubescent racemes having 3-4 mm long pedicels. The flowers are greenish yellow and are usually unisexual having 4, rarely 3-6, sepals. Petals are absent. Male flower has 8, orange or yellow white and fleshy disk lobes and numerous stamens. Female flower is usually without stamens, 4-6 free styles and indistinctly bilobed stigmas. Fruit is a globose, depressed globose to obovate berry, 2-2.5 cm in diameter and light green to pink or purplish green in colour and turns dark red at maturity. The pulp is whitish, juicy and acidic, crowned by the 4-6 small, peg-like styles set in a circle having 4-7 flat seeds (Verheij and Coronel, 1991).

Family Caryocaraceae

It contains about 2 genera and 25 species (Heywood *et al*., 2007) found in tropical region. The plants are small to large evergreen trees, sometimes with large buttresses, and occasionally shrublike. The leaves are opposite (*Caryocar*) or alternate, usually palmate and mostly 3-foliate, with usually caducous stipules, the lamina is serrate or serrulate. The flowers are actinomorphic, bisexual, large and showy borne in terminal racemes, nocturnally pollinated by bats (*Caryocar*). The calyx has 5(6) lobes but is rudimentary in *Anthodiscus*. The petals are 4(5), free, slightly connate at the base (*Caryocar*) or fused at the apex (*Anthodiscus*). The stamens are 55-750, the innermost shorter and staminodial, the filaments often fused at the base. In *Caryocar*, the petals and stamens fall after anthesis, while in *Anthodiscus*, the petals fall as a unit. The ovary is superior, of 4-20 fused carpels having 4(-6) (*Caryocar*) or 8-20 (*Anthodiscus*) locules with axile placentation and one ovule per locule. The fruit is drupaceous, separating into 1-seeded pyrenes on maturity. The fruit has 1 to 4 (*Caryocar*) or 8 to 20 (*Anthodiscus*) seeds.

Genus *Caryocar* F. Allam ex L. (souari trees)

The 15 species in this genus are all trees that yield strong timber, 8 species yield edible fruits called souari nuts or sawarri nuts. The most well known species is probably the pekea nut (*C. nuciferum*). In Brazil, the pequi (*C. brasiliense*) is most popular. It has a variety of uses, one among them being the production of pequi oil. Some species are useful indigenously to produce poisons used for hunting.

Pequi
(***Caryocar brasiliense*** Cam.; piqui; piquia oil plant)

The small pequi tree is a twisted shrub growing up to 10 m tall. Leaves are alternate, up to 18x12 cm in size with rounded apex and base, without stipules and are 3-foliate. The leaflets are elliptic ovate. Inflorescence is a terminal raceme. Calyx is broadly cup-shaped, 10-13 cm long, 5-6 lobed and rounded. The corolla is 5-6 lobed and white to yellow. Stamens are numerous and ovary is globose and 4-locular. Fruit is irregular, ovoid globose, usually 1-2 locular, 4-5 cm in diameter having more or less smooth exocarp, thick and fleshy pericarp attached to the mesocarp. The mesocarp and endocarp envelop the seed to form an oval stone, 2.5-3 cm in diameter. Endocarp is spiny, up to 2-3 cm long and contains 1-4 kidney shaped kernels. The kernel is white and oily (FAO, 1986; Brücher, 1989; Wickens, 1995).

Family Irvingiaceae

It contains 3 genera and 10 species (Heywood *et al.*, 2007). One species of *Desbordesia* is distributed from Nigeria to western Democratic Republic of Congo, 2 species of *Klainedoxa* are distributed from Guinea-Bissau to southern Sudan and Zambia, and 6 species of *Irvingia* are distributed from Sierra Leone to southern Sudan, Democratic Republic of Congo and Angola, and one species from Thailand and Vietnam to Sumatra and Java. These occur in forests on dry grounds or occasionally on river banks or in seasonally flooded forest.

Chestnut

Colossal

Michigan Early

Benton Harbor

Everfresh

Pecan

Gafford

McMillan

Desirable

Carambola (TFNet, 2008)

Arkin

Golden Star

B 2

B 10

B 17

Passion fruit (Kaveri)

Aonla (Dr Sunil Pareek, MPUAT, Udaipur)

Chakaiya

Balawant

Krishna

Kanchan

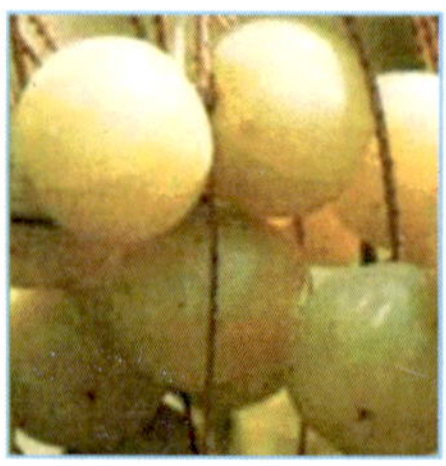
NA 6

NA 7

Anand 2

Garcinia (TFNet, 2008; CHES, Chethali)

G. mangostana Mangosteen

G. dulcis

G. livingstonei

G. cambogia

G. atroviridis

G. indica Kokam (GI-VIII-5)

(Choisy) W.F. Wight.), *G. cambogia* Desrouss., *G. pirainiana* King., *G. livingstonei* T Anders and *G. atroviridis* (Griff.) J. Anderson. Other important species are *G. atroviridis* (Assam gelugur), *G. hombroniana* (seashore mangosteen), *G. indica* (kokam), *G. Parvifolia* (Assam aur aur), *G. prainiana* (cerapu), *G. xanthochymus* (yellow mangosteen), *G. cambogia, G. livingstonei, G. intermedia* and *G. dulcis*.

Mangosteen
(***Garcinia mangostana*** L. syn. ***Mangostana garcinia*** Gaertn.) (2n=88, 90)

It is a tropical and evergreen tree and native of Burma and Malaya. It is also found at the foothills of Nilgiri and Tirunevalley in South India. Warm and moderately humid zones are suitable for its growth and production. The growth is poor if the humidity is high for long. It does not tolerate frost. Tree is very attractive, evergreen, rather slow growing, 6-25 m in height with a straight trunk, symmetrically branched forming a regular pyramidal crown. The original root system dies and is replaced by new one arising from the base of the trunk has more root hairs.

All parts of the plant exude yellow latex when injured. Leaves are opposite with short petioles clasping the shoot so that the apical pair conceals the terminal bud. Leaf blade is large, 15-25 x 7-13 cm in size, simple, oblong or elliptic, thick, leathery and shiny, entire, glabrous and olive green above, yellow green beneath with pale green central nerve and cuspidate apex. The tree is dioecious. Flowers are solitary or paired, polygamous, perfect and staminate, borne both on the same tree at the apices of branchlets with short and thick pedicels. The female flower is 5.5 cm in diameter having 4 sepals arranged in 2 pairs, 4 thick fleshy and yellow green petals with reddish edges, 1-2 seriate and sessile staminodes, 4-8 celled ovary with prominent, sessile and 4-8 lobed stigma. The tree takes too long to start bearing fruits, may be about 10 years. The fruit develops parthenocarpically. The fruit is a thick-shelled, globose and smooth berry, called *Bacca corticata*, capped by large persistent calyx at the stem end that has 5-7 fleshy segments. The fruit is 6-8 cm in diameter with purple or reddish purple external colour (FAO, 1982; Morton, 1987; Verheij and Coronel, 1991 Yaacob and Tindall, 1995). The flesh is white. The edible portion is aril. Seeds are brown and apomictic and 2.0-2.5 x 1.5-2.0 cm in size. The tree is propagated by seed.

Although mangosteen is apomictic and plants raised from seeds have little variation but no cultivars have been identified. According to Corner, the fruit from seedling trees is fairly uniform. Only one distinct variant is known and that is in the Sulu Islands. Its fruit is larger, the rind is thicker than normal, the flesh is more acid and the flavour is more pronounced. In North Borneo, a wild form has only 4 carpels, each containing a fully developed seed. The Malaysian Department of Agriculture has identified two clones, GA1 and GA2, whose fruits differ in shape, weight, external colour and number of seeds. The other less common type grown in Pahang and Sabah, Malaysia, known as Mester, produces obovoid fruit with slightly pointed distal ends.

Yellow mangosteen (Beeneke Puli) is a selection from more than 70 accessions at IIHR, Bengaluru. The tree is evergreen reaching up to 15-20 m height with straight trunk and dense pyramidal crown. The trees have long juvenile period and start flowering 8-10 year after planting. Flowering takes place during April-May and the fruits ripen during December-January. The fruit is subglobose with prominent beak and turns yellow on ripening. The seeds are embedded in the edible deep yellow pulp. The fruit weight varies from 100 to 150 g. The pulp recovery is 85-90%. The fruits are sweet acidic with 10-14°Brix TSS and 1% acidity and contain high amount of xanthones which are said to reduce cholesterol level and atherosclerosis (hardening of the arteries) as well as to naturally combat cancer.

Mundu
(***Garcinia dulcis*** Kurz)

It is a native of the Philippines, Borneo, Java and Thailand. It is a medium sized, dioecious tree with dark green leaves of 10-30 x 3-15 cm size. The fruit is round, 5-8 cm in diameter and contains 1-5 large brown seeds enveloped in the orange pulp. Pulp is eaten fresh or is used to make jams or candies.

Gamboge
(***Garcinia tinctoria*** W.F. Wight; asam kandis)

It is a native of India, Myanmar and Thailand. The tree is medium sized. The leaves are opposite and 7-15 cm x 4-6 cm in size. Male flowers are pink to red in colour. The fruit is small subglobose berry, 3-6 cm in diameter that turns yellow when ripe. The fruit is edible or is used to make sherbets, jam and to flavour other foods.

Som-Khack
(***Garcinia atrovirdis*** Griff. ex T. Anderson; asam gelugur)

It is a native of peninsular Malaysia, Thailand, Myanmar and Assam (India). The tree grows to a height of 20-30 m and has long trunk, smooth gray bark and drooping branches. Leaves are dark green, narrowly oblong and abruptly tapered at the apex. Flowers are dark red. The fruit is large, 6-10 cm wide, nearly round, fluted with 12-16 ribs and grooves. Fruits are cut into slices and dried and used as a substitute for flavouring.

Cerapu
(***Garcinia prainiana*** King)

It is a native of Malaysia and Thailand. The tree is small or medium sized. Leaves are large and elliptic in shape. The fruits are round and smooth, rather flattened, small and 2.5-4.5 cm wide.

Gorakha
(***Garcinia cambogia*** Desrouss; cambodge; Malabar tamarind)

It is native of Sri Lanka. It is a small or medium sized tree with dark green and elliptic obovate leaves. The fruits are ovoid, 5 cm in diameter, yellow or red in colour with 6-8 grooves. The dried rind of cambodge is used as a condiment for flavouring curries.

Imbe
(*Garcinia livingstonei* T. Anders.)

It is native of eastern and southern Africa. It is small tree up to 10 m in height or a shrub. It is evergreen with dense spreading growth with a twisted trunk. The fruits are ovoid globose, 2.5-3.5 x 2.5-3.0 cm, orange to reddish in colour with acid sweet pulp and are eaten raw or cooked.

Kokam
(*Garcinia indica* Choisy; kokam butter tree; mangosteen oil tree; brindonia tallow tree)

It is native of India and is found in the tropical rainforest of Western Ghats from Konkan to Mysore, Coorg and Wynad. It is commonly planted in South Gujarat and in Ratnagiri district of Maharashtra.

The tree is slender, evergreen and handsome having drooping branches. The leaves are ovate or oblong lanceolate, 6-9 x 2.5-3.8 cm in size, dark green above and pale beneath. Flowers are small and dioecious. Male flowers are borne in terminal pedunculate cyme in clusters of 3 to 7. The bisexual flowers are solitary. Stamens are 10-18, coherent in 4 bundles alternating with petals. Fruits are globose or spherical, 2.5-3.7 cm in diameter, dark purple when ripe enclosing 5-8 large seeds (Anon., 1956).

Cultivars

Considerable variation occurs particularly in Maharashtra and Karnataka both in natural habitats as well as in the cultivated areas (Arora and Pandey, 1996) in size and quality characters of the fruit such as flavour, colour, acidity in pulp, fat content and rind thickness. Konkan Krishi Vidyapeeth, Dapoli has developed an early maturing cultivar called Konkan Amruta that gives average fruit yield of 138 kg per tree. The fruit is 35 g in weight and has good shelf life (Dumbre, 1997). Some genotypes such as MLDK-5, MLDK-2, MLDK-3, MLDK-10 and MLDK-4 have been identified on the basis of characters relating to precocity and fruit yield (Gwankar *et al.*, 2004).

GI-V-8: The seedling selection has higher fruit weight. The tree has upright growth and medium size. The fruits ripen during May-June. The fruit has 75 to 85 g weight, dull red colour, dark red rind, 4-5 seeds, 8 segments and white, juicy and acid sweet flesh. The seeds are attached to flesh. The rind recovery is 62%. The flesh has 13.5°Brix TSS and 62 mg/100 g vitamin C. The average yield is 300-500 fruits per tree.

GI-VIII-5: It is a high yielding seedling selection. The tree is spreading and medium in size. The fruits ripen during May-June. The average fruit weight ranges between 50 and 60 g. The fruit is dull red having 6-7 seeds, dark red rind, white flesh and 8 segments. The flesh is juicy and acid sweet and the seeds are attached to flesh. The rind recovery is 59.5%. The flesh has 14.1°Brix TSS and 64 mg/100 g vitamin C. The average yield is 1000-1200 fruits per tree.

GI-V-4: The trees are spreading with 4-5 m spread, medium size, 3- 4 m height and high yielding. The fruits ripen during May-June. The fruit weight ranges from 45 to 50 g. Fruit is dull red having dark red rind, white flesh, 8 segments and acid sweet flesh. The seeds are attached to the flesh. The rind recovery is 48%. The flesh has 14.5°Brix TSS and 36 mg/100 g vitamin C. The average yield is 1000-1250 fruits per tree.

Cowphal
(***Garcinia cowa*** Roxb.)

It yields edible fruits that are used for making curry and beverage. A sort of butter is made from the seed. Its bark yields yellow dye (Anon., 1956). The plants can be used as rootstock.

Malabar tamarind
(***Garcinia gummi-gutta*** L., ***G. cambogia*** (Gaertn.) Desr.;
brindleberry, gamboge, gorakha, kudam puli)

It is native of Indonesia. It is a small or medium sized tree with dark green and elliptic obovate leaves. The fruits are ovoid, 5 cm in diameter, yellow or red in colour with 6-8 grooves. The dried rind of camboge is used as a condiment for flavouring curries.

A promising line GG-V-1 has been identified from the seedling population in Karnataka, India. The tree has upright growth and medium size. The fruits ripen during July. The fruit is large-sized (75-85 g) and dull yellow having 6-7 seeds, yellow rind, white flesh, 8 segments and acidic juice. The seeds are not attached to flesh. The rind recovery is 62%. The flesh has 13.5°Brix TSS and 62 mg/100 g vitamin C. The average yield is 400-700 fruits per tree.

Genus *Platonia* Mart.

The plants bear single flowers having broad petals, many stamens per fascicle, papillate filaments, 8-11 mm long ±locellate anthers, many ovules per carpel and long style. Exotegmen is absent. Germination is hypogeal. *Platonia insignis* is the sole species of the genus. It occurs in Guyanas, Brazil at low altitudes (Kubitzki, 2007) and in the humid forests of Brazil, Paraguay, parts of Colombia and northeast Guyana, especially in Amazon rainforest.

Bakuri
(***Platonia insignis*** Mart. syn. ***Platonia esculenta*** (Arruda) Rickett and Stafleu;
bacuri; bacuri do parana; pacuri; parcouri; bacupari Maniballi; Naranjillo;
Bacurizeiro)

It is a native of Brazil and Paraguay where it is found wild in the Amazon region of northern Brazil from Maranhao, Goias to Paraguay. It is also cultivated in Paraguay and Brazil but is little known elsewhere (Leaky and Newton, 1994). The bakuri is one of the most popular fruits of the Belem region and has good potential in the tropics (FAO, 1986; Martin *et al.,* 1987).

The tree is tall, erect and grows up to 25 m in height having pyramidal crown and copious latex in the bark. The leaves are opposite, oblong or elliptic, 15 cm long, dark green and glossy above and leathery with wavy margins. Flowers are solitary, 7 cm long, bisexual, rose coloured, 5-petalled with many stamens and emerge terminally at leaf fall on young branches. The mature fruit is spherical, 8-12 cm in diameter, weighing up to 900 g with smooth yellow to orange exocarp (rind). The rind is yellow, hard but fleshy inside, 1-2 cm thick and contains gummy, yellow and resinous latex. The white and pithy pulp having pleasant odour and agreeable subacid flavour contains 1 to 4, rarely 5, oblong, angular and dark brown and 5-6 cm long seeds. The infertile seed compartments are filled with pulp called "tilho" (Martin *et al.*, 1987).

No standard cultivar is known. However, lot of variability occurs in nature with regard to fruit size, quality and yield. A seedless type has been identified (FAO, 1996a,b).

Genus *Rheedia*

The important species that produce edible fruits are *Rheedia madruno* Planch. and Triana (Madrono), *R. brasiliensis* Planch. and Triana (bakupari), growing wild in Rio de Janerio and Paraguay and mameyito (*R. edulis* Planch. and Triana) and bacuripari (*R. macrophylla* Planch. and Triana), growing wild in the humid forests from Surinam and Brazil to northern Peru (Morton, 1987).

Madrono
(*Rheedia madruno* Planch. and Triana)

It is native of South America. It is distributed in Golfo Dulce region of Costa Rica, the Atlantic slope of Panama and northern South America from Colombia and Ecuador through Venezuela to Guyana and Bolivia. It is particularly common in the Cauca valley of Colombia.

Madrono tree is erect and compact with pyramidal or rounded crown growing up to 8 m in height and has much gummy yellow latex. Leaves are opposite, elliptic to oblong, wedge-shaped at the base and rounded or pointed at the apex, 6-20 x 2-7.5 cm in size, dark green above and paler beneath with numerous conspicuous veins on both the surfaces. The fragrant male and female flowers are borne on separate trees in clusters of up to 14 in the leaf axils and have 4 reflexed pale yellow petals. The male flowers have 20 to 30 light yellow stamens. The fruit is round or ellipsoidal with a prominent nipple at each end, 5-7.5 cm long with thick, leathery, warty and greenish yellow rind containing deep yellow resinous latex. The white translucent, juicy, sweet-acid, aromatic pulp adheres tightly to 1 to 3 ovate or oblong seeds, which are 2 cm long (Morton, 1987; Brücher, 1989).

Family Calophyllaceae

It has 14 genera and 595 species, mostly having milky sap. The genus *Mammea* has about 50 evergreen tree species.

Genus *Mammea* L.

Plants are trees, sometimes unbranched and schopfbaum rosette tree, glabrous having perulate terminal bud. The leaves are rarely spiral having distant secondary veins and fine reticulate venation. Resin canals are also rarely present. Plants are dioecious. Inflorescences are axillary, fasciculate having flowers with 2 connate sepals, 4-6 petals, 0.6-4 mm long anthers, large and single to small or no glands, 2(4), 2(4) ovules per carpel (8-locular ovary), short style and peltate stigma. The fruit is a fibrous berry, rarely a septifragal capsule having complex testa, no exotegmen, $\leq$ 1.2 cm long embryo and massive cotyledons. The germination is hypogeal. It contains 75 species, 2 in central America, 3 in Africa and the others from the centre of diversity in Madagascar to the Pacific and New Caledonia at low to medium altitudes. The plants appear to be andromonoecious (Kubitzki *et al.*, 2007).

Mammee apple
(***Mammea americana*** L.; mamme; mammey apple; mamey; South American apricot; 'mamey do santo domingo')

It is often confused with the sapote or mamey colorado (*Calocarpum sapota* Merr.) of Sapotaceae, which is commonly called mamey in Cuba. It is native of West Indies and northern South America and is cultivated in the Bahamas Islands and the Greater and Lesser Antilles. It is sparingly grown in E1 Salvador and in the lowlands of Costa Rica and Guatemala as ornamental shade tree. Its cultivation is scattered through the Guianas, Venezuela, Colombia, Ecuador, northern Brazil and southern Mexico. It has been introduced into West Africa, South East Asia, Java, Philippines, USA (California, Florida) and Hawaii (Morton, 1987). The fruits can be used in fresh and processed form. The related edible species is *M. africana* Sabine (African apricot), which is native to Africa.

The mamey tree is an evergreen, handsome and large tree growing up to 25 m in height. It has a short trunk and ascending branches forming an erect and oval head having dense foliage with opposite, glossy, leathery, dark green and broadly elliptic leaves of 20 x 10 cm size. The flowers are fragrant and have 4 to 6 white petals, numerous orange stamens and 2-4-celled ovary and are borne singly or in groups of 2 or 3 on short stalks in the axils of young shoots. Male, female and hermaphrodite flowers occur together or on separate trees.

The fruit is round or somewhat irregular in shape with short thick stem end and a more or less distinct tip having a diameter of 10 to 15 cm. The fruit is heavy and weighs up to several kg and remains hard until fully ripe. The skin is about 3 mm thick, bitter, light brown or grayish brown with small scattered, warty or scurfy and leathery areas. Beneath the skin, a thin, dry, whitish membrane or rag is present which adheres to the flesh and is astringent or bitter in taste. The flesh is light or golden yellow to orange, non-fibrous and may be firm and crisp or sometimes dry to tender, melting and juicy. The fruit is more or less free from seed, though bits of seed cover remain with it, which are bitter in taste. The ripe flesh is fragrant, pleasantly subacid and resembles the apricot or red raspberry in flavour. Fruits of poor quality may be sour or mawkishly sour. Small fruits are usually single seeded. The juice leaves an indelible stain (Page, 1984; Morton, 1987; Verheij and Coronel, 1991). Sweet and sour cultivars are available. The seeds are 1-4, russet brown, rough, ovoid or elliptic and about 6 cm long. There is a lot of scope for selecting superior types as lot of variability occurs in fruit size, yield and quality (Page, 1984; Morton, 1987).

⑧ ⑧ ⑧